A2-Level Mathematics

A2 Maths is seriously tricky — no question about that.
To do well, you're going to need to revise properly and practise hard.

This book has thorough notes on everything in modules C3, C4, S2 and M2.
It'll help you learn the stuff you need and take you step-by-step through loads of examples.

It's got practice questions... lots of them. For every topic there are warm-up and exam-style questions. Plus there are two full practice exams at the end of each module.

And of course, we've done our best to make the whole thing vaguely entertaining for you.

Complete Revision and Practice

Exam Board: Edexcel

Contents

Core Mathematics C3

C3 Section 1 — Algebra & Functions

C3 Section 2 — Trigonometry

C3 Section 3 — Exponentials & Logarithms

C3 Section 4 — Differentiation

C3 Section 5 — Numerical Methods

C3 Practice Exams

Core Mathematics C4

C4 Section 1 — Algebra & Functions

C4 Section 2 — Coordinate Geometry in the (x, y) Plane

C4 Section 3 — Sequences & Series

C4 Section 4 — Differentiation

C4 Section 5 — Integration 1

C4 Section 6 — Integration 2

C4 Section 7 — Vectors

C4 Practice Exams

Contents

Statistics S2

S2 Section 1 — The Binomial Distribution

S2 Section 2 — The Poisson Distribution

S2 Section 3 — Continuous Random Variables

S2 Section 4 — Continuous Distributions

S2 Section 5 — Hypothesis Tests

S2 Practice Exams

Mechanics M2

M2 Section 1 — Kinematics

M2 Section 2 — Centres of Mass

M2 Section 3 — Work & Energy

M2 Section 4 — Collisions

M2 Section 5 — Statics of Rigid Bodies

M2 Practice Exams

Contributors:
Mary Falkner, Paul Jordin, Sharon Keeley-Holden, Simon Little, Ali Palin, Andy Park, David Ryan, Lyn Setchell, Caley Simpson, Jane Towle, Jonathan Wray, Dawn Wright

Proofreaders:
Mona Allen, Alastair Duncombe, Ann Francis, Paul Garrett, Glenn Rogers

Published by CGP

ISBN: 978 1 84762 584 7

www.cgpbooks.co.uk

Printed by Elanders Ltd, Newcastle upon Tyne.

Based on the classic CGP style created by Richard Parsons.

Simplifying Expressions

What a lovely way to start a book — a page on algebraic fractions. Still, at least they're over with early on, so if they pop up later in C3 you'll know what to do. No, not run away and cower in a corner — use the things you learnt on this page.

Simplify algebraic fractions by Factorising and Cancelling Factors

Algebraic fractions are a lot like normal fractions — and you can treat them in the same way, whether you're multiplying, dividing, adding or subtracting them. All fractions are much easier to deal with when they're in their simplest form, so the first thing to do with algebraic fractions is to simplify them as much as possible.

1) Look for common factors in the numerator and denominator — factorise top and bottom and see if there's anything you can cancel.
2) If there's a fraction in the numerator or denominator (e.g. $\frac{1}{x}$), multiply the whole thing (i.e. top and bottom) by the same factor to get rid of it (for $\frac{1}{x}$, you'd multiply through by x).

EXAMPLES Simplify the following:

a) $\frac{3x+6}{x^2-4} = \frac{3\cancel{(x+2)}}{\cancel{(x+2)}(x-2)} = \frac{3}{x-2}$

Watch out for the difference of two squares — see C1.

b) $\frac{2+\frac{1}{2x}}{4x^2+x} = \frac{\left(2+\frac{1}{2x}\right)\times 2x}{x(4x+1)\times 2x} = \frac{\cancel{4x+1}}{2x^2\cancel{(4x+1)}} = \frac{1}{2x^2}$

3) You multiply algebraic fractions in exactly the same way as normal fractions — multiply the numerators together, then multiply the denominators. It's a good idea to cancel any common factors before you multiply.
4) To divide by an algebraic fraction, you just multiply by its reciprocal (the reciprocal is 1 ÷ the original thing — for fractions you just turn the fraction upside down).

EXAMPLES Simplify the following:

a) $\frac{x^2-2x-15}{2x+8} \times \frac{x^2-16}{x^2+3x} = \frac{\cancel{(x+3)}(x-5)}{2\cancel{(x+4)}} \times \frac{\cancel{(x+4)}(x-4)}{x\cancel{(x+3)}} = \frac{(x-5)(x-4)}{2x} \left(= \frac{x^2-9x+20}{2x}\right)$

Factorise both fractions.

b) $\frac{3x}{5} \div \frac{3x^2-9x}{20} = \frac{\cancel{3x}}{\cancel{5}} \times \frac{20}{\cancel{3x}(x-3)} = \frac{4}{x-3}$

Turn the second fraction upside down.

Add and Subtract fractions by finding a Common Denominator

You'll have come across adding and subtracting fractions before in C1, so here's a little reminder of how to do it:

EXAMPLE Simplify:

$$\frac{2y}{x(x+3)} + \frac{1}{y^2(x+3)} - \frac{x}{y}$$

The common denominator is the lowest common multiple (LCM) of all the denominators.

① **Find the Common Denominator**

Take all the individual 'bits' from the bottom lines and multiply them together. Only use each bit once unless something on the bottom line is raised to a power.

The individual 'bits' here are x, $(x+3)$ and y...

$$xy^2(x+3)$$

...but you need to use y^2 because there's a y^2 in the second fraction's denominator.

② **Put Each Fraction over the Common Denominator**

Make the denominator of each fraction into the common denominator.

$$\frac{y^2\times 2y}{y^2x(x+3)} + \frac{x\times 1}{xy^2(x+3)} - \frac{xy(x+3)\times x}{xy(x+3)y}$$

Multiply the top and bottom lines of each fraction by whatever makes the bottom line the same as the common denominator.

③ **Combine into One Fraction**

Once everything's over the common denominator you can just add the top lines together.

All the bottom lines are the same — so you can just add the top lines.

$$= \frac{2y^3+x-x^2y(x+3)}{xy^2(x+3)} = \frac{2y^3+x-x^3y-3x^2y}{xy^2(x+3)}$$

Who are you calling common...

Nothing on this page should be a big shock to you — it's all stuff you've done before. You've been using normal fractions for years, and algebraic fractions work in just the same way. They look a bit scary, but they're all warm and fuzzy inside.

Algebraic Division

I'll be honest with you, algebraic division is a bit tricky. But as long as you take it slowly and don't rush, it'll all fall into place. And it's really quick and easy to check your answer if you're not sure. What more could you want?

There are some Terms you need to Know

There are a few words that keep popping up in algebraic division, so make sure you know what they all mean.

1) DEGREE — the highest power of x in the polynomial (e.g. the degree of $4x^5 + 6x^2 - 3x - 1$ is 5).
2) DIVISOR — this is the thing you're dividing by (e.g. if you divide $x^2 + 4x - 3$ by $x + 2$, the divisor is $x + 2$).
3) QUOTIENT — the bit that you get when you divide by the divisor (not including the remainder — see p.3).

Method 1 — Divide by Subtracting Multiples of the Divisor

Back in C2, you learnt how to do algebraic division by subtracting chunks of the divisor.
Here's a quick reminder of how to divide a polynomial by $x - k$:

Algebraic Division

1) **Subtract a multiple of $(x - k)$ to get rid of the highest power of x.**
2) **Repeat step 1 until you've got rid of all the powers of x.**
3) **Work out how many lumps of $(x - k)$, you've subtracted, and read off the remainder.**

Have a look back at your C2 notes if you can't remember how to do this.

EXAMPLE Divide $2x^3 - 3x^2 - 3x + 7$ by $x - 2$.

① Start with $2x^3 - 3x^2 - 3x + 7$, and subtract $2x^2$ lots of $(x - 2)$ to get rid of the x^3 term. $\Rightarrow (2x^3 - 3x^2 - 3x + 7) - 2x^2(x - 2) = x^2 - 3x + 7$

② Now start again with $x^2 - 3x + 7$. The highest power of x is the x^2 term, so subtract x lots of $(x - 2)$ to get rid of that. $\Rightarrow (x^2 - 3x + 7) - x(x - 2) = -x + 7$

③ All that's left now is $-x + 7$. Get rid of $-x$ by subtracting $-1 \times (x - 2)$. $\Rightarrow (-x + 7) - (-1(x - 2)) = 5$

So $(2x^3 - 3x^2 - 3x + 7) \div (x - 2) = 2x^2 + x - 1$ remainder 5.

Method 2 — use Algebraic Long Division

To divide two algebraic expressions, you can use long division (using the same method you'd use for numbers).

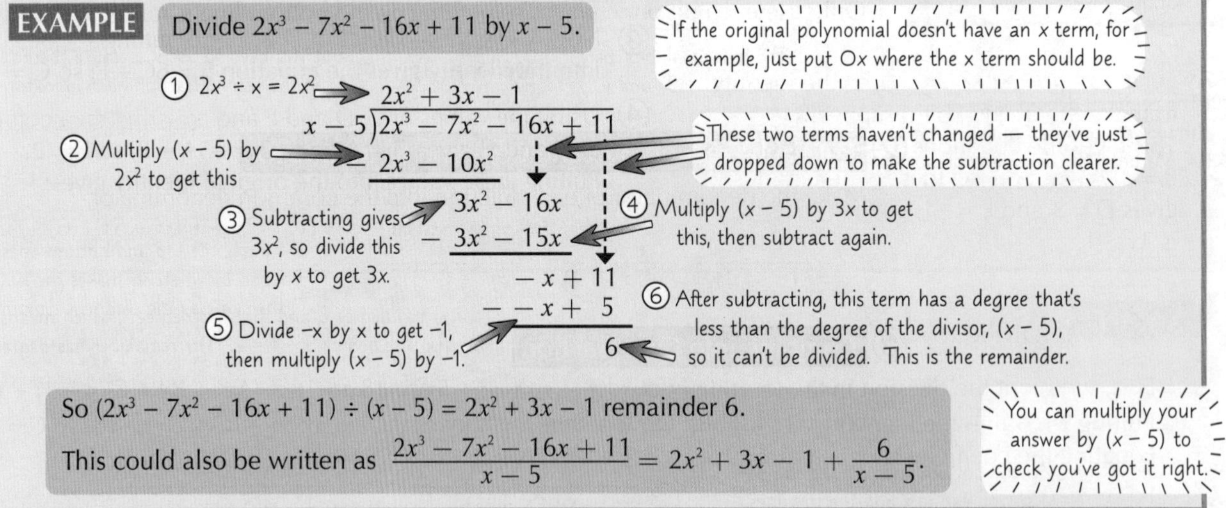

EXAMPLE Divide $2x^3 - 7x^2 - 16x + 11$ by $x - 5$.
If the original polynomial doesn't have an x term, for example, just put 0x where the x term should be.
① $2x^3 \div x = 2x^2$
$2x^2 + 3x - 1$
$x - 5 \overline{) 2x^3 - 7x^2 - 16x + 11}$
② Multiply $(x - 5)$ by $2x^2$ to get this
$- \quad 2x^3 - 10x^2$
These two terms haven't changed — they've just dropped down to make the subtraction clearer.
$3x^2 - 16x$
③ Subtracting gives $3x^2$, so divide this by x to get $3x$.
$- \quad 3x^2 - 15x$
④ Multiply $(x - 5)$ by $3x$ to get this, then subtract again.
$-x + 11$
$- \quad -x + 5$
⑤ Divide $-x$ by x to get -1, then multiply $(x - 5)$ by -1.
6
⑥ After subtracting, this term has a degree that's less than the degree of the divisor, $(x - 5)$, so it can't be divided. This is the remainder.

So $(2x^3 - 7x^2 - 16x + 11) \div (x - 5) = 2x^2 + 3x - 1$ remainder 6.

This could also be written as $\dfrac{2x^3 - 7x^2 - 16x + 11}{x - 5} = 2x^2 + 3x - 1 + \dfrac{6}{x - 5}$.

You can multiply your answer by $(x - 5)$ to check you've got it right.

Just keep repeating — divide and conquer, divide and conquer...

For algebraic division to work, the degree of the divisor has to be less than (or equal to) the degree of the original polynomial (for example, you couldn't divide $x^2 + 2x + 3$ by $x^3 + 4$ as $3 > 2$, but you could do it the other way around). If you don't like either of these methods, you'll be pleased to know there's another way to divide coming up on the next page.

Algebraic Division

I really spoil you — as if two different methods for doing algebraic division weren't enough, I'm going to give you a third. If you're not sure about any of the terms, look back at the definitions on p.2.

Method 3 — use the Formula f(x) = q(x)d(x) + r(x)

There's a handy formula you can use to do algebraic division. It looks like this:

> A polynomial $f(x)$ can be written in the form $f(x) \equiv q(x)d(x) + r(x)$, where $q(x)$ is the quotient, $d(x)$ is the divisor and $r(x)$ is the remainder.

This comes from the Remainder Theorem that you met in C2. It's a good method for when you're dividing by a quadratic — long division can get a bit tricky when the divisor has 3 terms.

You'll be given $f(x)$ and $d(x)$ in the question, and it's down to you to work out $q(x)$ and $r(x)$. Here's how you do it:

Using the Formula

1) **First, you have to work out the degrees of the quotient and remainder, which depend on the degrees of the polynomial and the divisor. The degree of the quotient is $\deg f(x) - \deg d(x)$, and the degree of the remainder has to be less than the degree of the divisor.**
2) **Write out the division using the formula above, but replace $q(x)$ and $r(x)$ with general polynomials (i.e. a general polynomial of degree 2 is $Ax^2 + Bx + C$, and a general polynomial of degree 1 is $Ax + B$, where A, B, C, etc. are constants to be found).**
3) **The next step is to work out the values of the constants — you do this by substituting in values for x to make bits disappear, and by equating coefficients.**
4) **It's best to start with the constant term and work backwards from there.**
5) **Finally, write out the division again, replacing A, B, C, etc. with the values you've found.**

Equating coefficients means comparing the coefficients of each power of x on the LHS and the RHS.

The method looks a bit intense, but follow through the examples below to see how it works.

Start with the Remainder and Work Backwards

When you're using this method, you might have to use simultaneous equations to work out some of the coefficients. Have a look back at your C1 notes for a reminder of how to do this if you need to.

EXAMPLE Divide $x^4 - 3x^3 - 3x^2 + 10x + 5$ by $x^2 - 5x + 6$.

① First, write out the division in the form $f(x) \equiv q(x)d(x) + r(x)$:

$$x^4 - 3x^3 - 3x^2 + 10x + 5 \equiv (Ax^2 + Bx + C)(x^2 - 5x + 6) + Dx + E$$
$$\equiv (Ax^2 + Bx + C)(x - 2)(x - 3) + Dx + E.$$

f(x) has degree 4 and d(x) has degree 2, which means that q(x) has degree 4 – 2 = 2. The remainder has degree 1 or 0 — put in Dx + E, as D can always be 0.

d(x) factorises to give $(x - 2)(x - 3)$.

② Substitute $x = 2$ and $x = 3$ into the identity to make the q(x)d(x) bit disappear. This gives the equations $5 = 2D + E$ and $8 = 3D + E$. Solving these simultaneously gives $D = 3$ and $E = -1$, so the remainder is $3x - 1$.

③ Now, using these values of D & E and putting $x = 0$ into the identity gives the equation $5 = 6C + E$, so $C = 1$.

④ Using the values of C, D and E and equating the coefficients of x^4 and x^3 gives: $1 = A$ and $-3 = -5A + B$, so $B = 2$. Putting these values into the original identity gives:

$$x^4 - 3x^3 - 3x^2 + 10x + 5 \equiv (x^2 + 2x + 1)(x^2 - 5x + 6) + 3x - 1.$$

EXAMPLE Divide $x^3 + 5x^2 - 18x - 10$ by $x - 3$.

f(x) has degree 3 and d(x) has degree 1, which means that q(x) has degree 3 – 1 = 2. The remainder has degree 0.

First, write out the division in the form $f(x) \equiv q(x)d(x) + r(x)$: $x^3 + 5x^2 - 18x - 10 \equiv (Ax^2 + Bx + C)(x - 3) + D$.
Putting $x = 3$ into the identity gives $D = 8$. Now, setting $x = 0$ gives the equation $-3C + D = -10$, so $C = 6$.
Equating the coefficients of x^3 and x^2 gives $A = 1$ and $-3A + B = 5$, so $B = 8$.
So $x^3 + 5x^2 - 18x - 10 \equiv (x^2 + 8x + 6)(x - 3) + 8$.

A reminder about remainders...

The degree of the remainder has to be less than the degree of the divisor, otherwise it would be included in the quotient.
E.g. if $r(x) = (x + 1)$ and $d(x) = (x - 3)$, then $r(x)$ can be divided by $d(x)$, giving a remainder of 4 (so $x + 1$ wasn't the remainder).

Functions and Mappings

In A2 maths, your teacher might ask you to draw a mapping diagram. Sadly, they don't want you to draw an exciting map with rivers, mountains, caves and secret tunnels on it — they want you to draw a boring diagram. Shame.

Values in the *Domain* are *Mapped* to values in the *Range*

1) A mapping is an operation that takes one number and transforms it into another. E.g. 'multiply by 5', 'square root' and 'divide by 7' are all mappings.
2) The set of numbers you can start with is called the domain, and the set of numbers they can become is called the range. Mappings can be drawn as diagrams like this: You can also draw mappings as graphs (see below).

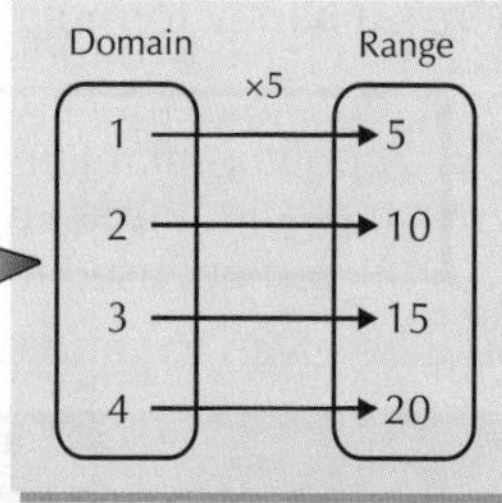

3) The domain and / or range will often be the set of real numbers, $\mathbb{R}$ (a real number is any positive or negative number (or 0) — fractions, decimals, integers, surds). If x can take any real value, it's usually written as $x \in \mathbb{R}$.
4) You might have to work out the range of a mapping from the domain you're given. For example, $y = x^2$, $x \in \mathbb{R}$ has the range $f(x) \geq 0$, as all square real numbers are positive (or zero).

Other sets of numbers include $\mathbb{Z}$, the set of integers, $\mathbb{N}$, the set of natural numbers (positive integers, not including 0) and $\mathbb{C}$, the complex numbers (made up of 'imaginary' numbers — you don't meet these in C3 or C4).

A *Function* is a type of *Mapping*

1) Some mappings take every number in the domain to only one number in the range. These mappings are called functions. If a mapping takes a number from the domain to more than one number in the range (or if it isn't mapped to any number in the range), it's not a function.

Functions (e.g. x^2) are usually written as $f(x) = x^2$ or $f : x \to x^2$.

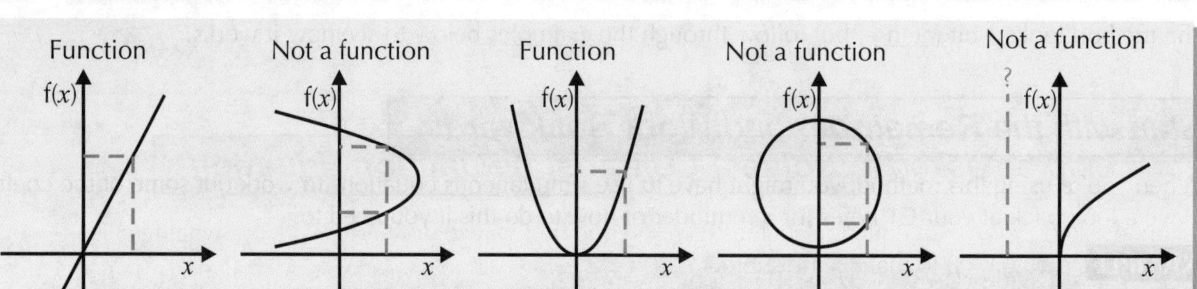

2) For the graphs above, the first and third are functions because each value of x is mapped to a single value of $f(x)$. The second and fourth aren't functions because the values of x are mapped to two different values of $f(x)$. The fifth also isn't a function, this time because $f(x)$ is not defined for $x < 0$.
3) Some mappings that aren't functions can be turned into functions by restricting their domain. For example, the mapping $y = \frac{1}{x-1}$ for $x \in \mathbb{R}$ is not a function, because it's not defined at $x = 1$ (draw the graph if you're not convinced). But if you change the domain to $x > 1$, the mapping is now a function.

Functions can be *One-to-One* or *Many-to-One*

1) A one-to-one function maps one element in the domain to one element in the range — e.g. $f : x \to 2x$, $x \in \mathbb{R}$ is one-to-one, as every x is mapped to a unique value in the range (the range is also $\mathbb{R}$). So only 3 in the domain is mapped to 6 in the range.
2) A many-to-one function maps more than one element in the domain to one element in the range (remember that no element in the domain can map to more than one element in the range, otherwise it wouldn't be a function). $f(x) = x^2$, $x \in \mathbb{R}$ is a many-to-one function, as two elements in the domain map to the same element in the range — e.g. both 3 and −3 map to 9.

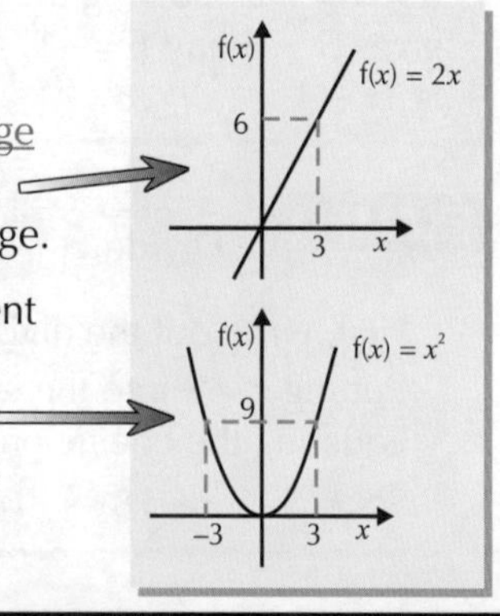

Welcome to my domain...

When you're drawing a function or a mapping, you should draw a mapping diagram if you're given a discrete set of numbers (e.g. $x \in \{0, 1, 2, 3\}$), but you should draw a graph if the domain is continuous (e.g. $x \in \mathbb{R}$).

Composite Functions

You're not done with functions yet. Oh no. You need to know what happens if you put two (or more) functions together. There's only one way to find out...

Functions can be Combined to make a Composite Function

1) If you have two functions f and g, you can combine them (do one followed by the other) to make a new function. This is called a composite function.
2) Composite functions are written fg(x) — this means do g first, then f. If it helps, put brackets in until you get used to it, so fg(x) = f(g(x)). The order is really important — usually fg(x) ≠ gf(x).
3) If you get a composite function that's written $f^2(x)$, it means ff(x) — you do f twice.

Composite functions made up of three or more functions work in exactly the same way.

EXAMPLE For the functions $f : x \to 2x^3$ $\{x \in \mathbb{R}\}$ and $g : x \to x - 3$ $\{x \in \mathbb{R}\}$, find:

a) fg(4) b) fg(0) c) gf(0) d) fg(x) e) gf(x) f) $f^2(x)$.

a) $fg(4) = f(g(4)) = f(4-3) = f(1) = 2 \times 1^3 = 2$

b) $fg(0) = f(g(0)) = f(0-3) = f(-3) = 2 \times (-3)^3 = 2 \times -27 = -54$

c) $gf(0) = g(f(0)) = g(2 \times 0^3) = g(0) = 0 - 3 = -3$

From parts b) and c) you can see that fg(x) ≠ gf(x).

d) $fg(x) = f(g(x)) = f(x-3) = 2(x-3)^3$

e) $gf(x) = g(f(x)) = g(2x^3) = 2x^3 - 3$

f) $f^2(x) = f(f(x)) = f(2x^3) = 2(2x^3)^3 = 16x^9$

You could be asked to Solve a Composite Function Equation

If you're asked to solve an equation such as fg(x) = 8, the best way to do it is to work out what fg(x) is, then rearrange fg(x) = 8 to make x the subject.

EXAMPLE For the functions $f : x \to \sqrt{x}$ with domain $\{x \geq 0\}$ and $g : x \to \frac{1}{x-1}$ with domain $\{x > 1\}$, solve the equation fg(x) = ½. Also, state the range of fg(x).

First, find fg(x): $fg(x) = f\left(\frac{1}{x-1}\right) = \sqrt{\frac{1}{x-1}} = \frac{1}{\sqrt{x-1}}$

So $\frac{1}{\sqrt{x-1}} = \frac{1}{2}$

Rearrange this equation to find x:

$$\frac{1}{\sqrt{x-1}} = \frac{1}{2} \Rightarrow \sqrt{x-1} = 2 \Rightarrow x - 1 = 4 \Rightarrow x = 5$$

To find the range, it's often helpful to draw the graph of fg(x):

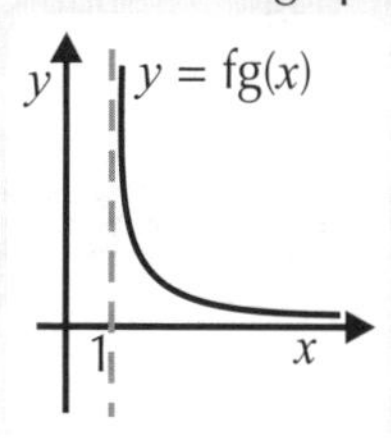

The domain of fg(x) is $x > 1$ (though the question doesn't ask for this) and the range is fg(x) > 0.

Be careful with the domains and ranges of composite functions.

EXAMPLE For the functions $f : x \to 2x + 1$ $\{x \in \mathbb{R}\}$ and $g : x \to x^2$ $\{x \in \mathbb{R}\}$, solve gf(x) = 16.

Find gf(x): $gf(x) = g(2x + 1) = (2x + 1)^2$.

Now solve gf(x) = 16: $(2x + 1)^2 = 16 \Rightarrow 4x^2 + 4x + 1 = 16$
$\Rightarrow 4x^2 + 4x - 15 = 0$
$\Rightarrow (2x - 3)(2x + 5) = 0$ so $x = \frac{3}{2}$ or $x = -\frac{5}{2}$

Compose a concerto for f(x) and orchestra...

The most important thing to remember on this page is the order you do the functions in — for fg(x) you always do g first as g is next to x. It's like getting dressed — you wouldn't put your shoes on before your socks, as your socks go next to your feet.

Inverse Functions

Just when you'd got your head around functions, ranges, domains and composite functions, they go and turn it all back to front by introducing inverses.

Only One-to-One Functions have Inverses

1) An inverse function does the opposite to the function. So if the function was '+ 1', the inverse would be '– 1', if the function was '× 2', the inverse would be '÷ 2' etc. The inverse for a function f(x) is written $f^{-1}(x)$.
2) An inverse function maps an element in the range to an element in the domain — the opposite of a function. This means that only one-to-one functions have inverses, as the inverse of a many-to-one function would be one-to-many, which isn't a function (see p.4).
3) For any inverse $f^{-1}(x)$,

Doing the function and then the inverse...

$$f^{-1}f(x) = x = ff^{-1}(x)$$

...is the same as doing the inverse then doing the function — both just give you x.

4) The domain of the inverse is the range of the function, and the range of the inverse is the domain of the function.

EXAMPLE The function $f(x) = x + 7$ with domain $x \geq 0$ and range $f(x) \geq 7$ is one-to-one, so it has an inverse.

The inverse of + 7 is – 7, so $f^{-1}(x) = x - 7$. $f^{-1}(x)$ has domain $x \geq 7$ and range $f^{-1}(x) \geq 0$.

Work out the Inverse using Algebra

For simple functions (like the one in the example above), it's easy to work out what the inverse is just by looking at it. But for more complex functions, you need to rearrange the original function to change the subject.

Finding the Inverse

1) **Replace f(x) with y to get an equation for y in terms of x.**
2) **Rearrange the equation to make x the subject.**
3) **Replace x with $f^{-1}(x)$ and y with x — this is the inverse function.**
4) **Swap round the domain and range of the function.**

EXAMPLE Find the inverse of the function $f(x) = 3x^2 + 2$ with domain $x \geq 0$, and state its domain and range.

1) First, replace f(x) with y: $y = 3x^2 + 2$.
2) Rearrange the equation to make x the subject:

$$y - 2 = 3x^2 \Rightarrow \frac{y-2}{3} = x^2 \Rightarrow \sqrt{\frac{y-2}{3}} = x$$

$x \geq 0$ so you don't need the negative square root.

It's easier to work with y than f(x).

3) Replace x with $f^{-1}(x)$ and y with x:

$$f^{-1}(x) = \sqrt{\frac{x-2}{3}}$$

4) Swap the domain and range: the range of f(x) is $f(x) \geq 2$, so $f^{-1}(x)$ has domain $x \geq 2$ and range $f^{-1}(x) \geq 0$.

You might have to Draw the Graph of the Inverse

The inverse of a function is its reflection in the line $y = x$.

EXAMPLE Sketch the graph of the inverse of the function $f(x) = x^2 - 8$ with domain $x \geq 0$.

It's easy to see what the domains and ranges are from the graph — f(x) has domain $x \geq 0$ and range $f(x) \geq -8$, and $f^{-1}(x)$ has domain $x \geq -8$ and range $f^{-1}(x) \geq 0$.

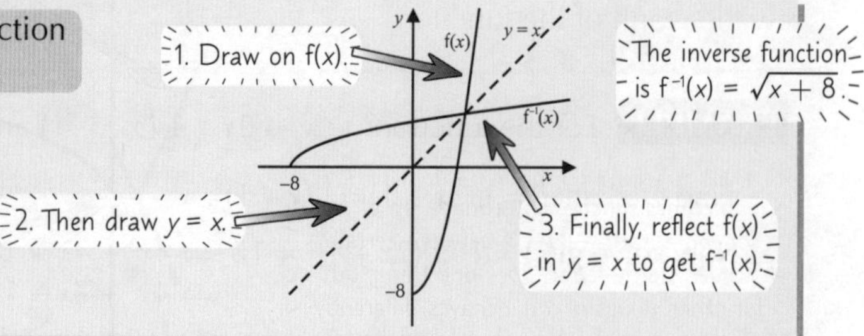
1. Draw on f(x).
2. Then draw y = x.
3. Finally, reflect f(x) in y = x to get f⁻¹(x).
The inverse function is f⁻¹(x) = √(x + 8).
y
x
f(x)
y = x
f⁻¹(x)
–8
–8

Line y = x on the wall — who is the fairest of them all...

I think I've got the hang of this inverse stuff now — so the inverse of walking to the shops and buying some milk would be taking the money out the till, putting the milk back on the shelf, leaving the shop and walking home backwards. Sorted.

Modulus

The modulus of a number is really useful if you don't care whether something's positive or negative — like if you were finding the difference between two numbers (e.g. 7 and 12). It doesn't matter which way round you do the subtraction (i.e. 12 – 7 or 7 – 12) — the difference between them is still 5.

Modulus is the Size of a number

1) The modulus of a number is its size — it doesn't matter if it's positive or negative. So for a positive number, the modulus is just the same as the number itself, but for a negative number, the modulus is its positive value. For example, the modulus of 8 is 8, and the modulus of –8 is also 8.
2) The modulus of a number, x, is written $|x|$. So the example above would be written $|8| = |-8| = 8$.
3) In general terms, for $x \geq 0$, $|x| = x$ and for $x < 0$, $|x| = -x$.
4) Functions can have a modulus too — the modulus of a function f(x) is its positive value. Suppose $f(x) = -6$, then $|f(x)| = 6$. In general terms,
5) If the modulus is inside the brackets in the form $f(|x|)$, then you make the x-value positive before applying the function. So $f(|-2|) = f(2)$.

The modulus is sometimes called the absolute value.

$|f(x)| = f(x)$ when $f(x) \geq 0$ and $|f(x)| = -f(x)$ when $f(x) < 0$.

The Graphs of |f(x)| and f(|x|) are Different

You'll probably have to draw the graph of a modulus function — and there are two different types.

1) For the graph of $y = |f(x)|$, any negative values of f(x) are made positive by reflecting them in the x-axis. This restricts the range of the modulus function to $|f(x)| \geq 0$ (or some subset within $|f(x)| \geq 0$, e.g. $|f(x)| \geq 1$).
2) For the graph of $y = f(|x|)$, the negative x-values produce the same result as the corresponding positive x-values. So the graph of f(x) for $x \geq 0$ is reflected in the y-axis for the negative x-values.
3) The easiest way to draw these graphs is to draw f(x) (ignoring the modulus for now), then reflect it in the appropriate axis. This will probably make more sense when you've had a look at a couple of examples:

EXAMPLE Draw the graphs of $y = |f(x)|$ and $y = f(|x|)$ for the functions $f(x) = 5x - 5$ and $f(x) = x^2 - 4x$.

y = |f(x)|
f(x) = 5x – 5
y = f(|x|)
For negative x-values, reflect the line in the y-axis.
Reflect the negative part of the line in the x-axis.
y = |f(x)|
y = f(|x|)
f(x) = x² – 4x

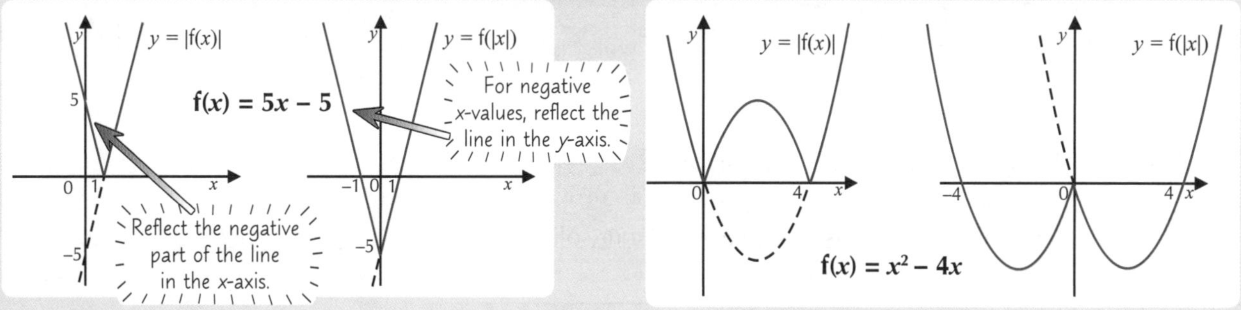

EXAMPLE

Draw the graph of the function $f(x) = \begin{cases} |2x+1| & x < 0 \\ \sqrt{x} & x \geq 0 \end{cases}$.

Sometimes functions are made up of two or more parts — for x between certain values, the function does one thing, but for other values of x it behaves differently.

Draw on each part of the graph separately.
y = |2x + 1|
y = √x

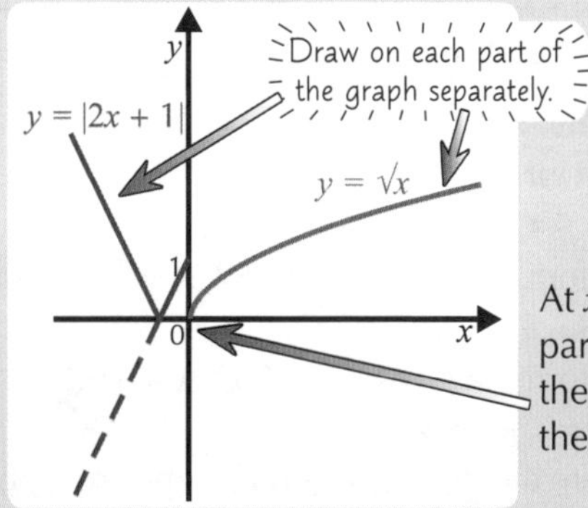

At $x = 0$, $y = |2(0) + 1| = 1$ for the first part of the function and $y = \sqrt{0} = 0$ for the second part of the function — so there'll be a gap in the graph.

Modulus built the city of Mode...

You might have to draw modulus graphs for functions like f(x) = ax + b from scratch. You could be asked for trig graphs and exponentials too. For harder graphs, you'll often be given a graph which you can use as a starting point for the modulus.

Modulus

An exam question might ask you to solve an equation like '$|f(x)| = n$' (for a constant n) or '$|f(x)| = g(x)$' for a function g. I admit, it would be more exciting to solve a crime, but I'm afraid modulus functions must come first...

Solving modulus functions usually produces More Than One solution

Here comes the method for solving '$|f(x)| = n$'. Solving '$|f(x)| = g(x)$' is exactly the same — just replace n with $g(x)$.

Solving Modulus Equations of the form $|f(x)| = n$

1) **First, sketch the functions $y = |f(x)|$ and $y = n$, on the same axes.** ← The solutions you're trying to find are where they intersect.
2) **From the graph, work out the ranges of x for which $f(x) \geq 0$ and $f(x) < 0$:**
   E.g. $f(x) \geq 0$ for $x \leq a$ or $x \geq b$ and $f(x) < 0$ for $a < x < b$ ← These ranges should 'fit together' to cover all possible x values.
3) **Use this to write two new equations, one true for each range of x...**
   (1) $f(x) = n$ for $x \leq a$ or $x \geq b$ ← The original equation '$|f(x)| = n$' becomes '$f(x) = n$' in the range where $f(x) \geq 0$...
   (2) $-f(x) = n$ for $a < x < b$ ← ...and it becomes '$-f(x) = n$' in the range where $f(x) < 0$.
4) **Now just solve each equation and check that any solutions are valid — get rid of any solutions outside the range of x you've got for that equation.**
5) **Look at the graph and check that your solutions look right.**

Sketch the Graph to see How Many Solutions there are

EXAMPLE Solve $|x^2 - 9| = 7$.

1) First off, sketch the graphs of $y = |x^2 - 9|$ and $y = 7$. They cross at 4 different points, so there should be 4 solutions.
2) Now find out where $f(x) \geq 0$ and $f(x) < 0$:
   $x^2 - 9 \geq 0$ for $x \leq -3$ or $x \geq 3$, and $x^2 - 9 < 0$ for $-3 < x < 3$

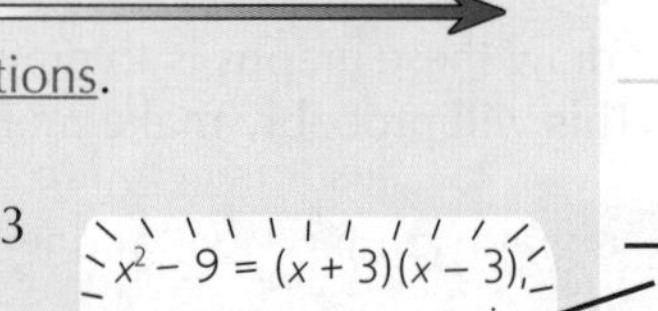

$x^2 - 9 = (x + 3)(x - 3)$,
so curve crosses x-axis
at 3 and -3.

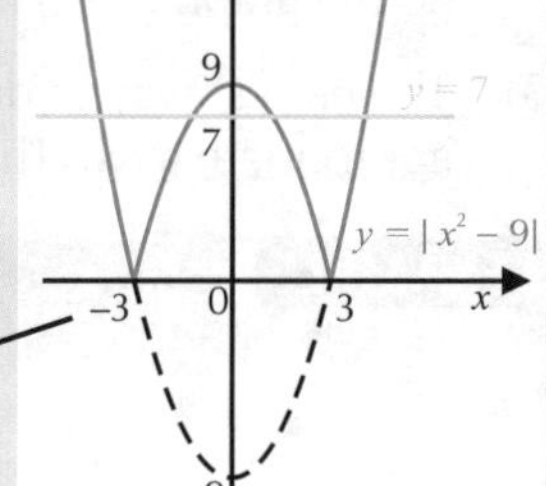

3) Form two equations for the different ranges of x:
   (1) $x^2 - 9 = 7$ for $x \leq -3$ or $x \geq 3$
   (2) $-(x^2 - 9) = 7$ for $-3 < x < 3$
4) Solving (1) gives: $x^2 = 16 \Rightarrow x = 4, x = -4$
   Check they're valid: $x = -4$ is in '$x \leq -3$' and $x = 4$ is in '$x \geq 3$' — so they're both valid.
   Solving (2) gives: $x^2 - 2 = 0 \Rightarrow x^2 = 2$ so $x = \sqrt{2}, x = -\sqrt{2}$.
   Check they're valid: $x = \sqrt{2}$ and $x = -\sqrt{2}$ are both within $-3 < x < 3$ — so they're also both valid.
5) Check back against the graphs — we've found four solutions and they're in the right places. Nice.

EXAMPLE Solve $|x^2 - 2x - 3| = 1 - x$.

1) Sketch $y = |x^2 - 2x - 3|$ and $y = 1 - x$. The graphs cross twice.
2) Looking at where $f(x) \geq 0$ and where $f(x) < 0$ gives...
3) (1) $x^2 - 2x - 3 = 1 - x$ for $x \leq -1$ or $x \geq 3$
   (2) $-(x^2 - 2x - 3) = 1 - x$ for $-1 < x < 3$.

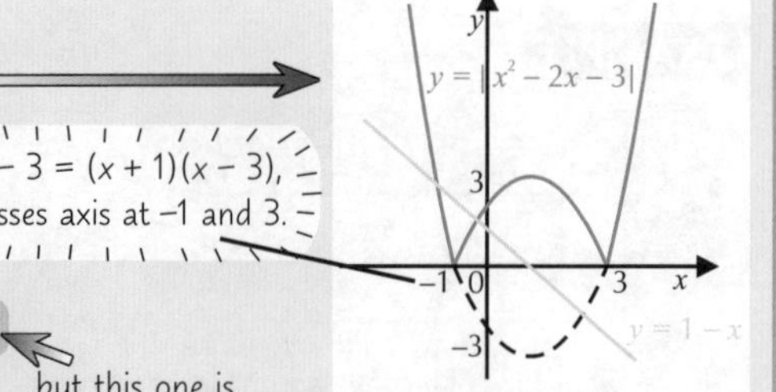

$x^2 - 2x - 3 = (x + 1)(x - 3)$,
so it crosses axis at -1 and 3.

4) Solving (1) using the quadratic formula gives $x = 2.562$, $x = -1.562$.
   $x \leq -1$ or $x \geq 3$, so this solution is not valid... ...but this one is.

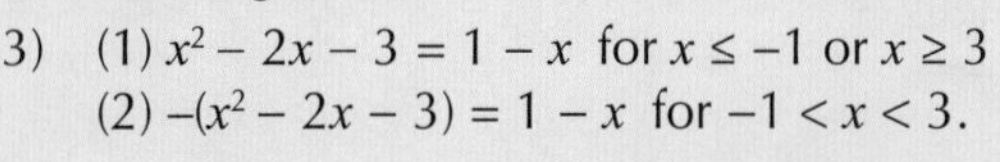

   Solving (2) using the quadratic formula gives $x = 3.562$, $x = -0.562$.
   $-1 < x < 3$, so this solution is not valid... ...but this one is.
5) Checking against the graph, there are two solutions and they're where we expected. El coolio.

How very interesting...

So if the effect of the modulus is to make a negative positive, I guess that means that |exam followed by detention followed by getting splashed by a car on the way home| = sleep-in followed by picnic followed by date with Hugh Jackman. I wish.

Transformations of Graphs

Back in C1, you came across transformations of graphs — vertical and horizontal translations, stretches and reflections. In C2, you saw the same transformations on trig graphs. As if that wasn't enough for you, you now need to be able to do combinations of transformations — more than one applied to the same graph.

There are Four main Transformations

The transformations you met in C1 and C2 are translations (adding things — a vertical or horizontal shift), stretches or squeezes (either vertical or horizontal) and reflections in the x- or y- axis. Here's a quick reminder of what each one does:

$y = f(x + c)$

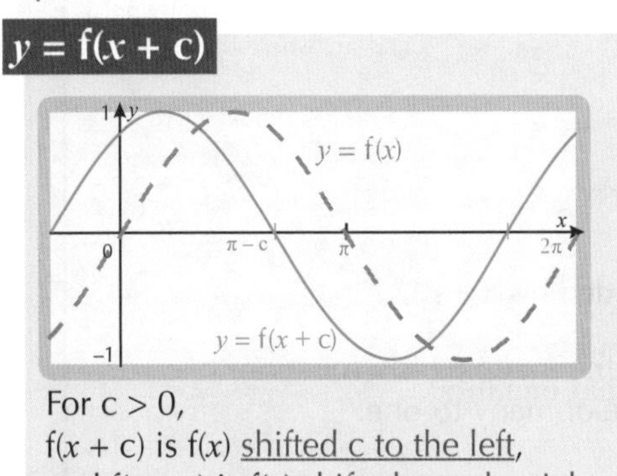

For c > 0, f(x + c) is f(x) shifted c to the left, and f(x – c) is f(x) shifted c to the right.

$y = f(x) + c$

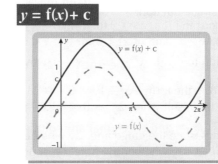

For c > 0, f(x) + c is f(x) shifted c upwards, and f(x) – c is f(x) shifted c downwards.

All these graphs use f(x) = sin x.

$y = af(x)$

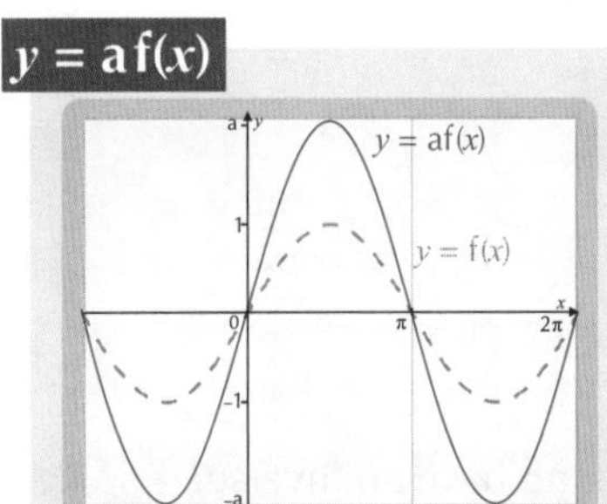

If a > 1, the graph of af(x) is f(x) stretched vertically by a factor of a.

If 0 < a < 1, the graph is squashed.

And if a < 0, the graph is also reflected in the x-axis.

Remember that a squash by a factor of a is really a stretch by a factor of $1/a$.

$y = f(ax)$

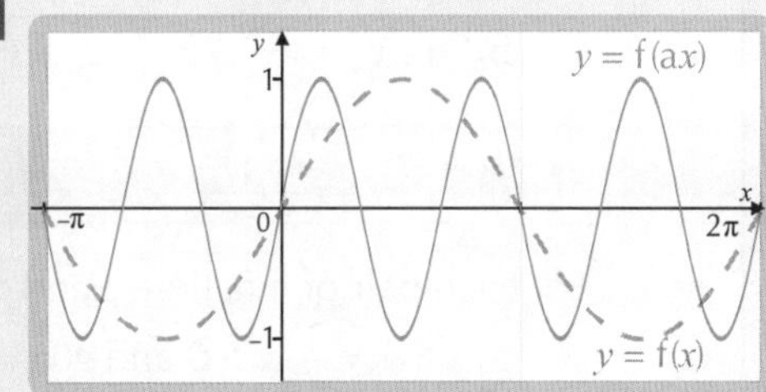

If a > 1, the graph of f(ax) is f(x) squashed horizontally by a factor of a.

If 0 < a < 1, the graph is stretched horizontally.

And if a < 0, the graph is also reflected in the y-axis.

Do Combinations of Transformations One at a Time

Combinations of transformations can look a bit tricky, but if you take them one step at a time they're not too bad. Don't try and do all the transformations at once — break it up into separate bits (as above) and draw a graph for each stage.

EXAMPLE The graph shows the function $y = f(x)$. Draw the graph of $y = 3f(x + 2)$, showing the coordinates of the turning points.

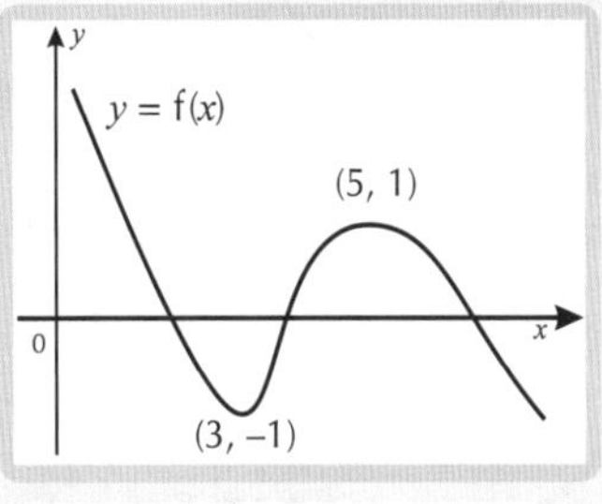

Make sure you do the transformations the right way round — you should do the bit in the brackets first.

Don't try to do everything at once. First draw the graph of $y = f(x + 2)$ and work out the coordinates of the turning points.

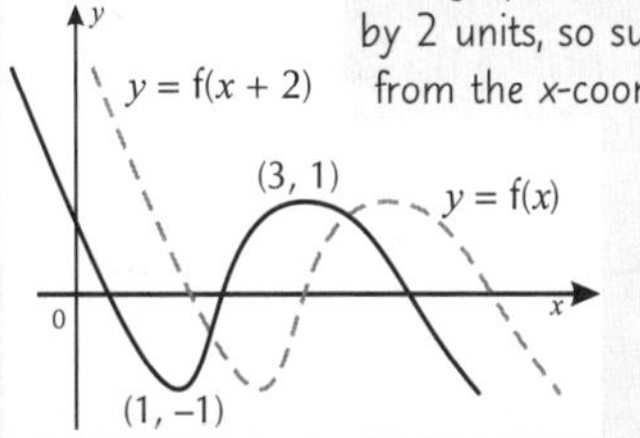

The graph is shifted left by 2 units, so subtract 2 from the x-coordinates.

Now use your graph of $y = f(x + 2)$ to draw the graph of $y = 3f(x + 2)$.

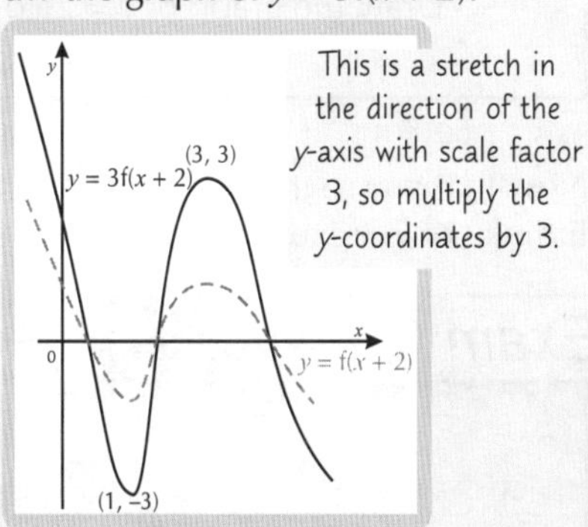

This is a stretch in the direction of the y-axis with scale factor 3, so multiply the y-coordinates by 3.

Tea and cake — the perfect combination...

Working out coordinates can be a bit tricky. The easiest way to do it is to work out what you're doing to the graph, then think about what that does to each point. Have a look at your transformed graph and check that the new coordinates make sense.

C3 Section 1 — Practice Questions

Well, that's the first section over and done with, and what better way to round it off than with some lovely questions. Have a go at these warm-up questions to get you in the mood.

Warm-up Questions

1) Simplify the following:

   a) $\frac{4x^2 - 25}{6x - 15}$ b) $\frac{2x+3}{x-2} \times \frac{4x-8}{2x^2-3x-9}$ c) $\frac{x^2-3x}{x+1} \div \frac{x}{2}$

2) Write the following as a single fraction:

   a) $\frac{x}{2x+1} + \frac{3}{x^2} + \frac{1}{x}$ b) $\frac{2}{x^2-1} - \frac{3x}{x-1} + \frac{x}{x+1}$

3) Use algebraic long division to divide $x^3 + 2x^2 - x + 19$ by $x + 4$.

4) Write $2x^3 + 8x^2 + 7x + 8$ in the form $(Ax^2 + Bx + C)(x + 3) + D$.
   Using your answer, state the result when $2x^3 + 8x^2 + 7x + 8$ is divided by $(x + 3)$.

5) For the following mappings, state the range and say whether or not the mapping is a function.
   If not, explain why, and if so, say whether the function is one-to-one or many-to-one.

   a) $f(x) = x^2 - 16,\ x \geq 0$
   b) $f : x \to x^2 - 7x + 10,\ x \in \mathbb{R}$
   c) $f(x) = \sqrt{x},\ x \in \mathbb{R}$
   d) $f : x \to \frac{1}{x-2},\ x \in \mathbb{R}$

6) For each pair of functions f and g, find fg(2), gf(1) and fg(x).

   a) $f(x) = \frac{3}{x},\ x > 0$ and $g(x) = 2x + 3,\ x \in \mathbb{R}$
   b) $f(x) = 3x^2,\ x \geq 0$ and $g(x) = x + 4,\ x \in \mathbb{R}$

7) A one-to-one function f has domain $x \in \mathbb{R}$ and range $f(x) \geq 3$. Does this function have an inverse?
   If so, state its domain and range.

8) Using algebra, find the inverse of the function $f(x) = \sqrt{2x-4},\ x \geq 2$.
   State the domain and range of the inverse.

9) For the function $f(x) = 2x - 1\ \{x \in \mathbb{R}\}$, sketch the graphs of:

   a) $|f(x)|$
   b) $f(|x|)$

10) Use your graph from part 9) a) to help you solve the equation
   $|2x - 1| = 5$.

11) The function $y = f(x)$ is shown on the graph on the right.
   Draw the graph of $y = 2f(x) + 1$.

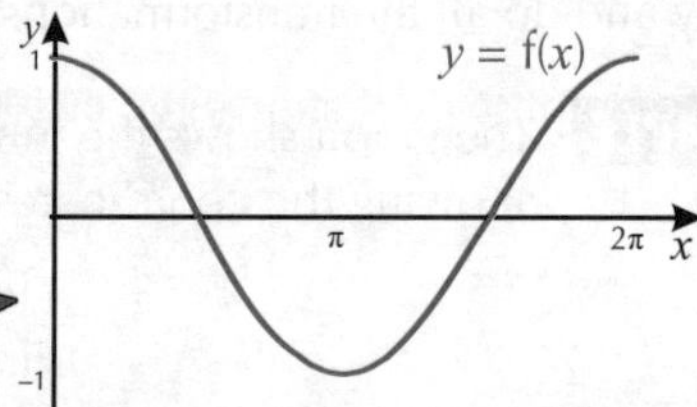

Now that you're in the algebra and functions zone (not to be confused with the twilight zone or the phantom zone), I think you're ready to have a go at some exam-style questions.

Exam Questions

1 Write $\frac{2x^2 - 9x - 35}{x^2 - 49}$ as a fraction in its simplest form.

(3 marks)

2 In words, describe what happens to the curve $y = x^3$ to transform it into the curve $y = 2(x-1)^3 + 4$.

(6 marks)

C3 Section 1 — Practice Questions

They were nice questions to ease you in gently. I have to warn you, they get a bit harder on this page. It's nothing you can't handle though. Just arm yourself with a mosquito net, an invisibility cloak and some algebraic knowledge and you'll be fine.

3 The functions f and g are given by: $f(x) = x^2 - 3$, $x \in \mathbb{R}$ and $g(x) = \frac{1}{x}$, $x \in \mathbb{R}, x \neq 0$.

a) Find an expression for $gf(x)$. *(2 marks)*

b) Solve $gf(x) = \frac{1}{6}$. *(3 marks)*

4 Write $x^3 + 15x^2 + 43x - 30$ in the form $(Ax^2 + Bx + C)(x + 6) + D$, where A, B, C and D are constants to be found. *(3 marks)*

5 For the functions f and g, where

$$f(x) = 2^x,\ x \in \mathbb{R} \qquad \text{and} \qquad g(x) = \sqrt{3x - 2},\ x \geq \tfrac{2}{3},$$

find:

a) $fg(6)$ *(2 marks)*

b) $gf(2)$ *(2 marks)*

c) (i) $g^{-1}(x)$ *(2 marks)*

(ii) $fg^{-1}(x)$ *(2 marks)*

6 The function f(x) is defined as follows: $f: x \to \frac{1}{x+5}$, domain $x > -5$.

a) State the range of f(x). *(1 mark)*

b) (i) Find the inverse function, $f^{-1}(x)$. *(3 marks)*

(ii) State the domain and range of $f^{-1}(x)$. *(2 marks)*

c) On the same axes, sketch the graphs of $y = f(x)$ and $y = f^{-1}(x)$. *(2 marks)*

7 The graph below shows the curve $y = f(x)$, and the intercepts of the curve with the x- and y-axes.

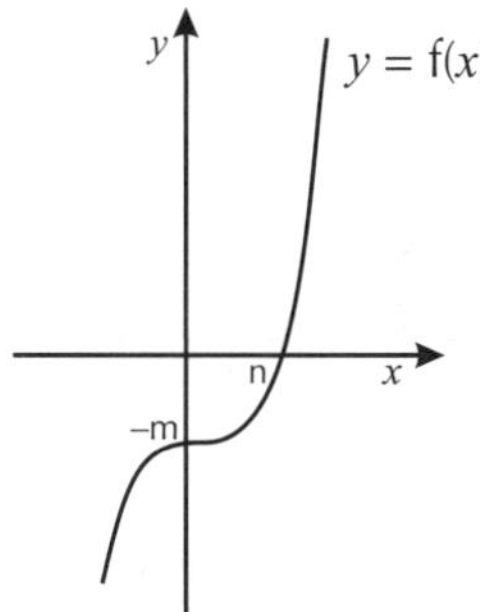

Sketch the graphs of the following transformations on separate axes, clearly labelling the points of intersection with the x- and y-axes in terms of m and n.

a) $y = |f(x)|$ *(2 marks)*

b) $y = -3f(x)$ *(2 marks)*

c) $y = f(|x|)$ *(2 marks)*

Arcsine, Arccosine and Arctangent

So here we go, forging deep into the mathematical jungle that is trigonometry.
Up first it's inverse trig functions — you need to know what they are, and what their graphs look like...

Arcsin, Arccos and Arctan are the Inverses of Sin, Cos and Tan

In Section 1 you saw that some functions have inverses, which reverse the effect of the function. The trig functions have inverses too.

ARCSINE is the inverse of sine. You might see it written as arcsin or $\sin^{-1}$.

ARCCOSINE is the inverse of cosine. You might see it written as arccos or $\cos^{-1}$.

ARCTANGENT is the inverse of tangent. You might see it written as arctan or $\tan^{-1}$.

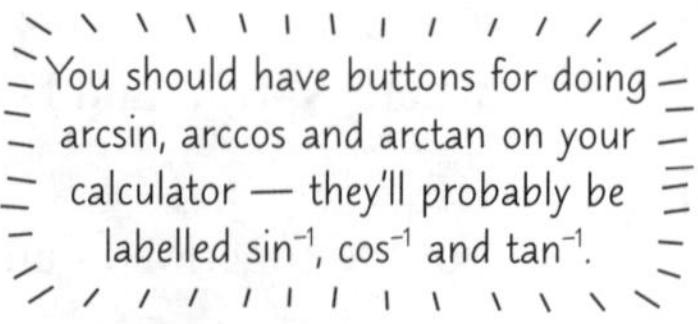

You should have buttons for doing arcsin, arccos and arctan on your calculator — they'll probably be labelled sin⁻¹, cos⁻¹ and tan⁻¹.

The inverse trig functions reverse the effect of sin, cos and tan.
For example, if sin 30° = 0.5, then arcsin 0.5 = 30°.

To Graph the Inverse Functions you need to Restrict their Domains

1) The functions sine, cosine and tangent are NOT one-to-one mappings (see p.4) — lots of values of x give the same value for $\sin x$, $\cos x$ or $\tan x$. For example: $\cos 0 = \cos 2\pi = \cos 4\pi = 1$, and $\tan 0 = \tan \pi = \tan 2\pi = 0$.
2) Only one-to-one functions have inverses, so for the inverse to be a function you have to restrict the domain of the trig function to make it one-to-one (see graphs below). This means that you only plot the graphs between certain x values, so that for each x value, you end up with one y value.
3) As the graphs are inverse functions, they're also reflections of the sin, cos and tan functions in the line $y = x$.

ARCSINE

For arcsin, limit the domain of $\sin x$ to $-\frac{\pi}{2} \leq x \leq \frac{\pi}{2}$ (the range of $\sin x$ is still $-1 \leq \sin x \leq 1$).

This means the domain of $\arcsin x$ is $-1 \leq x \leq 1$ and its range is $-\frac{\pi}{2} \leq \arcsin x \leq \frac{\pi}{2}$.

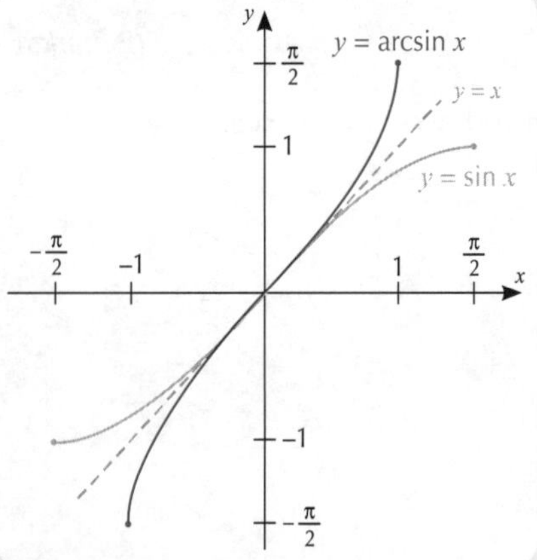

This graph goes through the origin.

The coordinates of its endpoints are $(1, \frac{\pi}{2})$ and $(-1, -\frac{\pi}{2})$.

ARCCOSINE

For arccos, limit the domain of $\cos x$ to $0 \leq x \leq \pi$ (the range of $\cos x$ is still $-1 \leq \cos x \leq 1$).

This means the domain of $\arccos x$ is $-1 \leq x \leq 1$ and its range is $0 \leq \arccos x \leq \pi$.

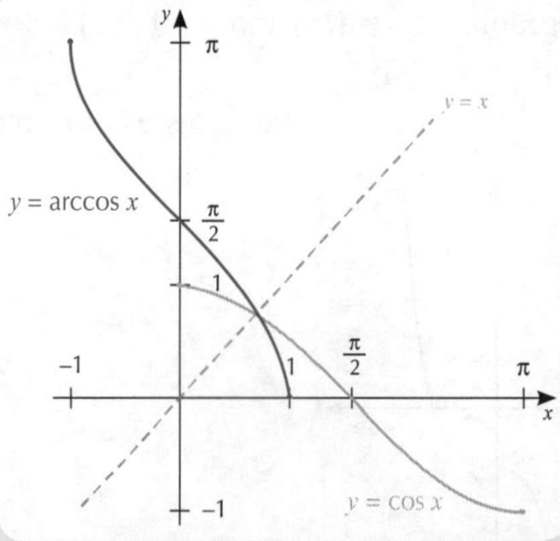

This graph crosses the y-axis at $(0, \frac{\pi}{2})$.

The coordinates of its endpoints are $(-1, \pi)$ and $(1, 0)$.

ARCTANGENT

For arctan, limit the domain of $\tan x$ to $-\frac{\pi}{2} \leq x \leq \frac{\pi}{2}$ (this doesn't limit the range of $\tan x$).

This means that the domain of $\arctan x$ isn't limited, but its range is limited to $-\frac{\pi}{2} \leq \arctan x \leq \frac{\pi}{2}$.

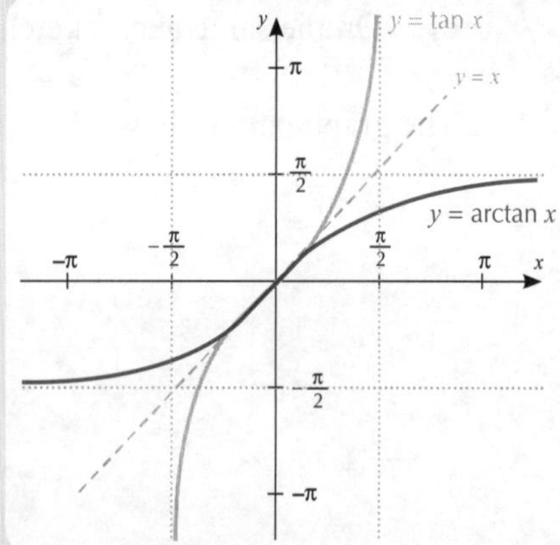

This graph goes through the origin.

It has asymptotes at $y = \frac{\pi}{2}$ and $y = -\frac{\pi}{2}$.

So applying the inverse function reverses everything...

It's really important that you can recognise the graphs of the inverse trig functions — you need to know what shape they are, what restricted domains you need to use to draw them, and any significant points, like where they end or where they cross the axes. You can check the graph by reflecting the curve in the line $y = x$ and seeing if you get the trig function you want.

Secant, Cosecant and Cotangent

Just when you thought you'd seen all the functions that trigonometry could throw at you, here come three more. These ones are pretty important — they'll come in really handy when you're solving trig equations.

Cosec, Sec and Cot are the Reciprocals of Sin, Cos and Tan

When you take the reciprocal of the three main trig functions, sin, cos and tan, you get three new trig functions — cosecant (or cosec), secant (or sec) and cotangent (or cot).

$$\text{cosec}\,\theta \equiv \frac{1}{\sin\theta} \qquad \sec\theta \equiv \frac{1}{\cos\theta} \qquad \cot\theta \equiv \frac{1}{\tan\theta}$$

The trick for remembering which is which is to look at the third letter — co*s*ec (1/*s*in), se*c* (1/*c*os) and co*t* (1/*t*an).

Since $\tan\theta = \frac{\sin\theta}{\cos\theta}$, you can also think of cot θ as being $\frac{\cos\theta}{\sin\theta}$.

Graphing Cosec, Sec and Cot

COSEC This is the graph of $y = \text{cosec}\,x$.

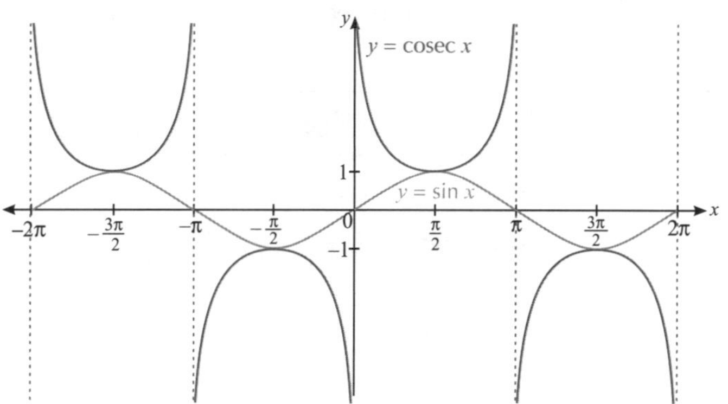

1) Since $\text{cosec}\,x = \frac{1}{\sin x}$, $y = \text{cosec}\,x$ is undefined at any point where $\sin x = 0$. So cosec x has asymptotes at $x = n\pi$ (where n is any integer).
2) The graph of cosec x has minimum points at $y = 1$ (wherever the graph of sin x has a maximum).
3) It has maximum points at $y = -1$ (wherever sin x has a minimum).

SEC This is the graph of $y = \sec x$.

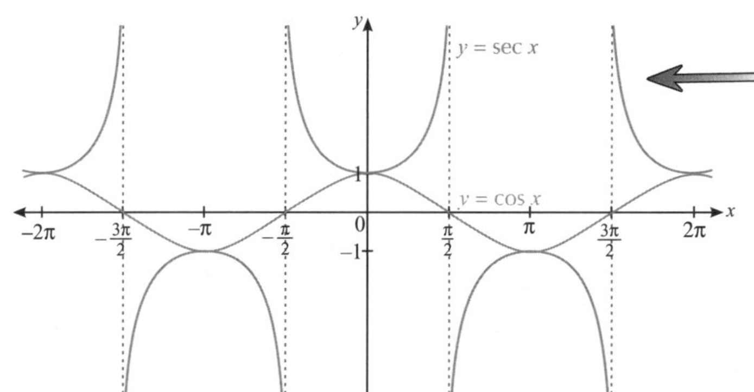

1) As $\sec x = \frac{1}{\cos x}$, $y = \sec x$ is undefined at any point where $\cos x = 0$. So sec x has asymptotes at $x = \left(n\pi + \frac{\pi}{2}\right)$ (where n is any integer).
2) The graph of sec x has minimum points at $y = 1$ (wherever the graph of cos x has a maximum).
3) It has maximum points at $y = -1$ (wherever cos x has a minimum).

COT This is the graph of $y = \cot x$.

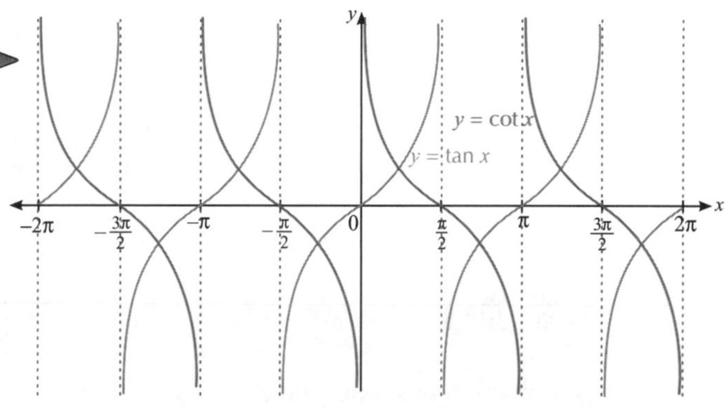

1) Since $\cot x = \frac{1}{\tan x}$, $y = \cot x$ is undefined at any point where $\tan x = 0$. So cot x has asymptotes at $x = n\pi$ (where n is any integer).
2) $y = \cot x$ crosses the x-axis at every place where the graph of tan x has an asymptote — this is any point with the coordinates $\left(\left(n\pi + \frac{\pi}{2}\right), 0\right)$.

Why did I multiply cot x by sin x? Just 'cos...

Remember to look at the third letter to work out which trig function it's the reciprocal of. I'm afraid you do need to be able to sketch the three graphs from memory. Someone in examiner world clearly has a bit of a graph-sketching obsession. You might have to transform a trig graph too — you use the same method as you would for other graphs (see p.9).

Using Trigonometric Identities

Ahh, trig identities. More useful than a monkey wrench, and more fun than rice pudding. Probably.

Learn these Three Trig Identities

Hopefully you remember using this handy little trig identity before:

IDENTITY 1: $\cos^2\theta + \sin^2\theta \equiv 1$

The ≡ sign tells you that this is true for all values of θ, rather than just certain values.

You can use it to produce a couple of other identities that you need to know about...

IDENTITY 2: $\sec^2\theta \equiv 1 + \tan^2\theta$

To get this, you just take everything in Identity 1, and divide it by $\cos^2\theta$:

$$\frac{\cos^2\theta}{\cos^2\theta} + \frac{\sin^2\theta}{\cos^2\theta} \equiv \frac{1}{\cos^2\theta}$$
$$1 + \tan^2\theta \equiv \sec^2\theta$$

Remember that $\cos^2\theta = (\cos\theta)^2$.

IDENTITY 3: $\text{cosec}^2\theta \equiv 1 + \cot^2\theta$

You get this one by dividing everything in Identity 1 by $\sin^2\theta$:

$$\frac{\cos^2\theta}{\sin^2\theta} + \frac{\sin^2\theta}{\sin^2\theta} \equiv \frac{1}{\sin^2\theta}$$
$$\cot^2\theta + 1 \equiv \text{cosec}^2\theta$$

Use the Trig Identities to Simplify Equations...

You can use identities to get rid of any trig functions that are making an equation difficult to solve.

EXAMPLE Solve the equation $\cot^2 x + 5 = 4\,\text{cosec}\,x$ in the interval $0° \le x \le 360°$.

You can't solve this while it has both cot and cosec in it, so use Identity 3 to swap $\cot^2 x$ for $\text{cosec}^2 x - 1$.

$$\text{cosec}^2 x - 1 + 5 = 4\,\text{cosec}\,x$$

Now rearranging the equation gives: $\text{cosec}^2 x + 4 = 4\,\text{cosec}\,x \Rightarrow \text{cosec}^2 x - 4\,\text{cosec}\,x + 4 = 0$

So you've got a quadratic in cosec x — factorise it like you would any other quadratic equation.

$$\text{cosec}^2 x - 4\,\text{cosec}\,x + 4 = 0$$
$$(\text{cosec}\,x - 2)(\text{cosec}\,x - 2) = 0$$

If it helps, think of this as $y^2 - 4y + 4 = 0$. Factorise it, and then replace the y with cosec x.

One of the brackets must be equal to zero — here they're both the same, so you only get one equation:

$$(\text{cosec}\,x - 2) = 0 \Rightarrow \text{cosec}\,x = 2$$

Now you can convert this into $\sin x$, and solve it easily:

$$\text{cosec}\,x = 2 \Rightarrow \sin x = \tfrac{1}{2}$$
$$x = 30° \text{ or } x = 150°$$

To find the other values of x, draw a quick sketch of the sin curve: From the graph, you can see that $\sin x$ takes the value of ½ twice in the given interval, once at $x = 30°$ and once at $x = 180 - 30 = 150°$.

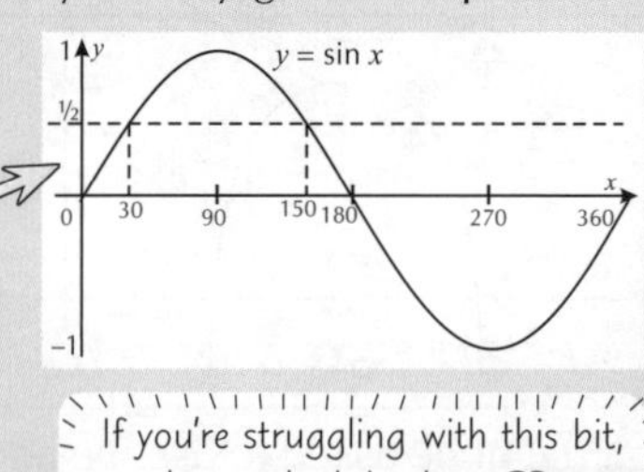

If you're struggling with this bit, have a look back at C2.

...or to Prove that two things are The Same

You can also use identities to prove that two trig expressions are the same, like this:

EXAMPLE Show that $\frac{\tan^2 x}{\sec x} \equiv \sec x - \cos x$.

You need to take one side of the identity and play about with it until you get the other side. ⟹ Left-hand side: $\frac{\tan^2 x}{\sec x}$.

Try replacing $\tan^2 x$ with $\sec^2 x - 1$: $\equiv \frac{\sec^2 x - 1}{\sec x} \equiv \frac{\sec^2 x}{\sec x} - \frac{1}{\sec x} \equiv \sec x - \cos x$ ...which is the right-hand side.

The Addition Formulas

You might have noticed that there are quite a lot of formulas lurking in this here trigonometry jungle. There are some more coming up on this page I'm afraid, so brace yourself — they're all about adding and subtracting angles...

You can use the *Addition Formulas* to find *Sums of Angles*

You can use the addition formulas to find the sin, cos or tan of the sum or difference of two angles.

When you have an expression like sin $(x + 60°)$ or cos $(n - \frac{\pi}{2})$, you can use these formulas to expand the brackets.

These formulas are given to you on the formula sheet.

$$\sin(A \pm B) \equiv \sin A \cos B \pm \cos A \sin B$$

$$\cos(A \pm B) \equiv \cos A \cos B \mp \sin A \sin B$$

$$\tan(A \pm B) \equiv \frac{\tan A \pm \tan B}{1 \mp \tan A \tan B}$$

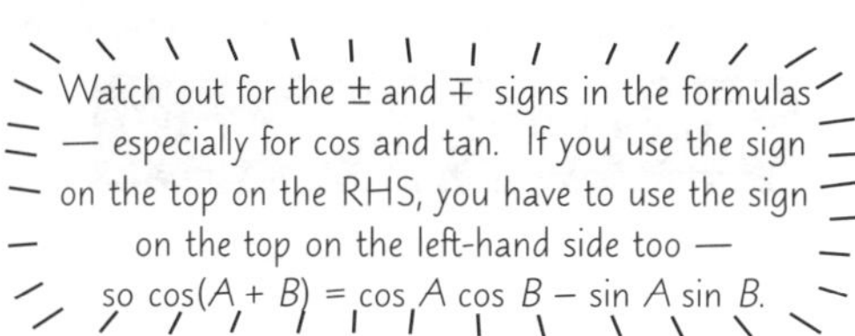

Watch out for the ± and ∓ signs in the formulas — especially for cos and tan. If you use the sign on the top on the RHS, you have to use the sign on the top on the left-hand side too — so cos(A + B) = cos A cos B – sin A sin B.

Use the *Formulas* to find the *Exact Value* of trig expressions

1) You should know the value of sin, cos and tan for common angles (in degrees and radians). These values come from using Pythagoras on right-angled triangles — you did it in C2.
2) In the exam you might be asked to calculate the exact value of sin, cos or tan for another angle using your knowledge of those angles and the addition formulas.
3) Find a pair of angles from the table which add or subtract to give the angle you're after. Then plug them into the addition formula, and work it through.

	0° 0	30° $\frac{\pi}{6}$	45° $\frac{\pi}{4}$	60° $\frac{\pi}{3}$	90° $\frac{\pi}{2}$
sin	0	$\frac{1}{2}$	$\frac{1}{\sqrt{2}}$	$\frac{\sqrt{3}}{2}$	1
cos	1	$\frac{\sqrt{3}}{2}$	$\frac{1}{\sqrt{2}}$	$\frac{1}{2}$	0
tan	0	$\frac{1}{\sqrt{3}}$	1	$\sqrt{3}$	n/a

EXAMPLE Using the addition formula for tangent, show that $\tan 15° = 2 - \sqrt{3}$.

Pick two angles that add or subtract to give 15°, and put them into the tan addition formula. It's easiest to use tan 60° and tan 45° here, since neither of them are fractions.

$$\tan 15° = \tan(60° - 45°) = \frac{\tan 60° - \tan 45°}{1 + \tan 60° \tan 45°}$$

Using $\tan(A - B) = \frac{\tan A - \tan B}{1 + \tan A \tan B}$

Substitute the values for tan 60° and tan 45° into the equation:

$$= \frac{\sqrt{3} - 1}{1 + (\sqrt{3} \times 1)} = \frac{\sqrt{3} - 1}{\sqrt{3} + 1}$$

Now rationalise the denominator of the fraction to get rid of the $\sqrt{3}$.

$$\frac{\sqrt{3} - 1}{\sqrt{3} + 1} \times \frac{\sqrt{3} - 1}{\sqrt{3} - 1} = \frac{3 - 2\sqrt{3} + 1}{3 - \sqrt{3} + \sqrt{3} - 1}$$

If you can't remember how to rationalise the denominator have a peek at your C1 notes.

Simplify the expression... $= \frac{4 - 2\sqrt{3}}{2} = 2 - \sqrt{3}$ ...and there's the right-hand side.

You can use these formulas to *Prove Identities* too

You might be asked to use the addition formulas to prove an identity. All you need to do is put the numbers and variables from the left-hand side into the addition formulas and simplify until you get the expression you're after.

EXAMPLE Prove that $\cos(a + 60°) + \sin(a + 30°) \equiv \cos a$

Be careful with the + and – signs here.

Put the numbers from the question into the addition formulas:

$$\cos(a + 60°) + \sin(a + 30°) \equiv (\cos a \cos 60° - \sin a \sin 60°) + (\sin a \cos 30° + \cos a \sin 30°)$$

Now substitute in any sin and cos values that you know...

$$= \frac{1}{2}\cos a - \frac{\sqrt{3}}{2}\sin a + \frac{\sqrt{3}}{2}\sin a + \frac{1}{2}\cos a$$

..and simplify:

$$= \frac{1}{2}\cos a + \frac{1}{2}\cos a = \cos a$$

This section's got more identities than Clark Kent...

I was devastated when my secret identity was revealed — I'd been masquerading as a mysterious caped criminal mastermind with an army of minions and a hidden underground lair. It was great fun, but I had to give it all up and write about trig.

The Double Angle Formulas

Whenever you see a trig expression with an even multiple of x in it, like $\sin 2x$, you can use one of the double angle formulas to prune it back to an expression just in terms of a single x.

There's a **Double Angle Formula** for **Each Trig Function**

Double angle formulas are just a slightly different kind of identity. They're called "double angle" formulas because they turn any tricky $2x$ type terms in trig equations back into plain x terms.

You need to know the double angle formulas for sin, cos and tan:

$$\cos 2A \equiv \cos^2 A - \sin^2 A$$
$$\text{or} \quad \equiv 2\cos^2 A - 1$$
$$\text{or} \quad \equiv 1 - 2\sin^2 A$$

$$\tan 2A \equiv \frac{2\tan A}{1 - \tan^2 A}$$

You can use the identity $\cos^2 A + \sin^2 A \equiv 1$ to get the other versions of the cos $2A$ formula.

You get these formulas by writing $2A$ as $A + A$ and using the addition formulas from the previous page.

Use the **Double Angle Formulas** to **Simplify** and **Solve Equations**

If an equation has a mixture of $\sin x$ and $\sin 2x$ terms in it, there's not much that you can do with it. So that you can simplify it, and then solve it, you have to use one of the double angle formulas.

EXAMPLE Solve the equation $\cos 2x - 5\cos x = 2$ in the interval $0 \leq x \leq 2\pi$.

First use the double angle formula $\cos 2A \equiv 2\cos^2 A - 1$ to get rid of $\cos 2x$ (use this version so that you don't end up with a mix of sin and cos terms).

$$2\cos^2 x - 1 - 5\cos x = 2$$

Simplify so you have zero on one side...
...then factorise and solve the quadratic that you've made:

$$2\cos^2 x - 5\cos x - 3 = 0$$
$$(2\cos x + 1)(\cos x - 3) = 0$$
$$\text{So } (2\cos x + 1) = 0 \text{ or } (\cos x - 3) = 0$$

The second bracket gives you $\cos x = 3$, which has no solutions since $-1 \leq \cos x \leq 1$.

So all that's left is to solve the first bracket to find x:

$$2\cos x + 1 = 0$$
$$\cos x = -\frac{1}{2} \Rightarrow x = \frac{2}{3}\pi \text{ or } x = \frac{4}{3}\pi.$$

Sketch the graph of $\cos x$ to find all values of x in the given interval: $\cos x = -½$ twice, once at $\frac{2}{3}\pi$ and once at $2\pi - \frac{2}{3}\pi = \frac{4}{3}\pi$.

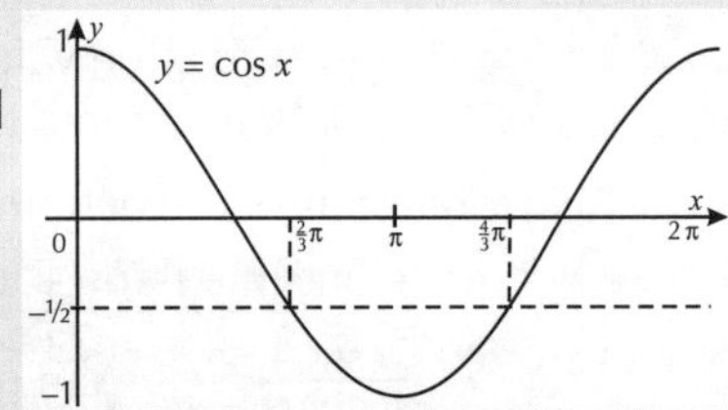

You can use a **Double Angle Formula** even when the x term **Isn't 2x**

Whenever you have an expression that contains any angle that's twice the size of another, you can use the double angle formulas — whether it's $\sin x$ and $\sin 2x$, $\cos 2x$ and $\cos 4x$ or $\tan x$ and $\tan \frac{x}{2}$.

EXAMPLE Prove that $2\cot \frac{x}{2}(1 - \cos^2 \frac{x}{2}) \equiv \sin x$

Use the identity $\sin^2\theta + \cos^2\theta \equiv 1$ to replace $1 - \cos^2 \frac{x}{2}$ on the left-hand side:

Left-hand side: $2\cot \frac{x}{2} \sin^2 \frac{x}{2}$

Now write $\cot\theta$ as $\frac{\cos\theta}{\sin\theta}$:

$$2\frac{\cos\frac{x}{2}}{\sin\frac{x}{2}}\sin^2\frac{x}{2} \equiv 2\cos\frac{x}{2}\sin\frac{x}{2}$$

Now you can use the sin $2A$ double angle formula to write $\sin x \equiv 2\sin\frac{x}{2}\cos\frac{x}{2}$ (using $A = \frac{x}{2}$).

So using the sin double angle formula... $\equiv \sin x$ ...you get the right-hand side.

You can work out half-angle formulas for cos and tan from the double angle formulas. This example uses the one for sin.

Double the angles, double the fun...

You definitely need to know the double angle formulas off by heart, because they won't be on the exam formula sheet. So it's a case of the old "learn 'em, write 'em out, and keep going until you can do all three perfectly" strategy. And don't forget to be on the lookout for sneaky questions that want you to use a double angle formula but don't contain a "$2x$" bit.

The R Addition Formulas

A different kind of addition formula this time — one that lets you go from an expanded expression to one with brackets...

Use the R Formulas when you've got a Mix of Sin and Cos

If you're solving an equation that contains both $\sin\theta$ and $\cos\theta$ terms, e.g. $3\sin\theta + 4\cos\theta = 1$, you need to rewrite it so that it only contains one trig function. The formulas that you use to do that are known as the *R* formulas:

One set for sine: $a\sin\theta \pm b\cos\theta \equiv R\sin(\theta \pm \alpha)$

And one set for cosine: $a\cos\theta \pm b\sin\theta \equiv R\cos(\theta \mp \alpha)$

where a and b are positive. Again, you need to be careful with the + and – signs here — see p.15.

Using the R Formulas

1) **You'll start with an identity like $2\sin x + 5\cos x \equiv R\sin(x + \alpha)$, where R and α need to be found.**
2) **First, expand the RHS using the addition formulas (see p.15): $2\sin x + 5\cos x \equiv R\sin x\cos\alpha + R\cos x\sin\alpha$.**
3) **Equate the coefficients of $\sin x$ and $\cos x$. You'll get two equations: ① $R\cos\alpha = 2$ and ② $R\sin\alpha = 5$.**
4) **To find α, divide equation ② by equation ①, then take $\tan^{-1}$ of the result.**
5) **To find R, square equations ① and ② and add them together, then take the square root of the answer.**

This is because $\frac{R\sin\alpha}{R\cos\alpha} = \tan\alpha$.

$(R\sin\alpha)^2 + (R\cos\alpha)^2 \equiv R^2(\sin^2\alpha + \cos^2\alpha) \equiv R^2$ (using the identity $\sin^2\alpha + \cos^2\alpha \equiv 1$).

This method looks a bit scary, but follow the example below through and it should make more sense.

Solve the equation in Stages

You'll almost always be asked to solve equations like this in different stages — first writing out the equation in the form of one of the *R* formulas, then solving it. You might also have to find the maximum or minimum value.

EXAMPLE (Part 1): Express $2\sin x - 3\cos x$ in the form $R\sin(x - \alpha)$, given that $R > 0$ and $0 \le \alpha \le 90°$.

$2\sin x - 3\cos x \equiv R\sin(x - \alpha)$, so expand the RHS to get $2\sin x - 3\cos x \equiv R(\sin x\cos\alpha - \cos x\sin\alpha)$.

Equating coefficients gives the equations $R\cos\alpha = 2$ and $R\sin\alpha = 3$.

Look at the coefficients of $\sin x$ on each side of the equation — on the LHS it's 2 and on the RHS it's $R\cos\alpha$, so $2 = R\cos\alpha$. You find the coefficient of $\cos x$ in the same way.

Solving for α: $\frac{R\sin\alpha}{R\cos\alpha} = \frac{3}{2} = \tan\alpha$

$\alpha = \tan^{-1} 1.5 = 56.31°$

This value fits into the correct range so you can leave it as it is.

Solving for R: $(R\cos\alpha)^2 + (R\sin\alpha)^2 = 2^2 + 3^2 = R^2$

$R = \sqrt{2^2 + 3^2} = \sqrt{13}$

So $2\sin x - 3\cos x = \sqrt{13}\sin(x - 56.31°)$

EXAMPLE (Part 2): Hence solve $2\sin x - 3\cos x = 1$ in the interval $0 \le x \le 360°$.

If $2\sin x - 3\cos x = 1$, that means $\sqrt{13}\sin(x - 56.31°) = 1$, so $\sin(x - 56.31°) = \frac{1}{\sqrt{13}}$.

$0 \le x \le 360°$, so $-56.31° \le x - 56.31° \le 303.69°$.

Careful — you're looking for solutions between $-56.31°$ and $303.69°$ here.

Solve the equation using arcsin:

$x - 56.31° = \sin^{-1}\left(\frac{1}{\sqrt{13}}\right) = 16.10°$ or $180 - 16.10 = 163.90°$.

So $x = 16.10 + 56.31 = 72.4°$ or $x = 163.90 + 56.31 = 220.2°$

EXAMPLE (Part 3): What are the max and min values of $2\sin x - 3\cos x$?

The maximum and minimum values of sin (and cos) are ± 1, so the maximum and minimum values of $R\sin(x - \alpha)$ are $\pm R$.

As $2\sin x - 3\cos x = \sqrt{13}\sin(x - 56.31°)$, $R = \sqrt{13}$, so the maximum and minimum values are $\pm\sqrt{13}$.

A pirate's favourite trigonometry formula...

The *R* formulas might look a bit scary, but they're OK really — just do lots of examples until you're happy with the method. Careful with the adjusting the interval bit that came up in part 2 above — it's pretty fiddly and easy to get muddled over.

More Trigonometry Stuff

And here we have the final trig page... a collection of random bits that didn't really fit on the other pages. That's one of the scary things about trig questions — you never know what you're going to get.

*The **Factor Formulas** come from the **Addition Formulas***

As if there weren't enough trig formulas already, here come a few more. Don't worry though — these ones are given to you on the exam formula sheet so you don't need to learn them off by heart.

$$\sin A + \sin B \equiv 2\sin\left(\frac{A+B}{2}\right)\cos\left(\frac{A-B}{2}\right)$$

$$\sin A - \sin B \equiv 2\cos\left(\frac{A+B}{2}\right)\sin\left(\frac{A-B}{2}\right)$$

$$\cos A + \cos B \equiv 2\cos\left(\frac{A+B}{2}\right)\cos\left(\frac{A-B}{2}\right)$$

$$\cos A - \cos B \equiv -2\sin\left(\frac{A+B}{2}\right)\sin\left(\frac{A-B}{2}\right)$$

These are the factor formulas, and they come from the addition formulas (see below). They come in handy for some integrations — it's a bit tricky to integrate $2\cos 3\theta\cos\theta$, but integrating $\cos 4\theta + \cos 2\theta$ is much easier.

EXAMPLE Use the addition formulas to show that $\cos A + \cos B \equiv 2\cos\left(\frac{A+B}{2}\right)\cos\left(\frac{A-B}{2}\right)$

You can derive the other formulas using the same method.

Use the cos addition formulas: $\cos(x+y) \equiv \cos x\cos y - \sin x\sin y$ and $\cos(x-y) \equiv \cos x\cos y + \sin x\sin y$.

Add them together to get: $\cos(x+y) + \cos(x-y) \equiv \cos x\cos y - \sin x\sin y + \cos x\cos y + \sin x\sin y$
$\equiv 2\cos x\cos y$.

Now substitute in $A = x + y$ and $B = x - y$.

Subtracting these gives $A - B = x + y - (x - y) = 2y$, so $y = \frac{A-B}{2}$.

Adding gives $A + B = x + y + (x - y) = 2x$, so $x = \frac{A+B}{2}$.

So $\cos A + \cos B \equiv 2\cos\left(\frac{A+B}{2}\right)\cos\left(\frac{A-B}{2}\right)$.

*You might have to use **Different Bits** of **Trig** in the **Same Question***

Some exam questions might try and catch you out by making you use more than one identity to show that two things are equal...

EXAMPLE Show that $\cos 3\theta \equiv 4\cos^3\theta - 3\cos\theta$.

You have to use both the addition formula and the double angle formulas in this question.

First, write $\cos 3\theta$ as $\cos(2\theta + \theta)$, then you can use the cos addition formula:
$\cos(3\theta) \equiv \cos(2\theta + \theta) \equiv \cos 2\theta\cos\theta - \sin 2\theta\sin\theta$.

Now you can use the cos and sin double angle formulas to get rid of the 2θ:
$\cos 2\theta\cos\theta - \sin 2\theta\sin\theta \equiv (2\cos^2\theta - 1)\cos\theta - (2\sin\theta\cos\theta)\sin\theta$

$\equiv 2\cos^3\theta - \cos\theta - 2\sin^2\theta\cos\theta \equiv 2\cos^3\theta - \cos\theta - 2(1 - \cos^2\theta)\cos\theta$

$\equiv 2\cos^3\theta - \cos\theta - 2\cos\theta + 2\cos^3\theta \equiv 4\cos^3\theta - 3\cos\theta$.

This uses the identity $\sin^2\theta + \cos^2\theta \equiv 1$ in the form $\sin^2\theta \equiv 1 - \cos^2\theta$.

...or even drag up trig knowledge from C2 or even GCSE. This question looks short and sweet, but it's actually pretty nasty — you need to know a sneaky conversion between sin and cos.

EXAMPLE If $y = \arcsin x$ for $-1 \le x \le 1$ and $-\frac{\pi}{2} \le y \le \frac{\pi}{2}$, show that $\arccos x = \frac{\pi}{2} - y$.

$y = \arcsin x$, so $x = \sin y$ (as arcsin is the inverse of sin).

Now the next bit isn't obvious — you need to use an identity to switch from sin to cos. This gives... $x = \cos(\frac{\pi}{2} - y)$.

Now, taking inverses gives $\arccos x = \arccos(\cos(\frac{\pi}{2} - y))$, so $\arccos x = \frac{\pi}{2} - y$.

Converting Sin to Cos (and back):
$\sin t \equiv \cos(\frac{\pi}{2} - t)$
and $\cos t \equiv \sin(\frac{\pi}{2} - t)$.
Remember sin is just cos shifted by $\frac{\pi}{2}$ and vice versa.

Trig is like a box of chocolates...

You'll be pleased to know that you've seen all the trig formulas you need for C3. I know there are about 1000 of them (N.B. exaggerations like this may lose you marks in the exam), but any of them could pop up. Examiners particularly like it when you have to use one identity or formula to prove or derive another, so get practising. Then go off and have a nice cup of tea.

C3 Section 2 — Practice Questions

There are a lot of formulas in this section — try writing them all out and sticking them somewhere so you can learn them. The best way to get to grips with them is to practise using them — so here are some questions for you to have a go at.

Warm-up Questions

1) Using your vast knowledge of trig values for common angles, evaluate these (in radians, between 0 and $\frac{\pi}{2}$):
   a) $\sin^{-1}\frac{1}{\sqrt{2}}$ b) $\cos^{-1}0$ c) $\tan^{-1}\sqrt{3}$
2) Sketch the graphs of arcsine, arccosine and arctangent. Make sure you show their domains and ranges.
3) For $\theta = 30°$, find the exact values of:
   a) cosec θ b) sec θ c) cot θ
4) Sketch the graphs of cosecant, secant and cotangent for $-2\pi \le x \le 2\pi$.
5) Use the identity $\cos^2\theta + \sin^2\theta \equiv 1$ to produce the identity $\sec^2\theta \equiv 1 + \tan^2\theta$.
6) Use the trig identities to show that $\cot^2\theta + \sin^2\theta \equiv \mathrm{cosec}^2\theta - \cos^2\theta$.
7) State the three different versions of the double angle formula for cos.
8) Use the double angle formula to solve the equation: $\sin 2\theta = -\sqrt{3}\sin\theta,\ 0 \le \theta \le 360°$.
9) Using the addition formula for cos, find the exact value of $\cos\frac{\pi}{12}$.
10) Find $\sin(A + B)$, given that $\sin A = \frac{4}{5}$ and $\sin B = \frac{7}{25}$.
    You might find these triangles useful:

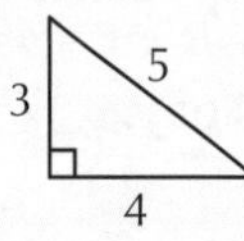

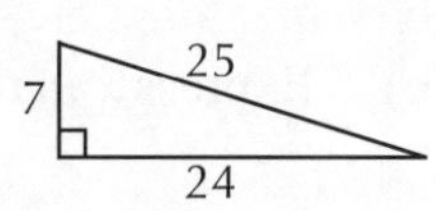

11) Which two R formulas could you use to write $a\cos\theta + b\sin\theta$ $(a, b > 0)$ in terms of just sin or just cos?
12) Write $5\sin\theta - 6\cos\theta$ in the form $R\sin(\theta - \alpha)$, where $R > 0$ and $0 \le \alpha \le 90°$.
13) Use the addition formulas to show that $\sin A - \sin B \equiv 2\cos\left(\frac{A+B}{2}\right)\sin\left(\frac{A-B}{2}\right)$.
14) Show that $\frac{\cos\theta}{\sin\theta} + \frac{\sin\theta}{\cos\theta} \equiv 2\,\mathrm{cosec}\,2\theta$.

Here is a selection of the finest trigonometry exam questions available, matured for 21 days and served with a delicious peppercorn sauce.

Exam Questions

1 a) Sketch the graph of $y = \mathrm{cosec}\,x$ for $-\pi \le x \le \pi$. *(3 marks)*

Don't forget to put your calculator in RAD mode when you're using radians (and DEG mode when you're using degrees)...

b) Solve the equation $\mathrm{cosec}\,x = \frac{5}{4}$ for $-\pi \le x \le \pi$.
Give your answers correct to 3 significant figures. *(3 marks)*

c) Solve the equation $\mathrm{cosec}\,x = 3\sec x$ for $-\pi \le x \le \pi$.
Give your answers correct to 3 significant figures. *(3 marks)*

2 a) Write $9\sin\theta + 12\cos\theta$ in the form $R\sin(\theta + \alpha)$, where $R > 0$ and $0 \le \alpha \le \frac{\pi}{2}$. *(3 marks)*

b) Using the result from part (a) solve $9\sin\theta + 12\cos\theta = 3$, giving all solutions for θ in the range $0 \le \theta \le 2\pi$. *(5 marks)*

C3 Section 2 — Practice Questions

Take a deep breath and get ready to dive in again — here come some more lovely trig questions...

3 Using the double angle and addition identities for sin and cos, find an expression for $\sin 3x$ in terms of $\sin x$ only. *(4 marks)*

4 **Figure 1** shows the graph of $y = \arccos x$, where y is in radians. A and B are the end points of the graph.

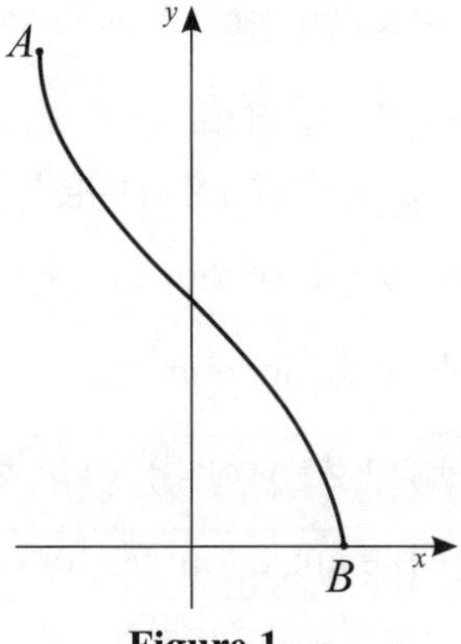

Figure 1

a) Write down the coordinates of A and B. *(2 marks)*

b) Express x in terms of y. *(1 mark)*

c) Solve, to 3 significant figures, the equation $\arccos x = 2$ for the interval shown on the graph. *(2 marks)*

5 a) Show that $\dfrac{2\sin x}{1 - \cos x} - \dfrac{2\cos x}{\sin x} \equiv 2\operatorname{cosec} x$ *(4 marks)*

b) Use this result to find all the solutions for which

$$\frac{2\sin x}{1 - \cos x} - \frac{2\cos x}{\sin x} = 4 \qquad 0 < x < 2\pi.$$

(3 marks)

6 a) Write $5\cos\theta + 12\sin\theta$ in the form $R\cos(\theta - \alpha)$, where $R > 0$ and $0 \le \alpha \le 90°$. *(4 marks)*

b) Hence solve $5\cos\theta + 12\sin\theta = 2$ for $0 \le \theta \le 360°$, giving your answers to 2 decimal places. *(5 marks)*

c) Use your results from part a) above to find the minimum value of $(5\cos\theta + 12\sin\theta)^3$. *(2 marks)*

7 a) (i) Using an appropriate identity, show that $3\tan^2\theta - 2\sec\theta = 5$ can be written as $3\sec^2\theta - 2\sec\theta - 8 = 0$. *(2 marks)*

(ii) Hence or otherwise show that $\cos\theta = -\frac{3}{4}$ or $\cos\theta = \frac{1}{2}$. *(3 marks)*

b) Use your results from part a) above to solve the equation $3\tan^2 2x - 2\sec 2x = 5$ for $0 \le x \le 180°$. Give your answers to 2 decimal places. *(3 marks)*

e^x, ln x and Graphs

This section is useful 'cos lots of 'real' things increase (or decrease) exponentially — student debts, horrible diseases... We'll start off with a quick recap of some things from C2, then I'll introduce you to some very special functions...

Graphs of $y = a^x$ and $y = a^{-x}$ show Exponential Growth and Decay

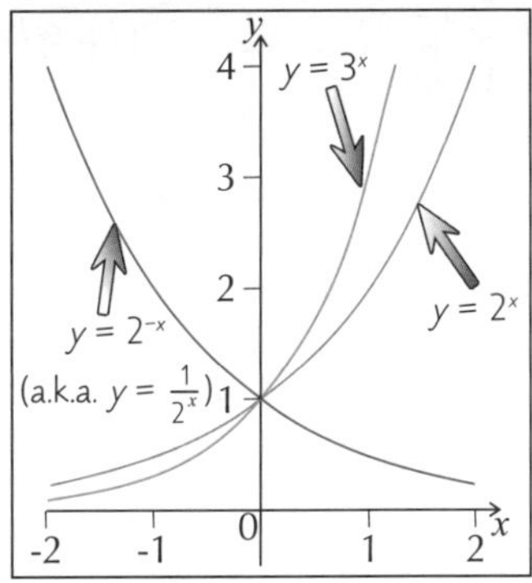

You should be familiar with these graphs from C2.
The main feature of exponential growth / decay is that the rate of increase / decrease of the function is proportional to the function itself.
So if we plotted the gradient of $y = a^x$, it would have the same shape as $y = a^x$.

The main points to remember for $y = a^x$ functions ($a > 0$) are:

1) As $x \to \infty$, $y \to \infty$ (and the gradient also $\to \infty$).
2) As $x \to -\infty$, $y \to 0$ (which means that a^x is always positive).
3) When $x = 0$, $y = 1$ (so they all pass through $(0, 1)$ on the y-axis).

The Gradient of the Exponential Function $y = e^x$ is e^x

There is a value of 'a' for which the gradient of $y = a^x$ is exactly the same as a^x. That value is known as e, an irrational number around 2.7183 (it's stored in your calculator just like π). Because e is just a number, the graph of $y = e^x$ has all the properties of $y = a^x$...

1) $y = e^x$ cuts the y-axis at $(0, 1)$.
2) As $x \to \infty$, $e^x \to \infty$ and as $x \to -\infty$, $e^x \to 0$.
3) $y = e^x$ does not exist for $y \leq 0$ (i.e. e^x can't be zero or –ve).

The disturbingly interesting fact that e^x doesn't change when you differentiate is used lots in the differentiation section — see p.27.

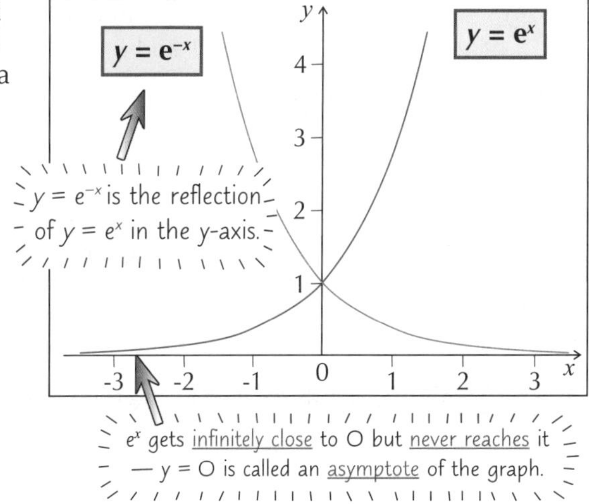

eˣ gets infinitely close to 0 but never reaches it — y = 0 is called an asymptote of the graph.

ln x is the Inverse Function of e^x

ln x (also known as $\log_e x$, or 'natural log'*) is the inverse function of e^x (see p.6):

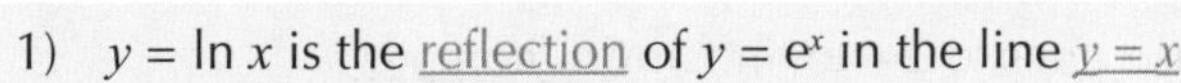

1) $y = \ln x$ is the reflection of $y = e^x$ in the line $y = x$.
2) It cuts the x-axis at $(1, 0)$ (so $\ln 1 = 0$).
3) As $x \to \infty$, $\ln x \to \infty$ (but 'slowly'), and as $x \to 0$, $\ln x \to -\infty$.
4) $\ln x$ does not exist for $x \leq 0$ (i.e. x can't be zero or negative).

$y = \ln x$ has an asymptote at $x = 0$.

Because ln x is a logarithmic function and the inverse of e^x, we get these juicy formulas and log laws...

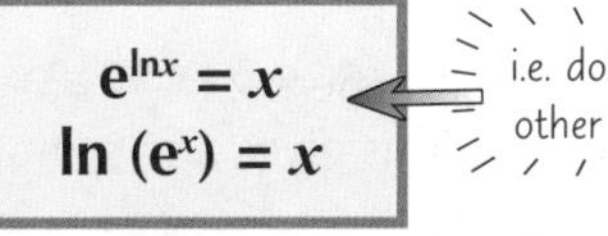

$$e^{\ln x} = x$$
$$\ln (e^x) = x$$

i.e. doing one function then the other to x takes you back to x.

'Log laws' for ln x

$$\ln x + \ln y = \ln (xy)$$
$$\ln x - \ln y = \ln \left(\frac{x}{y}\right)$$
$$\ln x^k = k \ln x$$

These are the same old log laws you saw in C2, applied to ln x.

These formulas are extremely useful for dealing with equations containing 'e^x's or 'ln x's, as you'll see on the next page...

*Certified organic

'e' is for exponential, but also for easy exam questions — no excuses...

When it comes to logs, I prefer the natural look. Remember the limits of $y = e^x$, $y = e^{-x}$ and $y = \ln x$ from the graphs, and polish up your skills with the log laws from C2, and the rest of the section should be a breeze. Naturally.

Using eˣ and ln x — Solving Equations

Now what makes e^x and $\ln x$ so clever is that you can use one to cancel out the other, which comes in very handy for solving equations. You'll need all those fruity formulas from the previous page to get through this one...

Use the Inverse Functions and Log Laws to Solve Equations

EXAMPLES a) Solve the equation $2\ln x - \ln 2x = 6$, giving your answer as an exact value of x.

1) Use the log laws (see previous page) to simplify $2\ln x - \ln 2x = 6$ into:
$\ln x^2 - \ln 2x = 6 \Rightarrow \ln(x^2 \div 2x) = 6 \Rightarrow \ln(\frac{x}{2}) = 6$.

2) Now apply the inverse function e^x to both sides — this will remove the $\ln(\frac{x}{2})$:
$e^{\ln(\frac{x}{2})} = e^6 \Rightarrow \frac{x}{2} = e^6 \Rightarrow x = 2e^6$. And since we need an exact value, leave it as that.

Using $e^{\ln x} = x$ from the last page

b) Find the exact solutions of the equation $e^x + 5e^{-x} = 6$.

1) A big clue here is that you're asked for more than one solution. Think quadratics...
2) Multiply each part of the equation by e^x to get rid of that e^{-x}:
$e^x + 5e^{-x} = 6 \Rightarrow e^{2x} + 5 = 6e^x \Rightarrow e^{2x} - 6e^x + 5 = 0$.
3) It starts to look a bit nicer if you substitute y for e^x: $y^2 - 6y + 5 = 0$.
4) Since we're asked for exact solutions, it will probably factorise:
$(y - 1)(y - 5) = 0 \Rightarrow y = 1$ and $y = 5$.
5) Put e^x back in: $e^x = 1$ and $e^x = 5$.
6) Take 'ln' of both sides to solve: $\ln e^x = \ln 1 \Rightarrow x = \ln 1 = 0$ and $\ln e^x = \ln 5 \Rightarrow x = \ln 5$.

Basic power laws — $(e^x)^2 = e^{2x}$ and $e^{-x} \times e^x = e^0 = 1$.

Using $\ln e^x = x$

Real-Life functions look like $y = e^{ax+b} + c$ and $y = \ln(ax + b)$

You should be familiar with the shape of the bog-standard exponential graphs, but most exponential functions will be transformed in some way. You need to know how the key features of the graph change depending on the function.

EXAMPLES Sketch the graphs of the following functions, labelling any key points and stating the value of 'a':
a) $y = e^{-7x+1} - 5$ ($x \in \mathbb{R}, y > a$) and b) $y = \ln(2x + 4)$ ($x \in \mathbb{R}, x > a$).

$y = e^{-7x+1} - 5$

1) 'Key points' usually means where the graph crosses the axes, i.e. where x and y are 0:
When $x = 0$, $y = e^1 - 5 = -2.28$. When $y = 0$, $e^{-7x+1} = 5 \Rightarrow -7x + 1 = \ln 5 \Rightarrow x = -0.0871$.
2) Next see what happens as x goes to $\pm\infty$ to find any asymptotes:
As $x \to \infty$, $e^{-7x+1} \to 0$, so $y \to -5$. As $x \to -\infty$, $e^{-7x+1} \to \infty$, so $y \to \infty$.
3) Now use this information to sketch out a graph. y can't go below -5, so if $y > a$, $a = -5$.

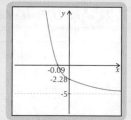

This tells you the range of values for the function (see p.4).

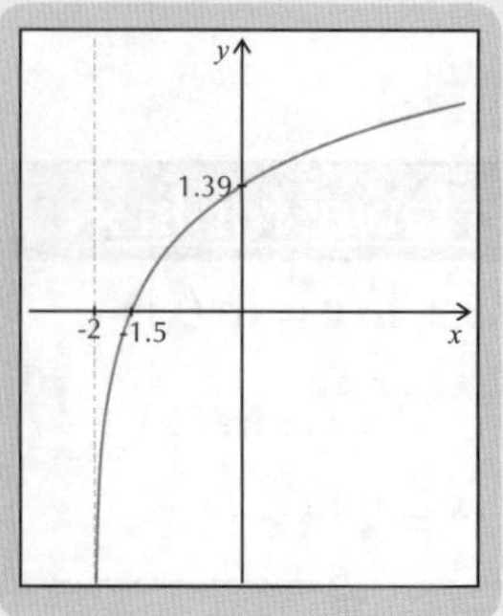

$y = \ln(2x + 4)$

1) First the intercepts: When $x = 0$, $y = \ln 4 = 1.39$. When $y = 0$, $2x + 4 = e^0 = 1 \Rightarrow x = -1.5$.
2) As $x \to \infty$, $y \to \infty$ (gradually).
3) As $x \to -\infty$, y decreases up to the point where $2x + 4 = 0$, at which it can no longer exist (since $\ln x$ can only exist for $x > 0$). This gives an asymptote at $2x + 4 = 0$, i.e. $x = -2$.
4) Sketch the graph using this information. x can't go below -2, so if $x > a$, $a = -2$.

This tells you the domain (see p.4).

No problems — only solutions...

All the individual steps to solving these equations are easy — the hard bit is spotting what combination of things to try. A good thing to look for is hidden quadratics, so try and substitute for e^x or $\ln x$ to make things look a bit nicer. The sketches get easier with practice, so you'd best get cracking.

Using e^x and ln x — Solving Equations

This page is all about models. Except they're modelling exponential growth and decay in real-world applications rather than the Chanel Autumn/Winter collection. Sorry.

Use the Exponential Functions to Model real-life Growth and Decay

In the exam you'll usually be given a background story to an exponential equation.
They may then ask you to find some values, work out a missing part of the equation, or even sketch a graph.
There's nothing here you haven't seen before — you just need to know how to deal with all the wordy bits.

EXAMPLE The exponential growth of a colony of bacteria can be modelled by the equation $B = 60e^{0.03t}$, where B is the number of bacteria, and t is the time in hours from the point at which the colony is first monitored ($t \geq 0$). Use the model to predict:

a) the number of bacteria after 4 hours.

You need to find B when $t = 4$, so put the numbers into the equation:

$B = 60 \times e^{(0.03 \times 4)}$
$= 60 \times 1.1274...$
$= 67.6498...$

So B = 67 bacteria.

You shouldn't round up here — there are only 67 whole bacteria, not 68.

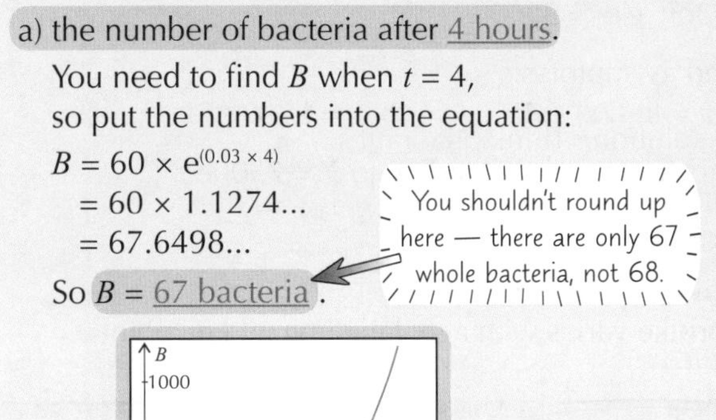

b) the time taken for the colony to grow to 1000.

1) You need to find t when B = 1000, so put the numbers into the equation:
$1000 = 60e^{0.03t}$
$\Rightarrow e^{0.03t} = 1000 \div 60 = 16.6666...$

2) Now take 'ln' of both sides as usual:
$\ln e^{0.03t} = \ln(16.6666...)$
$\Rightarrow 0.03t = 2.8134...$
$\Rightarrow t = 2.8134... \div 0.03 =$ 93.8 hours to 3 s.f.

Even if the question doesn't ask for a sketch of the equation, you may still find it useful to do one to give you an idea of what's going on.

EXAMPLE The concentration (C) of a drug in the bloodstream, t hours after taking an initial dose, decreases exponentially according to $C = Ae^{-kt}$, where k is a constant. If the initial concentration is 0.72, and this halves after 5 hours, find the values of A and k and sketch a graph of C against t.

1) The 'initial concentration' is 0.72 when $t = 0$, so put this information in the equation to find the missing constant A:
$0.72 = A \times e^0 \Rightarrow 0.72 = A \times 1 \Rightarrow A = 0.72$.

2) The question also says that when $t = 5$ hours, C is half of 0.72. So using the value for A found above:
$C = 0.72e^{-kt}$
$0.72 \div 2 = 0.72 \times e^{(-k \times 5)}$
$\Rightarrow 0.36 = 0.72 \times e^{-5k} \Rightarrow 0.36 = \frac{0.72}{e^{5k}} \Rightarrow e^{5k} = \frac{0.72}{0.36} = 2.$

3) Now take 'ln' of both sides to solve:
$\ln e^{5k} = \ln 2 \Rightarrow 5k = \ln 2$
$\Rightarrow k = \ln 2 \div 5 = 0.139$ to 3 s.f.

4) So the equation is $C = 0.72e^{-0.139t}$.
You still need to do a sketch though, so find the intercepts and asymptotes as you did on the last page:
When $t = 0$, $C = 0.72$. As $t \to \infty$, $e^{-0.139t} \to 0$, so $C \to 0$.

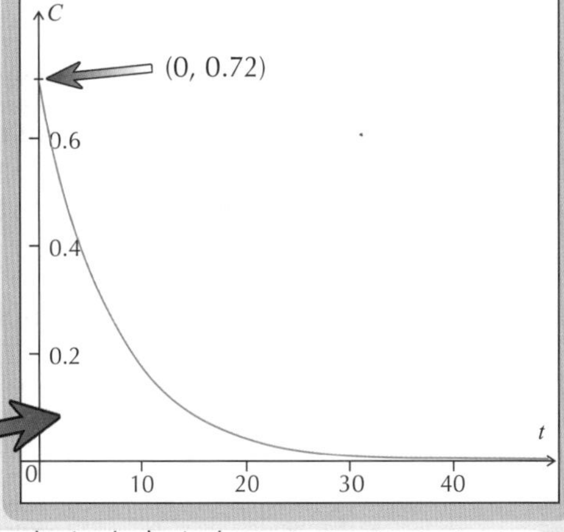

The sketch should make sense for the situation in the question — here t can only be positive as it is the time after an event, so only sketch the graph for $t \geq 0$.

Learn this and watch your knowledge grow exponentially...

For these wordy problems the key is just to extract the relevant information and solve like you did on the last page. The more you practise, the more familiar they'll become — fortunately there's a fair bit of practice on the next two pages. You've probably got time to make a quick cuppa beforehand though. Milk, two sugars please. And a custard cream. Ta.

C3 Section 3 — Practice Questions

Well that section was short and sweet, rather like that lovely Richard Hammond.
While it's all fresh in your mind, have a go at these little hamsters...

Warm-up Questions

1) Plot the following graphs on the same axes, for $-2 \leq x \leq 2$:
   a) $y = 4e^x$ b) $y = 4e^{-x}$ c) $y = 4 \ln x$ d) $y = \ln 4x$.
2) Find the value of x, to 4 decimal places, when:
   a) $e^{2x} = 6$ b) $\ln (x + 3) = 0.75$ c) $3e^{-4x+1} = 5$ d) $\ln x + \ln 5 = \ln 4$.
3) Solve the following equations, giving your solutions as exact values:
   a) $\ln (2x - 7) + \ln 4 = -3$ b) $2e^{2x} + e^x = 3$.
4) Sketch graphs of the following, labelling key points and asymptotes:
   a) $y = 2 - e^{x+1}$ b) $y = 5e^{0.5x} + 5$ c) $y = \ln (2x) + 1$ d) $y = \ln (x + 5)$
5) The value of a motorbike (£V) varies with age (in t years from new) according to $V = 7500e^{-0.2t}$.
   a) How much did it originally cost?
   b) What is its value after 10 years (to the nearest £)?
   c) After how many years will the motorbike's value have fallen below £500?
   d) Sketch a graph showing how the value of the motorbike varies with age, labelling all key points.

Feeling confident? Thought so.
Let's see how you handle these exam-style problems — they're a wee bit more problematic...

Exam Questions

1 a) Given that $6e^x = 3$, find the exact value of x. *(2 marks)*

b) Find the exact solutions to the equation:

$$e^{2x} - 8e^x + 7 = 0.$$

(4 marks)

c) Given that $4 \ln x = 3$, find the exact value of x. *(2 marks)*

d) Solve the equation:

$$\ln x + \frac{24}{\ln x} = 10$$

giving your answers as exact values of x. *(4 marks)*

2 The sketch below shows the function $y = e^{ax} + b$, where a and b are constants.

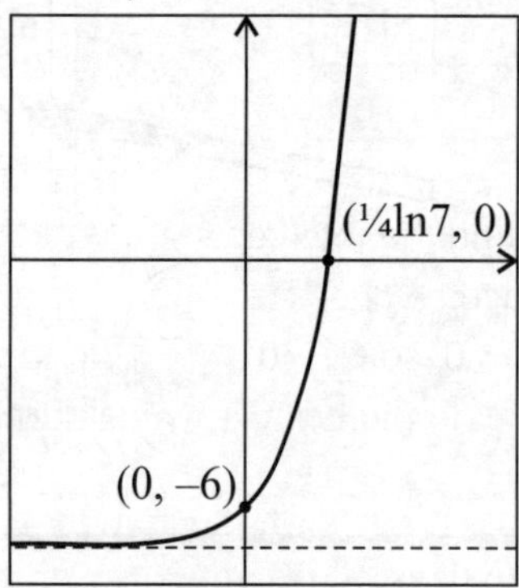

Find the values of a and b, and the equation of the asymptote shown on the sketch. *(5 marks)*

C3 Section 3 — Practice Questions

3 A breed of mink is introduced to a new habitat.
The number of mink, M, after t years in the habitat, is modelled by:

$$M = 74e^{0.6t} \quad (t \geq 0)$$

a) State the number of mink that were introduced to the new habitat originally. *(1 mark)*

b) Predict the number of mink after 3 years in the habitat. *(2 marks)*

c) Predict the number of complete years it would take for the population of mink to exceed 10 000. *(2 marks)*

d) Sketch a graph to show how the mink population varies with time in the new habitat. *(2 marks)*

4 A curve has the equation $y = \ln(4x - 3)$.

a) The point A with coordinate $(a, 1)$ lies on the curve. Find a to 2 decimal places. *(2 marks)*

b) The curve only exists for $x > b$. State the value of b. *(2 marks)*

c) Sketch the curve, labelling any important points. *(2 marks)*

5 Solve the following equations, giving your answers as exact values of x.

a) $2e^x + 18e^{-x} = 20$ *(4 marks)*

b) $2 \ln x - \ln 3 = \ln 12$ *(3 marks)*

6 A radioactive substance decays exponentially so that its activity, A, can be modelled by

$$A = Be^{-kt}$$

where t is the time in days, and $t \geq 0$. Some experimental data is shown below.

t	0	5	10
A	50	42	

a) State the value of B. *(1 mark)*

b) Find the value of k, to 3 significant figures. *(2 marks)*

c) Find the missing value from the table, to the nearest whole number. *(2 marks)*

d) The half-life of a substance is the time it takes for the activity to halve.
Find the half-life of this substance, in days. Give your answer to the nearest day. *(3 marks)*

Chain Rule

That's right — our old friend differentiation is back again, this time with some new exciting features. Before you start panicking about how much you've already forgotten, all you need for now is: $\frac{d}{dx}(x^n) = nx^{n-1}$

The Chain Rule is used for Functions of Functions

The chain rule is a nifty little tool that allows you to differentiate complicated functions by splitting them up into easier ones. The trick is spotting how to split them up, and choosing the right bit to substitute.

Chain Rule Method

- **Pick a suitable function of x for 'u' and rewrite y in terms of u.**
- **Differentiate u (with respect to x) to get $\frac{du}{dx}$, and differentiate y (with respect to u) to get $\frac{dy}{du}$.**
- **Stick it all in the formula.**

If $y = f(u)$ and $u = g(x)$ then:
$$\frac{dy}{dx} = \frac{dy}{du} \times \frac{du}{dx}$$

EXAMPLE Find the exact value of $\frac{dy}{dx}$ when $x = 1$ for $y = \frac{1}{\sqrt{x^2 + 4x}}$.

1) First, write y in terms of powers to make it easier to differentiate: $y = (x^2 + 4x)^{-\frac{1}{2}}$.
2) Pick a chunk of the equation to call 'u', and rewrite y in terms of u:
e.g. in this case let $u = x^2 + 4x$, so $y = u^{-\frac{1}{2}}$.
3) Now differentiate both bits separately: $u = x^2 + 4x$, so $\frac{du}{dx} = 2x + 4$ and $y = u^{-\frac{1}{2}}$, so $\frac{dy}{du} = -\frac{1}{2}u^{-\frac{3}{2}}$.
4) Use the chain rule to find $\frac{dy}{dx}$: $\frac{dy}{dx} = \frac{dy}{du} \times \frac{du}{dx} = -\frac{1}{2}u^{-\frac{3}{2}} \times (2x + 4)$.
5) Substitute in for u and rearrange: $u = x^2 + 4x$, so $\frac{dy}{dx} = -\frac{1}{2}(x^2 + 4x)^{-\frac{3}{2}}(2x + 4) = -\frac{x + 2}{(\sqrt{x^2 + 4x})^3}$.
6) Finally, put in $x = 1$ to answer the question: $\frac{dy}{dx} = -\frac{1 + 2}{(\sqrt{1^2 + (4 \times 1)})^3} = \frac{-3}{5\sqrt{5}} = \frac{-3\sqrt{5}}{25}$.

Write down all the steps — it'll help you avoid small mistakes that could affect your final answer.

'Exact' means leave in surd form where necessary.

Use dy/dx = 1 ÷ dx/dy for x = f(y)

For $x = f(y)$, use $\frac{dy}{dx} = \frac{1}{\left(\frac{dx}{dy}\right)}$

The principle of the chain rule can also be used where x is given in terms of y (i.e. $x = f(y)$). This comes from a bit of mathematical fiddling, but it's quite useful:

$\frac{dy}{dx} \times \frac{dx}{dy} = \frac{dy}{dy} = 1$, so rearranging gives $\frac{dy}{dx} = \frac{1}{\left(\frac{dx}{dy}\right)}$. Here's how to use it...

EXAMPLE A curve has the equation $x = y^3 + 2y - 7$. Find $\frac{dy}{dx}$ at the point $(-4, 1)$.

1) Forget that the xs and ys are in the 'wrong' places and differentiate as usual:
$x = y^3 + 2y - 7$, so $\frac{dx}{dy} = 3y^2 + 2$.
2) Use $\frac{dy}{dx} = \frac{1}{\left(\frac{dx}{dy}\right)}$ to find $\frac{dy}{dx}$: $\frac{dy}{dx} = \frac{1}{3y^2 + 2}$.
3) $y = 1$ at the point $(-4, 1)$, so put this in the equation:
$\frac{dy}{dx} = \frac{1}{3(1)^2 + 2} = \frac{1}{5} = 0.2$, so $\frac{dy}{dx} = 0.2$ at the point $(-4, 1)$.

You'll be using this again on the next page so make sure you've learnt it now.

I'm in the middle of a chain rule differentiation...

You know, I'm not sure I've stressed enough just how important differentiation is. It's one of those bits of maths that examiners can tag on to almost any other A-Level topic. It's almost like they have a mantra: 'Give me ANY function and I will ask you to differentiate it, in a multitude of intricate ways'. To which you should respond: 'Bring. It. On.'

Differentiation of e^x and ln x

Remember those special little functions from Section Three? Well you're about to find out just how special they are as we take a look at how to differentiate them. I can tell you're overcome by excitement so I'll not keep you waiting...

The Gradient of $y = e^x$ is e^x by Definition

$$y = e^x \qquad \frac{dy}{dx} = e^x$$

OR

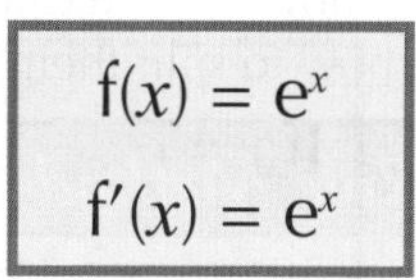

Get used to using both types of function notation. You should remember from C2 that $f'(x)$ means the same as dy/dx.

In the last section (see p.21) we saw that 'e' was just a number for which the gradient of e^x was e^x. Which makes it pretty simple to differentiate.

EXAMPLE If $f(x) = e^{x^2} + 2e^x$, find $f'(x)$ for $x = 0$.

1) Let's break down the function into its two bits and differentiate them separately:

$y = e^{x^2}$ and $y = 2e^x$

2) This is the tricky bit. Use the chain rule from the last page: $u = x^2$ and $y = e^u$

3) Both u and y are now easy to differentiate: $\frac{du}{dx} = 2x$ and $\frac{dy}{du} = e^u$

4) $\frac{dy}{dx} = \frac{du}{dx} \times \frac{dy}{du} = 2x \cdot e^u = 2x \cdot e^{x^2}$

5) This bit's easy. If $y = 2e^x$ then $\frac{dy}{dx} = 2e^x$ too.

When $y = kf(x)$ where k is a constant, then dy/dx is just $kf'(x)$.

6) Put the bits back together and you end up with $f'(x) = 2xe^{x^2} + 2e^x$.

7) So when $x = 0$, $f'(x) = 0 + 2e^0 = 2$.

Turn $y = \ln x$ into $x = e^y$ to Differentiate

$$y = \ln x \qquad \frac{dy}{dx} = \frac{1}{x}$$

This result you can just learn, but it comes from another bit of mathematical fiddling:

If $y = \ln x$, then $x = e^y$ (see p.21).

Differentiating gives $\frac{dx}{dy} = e^y$, and $\frac{dy}{dx} = \frac{1}{\left(\frac{dx}{dy}\right)} = \frac{1}{e^y} = \frac{1}{x}$ (since $x = e^y$). Nice eh.

EXAMPLE Find $\frac{dy}{dx}$ if $y = \ln(x^2 + 3)$.

1) Use the chain rule again for this one: $y = \ln u$ and $u = x^2 + 3$.

2) $\frac{dy}{du} = \frac{1}{u}$ (from above) and $\frac{du}{dx} = 2x$.

3) So $\frac{dy}{dx} = \frac{dy}{du} \times \frac{du}{dx} = \frac{1}{u} \times 2x = \frac{2x}{x^2+3}$.

Look again at your final answer. It comes out to $\frac{f'(x)}{f(x)}$.

This will always be the case for $y = \ln(f(x))$ so you can just learn this result:

$$y = \ln(f(x)) \qquad \frac{dy}{dx} = \frac{f'(x)}{f(x)}$$

These functions pop up everywhere in the e^xams...

There's nothing too tough on this page, so you have no excuse for not getting a good grasp of the basics while you can. The derivatives of e^x and $\ln x$ are just a couple more of those essential little things you've just got to learn. If you don't, you could get stumped by a fairly easy exam question. I know I'd gladly spend every waking hour learning this stuff if I could...

Differentiation of Sin, Cos and Tan

So you think you know all there is to know about trigonometry. Well think again, 'cos here it comes again. (You see what I did there with the 'cos'? Pun #27 from 'Ye Olde Booke of Maths Punnes'...)

The Rules for dy/dx of Sin, Cos and Tan only work in Radians

For trigonometric functions, where the angle is measured in radians, the following rules apply:

If $y =$	$\frac{dy}{dx} =$
$\sin x$	$\cos x$
$\cos x$	$-\sin x$
$\tan x$	$\sec^2 x$

There's loads more about sec (and cosec and cot) on p.13.

Use the Chain Rule with Sin/Cos/Tan (f(x))

If you can't follow what's happening here, go back to p.26 and brush up on the chain rule.

EXAMPLE: Differentiate $y = \cos 2x + \sin (x + 1)$ with respect to x.

It's the chain rule (again) for both parts of this equation:

1) Differentiate '$y = \cos 2x$': $y = \cos u$, $u = 2x$,
so $\frac{dy}{du} = -\sin u$ (see above) and $\frac{du}{dx} = 2 \Rightarrow \frac{dy}{dx} = -2\sin 2x$.
2) Differentiate '$y = \sin (x + 1)$': $y = \sin u$, $u = x + 1$,
so $\frac{dy}{du} = \cos u$ (see above) and $\frac{du}{dx} = 1 \Rightarrow \frac{dy}{dx} = \cos (x + 1)$.
3) Put it all together to get $\frac{dy}{dx} = -2\sin 2x + \cos (x + 1)$.

EXAMPLE: Find $\frac{dy}{dx}$ when $x = \tan 3y$.

1) First find $\frac{dx}{dy}$ using the chain rule: $x = \tan u$, $u = 3y$, $\frac{dx}{du} = \sec^2 u$, $\frac{du}{dy} = 3$, so $\frac{dx}{dy} = 3\sec^2 3y$.
2) Then use $\frac{dy}{dx} = \frac{1}{\left(\frac{dx}{dy}\right)}$ to get the final answer: $\frac{dy}{dx} = \frac{1}{3\sec^2 3y} = \frac{1}{3}\cos^2 3y$.

See p.26 if you can't remember this.

Remember to use Trig Identities where Necessary

EXAMPLE For $y = 2\cos^2 x + \sin 2x$, show that $\frac{dy}{dx} = 2(\cos 2x - \sin 2x)$.

1) Writing out the equation in a slightly different way helps with the chain rule: $y = 2(\cos x)^2 + \sin 2x$.
2) For the first bit, $y = 2u^2$, $u = \cos x$, so $\frac{dy}{du} = 4u$ and $\frac{du}{dx} = -\sin x$.
For the second bit, $y = \sin u$, $u = 2x$, so $\frac{dy}{du} = \cos u$ and $\frac{du}{dx} = 2$.
3) Putting it all in the chain rule formula gives $\frac{dy}{dx} = -4\sin x \cos x + 2\cos 2x$.
4) From the target answer in the question it looks like we need a $\sin 2x$ from somewhere, so use the 'double angle' formula (see p.16) $\sin 2x \equiv 2 \sin x \cos x$:
$\frac{dy}{dx} = -2\sin 2x + 2 \cos 2x$, which rearranges nicely to give $\frac{dy}{dx} = 2(\cos 2x - \sin 2x)$. Et voilà.

You could also use the identity $\cos 2x \equiv 2 \cos^2 x - 1$ before differentiating. You'll get the same answer.

I'm having an identity crisis — I can't differentiate between sin and cos...

Don't get tied down by the chain rule (pun #28...). After a bit of practice you'll be able to do it a lot quicker in one step — just say in your working 'using the chain rule...' so the examiner can see how clever you are.

Product Rule

In maths-speak, a 'product' is what you get when you multiply things together. So the 'product rule' is a rule about differentiating things that are multiplied together. And it's yet another rule you have to learn I'm afraid.

Use the Product Rule to differentiate Two Functions Multiplied Together

This is what it looks like:

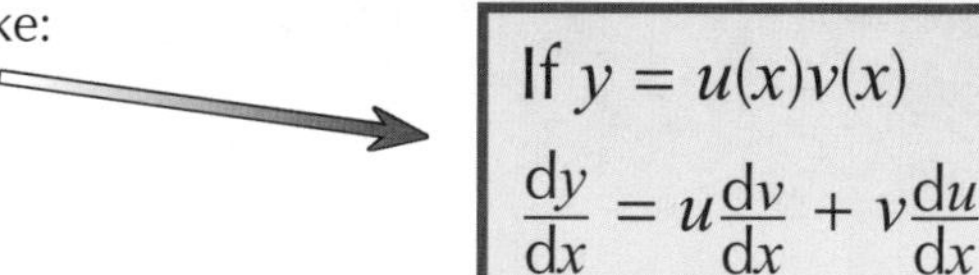

If $y = u(x)v(x)$

$$\frac{dy}{dx} = u\frac{dv}{dx} + v\frac{du}{dx}$$

And here's how to use it: (u and v are functions of x.)

EXAMPLES Differentiate the following with respect to x: a) $x^3 \tan x$ and b) $e^{2x}\sqrt{2x-3}$.

a) $x^3 \tan x$

1) The crucial thing is to write down everything in steps. Start with identifying 'u' and 'v':
$u = x^3$ and $v = \tan x$.
2) Now differentiate these two separately, with respect to x:
$\frac{du}{dx} = 3x^2$ and $\frac{dv}{dx} = \sec^2 x$.
3) Very carefully put all the bits into the formula:
$\frac{dy}{dx} = u\frac{dv}{dx} + v\frac{du}{dx} = (x^3 \cdot \sec^2 x) + (\tan x \cdot 3x^2)$
4) Finally, rearrange to make it look nicer:
$\frac{dy}{dx} = x^3 \sec^2 x + 3x^2 \tan x$.

b) $e^{2x}\sqrt{2x-3}$

1) Again, start with identifying 'u' and 'v':
$u = e^{2x}$ and $v = \sqrt{2x-3}$.
2) Each of these needs the chain rule to differentiate:
$\frac{du}{dx} = 2e^{2x}$ and $\frac{dv}{dx} = \frac{1}{\sqrt{2x-3}}$ (do it in steps if you need to...)
3) Put it all into the product rule formula:
$\frac{dy}{dx} = u\frac{dv}{dx} + v\frac{du}{dx} = (e^{2x} \cdot \frac{1}{\sqrt{2x-3}}) + (\sqrt{2x-3} \cdot 2e^{2x})$
4) Rearrange and simplify:
$\frac{dy}{dx} = e^{2x}\left(\frac{1}{\sqrt{2x-3}} + 2\sqrt{2x-3}\right) = e^{2x}\left(\frac{1+2(2x-3)}{\sqrt{2x-3}}\right)$
$= \frac{e^{2x}(4x-5)}{\sqrt{2x-3}}$.

Use the Rules Together to differentiate Complicated Functions

In the exam they might tell you which rules to use, but chances are they won't.
And you'll probably have to throw a whole load of rules at any one question.

EXAMPLE Solve the equation $\frac{d}{dx}((x^3 + 3x^2)\ln x) = 2x^2 + 5x$, leaving your answer as an exact value of x.

1) The $\frac{d}{dx}$ just tells you to differentiate the bit in brackets first.

And since $(x^3 + 3x^2)\ln x$ is a product of two functions, use the product rule:
$u = x^3 + 3x^2 \Rightarrow \frac{du}{dx} = 3x^2 + 6x$ and $v = \ln x \Rightarrow \frac{dv}{dx} = \frac{1}{x}$ (see p.27)

So $\frac{d}{dx}((x^3 + 3x^2)\ln x) = [(x^3 + 3x^2) \cdot \frac{1}{x}] + [\ln x \cdot (3x^2 + 6x)] = x^2 + 3x + (3x^2 + 6x)\ln x$.

You should be well up on $\ln x$ and e^x after Section 3, but glance back at pages 21-23 if you need to.

2) Now put this into the equation from the question in place of $\frac{d}{dx}((x^3 + 3x^2)\ln x)$:
$x^2 + 3x + (3x^2 + 6x)\ln x = 2x^2 + 5x$

You're asked for an exact value so leave in terms of e.

3) Rearrange and solve as follows:
$(3x^2 + 6x)\ln x = 2x^2 + 5x - x^2 - 3x \Rightarrow (3x^2 + 6x)\ln x = x^2 + 2x \Rightarrow \ln x = \frac{x^2 + 2x}{3(x^2 + 2x)} = \frac{1}{3} \Rightarrow x = e^{\frac{1}{3}}$.

The first rule of maths club is — you do not talk about maths club...

These rules are supposed to make your life easier when differentiating. Learning them means you don't have to do everything from first principles every time. Try not to get the product rule mixed up with the chain rule. Repeat after me: 'The chain rule is for functions of functions but the product rule is for products of functions'. Snappy, I know...

Quotient Rule

The world is a beautiful, harmonious place full of natural symmetry. So of course, if we have a 'product rule' to differentiate products, we must also have a 'quotient rule' to differentiate... er... quotients. Read on and learn.

Use the Quotient Rule for one function Divided By another

A quotient is one function divided by another one.
The rule for differentiating quotients looks like this:

$$\text{If } y = \frac{u(x)}{v(x)}$$

$$\frac{dy}{dx} = \frac{v\frac{du}{dx} - u\frac{dv}{dx}}{v^2}$$

You could, if you wanted to, just use the product rule on $y = uv^{-1}$ (try it — you'll get the same answer).
This way is so much quicker and easier though — and it's on the formula sheet.

EXAMPLE: Find the gradient of the tangent to the curve with equation $y = \frac{(2x^2 - 1)}{(3x^2 + 1)}$, at the point (1, 0.25).

1) 'Gradient of tangent' means differentiate.
2) First identify u and v for the quotient rule, and differentiate separately:
   $u = 2x^2 - 1 \Rightarrow \frac{du}{dx} = 4x$ and $v = 3x^2 + 1 \Rightarrow \frac{dv}{dx} = 6x$.
3) It's very important that you get things in the right order, so concentrate on what's going where:
   $$\frac{dy}{dx} = \frac{v\frac{du}{dx} - u\frac{dv}{dx}}{v^2} = \frac{(3x^2 + 1)(4x) - (2x^2 - 1)(6x)}{(3x^2 + 1)^2}$$
4) Now you can simplify things:
   $$\frac{dy}{dx} = \frac{x[4(3x^2 + 1) - 6(2x^2 - 1)]}{(3x^2 + 1)^2} = \frac{x[12x^2 + 4 - 12x^2 + 6]}{(3x^2 + 1)^2} = \frac{10x}{(3x^2 + 1)^2}.$$
5) Finally, put in $x = 1$ to find the gradient at (1, 0.25): $\frac{dy}{dx} = \frac{10}{(3 + 1)^2} = 0.625.$

This bit's just like the product rule from the last page.

Don't try and simplify straight away or you'll get things mixed up.

If it's a 'normal' rather than a 'tangent' do −1 ÷ gradient.

Find Further Rules using the Quotient Rule

EXAMPLE Use the quotient rule to differentiate $y = \frac{\cos x}{\sin x}$, and hence show that for $y = \cot x$, $\frac{dy}{dx} = -\text{cosec}^2\, x$.

1) Start off identifying $u = \cos x$ and $v = \sin x$.
2) Differentiating separately gives: $\frac{du}{dx} = -\sin x$, and $\frac{dv}{dx} = \cos x$ (see p.28).
3) Putting everything in the quotient rule formula gives:
   $$\frac{dy}{dx} = \frac{(\sin x \times -\sin x) - (\cos x \times \cos x)}{(\sin x)^2} = \frac{-\sin^2 x - \cos^2 x}{\sin^2 x}.$$
4) Use a trig identity to simplify this ($\sin^2 x + \cos^2 x \equiv 1$ should do the trick...):
   $$\frac{dy}{dx} = \frac{-(\sin^2 x + \cos^2 x)}{\sin^2 x} = \frac{-1}{\sin^2 x}.$$
5) Linking this back to the question, since $\tan x = \frac{\sin x}{\cos x}$, and $\cot x = \frac{1}{\tan x}$, then $y = \frac{\cos x}{\sin x} = \cot x$.
   And since $\text{cosec}\, x = \frac{1}{\sin x}$, then $\frac{dy}{dx} = \frac{-1}{\sin^2 x} = -\text{cosec}^2\, x$. QED*

Don't forget your easy C2 trig identities as well as the ones covered in Section 2.

There's more of this trig stuff on the next page. This was just a taste of things to come...

*Quite Exciting Differentiation

The second rule of maths club is — you do not talk about maths club...

Confused yet? Yes I know, there are three very similar looking rules in this section, all using us and vs and xs and ys all over the shop. You won't remember them by reading them over and over again like some mystical code. You will remember them by using them lots and lots in practice questions. Plain and simple — just how I like my men...

More Trig Differentiation

After whetting your appetite with the little proof on the last page, let's have a gander at some more trig differentiation. Namely, the rules for differentiating cosec x, sec x and cot x, and the vast array of things you can do with them.

d/dx of Cosec, Sec and Cot come from the Quotient Rule

Since cosec, sec and cot are just the reciprocals of sin, cos and tan, the quotient rule can be used to differentiate them. You have to know these results, and it will help a lot if you can show where they come from too.

$y = \operatorname{cosec} x = \frac{1}{\sin x}$

1) For the quotient rule:
   $u = 1 \Rightarrow \frac{du}{dx} = 0$ and $v = \sin x \Rightarrow \frac{dv}{dx} = \cos x$
2) $\frac{dy}{dx} = \frac{v\frac{du}{dx} - u\frac{dv}{dx}}{v^2} = \frac{(\sin x \cdot 0) - (1 \cdot \cos x)}{\sin^2 x} = -\frac{\cos x}{\sin^2 x}$
3) Since $\cot x = \frac{\cos x}{\sin x}$, and $\operatorname{cosec} x = \frac{1}{\sin x}$,
   $\frac{dy}{dx} = -\frac{\cos x}{\sin x} \times \frac{1}{\sin x} = -\operatorname{cosec} x \cot x$.

$y = \sec x = \frac{1}{\cos x}$

1) For the quotient rule:
   $u = 1 \Rightarrow \frac{du}{dx} = 0$ and $v = \cos x \Rightarrow \frac{dv}{dx} = -\sin x$
2) $\frac{dy}{dx} = \frac{v\frac{du}{dx} - u\frac{dv}{dx}}{v^2} = \frac{(\cos x \cdot 0) - (1 \cdot -\sin x)}{\cos^2 x} = \frac{\sin x}{\cos^2 x}$
3) Since $\tan x = \frac{\sin x}{\cos x}$, and $\sec x = \frac{1}{\cos x}$,
   $\frac{dy}{dx} = \frac{\sin x}{\cos x} \times \frac{1}{\cos x} = \sec x \tan x$.

If $y =$	$\frac{dy}{dx} =$
$\operatorname{cosec} x$	$-\operatorname{cosec} x \cot x$
$\sec x$	$\sec x \tan x$
$\cot x$	$-\operatorname{cosec}^2 x$

Go back a page for this one. Have a go at writing it out like the ones above, starting with $y = \cos x / \sin x$.

If you can't remember which trig functions give a negative result when you differentiate them, just remember it's all the ones that begin with c — cos, cosec and cot.

Use the Chain, Product and Quotient Rules with Cosec, Sec and Cot

So once you're familiar with the three rules in the box above you can use them with the chain, product and quotient rules and in combination with all the other functions we've seen so far.

EXAMPLES Find $\frac{dy}{dx}$ for the following functions: a) $y = \sec(2x^2)$ and b) $y = e^x \cot x$.

a) $y = \sec(2x^2)$

1) This is a function of a function, so think 'chain rule':
   $y = \sec u$ and $u = 2x^2$
2) $\frac{dy}{du} = \sec u \tan u$ (see above) $= \sec(2x^2)\tan(2x^2)$
3) $\frac{du}{dx} = 4x$
4) So $\frac{dy}{dx} = \frac{dy}{du} \times \frac{du}{dx} = 4x\sec(2x^2)\tan(2x^2)$.

b) $y = e^x \cot x$

1) This is a product of two functions, so think 'product rule':
   $u = e^x$ and $v = \cot x$
2) $\frac{du}{dx} = e^x$
3) $\frac{dv}{dx} = -\operatorname{cosec}^2 x$ (see above)
4) So $\frac{dy}{dx} = u\frac{dv}{dx} + v\frac{du}{dx} = (e^x \cdot -\operatorname{cosec}^2 x) + (\cot x \cdot e^x)$
   $= e^x(\cot x - \operatorname{cosec}^2 x)$.

Get it? Got it? Good.

I'm co-sec-sy for my shirt — co-sec-sy it hurts...

I have some good news and some good news. The good news is — there are no more rules in boxes to learn for differentiation. The other good news is — the ones on this page will be on the formula sheet in the exam so you only need to know how to use them. So there's no excuse for anything less than excellence.

More Differentiation

What?! More differentiation?! Surely not. This page is all about using what you know.

*Finding the **Gradient**, **Tangent**, **dy/dx**, **f'(x)**, **d/dx(f(x))** — all mean '**Differentiate**'*

Usually in exams, differentiation will be disguised as something else — either through different notation ($f'(x)$, $\frac{dy}{dx}$ etc.) or by asking for the gradient or rate of change of something.
You could also be asked to find the equation of a tangent or normal to a curve at a given point:

EXAMPLE Find the equation of the tangent to the curve $y = \frac{5x+2}{3x-2}$ at the point (1, 7), in the form $y = mx + c$.

1) The gradient of the tangent is just the gradient of the curve at that point. So differentiate...
2) Use the quotient rule: $u = 5x + 2 \Rightarrow \frac{du}{dx} = 5$ and $v = 3x - 2 \Rightarrow \frac{dv}{dx} = 3$.
   So $\frac{dy}{dx} = \frac{5(3x-2) - 3(5x+2)}{(3x-2)^2} = -\frac{16}{(3x-2)^2}$.
3) Gradient of tangent at (1, 7) is $\frac{dy}{dx}$ at $x = 1$, which is $-\frac{16}{(3-2)^2} = -16$.
4) Use the equation of a straight line $y - y_1 = m(x - x_1)$ with $m = -16$, $y_1 = 7$ and $x_1 = 1$, to give:
   $y - 7 = -16(x - 1) \Rightarrow y = -16x + 23$ is the equation of the tangent.

If you're asked for a 'normal', do $-1 \div$ gradient of tangent here — then the rest is the same.

*The **Rules** might need to be used **Twice***

Some questions will really stretch your alphabet with a multitude of *u*s and *v*s:

EXAMPLE Differentiate $y = e^x \tan^2(3x)$

1) First off, this is product rule: $u = e^x$ (so $\frac{du}{dx} = e^x$) and $v = \tan^2(3x)$.
2) To find $\frac{dv}{dx}$ for the product rule, we need the chain rule twice:
   $v = u_1^2$, where $u_1 = \tan(3x)$.
   $\frac{dv}{du_1} = 2u_1 = 2\tan(3x)$, and $\frac{du_1}{dx} = 3\sec^2(3x)$ (which is an easy chain rule solution itself). So $\frac{dv}{dx} = 6\tan(3x)\sec^2(3x)$.
3) Now we can put this result in the product rule formula to get $\frac{dy}{dx}$:
   $\frac{dy}{dx} = (e^x \cdot 6\tan(3x)\sec^2(3x)) + (\tan^2(3x) \cdot e^x) = e^x \tan(3x)[6\sec^2(3x) + \tan(3x)]$. Job done.
   (labels: u, $\frac{dv}{dx}$, v, $\frac{du}{dx}$)

*Differentiate **Again** for **d²y/dx²**, **Turning Points**, **Stationary Points** etc.*

Refresh your memory on C2, where you learnt all about maximums and minimums...

EXAMPLE Determine the nature of the stationary point of the curve $y = \frac{\ln x}{x^2}$ $(x > 0)$.

1) First use the quotient rule to find $\frac{dy}{dx}$: $u = \ln x \Rightarrow \frac{du}{dx} = \frac{1}{x}$, $v = x^2 \Rightarrow \frac{dv}{dx} = 2x$. So $\frac{dy}{dx} = \frac{1 - 2\ln x}{x^3}$.
2) The stationary points occur where $\frac{dy}{dx} = 0$ (i.e. zero gradient) so this is when:
   $\frac{1 - 2\ln x}{x^3} = 0 \Rightarrow \ln x = \frac{1}{2} \Rightarrow x = e^{\frac{1}{2}}$.
3) To find out whether it's a maximum or minimum, differentiate $\frac{dy}{dx}$ to get $\frac{d^2y}{dx^2}$:
   $u = 1 - 2\ln x \Rightarrow \frac{du}{dx} = -\frac{2}{x}$, $v = x^3 \Rightarrow \frac{dv}{dx} = 3x^2$. So $\frac{d^2y}{dx^2} = \frac{6\ln x - 5}{x^4}$.
4) When $x = e^{\frac{1}{2}}$, $\frac{d^2y}{dx^2} < 0$ (i.e. negative), which means it's a maximum point.

Positive means minimum, negative means maximum — it's all there in C2.

Parlez vous exam?

It's often noted that mathematics has its own language — you need to make sure you're fluent or all your hard work will go to waste. Become an expert in deciphering exam questions so you do exactly what's expected with the minimum of fuss.

C3 Section 4 — Practice Questions

Those who know it, know they know it. Those who think they know it, need to know they know it. So, you think you know it, no? Try these to make sure.

Warm-up Questions

1) Differentiate with respect to x:
   a) $y = \sqrt{x^3 + 2x^2}$ b) $y = \frac{1}{\sqrt{x^3 + 2x^2}}$ c) $y = e^{5x^2}$ d) $y = \ln(6 - x^2)$
2) Find $\frac{dy}{dx}$ when a) $x = 2e^y$ b) $x = \ln(2y + 3)$
3) Find $f'(x)$ for the following functions:
   a) $f(x) = \sin^2(x + 2)$ b) $f(x) = 2\cos 3x$ c) $f(x) = \sqrt{\tan x}$

   Assume that questions involving trig are using radians unless stated otherwise.
4) Find the value of the gradient for:
   a) $y = e^{2x}(x^2 - 3)$ when $x = 0$ b) $y = \ln x \sin x$ when $x = 1$
5) Find the equation of the tangent to the curve $y = \frac{6x^2 + 3}{4x^2 - 1}$ at the point (1, 3).
6) Find $\frac{dy}{dx}$ when $x = 0$ for $y = \operatorname{cosec}(3x - 2)$.

And finally — a megabeast of a question. You probably won't get anything as involved as this in the exam, but if you think you're hard enough...

7) Find the stationary point on the curve $y = \frac{e^x}{\sqrt{x}}$, and say whether it is a maximum or minimum.

Well that's put some colour in your cheeks. Now to really excel yourself on the exam practice, but try not to pull a muscle — you need to be match fit for the real thing.

Exam Questions

1 Find $\frac{dy}{dx}$ for each of the following functions. Simplify your answer where possible.

a) $y = \ln(3x + 1)\sin(3x + 1)$. *(4 marks)*

b) $y = \frac{\sqrt{x^2 + 3}}{\cos 3x}$. *(4 marks)*

c) $y = \sin^3(2x^2)$ *(3 marks)*

d) $y = 2\operatorname{cosec}(3x)$ *(2 marks)*

2 The curve shown below has the equation $x = \sqrt{y^2 + 3y}$.

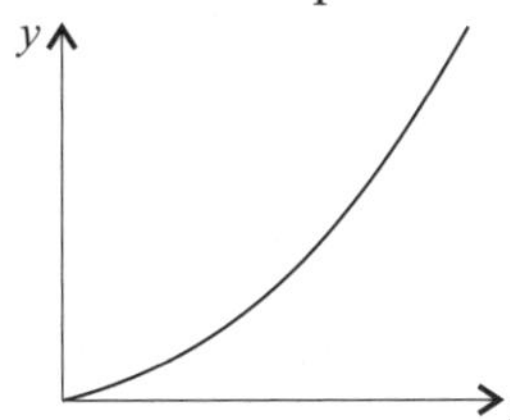

a) Find $\frac{dy}{dx}$ at the point (2, 1). *(5 marks)*

b) Hence find the equation of the tangent to the curve at (2, 1), in the form $y = ax + b$, where a and b are constants. *(2 marks)*

3 Use the quotient rule to show that, for the function $f(x) = \sec x$:

$$f'(x) = \sec x \tan x.$$

(4 marks)

C3 Section 4 — Practice Questions

4 Differentiate the following with respect to x.

a) $\sqrt{(e^x + e^{2x})}$. *(3 marks)*

b) $3e^{2x+1} - \ln(1 - x^2) + 2x^3$. *(3 marks)*

5 A sketch of the function $f(x) = 4\ln 3x$ is shown in the diagram.

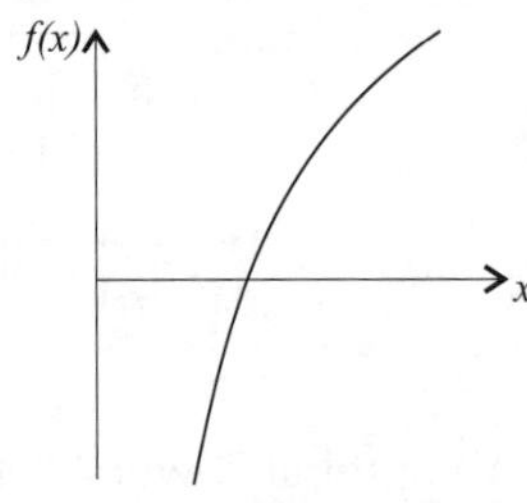

a) Find $f'(x)$ at the point where $x = 1$. *(3 marks)*

b) Find the equation of the tangent to the curve at the point $x = 1$. *(3 marks)*

6 Find the gradient of the tangent to the curve:

$$y = \sin^2 x - 2\cos 2x$$

at the point where $x = \frac{\pi}{12}$ radians. *(4 marks)*

7 Given that $y = \frac{e^x + x}{e^x - x}$, find $\frac{dy}{dx}$ when $x = 0$. *(3 marks)*

8 Find the equation of the normal to the curve $x = \sin 4y$ that passes through the point $\left(0, \frac{\pi}{4}\right)$.
Give your answer in the form $y = mx + c$, where m and c are constants to be found. *(6 marks)*

9 A curve with equation $y = e^x \sin x$ has 2 turning points in the interval $-\pi \le x \le \pi$.

a) Find the value of x at each of these turning points. *(6 marks)*

b) Determine the nature of each of the turning points. *(5 marks)*

Location of Roots

And now to the final leg of the magical mystery tour known as C3. And what a finale. Small but perfectly formed, this section will tell you everything you need to know (for now) about finding approximations of roots. Oh the thrills.

A Change of Sign from f(a) to f(b) means a Root Between a and b

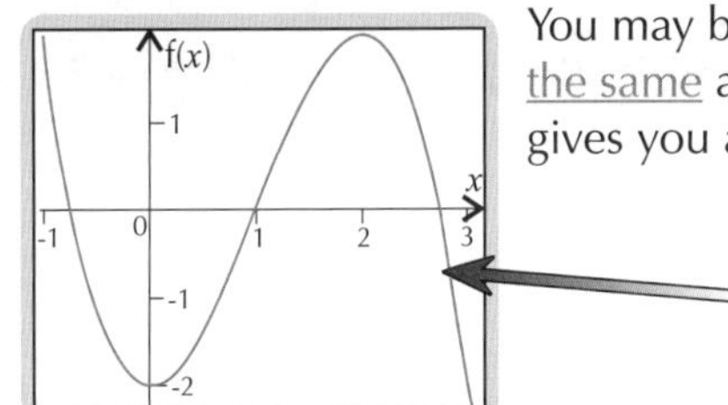

You may be asked to 'solve' or 'find the roots of' an equation (where $f(x) = 0$). This is exactly the same as finding the value of x where the graph crosses the x-axis. The graph of the function gives you a rough idea how many roots there are (if any) and where.

E.g. the function $f(x) = 3x^2 - x^3 - 2$ (shown here) has 3 roots in the interval $-1 \le x \le 3$, since it crosses the x-axis three times (i.e. there are 3 solutions to the equation $3x^2 - x^3 - 2 = 0$). You can also see from the graph that $x = 1$ is a root, and the other roots are close to $x = -1$ and $x = 3$.

Look at the graph above at the root $x = 1$. For x-values just before the root, $f(x)$ is negative, and just after the root, $f(x)$ is positive. It's the other way around for the other two roots, but either way:

f(x) changes sign as it passes through a root.

This is only true for continuous functions — ones that are joined up all the way along with no 'jumps' or gaps.

To show that a root lies in the interval between two values 'a' and 'b':

1) Find f(a) and f(b).
2) If the two answers have different signs, and the function is continuous, there's a root somewhere between 'em.

$f(x) = \tan x$ is an example of a non-continuous function — it has gaps where $f(x)$ changes sign even though there's no root.

EXAMPLE Show that $x^4 + 3x - 5 = 0$ has a root in the interval $1.1 \le x \le 1.2$.

1) Put both 1.1 and 1.2 into the expression:
$f(1.1) = (1.1)^4 + (3 \times 1.1) - 5 = -0.2359$. $f(1.2) = (1.2)^4 + (3 \times 1.2) - 5 = 0.6736$.
2) f(1.1) and f(1.2) have different signs, and $f(x)$ is continuous, so there's a root in the interval $1.1 \le x \le 1.2$.

Use an Iteration Formula to find Approximations of Roots

Some equations are just too darn tricky to solve properly. For these, you need to find approximations to the roots, to a certain level of accuracy. You'll usually be told the value of x that a root is close to, and then iteration does the rest.

Iteration is like fancy trial and improvement. You put an approximate value of a root x into an iteration formula, and out pops a slightly more accurate value. Then repeat as necessary until you have an accurate enough answer.

EXAMPLE Use the iteration formula $x_{n+1} = \sqrt[3]{x_n + 4}$ to solve $x^3 - 4 - x = 0$, to 2 d.p. Start with $x_0 = 2$.

1) The notation x_n just means the approximation of x at the nth iteration. So putting x_0 in the formula for x_n, gives you x_{n+1}, which is x_1, the first iteration.
2) $x_0 = 2$, so $x_1 = \sqrt[3]{x_0 + 4} = \sqrt[3]{2 + 4} = 1.8171...$ ← Leave this in your calculator for accuracy.
3) This value now gets put back into the formula to find x_2:
$x_1 = 1.8171...$, so $x_2 = \sqrt[3]{x_1 + 4} = \sqrt[3]{1.8171... + 4} = 1.7984...$ ← You should now just be able to type '$\sqrt[3]{(ANS + 4)}$' in your calculator and keep pressing enter for each iteration.
4) Carry on until you get answers that are the same when rounded to 2 d.p:
$x_2 = 1.7984...$, so $x_3 = \sqrt[3]{x_2 + 4} = \sqrt[3]{1.7984... + 4} = 1.7965...$
5) x_2, x_3, and all further iterations are the same when rounded to 2 d.p., so the root is $x = 1.80$ to 2 d.p.

The hat — an approximate solution to root problems...

Already one third of the way through this section, and, I hope you agree, it's been a pretty gentle start. Just to re-iterate (ho ho) the main ways to find those roots — sign changes and iteration formulas. It's a doddle.

Iterative Methods

Now we come to the trickier bits. It's all well and good being able to plug numbers into a formula, but where do those formulas come from? And why don't they always work? Read on to find out...

Rearrange the Equation to get the Iteration Formula

The iteration formula is just a rearrangement of the equation, leaving a single 'x' on one side.

There are often lots of different ways to rearrange the equation, so in the exam you'll usually be asked to 'show that' it can be rearranged in a certain way, rather than starting from scratch.

You can also rearrange $x^3 - x^2 - 9 = 0$ into the iteration formula $x_{n+1} = \sqrt{x_n^3 - 9}$, which behaves differently, as shown below.

EXAMPLE Show that $x^3 - x^2 - 9 = 0$ can be rearranged into $x = \sqrt{\frac{9}{x-1}}$.

1) The '9' is on its own in the fraction so try: $x^3 - x^2 - 9 = 0 \Rightarrow x^3 - x^2 = 9$
2) The LHS can be factorised now: $x^2(x - 1) = 9$
3) Get the x^2 on its own by dividing by $x - 1$: $x^2 = \frac{9}{x-1}$
4) Finally square root both sides: $x = \sqrt{\frac{9}{x-1}}$

You can now use the iteration formula $x_{n+1} = \sqrt{\frac{9}{x_n - 1}}$ to find approximations of the roots.

Sometimes an iteration formula just will not find a root. In these cases, no matter how close to the root you have x_0, the iteration sequence diverges — the numbers get further and further apart. The iteration also might stop working — e.g. if you have to take the square root of a negative number.

EXAMPLE The equation $x^3 - x^2 - 9 = 0$ has a root close to $x = 2.5$. What is the result of using $x_{n+1} = \sqrt{x_n^3 - 9}$ with $x_0 = 2.5$ to find this root?

1) Start with $x_1 = \sqrt{2.5^3 - 9} = 2.5739...$ (seems okay so far...)
2) Subsequent iterations give: $x_2 = 2.8376...$, $x_3 = 3.7214...$, $x_4 = 6.5221...$ — so the sequence diverges.

Usually though, in an exam question, you'll be given a formula that converges to a certain root — otherwise there's not much point in using it. If your formula diverges when it shouldn't, go back and check you've not made a mistake.

Use Upper and Lower Bounds to 'Show that' a root is correct

Quite often you'll be given an approximation to a root and be asked to show that it's correct to a certain accuracy. This is a lot like showing that the root lies in a certain interval (on the last page) — the trick is to work out the right interval.

EXAMPLE Show that $x = 2.472$ is a root of the equation $x^3 - x^2 - 9 = 0$ to 3 d.p.

1) If $x = 2.472$ is a root rounded to 3 decimal places, the exact root must lie between the upper and lower bounds of this value — 2.4715 and 2.4725. Any value in this interval would be rounded to 2.472 to 3 d.p.

2.471 2.4715 2.472 2.4725 2.473

2) The function $f(x) = x^3 - x^2 - 9$ is continuous, so you know the root lies in the interval $2.4715 \le x \le 2.4725$ if f(2.4715) and f(2.4725) have different signs.
3) $f(2.4715) = 2.4715^3 - 2.4715^2 - 9 = -0.0116...$ and $f(2.4725) = 2.4725^3 - 2.4725^2 - 9 = 0.0017...$
4) f(2.4715) and f(2.4725) have different signs, so the root must lie in between them. Since any value between would be rounded to 2.472 to 3 d.p. this answer must be correct.

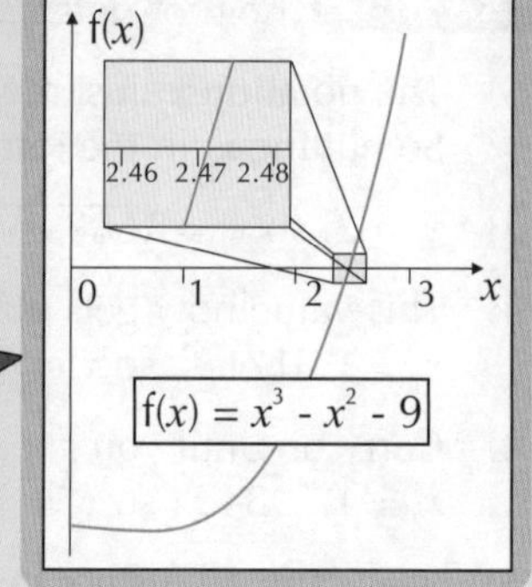

You're bound to be asked questions on this...

There are usually several parts to an exam question on iteration, but it's all pretty standard stuff. I'd put good money on you having to rearrange an equation to get an iteration formula, or show that an approximation to a root is correct.

Iterative Methods

So now that you know all you need to know to be able to tackle the exam questions, let's have a look at how it all fits together in a worked example. Brace yourself...

Questions on Locating Roots combine all the Different Methods

Obviously, the questions you come across in the exam won't be identical to the one below (if only...), but there are, after all, only a limited number of ways you can be asked to find a root using the numerical methods in this section. If you can follow the steps shown below you won't go far wrong.

EXAMPLE The graph below shows both roots of the continuous function $f(x) = 6x - x^2 + 13$.

a) Show that the positive root, α, lies in the interval $7 < x < 8$.

b) Show that $6x - x^2 + 13 = 0$ can be rearranged into the formula: $x = \sqrt{6x + 13}$.

c) Use the iteration formula $x_{n+1} = \sqrt{6x_n + 13}$ and $x_0 = 7$ to find α to 1 d.p.

d) Show that the negative root, β, is -1.690 to 3 d.p.

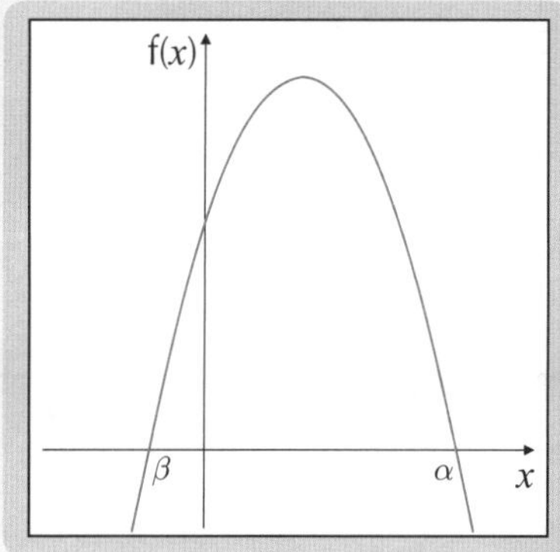

a) $f(x)$ is a continuous function, so if $f(7)$ and $f(8)$ have different signs then there is a root in the interval $7 < x < 8$:

$f(7) = (6 \times 7) - 7^2 + 13 = 6.$

$f(8) = (6 \times 8) - 8^2 + 13 = -3.$

There is a change of sign so $7 < \alpha < 8$.

b) Get the x^2 on its own to make: $6x + 13 = x^2$

Now take the (positive) square root to leave: $x = \sqrt{6x + 13}$.

c) Using $x_{n+1} = \sqrt{6x_n + 13}$ with $x_0 = 7$, gives $x_1 = \sqrt{6 \times 7 + 13} = 7.4161...$

Continuing the iterations:

$x_2 = \sqrt{6 \times 7.4161... + 13} = 7.5826...$ $\quad x_3 = \sqrt{6 \times 7.5826... + 13} = 7.6482...$

$x_4 = \sqrt{6 \times 7.6482... + 13} = 7.6739...$ $\quad x_5 = \sqrt{6 \times 7.6739... + 13} = 7.6839...$

$x_6 = \sqrt{6 \times 7.6839... + 13} = 7.6879...$ $\quad x_7 = \sqrt{6 \times 7.6879... + 13} = 7.6894...$

x_4 to x_7 all round to 7.7 to 1 d.p., so to 1 d.p. $\alpha = 7.7$.

The list of results from each iteration $x_1, x_2, x_3...$ is called the iteration sequence.

d) If $\beta = -1.690$ to 3 d.p. the upper and lower bounds are -1.6895 and -1.6905. The root must lie between these values in order to be rounded to -1.690.

As the function is continuous, if $f(-1.6895)$ and $f(-1.6905)$ have different signs then $-1.6905 \le \beta \le -1.6895$:

$f(-1.6895) = (6 \times -1.6895) - (-1.6895)^2 + 13 = 0.00858...$

$f(-1.6905) = (6 \times -1.6905) - (-1.6905)^2 + 13 = -0.00079...$

There is a change of sign, so $-1.6905 \le \beta \le -1.6895$, and so $\beta = -1.690$ to 3 d.p.

Trouble finding a root? Try sat-nav...

And that's your lot — wasn't so bad, was it? All done and dusted for C3, except for those practice questions you've come to know and love so well. Then it's just the tiny wee matter of passing the exam...
So calculators at the ready, grab your lucky pen and prepare to iterate your heart out...

C3 Section 5 — Practice Questions

Oh happy day, there's light at the end of the C3 tunnel. You're almost there now, but to make up for a very short section I'm giving you lots of lovely practice. Stretch those thinking muscles with this warm-up:

Warm-up Questions

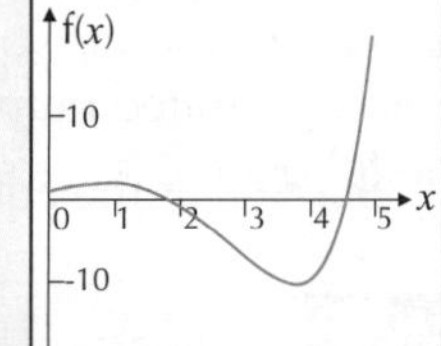

1) The graph shows the function $f(x) = e^x - x^3$ for $0 \leq x \leq 5$.
How many roots does the equation $e^x - x^3 = 0$ have in the interval $0 \leq x \leq 5$?

2) Show that there is a root in the interval:
   a) $3 < x < 4$ for $\sin(2x) = 0$, Don't forget to use radians when you're given trig functions.
   b) $2.1 < x < 2.2$ for $\ln(x - 2) + 2 = 0$,
   c) $4.3 < x < 4.5$ for $x^3 - 4x^2 = 7$.

3) By selecting an appropriate interval show that, to 1 d.p, $x = 1.2$ is a root of the equation $x^3 + x - 3 = 0$.

4) Use the formula $x_{n+1} = -\frac{1}{2}\cos x_n$, with $x_0 = -1$, to find a root of $\cos x + 2x = 0$ to 2 d.p.

5) Use the formula $x_{n+1} = \sqrt{\ln x_n + 4}$, with $x_0 = 2$, to find a root of $x^2 - \ln x - 4 = 0$ to 3 d.p.

6) a) Show that the equation $2x^2 - x^3 + 1 = 0$ can be written in the form:
   i) $x = \sqrt{\frac{-1}{2 - x}}$ ii) $x = \sqrt[3]{2x^2 + 1}$ iii) $x = \sqrt{\frac{x^3 - 1}{2}}$
   b) Use iteration formulas based on each of the above rearrangements with $x_0 = 2.3$ to find a root of $2x^2 - x^3 + 1 = 0$ to 2 d.p. Which of the three formulas converge to a root?

And for my final trick... Sadly no magic here, but all the right kinds of questions to prepare you for the exam. Which may not be what you want, but it's definitely what you need.

Exam Questions

1 The sketch below shows part of the graph of the function $f(x) = 2xe^x - 3$.
The curve crosses the x-axis at the point P $(p, 0)$, as shown, so p is a root of the equation $f(x) = 0$.

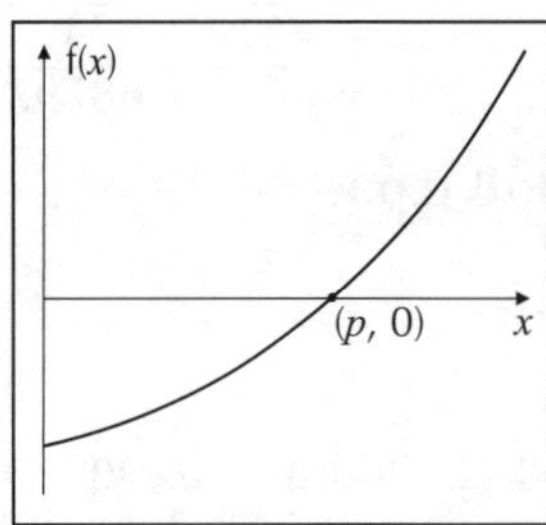

a) Show that $0.7 < p < 0.8$. *(3 marks)*

b) Show that $f(x) = 0$ can be rewritten as:

$$x = \frac{3}{2}e^{-x}.$$

(2 marks)

c) Starting with $x_0 = 0.7$, use the iteration

$$x_{n+1} = \frac{3}{2}e^{-x_n}$$

to find x_1, x_2, x_3 and x_4 to 4 d.p. *(3 marks)*

d) Show that $p = 0.726$, to 3 d.p. *(3 marks)*

C3 Section 5 — Practice Questions

2 The graph of the function:

$$y = \sin 3x + 3x, \quad 0 < x < \pi,$$

meets the line $y = 1$ when $x = a$.

a) Show that $0.1 < a < 0.2$. *(4 marks)*

b) Show that the equation:

$$\sin 3x + 3x = 1$$

can be written as:

$$x = \tfrac{1}{3}(1 - \sin 3x).$$

(2 marks)

c) Starting with $x_0 = 0.2$, use the iteration:

$$x_{n+1} = \tfrac{1}{3}(1 - \sin 3x_n)$$

to find x_4, to 3 d.p. *(2 marks)*

3 The sequence given by:

$$x_{n+1} = \sqrt[3]{x_n^2 - 4}, \quad x_0 = -1$$

converges to a number 'b'.

a) Find the values of x_1, x_2, x_3 and x_4 correct to 4 decimal places. *(3 marks)*

b) Show that $x = b$ is a root of the equation:

$$x^3 - x^2 + 4 = 0$$

(2 marks)

c) Show that $b = -1.315$ to 3 decimal places, by choosing an appropriate interval. *(3 marks)*

4 The function:

$$f(x) = \ln(x + 3) - x + 2, \quad x > -3$$

has a root at $x = m$.

a) Show that m lies between 3 and 4. *(3 marks)*

b) Find, using iteration, the value of m correct to 2 decimal places.
Use the iteration formula: $x_{n+1} = \ln(x_n + 3) + 2$
with $x_0 = 3$. *(3 marks)*

c) Use a suitable interval to verify that your answer to part b) is correct to 2 decimal places. *(3 marks)*

General Certificate of Education
Advanced Subsidiary (AS) and Advanced Level

Core Mathematics C3 — Practice Exam One

Time Allowed: 1 hour 30 min

Calculators may be used for this exam (except those with facilities for symbolic algebra, differentiation or integration).

Give any non-exact numerical answers to an appropriate degree of accuracy.

There are 75 marks available for this paper.

1 For the function:

$$f(x) = 3\ln x - \ln 3x, \qquad x > 0$$

find:

a) the exact value of x when $f(x) = 0$. *(2 marks)*

b) $f^{-1}(x)$. *(2 marks)*

c) the exact value of x when $f^{-1}(x) = 1$. *(2 marks)*

d) $f'(x)$ when $x = 1$. *(2 marks)*

2 The graph below shows the function $y = f(x)$, $x \in \mathbb{R}$, with turning points $A(-1, -2)$ and $B(3, 2)$.

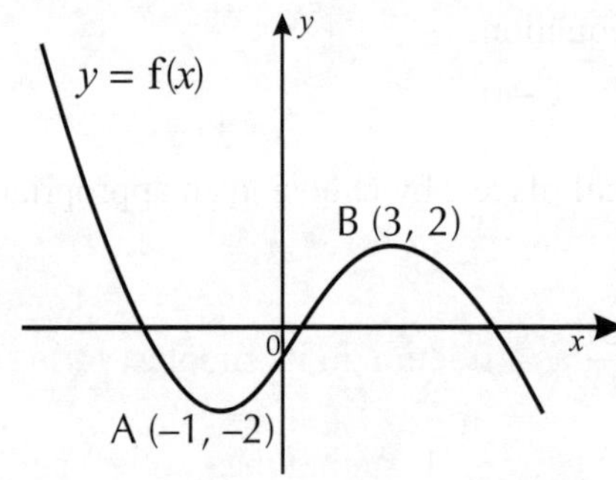

a) On separate axes, sketch the graphs of the following, clearly showing the coordinates of A and B where possible.

(i) $y = f(|x|)$. *(3 marks)*

(ii) $y = 3f(x + 2)$. *(3 marks)*

b) For the functions $g(x) = \sqrt{2x+3}$, $x \geq -1.5$ and $h(x) = \dfrac{6}{x^2 - 4}$, $x > 2$, find:

(i) gh(4) *(2 marks)*

(ii) hg(3) *(2 marks)*

(iii) hg(x) *(3 marks)*

3 Part of the curve

$$y = \frac{4x - 1}{\tan x}$$

is shown below.

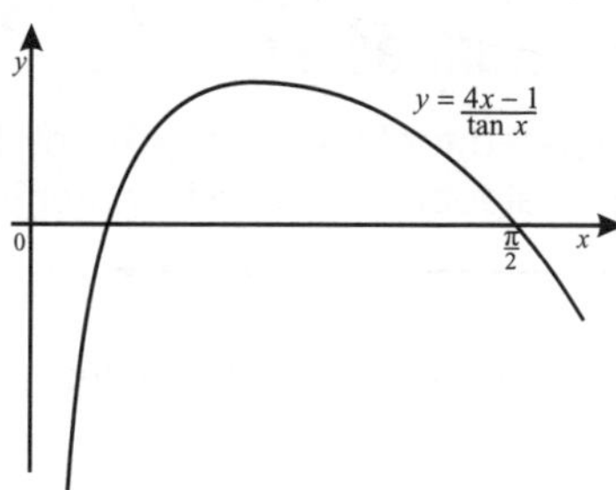

a) Show that:

$$4\cot x - (4x - 1)\text{cosec}^2 x$$

is an expression for $\frac{dy}{dx}$.

(3 marks)

b) The curve has a maximum in the range $0 < x < \frac{\pi}{2}$. Show that at the maximum point:

$$2\sin 2x - 4x + 1 = 0.$$

(3 marks)

4 a) On the same axes, draw the graphs of $f(x) = |2x + 3|$ and $g(x) = |5x - 4|$, showing clearly where each graph touches the coordinate axes.

(2 marks)

b) Hence or otherwise solve the equation $|2x + 3| = |5x - 4|$.

(4 marks)

5 a) Express $\frac{(x^2 - 9)(3x^2 - 10x - 8)}{(6x + 4)(x^2 - 7x + 12)}$ as a fraction in its simplest form.

(2 marks)

b) Divide $2x^3 - x^2 - 16x + 3$ by $x^2 - 3x - 1$, stating the quotient and remainder.

(4 marks)

6 a) Find the values of θ in the range $0 \le \theta \le 2\pi$ for which $\text{cosec}\ \theta = \frac{5}{3}$.
Give your answers to 3 significant figures.

(2 marks)

b) (i) Use an appropriate identity to show that $3\,\text{cosec}\ \theta = \cot^2\theta - 17$ can be written as $18 + 3\,\text{cosec}\ \theta - \text{cosec}^2\theta = 0$.

(2 marks)

(ii) Hence solve the equation $3\,\text{cosec}\ \theta = \cot^2\theta - 17$ for $0 \le \theta \le 2\pi$, giving your answers to 3 significant figures.

(4 marks)

7 The sketch below shows the intersection of the curve $y = 6^x$ with the line $y = x + 2$ at the point P.

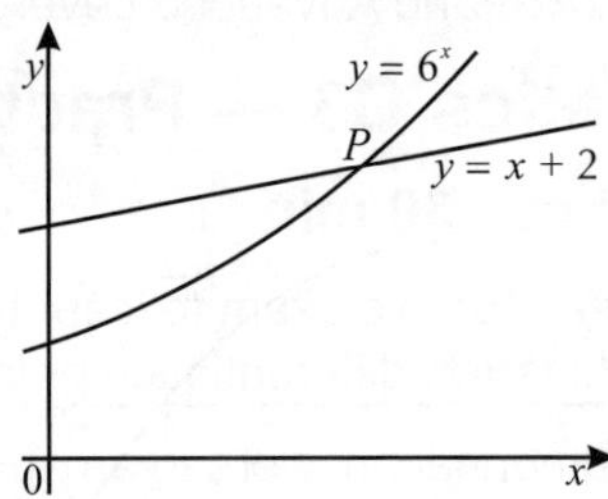

a) Show that the equation $6^x = x + 2$ can be written in the form:

$$x = \frac{\ln(x+2)}{\ln 6}.$$

(2 marks)

b) Starting with $x_0 = 0.5$, use the iteration formula:

$$x_{n+1} = \frac{\ln(x_n + 2)}{\ln 6}$$

to find x_1, x_2 and x_3 correct to 4 decimal places. *(3 marks)*

c) By selecting an appropriate interval, show that $x = 0.515$ to 3 decimal places at point P. *(3 marks)*

8 By writing $\sin 2\theta$ in terms of $\sin\theta$ and $\cos\theta$, solve the equation

$$3\sin 2\theta \tan\theta = 5, \qquad \text{for } 0 \le \theta \le 2\pi.$$

Give your answers to 3 significant figures. *(6 marks)*

9 A curve has the equation $x = \dfrac{e^y + 2y}{e^y - 2y}$.

a) Find $\dfrac{dy}{dx}$. *(3 marks)*

b) Find an equation of the normal to the curve at the point (1, 0) in the form $y = ax + b$. *(3 marks)*

10 Given that $\cos x = \frac{8}{9}$ for the acute angle x, find the exact values of:

a) $\sec x$. *(1 mark)*

b) $\operatorname{cosec} x$. *(2 marks)*

c) $\tan^2 x$. *(2 marks)*

d) $\cos 2x$. *(3 marks)*

General Certificate of Education
Advanced Subsidiary (AS) and Advanced Level

Core Mathematics C3 — Practice Exam Two

Time Allowed: 1 hour 30 min

Calculators may be used for this exam (except those with facilities for symbolic algebra, differentiation or integration).

Give any non-exact numerical answers to an appropriate degree of accuracy.

There are 75 marks available for this paper.

1 a) Write $\sqrt{2}\cos\theta - 3\sin\theta$ in the form $R\cos(\theta + \alpha)$, where $R > 0$ and $0 \leq \alpha \leq \frac{\pi}{2}$.
(3 marks)

b) Hence, or otherwise, solve the equation $\sqrt{2}\cos\theta - 3\sin\theta = 3$ for $0 \leq \theta \leq 2\pi$.
Give your answers to 3 significant figures.
(4 marks)

c) Hence find the maximum and minimum values of $(\sqrt{2}\cos\theta - 3\sin\theta)^4$, and state where the maximum and minimum points occur in the interval $0 \leq \theta \leq 2\pi$.
(4 marks)

2 The functions f and g are defined as follows:

$$f(x) = \frac{1}{x^2}, \quad x \in \mathbb{R}, \ x \neq 0$$
$$g(x) = x^2 - 9, \quad x \in \mathbb{R}$$

a) State the range of g.
(1 mark)

b) Neither f nor g have an inverse. Explain why.
(1 mark)

c) Find
(i) fg(4)
(2 marks)

(ii) gf(1)
(2 marks)

d) (i) Find fg(x), and write down the domain of the composite function fg.
(3 marks)

(ii) Hence solve $fg(x) = \frac{1}{256}$.
(4 marks)

3 a) Express $\frac{x^2 + 5x - 14}{2x^2 - 4x}$ as a fraction in its simplest form.
(3 marks)

b) Using your answer to part (a) or otherwise, write $\frac{x^2 + 5x - 14}{2x^2 - 4x} + \frac{14}{x(x-4)}$ as a single fraction, simplifying your answer as much as possible.
(3 marks)

4 For the function:

$$f(x) = (\sqrt{x+2})\ln(x+2) \quad (x > 0)$$

a) Show that $f(x) = 6 \ln 3$ when $x = 7$. *(2 marks)*

b) Show that $f'(x) = \frac{1}{3}(1 + \ln 3)$ when $x = 7$. *(4 marks)*

c) Hence show that the equation of the tangent to the curve:

$$y = (\sqrt{x+2})\ln(x+2).$$

at the point $x = 7$ can be written as:

$$3y = x + x\ln 3 + 11\ln 3 - 7.$$

(2 marks)

5 The graph below shows the curve of $y = \dfrac{1 + \cos x}{2}$:

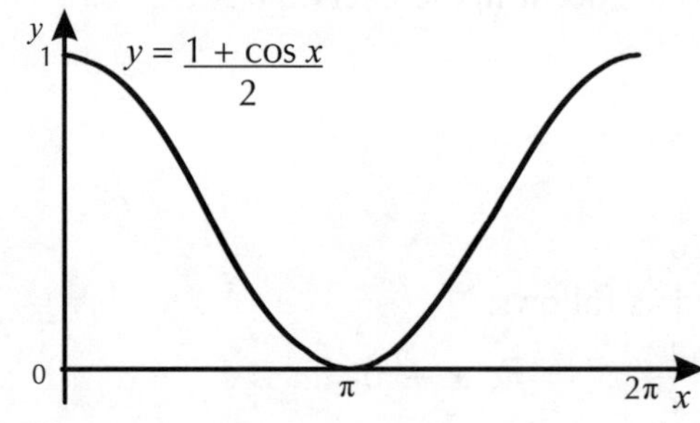

a) Use the double angle formula for cos to show that

$$\frac{1 + \cos x}{2} = \cos^2 \frac{x}{2}.$$

(3 marks)

b) Hence find the exact values of x for which $\cos^2 \frac{x}{2} = 0.75$ in the interval $0 \le x \le 2\pi$. *(4 marks)*

6 A curve has the equation:

$$y = e^{2x} - 5e^x + 3x.$$

a) Find $\dfrac{dy}{dx}$. *(2 marks)*

b) Find $\dfrac{d^2y}{dx^2}$. *(2 marks)*

c) Show that the stationary points on the curve occur when $x = 0$ and $x = \ln \frac{3}{2}$. *(4 marks)*

d) Determine the nature of each of the stationary points. *(4 marks)*

7 The UK population, P, of an endangered species of bird has been modelled over time, t years, by the function:

$$P = 5700e^{-0.15t} \quad (t \geq 0)$$

The time $t = 0$ is set as the beginning of the year 2010.

a) State the UK population of the species at the start of 2010. *(1 mark)*

b) Predict the UK population of the species at the start of 2020. *(2 marks)*

c) Predict the year that the population will drop to below 1000. *(2 marks)*

d) Sketch a graph to show the predicted UK population of the species between 2010 and 2025. *(3 marks)*

8 The graph below shows the function:

$$f(x) = 4(x^2 - 1), \qquad x \geq 0,$$

and its inverse function $f^{-1}(x)$.

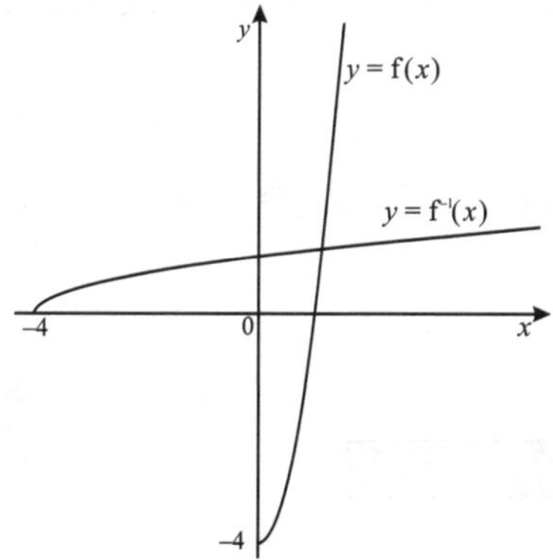

a) By finding an expression for $f^{-1}(x)$, and by considering how the graphs are related, show that $x = \sqrt{\frac{x}{4} + 1}$ at the points where the graphs meet. *(4 marks)*

b) Show that the expression from part a) has a root in the interval $1 < x < 2$. *(3 marks)*

c) Starting with $x_0 = 1$, use the iteration formula:

$$x_{n+1} = \sqrt{\frac{x_n}{4} + 1}$$

to find the x coordinate of the point of intersection, correct to 3 significant figures. *(3 marks)*

Partial Fractions

A nice straightforward start to this section. All the algebra is stuff you've been using for years — just keep a clear head.

'Expressing in Partial Fractions' is the Opposite of Adding Fractions (sort of)

1) You can split a fraction with more than one linear factor in the denominator into partial fractions.

$\frac{7x-7}{(2x+1)(x-3)}$ can be written as partial fractions of the form $\frac{A}{(2x+1)}+\frac{B}{(x-3)}$.

$\frac{9x^2+x+16}{(x+2)(2x-1)(x-3)}$ can be written as partial fractions of the form $\frac{A}{(x+2)}+\frac{B}{(2x-1)}+\frac{C}{(x-3)}$.

$\frac{x^2+17x+16}{(x+2)^2(3x-1)}$ can be written as partial fractions of the form $\frac{A}{(x+2)^2}+\frac{B}{(x+2)}+\frac{C}{(3x-1)}$.

Watch out here — this one doesn't quite follow the pattern.

2) The tricky bit is figuring out what A, B and C are.
You can use the substitution method or the equating coefficients method:

EXAMPLE Express $\frac{9x^2+x+16}{(x+2)(2x-1)(x-3)}$ in partial fractions.

You know that $\frac{9x^2+x+16}{(x+2)(2x-1)(x-3)} \equiv \frac{A}{(x+2)}+\frac{B}{(2x-1)}+\frac{C}{(x-3)}$. Now to work out A, B and C.

1 Add the partial fractions and cancel the denominators from both sides

$$\frac{A}{(x+2)}+\frac{B}{(2x-1)}+\frac{C}{(x-3)} \equiv \frac{A(2x-1)(x-3)+B(x+2)(x-3)+C(2x-1)(x+2)}{(x+2)(2x-1)(x-3)}$$

So the numerators are equal: $9x^2+x+16 \equiv A(2x-1)(x-3)+B(x+2)(x-3)+C(2x-1)(x+2)$

2 Substitute x for values which get rid of all but one of A, B and C...

Substituting $x = 3$ gets rid of A and B: $(9\times 3^2)+3+16 = 0+0+C((2\times 3)-1)(3+2)$
$100 = 25C \Rightarrow C = 4$

Substituting $x = -2$ gets rid of B and C: $(9\times(-2)^2)+(-2)+16 = A((2\times -2)-1)(-2-3)+0+0$
$50 = 25A \Rightarrow A = 2$

Substituting $x = 0.5$ gets rid of A and C: $(9\times(0.5^2))+0.5+16 = 0+B(0.5+2)(0.5-3)+0$
$18.75 = -6.25B \Rightarrow B = -3$

...OR compare coefficients in the numerators

$9x^2+x+16 \equiv A(2x-1)(x-3)+B(x+2)(x-3)+C(2x-1)(x+2)$

x^2 coefficients: $9 = 2A + B + 2C$
x coefficients: $1 = -7A - B + 3C$
constant terms: $16 = 3A - 6B - 2C$

Solving these equations simultaneously gives $A = 2$, $B = -3$ and $C = 4$ — the same as the substitution method.

3 Write out the solution $\frac{9x^2+x+16}{(x+2)(2x-1)(x-3)} \equiv \frac{2}{(x+2)}-\frac{3}{(2x-1)}+\frac{4}{(x-3)}$

Watch out for Difference of Two Squares Denominators

Just for added meanness, they might give you an expression like $\frac{4}{x^2-1}$ and tell you to express it as partial fractions.

You have to recognise that the denominator is a difference of two squares, write it as two linear factors, and then carry on as normal. E.g. $\frac{21x-2}{9x^2-4} \equiv \frac{21x-2}{(3x-2)(3x+2)} \equiv \frac{A}{(3x-2)}+\frac{B}{(3x+2)}$

All coefficients are not created equal — but some are...

It's worth getting to grips with both methods for step 2. Sometimes one's easier to use than the other, and sometimes you might want to mix and match. It's just another crucial step on the path to going down in history as a mathematical great.

Partial Fractions

Now things are hotting up in the partial fractions department — here's an example involving a repeated factor.

Sometimes it's best to use **Substitution** AND **Equate Coefficients**

EXAMPLE Express $\frac{x^2 + 17x + 16}{(x+2)^2(3x-1)}$ in partial fractions.

You know that $\frac{x^2 + 17x + 16}{(x+2)^2(3x-1)} \equiv \frac{A}{(x+2)^2} + \frac{B}{(x+2)} + \frac{C}{(3x-1)}$. Now to work out A, B and C.

1 Add the partial fractions

You end up with an extra $(x + 2)$ factor in each term that can be cancelled.

$$\frac{A}{(x+2)^2} + \frac{B}{(x+2)} + \frac{C}{(3x-1)} \equiv \frac{A(x+2)(3x-1) + B(x+2)^2(3x-1) + C(x+2)(x+2)^2}{(x+2)^2(x+2)(3x-1)}$$

Cancel the denominators from both sides $x^2 + 17x + 16 \equiv A(3x-1) + B(x+2)(3x-1) + C(x+2)^2$

2 Substitute x for values which get rid of all but one of A, B and C

Substituting $x = -2$ gets rid of B and C: $(-2)^2 + (17 \times -2) + 16 = A((3 \times -2) - 1) + 0 + 0$

$-14 = -7A \Rightarrow \underline{A = 2}$

Substituting $x = \frac{1}{3}$ gets rid of A and B: $\left(\frac{1}{3}\right)^2 + \left(17 \times \frac{1}{3}\right) + 16 = 0 + 0 + C\left(\frac{1}{3} + 2\right)^2$

$\frac{196}{9} = \frac{49}{9}C \Rightarrow \underline{C = 4}$

The trouble is, there's no value of x you can substitute to get rid of A and C to just leave B.

So: **Equate coefficients of x^2**

From $x^2 + 17x + 16 \equiv A(3x-1) + B(x+2)(3x-1) + C(x+2)^2$

Coefficients of x^2 are: $1 = 3B + C$

You know $C = 4$, so: $1 = 3B + 4 \Rightarrow \underline{B = -1}$

3 Write out the solution You now know A, B and C, so: $\frac{x^2 + 17x + 16}{(x+2)^2(3x-1)} \equiv \frac{2}{(x+2)^2} - \frac{1}{(x+2)} + \frac{4}{(3x-1)}$

Divide Before Expressing **Improper Fractions** as Partial Fractions

The numerator of an improper algebraic fraction has a degree equal to or greater than the degree of the denominator.

E.g. $\frac{x^2 + 4}{(x+3)(x+2)}$ (numerator: degree 2; denominator: degree 2) $\qquad \frac{x^4 + 2x}{(x-1)^2(x+2)}$ (numerator: degree 4; denominator: degree 3)

The degree of a polynomial is the highest power of x.

There's an extra step involved in expressing an improper fraction as partial fractions:

1) Divide the numerator by the denominator to get the quotient (q(x)) + a proper fraction (r(x) / d(x))
2) Express the proper fraction as partial fractions.

See pages 2-3 for algebraic division methods.

EXAMPLE Express $\frac{x^4 - 3x^3 - 3x^2 + 10x + 5}{(x-3)(x-2)}$ as partial fractions.

This is $(x - 3)(x - 2)$ multiplied out.

1) First work out $(x^4 - 3x^3 - 3x^2 + 10x + 5) \div (x^2 - 5x + 6)$:
   - Write out the result in the form $f(x) \equiv q(x)d(x) + r(x)$:

     $x^4 - 3x^3 - 3x^2 + 10x + 5 \equiv (x^2 + 2x + 1)(x^2 - 5x + 6) + 3x - 1.$

     Exactly as on page 3 — $q(x)$ = quotient, $d(x)$ = divisor and $r(x)$ = remainder.
   - Divide through by d(x): $\frac{x^4 - 3x^3 - 3x^2 + 10x + 5}{(x-3)(x-2)} \equiv (x^2 + 2x + 1) + \frac{3x-1}{(x-3)(x-2)}$ ← $q(x) + \frac{r(x)}{d(x)}$
2) Now just express the proper fraction as partial fractions: $\frac{x^4 - 3x^3 - 3x^2 + 10x + 5}{(x-3)(x-2)} \equiv (x^2 + 2x + 1) + \frac{A}{(x-3)} + \frac{B}{(x-2)}$

Rid the partial fraction world of improperness — it's only proper...

After you've found the partial fractions, don't forget to go back to the original fraction and write out the full solution...

C4 Section 1 — Practice Questions

Lots of variations on the partial fractions theme — check you've got it with these lovely jubbly questions.

Warm-up Questions

You have to factorise the denominator in Q1 parts d, e and g, and in Q2, part d.

1) Express the following as partial fractions.

a) $\dfrac{4x+5}{(x+4)(2x-3)}$ b) $\dfrac{-7x-7}{(3x+1)(x-2)}$ c) $\dfrac{x-18}{(x+4)(3x-4)}$ d) $\dfrac{5x}{x^2+x-6}$

e) $\dfrac{6+4y}{9-y^2}$ f) $\dfrac{10x^2+32x+16}{(x+3)(2x+4)(x-2)}$ g) $\dfrac{4x^2+12x+6}{x^3+3x^2+2x}$ h) $\dfrac{-11x^2+6x+11}{(2x+1)(3-x)(x+2)}$

2) Express the following as partial fractions — watch out for the repeated factors.

a) $\dfrac{2x+2}{(x+3)^2}$ b) $\dfrac{6x^2+17x+5}{x(x+2)^2}$ c) $\dfrac{-18x+14}{(2x-1)^2(x+2)}$ d) $\dfrac{8x^2-x-5}{x^3-x^2}$

3) Express the following as partial fractions — they're all improper, so divide them first.

a) $\dfrac{2x^2+18x+26}{(x+2)(x+4)}$ b) $\dfrac{3x^2+9x+2}{x(x+1)}$ c) $\dfrac{24x^2-70x+53}{(2x-3)^2}$ d) $\dfrac{3x^3-2x^2-2x-3}{(x+1)(x-2)}$

That should have got the neurones nicely warmed up. Unless it made you very sleepy instead.
Try these exam questions and make sure you can handle them.

Exam Questions

1 Given that, for $x \neq -\frac{1}{3}$, $\dfrac{5+9x}{(1+3x)^2} \equiv \dfrac{A}{(1+3x)^2} + \dfrac{B}{(1+3x)}$, where A and B are integers,

find the values of A and B.

(3 marks)

2 $\dfrac{18x^2-15x-62}{(3x+4)(x-2)} \equiv A + \dfrac{B}{(3x+4)} + \dfrac{C}{(x-2)}$

Find the values of the integers A, B and C.

(4 marks)

3 $f(x) = \dfrac{5x^2+3x+6}{(3-x)(2x-1)^2}$

Given that f(x) can be expressed in the form $f(x) = \dfrac{A}{(3-x)} + \dfrac{B}{(2x-1)^2} + \dfrac{C}{(2x-1)}$,

find the values of A and B and C.

(4 marks)

4 The algebraic fraction $\dfrac{-80x^2+49x-9}{(5x-1)(2-4x)}$ can be written in the form $4 + \dfrac{A}{(5x-1)} + \dfrac{B}{(2-4x)}$,

where A and B are constants. Find the values of A and B.

(4 marks)

5 a) Express the algebraic fraction $\dfrac{3x^2+12x-11}{(x+3)(x-1)}$ in the form $A + \dfrac{B+Cx}{(x+3)(x-1)}$,

where A, B and C are constants.

(4 marks)

b) Express $\dfrac{3x^2+12x-11}{(x+3)(x-1)}$ as partial fractions.

(3 marks)

Parametric Equations of Curves

Parametric equations seem kinda weirdy to start with, but they're actually pretty clever.
You can use them to replace one horrifically complicated equation with two relatively normal-looking ones.
I bet that's just what you always wanted...

Parametric Equations split up x and y into Separate Equations

1) Normally, graphs in the (x, y) plane are described using a Cartesian equation — a single equation linking x and y.
2) Sometimes, particularly for more complicated graphs, it's easier to have two linked equations, called parametric equations.
3) In parametric equations x and y are each defined separately in terms of a third variable, called a parameter. The parameter is usually either t or θ.

EXAMPLE

This graph is given by the parametric equations $y = t^2 - 1$ and $x = t + 1$:

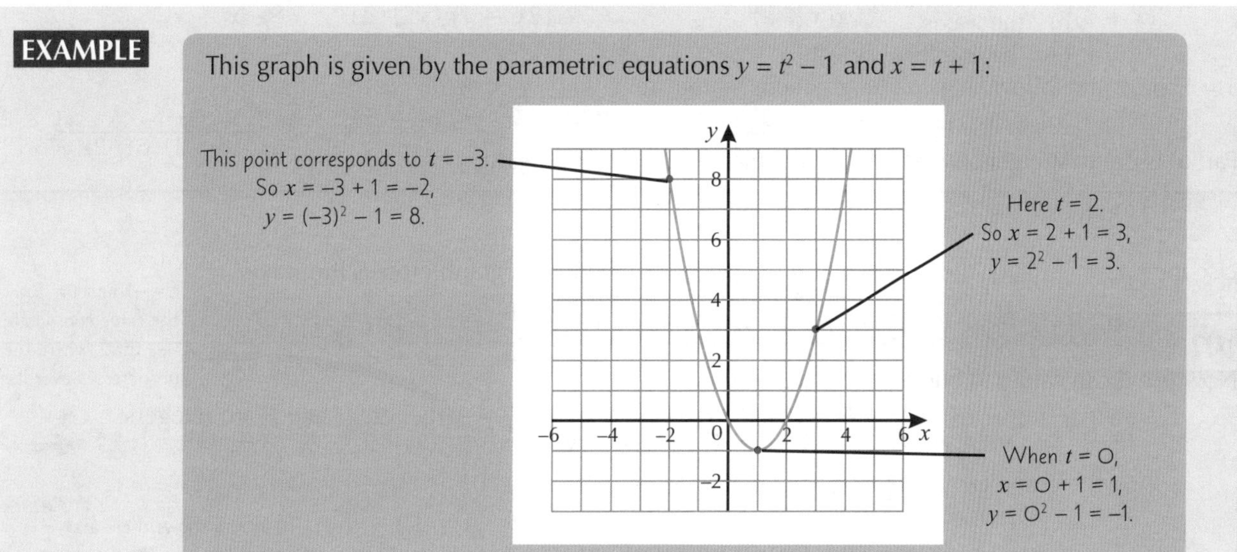
This point corresponds to t = –3.
So x = –3 + 1 = –2,
y = (–3)² – 1 = 8.
Here t = 2.
So x = 2 + 1 = 3,
y = 2² – 1 = 3.
When t = 0,
x = 0 + 1 = 1,
y = 0² – 1 = –1.
y
x
8
6
4
2
0
–2
–6
–4
–2
2
4
6

You can use the parametric equations of a graph to find coordinates of points on the graph, and to find the value of the parameter for given x- or y-coordinates.

EXAMPLE

A curve is defined by the parametric equations $y = \frac{1}{3t}$ and $x = 2t - 3$, $t \neq 0$.

a) Find the x- and y- values of the point the curve passes through when $t = 4$.

b) What value of t corresponds to the point where $y = 9$?

c) What is the value of y when $x = -15$?

Nothing to this question — just sub the right values into the right equations and you're away:

a) When $t = 4$, $x = 8 - 3 = 5$, and $y = \frac{1}{12}$

b) $9 = \frac{1}{3t} \Rightarrow t = \frac{1}{27}$

c) $-15 = 2t - 3 \Rightarrow t = -6 \Rightarrow y = -\frac{1}{18}$

Use the equation for x to find t first, then use that value of t in the other equation to find y.

Time to make like x and y in a set of parametric equations, and split...

Well that was a painless introduction to a topic if ever there was one. Yes, I can tell this section's going to be plain sailing... wait a minute... holy flip, would you look at the size of the example on the next page. And I think I see some trig functions looming in the distance. And that's either Godzilla or an integration sign on the horizon. Batten down the hatches...

Using Parametric Equations

There's plenty of tinkering around with equations to be done in this topic, so get your rearranging hat on. My rearranging hat is a jaunty straw boater.

Use *Parametric Equations* to find where graphs *Intersect*

A lot of parametric equations questions involve identifying points on the curve defined by the equations.

EXAMPLE

The curve shown in this sketch has the parametric equations $y = t^3 - t$ and $x = 4t^2 - 1$.

Find the coordinates of the points where the graph crosses:

a) the x-axis,
b) the y-axis,
c) the line $8y = 3x + 3$.

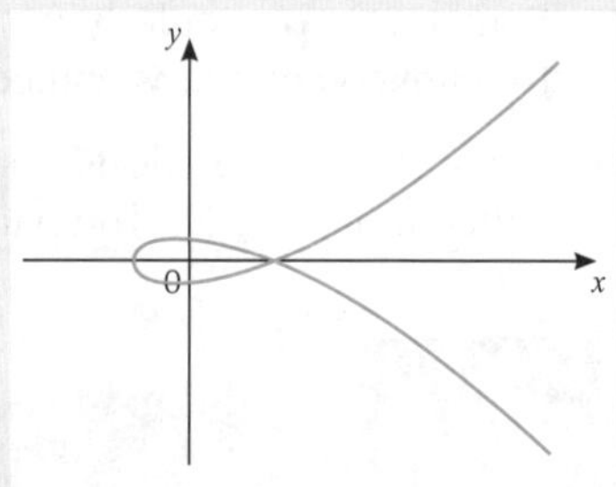

Part a) is pretty straightforward. You've got the y-coordinates already:

a) On the x-axis, $y = 0$.

Use the parametric equation for y to find the values of t where the graph crosses the x-axis:

So $0 = t^3 - t \Rightarrow t(t^2 - 1) = 0 \Rightarrow t(t + 1)(t - 1) = 0 \Rightarrow t = 0, t = -1, t = 1$

Now use those values to find the x-coordinates:

$t = 0 \Rightarrow x = 4(0)^2 - 1 = -1$ $\quad t = -1 \Rightarrow x = 4(-1)^2 - 1 = 3$ $\quad t = 1 \Rightarrow x = 4(1)^2 - 1 = 3$

So the graph crosses the x-axis at the points $(-1, 0)$ and $(3, 0)$.

t = –1 and t = 1 give the same coordinates — that's where the curve crosses over itself.

The sketch shows there are two points where the graph crosses each axis.

And b) is very similar: b) On the y-axis, $x = 0$.

So $0 = 4t^2 - 1 \Rightarrow t^2 = \frac{1}{4} \Rightarrow t = \pm\frac{1}{2}$

$t = \frac{1}{2} \Rightarrow y = \left(\frac{1}{2}\right)^3 - \frac{1}{2} = -\frac{3}{8}$ $\quad t = -\frac{1}{2} \Rightarrow y = \left(-\frac{1}{2}\right)^3 - \left(-\frac{1}{2}\right) = \frac{3}{8}$

So the graph crosses the y-axis at the points $(0, -\frac{3}{8})$ and $(0, \frac{3}{8})$.

Part c) is just a little trickier. First, sub the parametric equations into $8y = 3x + 3$:

c) $8y = 3x + 3 \Rightarrow 8(t^3 - t) = 3(4t^2 - 1) + 3$

Rearrange and factorise to find the values of t you need:

$\Rightarrow 8t^3 - 8t = 12t^2 \Rightarrow 8t^3 - 12t^2 - 8t = 0 \Rightarrow t(2t + 1)(t - 2) = 0 \Rightarrow t = 0, t = -\frac{1}{2}, t = 2$

Go back to the parametric equations to find the x- and y-coordinates:

$t = 0 \Rightarrow x = -1, y = 0$
$t = -\frac{1}{2} \Rightarrow x = 4(\frac{1}{4}) - 1 = 0, y = (-\frac{1}{2})^3 + \frac{1}{2} = \frac{3}{8}$
$t = 2 \Rightarrow x = 4(4) - 1 = 15, y = 2^3 - 2 = 6$

So the graph crosses the line $8y = 3x + 3$ at the points $(-1, 0)$, $(0, \frac{3}{8})$, $(15, 6)$.

You can check the answers by sticking these values back into $8y = 3x + 3$.

y-coordinates? y not...

You quite often get given a sketch of the curve that the parametric equations define. Don't forget that the sketch can be useful for checking your answers — if the curve crosses the x-axis twice, and you've only found one x-coordinate for when $y = 0$, you know something's gone a bit pear-shaped and you should go back and sort it out, sunshine.

Parametric and Cartesian Equations

If you've been dying for θ to put in an appearance since I mentioned it on page 49, then I've got good news. If, on the other hand, you're bored of parametric equations already... I'm sorry.

Rearrange Parametric Equations to get the *Cartesian Equation*

Some parametric equations can be converted into Cartesian equations. There are two main ways to do this:

To convert Parametric Equations to a Cartesian Equation:

 **Rearrange one of the equations to make the parameter the subject, then substitute the result into the other equation.**

or

 **If your equations involve trig functions, use trig identities (see C3 Section 2) to eliminate the parameter.**

You can use the first method to combine the parametrics used in the examples on p49:

EXAMPLE Give the Cartesian equations, in the form $y = f(x)$, of the curves represented by the following pairs of parametric equations:

a) $y = t^2 - 1$ and $x = t + 1$, b) $y = \frac{1}{3t}$ and $x = 2t - 3$, $t \neq 0$.

You want the answer in the form $y = f(x)$, so leave y alone for now, and rearrange the equation for x to make t the subject:

a) $x = t + 1 \Rightarrow t = x - 1$

Now you can eliminate t from the equation for y:

$$y = t^2 - 1 \Rightarrow y = (x-1)^2 - 1 = x^2 - 2x + 1 - 1$$
$$\Rightarrow y = x^2 - 2x$$

b) $x = 2t - 3 \Rightarrow t = \frac{x+3}{2}$

So $y = \frac{1}{3t} \Rightarrow y = \frac{1}{3\left(\frac{x+3}{2}\right)} \Rightarrow y = \frac{1}{\frac{3(x+3)}{2}} \Rightarrow y = \frac{2}{3x+9}$

If there are *Trig Functions*... use *Trig Identities*

Things get a little trickier when the likes of sin and cos decide to put in an appearance:

EXAMPLE A curve has parametric equations

$$x = 1 + \sin\theta, \quad y = 1 - \cos2\theta$$

Give the Cartesian equation of the curve in the form $y = f(x)$.

If you try to make θ the subject of these equations, things will just get messy. The trick is to find a way to get both x and y in terms of the same trig function.

You can get $\sin\theta$ into the equation for y using the identity $\cos2\theta = 1 - 2\sin^2\theta$:

$$y = 1 - \cos2\theta = 1 - (1 - 2\sin^2\theta) = 2\sin^2\theta$$

Rearranging the equation for x gives:

$$\sin\theta = x - 1, \quad \text{so } y = 2\sin^2\theta$$
$$\Rightarrow y = 2(x-1)^2 = 2x^2 - 4x + 2$$

If one of the parametric equations includes $\cos2\theta$ or $\sin2\theta$, that's probably the one you need to substitute — so make sure you know the double angle formulas.

Cartesy peasy, lemon squeezy...

Sometimes you'll get a nasty question where it's really difficult to get the parameter on its own — in that case you might have to do something clever like think about multiplying x and y or dividing y by x. If something like that comes up in an exam, they'll usually give you a hint — but be aware that you might need to think outside the box.

Areas Under Parametric Curves

Did I ever tell you about the time I spent the night under a parametric curve... or was it a bridge...

Learn the method for *Integrating Parametrics*

1) Normally, to find the area under a graph, you can do a simple integration.
   But if you've got parametric equations, things are more difficult — you can't find $\int y\,dx$ if y isn't written in terms of x.
2) There's a sneaky way to get around this. Suppose your parameter's t, then $\int y\,dx = \int y \frac{dx}{dt}\,dt$
3) Both y and $\frac{dx}{dt}$ are written in terms of t, so you can multiply them together to get an expression you can integrate with respect to t.

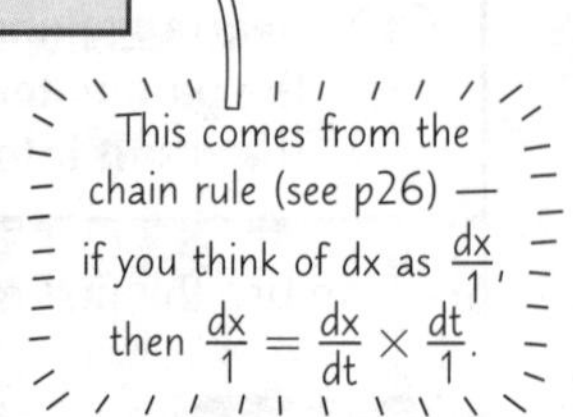

This comes from the chain rule (see p26) — if you think of dx as $\frac{dx}{1}$, then $\frac{dx}{1} = \frac{dx}{dt} \times \frac{dt}{1}$.

EXAMPLE A curve is defined by the parametric equations $y = t^2 + 2t + 3$ and $x = t^3 + 3$.
Show that $\int y\,dx = \int 3t^4 + 6t^3 + 9t^2\,dt$.

$\frac{dx}{dt} = 3t^2$, so using the formula above:

$$\int y\,dx = \int y\frac{dx}{dt}\,dt = \int (t^2 + 2t + 3)(3t^2)\,dt = \int 3t^4 + 6t^3 + 9t^2\,dt.$$

Remember to Convert the *Limits* of *Definite Integrals*

With a definite integral, you need to alter the limits as well. There's more about this sort of thing in C4 Sections 5 and 6.

EXAMPLE The shaded region marked A on this sketch is bounded by the lines $y = 0$ and $x = 2$, and by the curve with parametric equations $x = t^2 - 2$ and $y = t^2 - 9t + 20$, $t \geq 0$, which crosses the x-axis at $x = 14$.

Find the area of A.

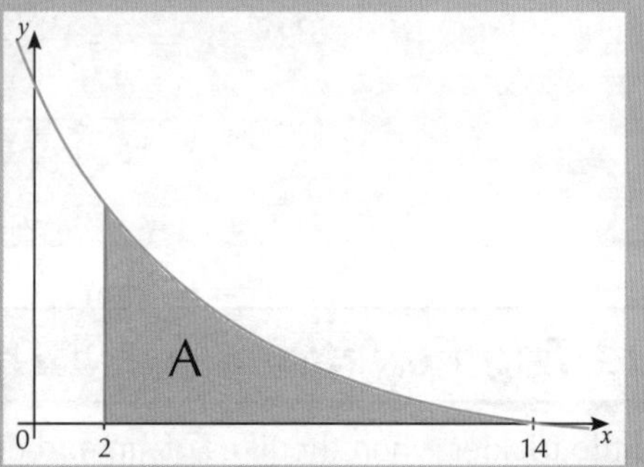

The area of A is $\int_2^{14} y\,dx$. We're going to use $\int y\,dx = \int y\frac{dx}{dt}\,dt$, so first we need to find $\frac{dx}{dt} = \frac{d}{dt}(t^2 - 2) = 2t$

Now we need to do something about those limits.
14 and 2 are the limits for integrating with respect to x.
We need to find the corresponding values of t.

$x = 2 \Rightarrow t^2 - 2 = 2 \Rightarrow t^2 = 4 \Rightarrow t = 2$
$x = 14 \Rightarrow t^2 - 2 = 14 \Rightarrow t^2 = 16 \Rightarrow t = 4$

Now we can integrate:

$$\begin{aligned}
A &= \int_2^{14} y\,dx = \int_2^4 y\frac{dx}{dt}\,dt \\
&= \int_2^4 (t^2 - 9t + 20)(2t)\,dt \\
&= \int_2^4 2t^3 - 18t^2 + 40t\,dt \\
&= \left[\tfrac{1}{2}t^4 - 6t^3 + 20t^2\right]_2^4 \\
&= \left(\tfrac{1}{2}(4)^4 - 6(4)^3 + 20(4)^2\right) - \left(\tfrac{1}{2}(2)^4 - 6(2)^3 + 20(2)^2\right) \\
&= 64 - 40 = 24
\end{aligned}$$

You might be having problems with premature integration...

Some of the stuff that's going on in these examples is covered in more depth in C4 Sections 5 and 6. If you can't wait till then, flick ahead and check it out. But I'll know you're only doing it to put off getting to the Practice Questions...

C4 Section 2 — Practice Questions

Before it became famous in the world of maths, the word 'parametric' had several other jobs. For example, it once starred as the last name of a Bond villain from the former Yugoslavia. Here are some questions. Enjoy.

Warm-up Questions

1) A curve is defined by the parametric equations $y = 2t^2 + t + 4$ and $x = \frac{6-t}{2}$.
   a) Find the values of x and y when $t = 0, 1, 2$ and 3.
   b) What are the values of t when: (i) $x = -7$ (ii) $y = 19$?
   c) Find the Cartesian equation of the curve, in the form $y = f(x)$.

2) The parametric equations of a curve are $x = 2\sin\theta$ and $y = \cos^2\theta + 4$, $-\frac{\pi}{2} \leq \theta \leq \frac{\pi}{2}$.
   a) What are the coordinates of the points where: (i) $\theta = \frac{\pi}{4}$ (ii) $\theta = \frac{\pi}{6}$
   b) What is the Cartesian equation of the curve?
   c) What restrictions are there on the values of x for this curve?

3) The curve C is defined by the parametric equations $x = \frac{\sin\theta}{3}$ and $y = 3 + 2\cos 2\theta$.
   Find the Cartesian equation of C.

4) A curve has parametric equations $y = 4 + \frac{3}{t}$ and $x = t^2 - 1$.
   a) What are the coordinates of the points where this curve crosses
      (i) the y-axis (ii) the line $x + 2y = 14$?
   b) Write the integral $\int y\,dx$ in the form $\int f(t)\,dt$. (You don't need to do the integration.)

Former career of the word 'parametric' #2 — stand-in for the word 'hallelujah' in an early draft of Handel's Messiah. Meanwhile, back at the practice questions...

Exam Questions

1 The curve C is defined by the parametric equations

$$x = 1 - \tan\theta, \quad y = \frac{1}{2}\sin 2\theta, \quad -\frac{\pi}{2} < \theta < \frac{\pi}{2}.$$

a) P is the point on curve C where $\theta = \frac{\pi}{3}$. Find the exact coordinates of P.
(2 marks)

b) Point Q on curve C has coordinates $(2, -\frac{1}{2})$. Find the value of θ at Q.
(2 marks)

c) Using the identity $\sin 2\theta \equiv \frac{2\tan\theta}{1 + \tan^2\theta}$, show that the Cartesian equation of C is $y = \frac{1-x}{x^2 - 2x + 2}$.
(3 marks)

2

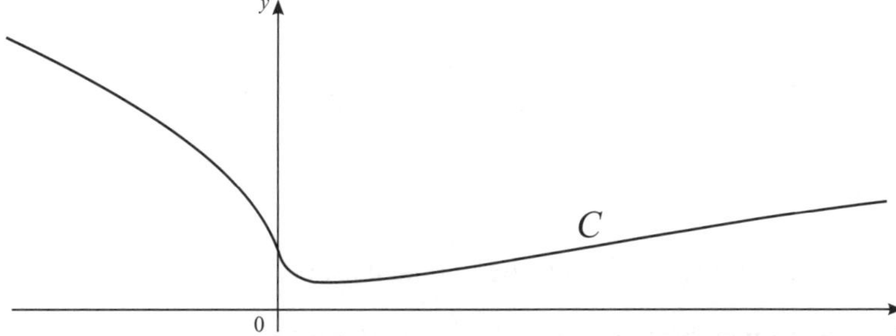

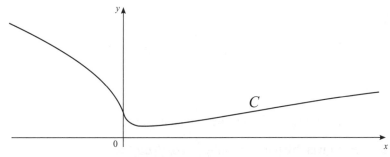

Curve C has parametric equations $x = t^3 + t$, $y = t^2 - 2t + 2$.

a) K is a point on C, and has the coordinates $(a, 1)$. Find the value of a.
(2 marks)

b) The line $8y = x + 6$ passes through C at points K, L and M.
Find the coordinates of L and M, given that the x-coordinate of M is greater than the x-coordinate of L.
(6 marks)

C4 Section 2 — Practice Questions

Former career of the word 'parametric' #3 — proposed name for the next ocean to be discovered. Unfortunately it turned out all the oceans have already been discovered. Ooh look, more questions...

3

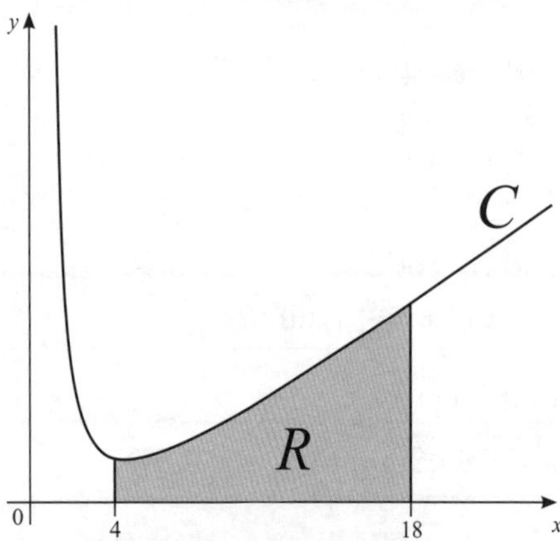

The curve C has parametric equations

$$x = t^2 + 3t, \qquad y = t^2 + \frac{1}{t^3}, \qquad t > 0.$$

The shaded region marked R is enclosed by C, the x-axis and the lines $x = 4$ and $x = 18$.

a) Show that the area of R is given by $\int_1^3 \frac{(t^5 + 1)(2t + 3)}{t^3}\,dt$. *(4 marks)*

b) Find the area of R. *(4 marks)*

4

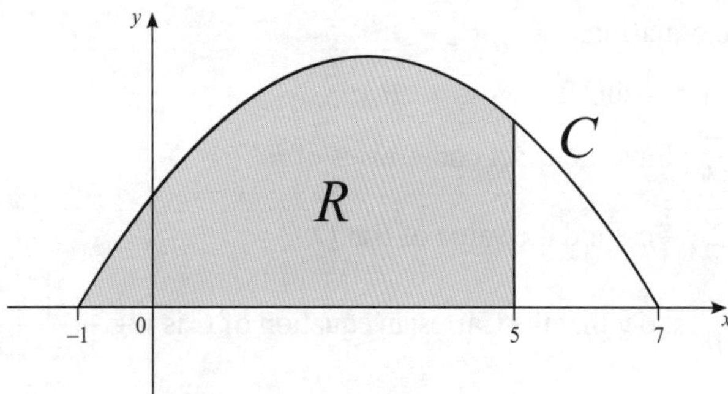

The parametric equations of curve C are

$$x = 3 + 4\sin\theta, \qquad y = \frac{1 + \cos 2\theta}{3}, \qquad -\frac{\pi}{2} \leq \theta \leq \frac{\pi}{2}.$$

Point H on C has coordinates $(5, \frac{1}{2})$.

a) Find the value of θ at point H. *(2 marks)*

The region R is enclosed by C, the line $x = 5$, and the x-axis, as shown.

b) Show that the area of R is given by the integral $\frac{8}{3}\int_{-\frac{\pi}{2}}^{\frac{\pi}{6}} \cos^3\theta\,d\theta$. *(5 marks)*

c) Show that the Cartesian equation of C can be written $y = \frac{-x^2 + 6x + 7}{24}$. *(4 marks)*

d) State the domain of values of x for the curve C. *(1 mark)*

The Binomial Expansion

Yeah, I know the binomial expansion. We spent some time together back in C2. Thought I'd never see it again. And then, of all the sections in all the maths books in all the world, the binomial expansion walks into mine...

The Binomial Expansion Formula is pretty useful

The binomial expansion is a way to raise a given expression to any power.

For simpler cases it's basically a fancy way of multiplying out brackets.
You can also use it to approximate more complicated expressions (see p58).

This is the general formula for binomial expansions:

$$(1+x)^n = 1 + nx + \frac{n(n-1)}{1\times 2}x^2 + \dots + \frac{n(n-1)\dots(n-r+1)}{1\times 2\times \dots \times r}x^r + \dots$$

The Binomial Expansion sometimes gives a Finite Expression

From the general formula, it looks like the expansion always goes on forever.
But if n is a positive integer, the binomial expansion is finite.

EXAMPLE Give the binomial expansion of $(1 + x)^5$.

You can use the general formula and plug in $n = 5$:

$$(1+x)^5 = 1 + 5x + \frac{5(5-1)}{1\times 2}x^2 + \frac{5(5-1)(5-2)}{1\times 2\times 3}x^3 + \frac{5(5-1)(5-2)(5-3)}{1\times 2\times 3\times 4}x^4$$
$$+ \frac{5(5-1)(5-2)(5-3)(5-4)}{1\times 2\times 3\times 4\times 5}x^5 + \frac{5(5-1)(5-2)(5-3)(5-4)(5-5)}{1\times 2\times 3\times 4\times 5\times 6}x^6 + \dots$$
$$= 1 + 5x + \frac{5\times 4}{1\times 2}x^2 + \frac{5\times 4\times 3}{1\times 2\times 3}x^3 + \frac{5\times 4\times 3\times 2}{1\times 2\times 3\times 4}x^4$$
$$+ \frac{5\times 4\times 3\times 2\times 1}{1\times 2\times 3\times 4\times 5}x^5 + \frac{5\times 4\times 3\times 2\times 1\times 0}{1\times 2\times 3\times 4\times 5\times 6}x^6 + \dots$$
$$= 1 + 5x + \frac{20}{2}x^2 + \frac{60}{6}x^3 + \frac{120}{24}x^4 + \frac{120}{120}x^5 + \frac{0}{720}x^6 + \dots$$
$$= 1 + 5x + 10x^2 + 10x^3 + 5x^4 + x^5$$

$n(n-1)$

$n = 5$

You can stop here — all the terms after this one are zero

The formula still works if the coefficient of x isn't 1.

EXAMPLE Give the binomial expansion of $(1 - 3x)^4$.

This time $n = 4$, but you also have to replace every x in the formula with $-3x$:

$(1-3x)^4$ ← Think of this as $(1 + (-3x))^4$ — you need to put the minus into the formula as well as the $3x$.

$n = 4$ $n(n-1)$ Don't forget to square the -3 as well. Stop here

$$= 1 + 4(-3x) + \frac{4\times 3}{1\times 2}(-3x)^2 + \frac{4\times \cancel{3}\times \cancel{2}}{1\times \cancel{2}\times \cancel{3}}(-3x)^3 + \frac{\cancel{4}\times \cancel{3}\times \cancel{2}\times \cancel{1}}{\cancel{1}\times \cancel{2}\times \cancel{3}\times \cancel{4}}(-3x)^4 + \frac{\cancel{4}\times \cancel{3}\times \cancel{2}\times \cancel{1}\times 0}{\cancel{1}\times \cancel{2}\times \cancel{3}\times \cancel{4}\times 5}(-3x)^5 + \dots$$
$$= 1 + 4(-3x) + \frac{12}{2}(9x^2) + \frac{4}{1}(-27x^3) + (81x^4) + \frac{0}{5}(-243x^5) + \dots$$
$$= 1 - 12x + 54x^2 - 108x^3 + 81x^4$$

Make life easier for yourself by cancelling down the fractions before you multiply.

The Binomial Expansion

Unfortunately, you only get a nice, neat, finite expansion when you've got a positive integer n.
But that pesky n sometimes likes to be a negative number or a fraction. n for nuisance. n for naughty.

If n is Negative the expansion gets more complicated...

EXAMPLE

Find the binomial expansion of $\frac{1}{(1+x)^2}$ up to and including the term in x^3.

This is where things start to get a bit more interesting.
First, rewrite the expression: $\frac{1}{(1+x)^2} = (1+x)^{-2}$.
You can still use the general formula. This time $n = -2$:

$n = -2$ $n(n-1)$

$$(1+x)^{-2} = 1 + (-2)x + \frac{(-2)\times(-2-1)}{1\times 2}x^2 + \frac{(-2)\times(-2-1)\times(-2-2)}{1\times 2\times 3}x^3 + \ldots$$
$$= 1 + (-2)x + \frac{(-2)\times(-3)}{1\times 2}x^2 + \frac{(-2)\times(-3)\times(-4)}{1\times 2\times 3}x^3 + \ldots$$
$$= 1 + (-2)x + \frac{3}{1}x^2 + \frac{-4}{1}x^3 + \ldots$$
$$= 1 - 2x + 3x^2 - 4x^3 + \ldots$$

With a negative n, you'll never get zero as a coefficient. If the question hadn't told you to stop, the expansion could go on forever.

Again, you can cancel down before you multiply — but be careful with those minus signs.

We've left out all the terms after $-4x^3$, so the cubic equation you've ended up with is an approximation to the original expression. You could also write the answer like this:

$$\frac{1}{(1+x)^2} \approx 1 - 2x + 3x^2 - 4x^3$$

... and if n is a Fraction things can be tricky too

The binomial expansion formula doesn't just work for integer values of n.

EXAMPLE

Find the binomial expansion of $\sqrt[3]{1+2x}$ up to and including the term in x^3.

This time we've got a fractional power: $\sqrt[3]{1+2x} = (1+2x)^{\frac{1}{3}}$

So this time $n = \frac{1}{3}$, and you also need to replace x with $2x$:

$n = \frac{1}{3}$ $n(n-1)$

$$(1+2x)^{\frac{1}{3}} = 1 + \tfrac{1}{3}(2x) + \frac{\frac{1}{3}\times\left(\frac{1}{3}-1\right)}{1\times 2}(2x)^2 + \frac{\frac{1}{3}\times\left(\frac{1}{3}-1\right)\times\left(\frac{1}{3}-2\right)}{1\times 2\times 3}(2x)^3 + \ldots$$
$$= 1 + \tfrac{2}{3}x + \frac{\frac{1}{3}\times\left(-\frac{2}{3}\right)}{1\times 2}4x^2 + \frac{\frac{1}{3}\times\left(-\frac{2}{3}\right)\times\left(-\frac{5}{3}\right)}{1\times 2\times 3}8x^3 + \ldots$$
$$= 1 + \tfrac{2}{3}x + \frac{\left(-\frac{2}{9}\right)}{2}4x^2 + \frac{\left(\frac{10}{27}\right)}{6}8x^3 + \ldots$$
$$= 1 + \tfrac{2}{3}x + \left(-\tfrac{2}{9}\times\tfrac{1}{2}\right)4x^2 + \left(\tfrac{10}{27}\times\tfrac{1}{6}\right)8x^3 + \ldots$$
$$= 1 + \tfrac{2}{3}x - \tfrac{4}{9}x^2 + \tfrac{40}{81}x^3 + \ldots$$

Cancelling down is much trickier with this type of expansion — it's usually safer to multiply everything out fully.

Exam questions often ask for the coefficients as simplified fractions.

The Binomial Expansion

More binomial goodness... this page is so jam-packed with the stuff, there's only room for a one-line intro...

*If the **Constant** in the brackets isn't **1**, you have to **Factorise** first*

So the general binomial expansion of $(1 + x)^n$ works fine for any n, and you can replace the x with other x-terms, but that 1 has to be a 1 before you can expand. That means you sometimes need to start with a sneaky bit of factorisation.

EXAMPLE Give the binomial expansion of $(3 - x)^4$.

To use the general formula, you need the constant term in the brackets to be 1.
You can take the 3 outside the brackets by factorising:

$$3 - x = 3(1 - \tfrac{1}{3}x)$$
$$\text{so} \quad (3 - x)^4 = [3(1 - \tfrac{1}{3}x)]^4 = 3^4(1 - \tfrac{1}{3}x)^4 = 81(1 - \tfrac{1}{3}x)^4$$

The aim here is to get an expression in the form $c(1 + dx)^n$, where c and d are constants.

Now we can use the general formula, with $n = 4$, and $-\frac{1}{3}x$ instead of x:

$$\left(1 - \tfrac{1}{3}x\right)^4 = 1 + 4\left(-\tfrac{1}{3}x\right) + \frac{4 \times 3}{1 \times 2}\left(-\tfrac{1}{3}x\right)^2 + \frac{4 \times 3 \times 2}{1 \times 2 \times 3}\left(-\tfrac{1}{3}x\right)^3 + \frac{4 \times 3 \times 2 \times 1}{1 \times 2 \times 3 \times 4}\left(-\tfrac{1}{3}x\right)^4$$
$$= 1 - \tfrac{4}{3}x + 6\left(\tfrac{1}{9}x^2\right) + 4\left(-\tfrac{1}{27}x^3\right) + \tfrac{1}{81}x^4$$
$$= 1 - \frac{4x}{3} + \frac{2x^2}{3} - \frac{4x^3}{27} + \frac{x^4}{81}$$

So now we can expand the original expression:

$$(3 - x)^4 = 81\left(1 - \tfrac{1}{3}x\right)^4$$
$$= 81\left(1 - \frac{4x}{3} + \frac{2x^2}{3} - \frac{4x^3}{27} + \frac{x^4}{81}\right)$$
$$= 81 - 108x + 54x^2 - 12x^3 + x^4$$

*Some **Binomial Expansions** are only **Valid** for **Certain Values** of x*

When you find a binomial expansion, you usually have to state which values of x the expansion is valid for.

If n is a positive integer, the binomial expansion of $(p + qx)^n$ is valid for all values of x.

If n is a negative integer or a fraction, the binomial expansion of $(p + qx)^n$ is valid when $\left|\frac{qx}{p}\right| < 1$.

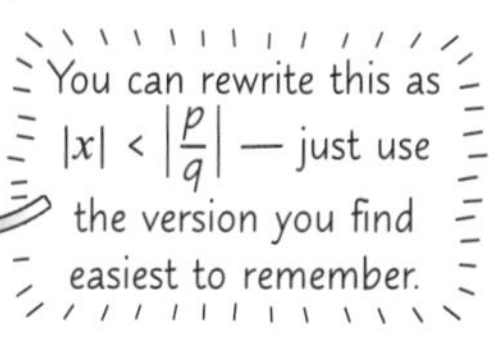

You can rewrite this as $|x| < \left|\frac{p}{q}\right|$ — just use the version you find easiest to remember.

This means there's a little bit more to do for the two examples on the previous page:

$(1 + x)^{-2} = 1 - 2x + 3x^2 - 4x^3 + ...$ This expansion is valid for $|x| < 1$.

$(1 + 2x)^{\frac{1}{3}} = 1 + \frac{2}{3}x - \frac{4}{9}x^2 + \frac{40}{81}x^3 + ...$

This expansion is valid if $|2x| < 1 \Rightarrow 2|x| < 1 \Rightarrow |x| < \frac{1}{2}$.

You might already know the rules $|ab| = |a||b|$ and $\left|\frac{a}{b}\right| = \frac{|a|}{|b|}$. If you don't, then get to know them — they're handy for rearranging these limits.

Lose weight and save money — buy no meals...

Two facts: 1) You can pretty much guarantee that there'll be a binomial expansion question on your C4 exam, and 2) any binomial expansion question they can throw at you will feature some combination of these adaptations of the general formula. So make sure you can deal with all the different variations by practising loads of questions.

Approximating with Binomial Expansions

Binomial expansions can give you a handy way to estimate various roots.
OK, so it's not that handy... just go with it for now...

*To find **Approximations**, substitute the right value of x*

When you've done an expansion, you can use it to estimate the value of the original expression for given values of x.

EXAMPLE

The binomial expansion of $(1 + 3x)^{\frac{1}{3}}$ up to the term in x^3 is $(1 + 3x)^{\frac{1}{3}} \approx 1 + x - x^2 + \frac{5}{3}x^3$.
The expansion is valid for $|x| < \frac{1}{3}$.
Use this expansion to approximate $\sqrt[3]{1.3}$. Give your answer to 4 d.p.

For this type of question, you need to find the right value of x to make the expression you're expanding equal to the thing you're looking for.

In this case it's pretty straightforward: $\sqrt[3]{1.3} = (1 + 3x)^{\frac{1}{3}}$ when $x = 0.1$.

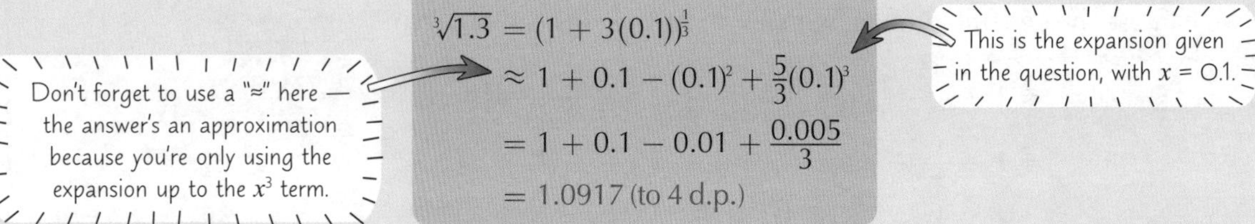

Don't forget to use a "≈" here — the answer's an approximation because you're only using the expansion up to the x^3 term.
This is the expansion given in the question, with $x = 0.1$.

$$\begin{aligned}\sqrt[3]{1.3} &= (1 + 3(0.1))^{\frac{1}{3}} \\ &\approx 1 + 0.1 - (0.1)^2 + \tfrac{5}{3}(0.1)^3 \\ &= 1 + 0.1 - 0.01 + \frac{0.005}{3} \\ &= 1.0917 \text{ (to 4 d.p.)}\end{aligned}$$

In trickier cases you have to do a spot of rearranging to get to the answer.

EXAMPLE

The binomial expansion of $(1 - 5x)^{\frac{1}{2}}$ up to the term in x^2 is $(1 - 5x)^{\frac{1}{2}} \approx 1 - \frac{5x}{2} - \frac{25}{8}x^2$.
The expansion is valid for $|x| < \frac{1}{5}$.
Use $x = \frac{1}{50}$ in this expansion to find an approximate value for $\sqrt{10}$.
Find the percentage error in your approximation, to 2 s.f.

First, sub $x = \frac{1}{50}$ into both sides of the expansion:

$$\begin{aligned}\sqrt{\left(1 - 5\left(\tfrac{1}{50}\right)\right)} &\approx 1 - \tfrac{5}{2}\left(\tfrac{1}{50}\right) - \tfrac{25}{8}\left(\tfrac{1}{50}\right)^2 \\ \sqrt{\left(1 - \tfrac{1}{10}\right)} &\approx 1 - \frac{1}{20} - \frac{1}{800} \\ \sqrt{\frac{9}{10}} &\approx \frac{759}{800}\end{aligned}$$

Now simplify the square root and rearrange to find an estimate for $\sqrt{10}$:

$$\sqrt{\frac{9}{10}} = \frac{\sqrt{9}}{\sqrt{10}} = \frac{3}{\sqrt{10}} \approx \frac{759}{800} \quad \Rightarrow \quad \sqrt{10} \approx 3 \div \frac{759}{800} = \frac{800}{253}$$

The percentage error is

$$\left|\frac{\text{real value} - \text{estimate}}{\text{real value}}\right| \times 100 = \left|\frac{\sqrt{10} - \frac{800}{253}}{\sqrt{10}}\right| \times 100 = 0.0070\% \text{ (to 2 s.f.)}$$

You never know when you might need to estimate the cube root of 1.3...

That percentage error bit in the second example is one of those ways they might sneak a seemingly unrelated topic into an exam question. The examiners are allowed to stick a bit from any of the earlier Core modules into C4, so don't freak out if they ask you something slightly unexpected — remember, you will have seen it before and you do know how to do it.

Binomial Expansions and Partial Fractions

Binomial expansions on their own are pretty nifty, but when you combine them with partial fractions (see p.46-47) they become all-powerful. I'm sure there's some sort of message about friendship or something in there...

Split functions into Partial Fractions, then add the Expansions

You can find the binomial expansion of even more complicated functions by splitting them into partial fractions first.

EXAMPLE

$$f(x) = \frac{x-1}{(3+x)(1-5x)}$$

a) f(x) can be expressed in the form $\frac{A}{(3+x)} + \frac{B}{(1-5x)}$. Find the values of A and B.

b) Use your answer to part a) to find the binomial expansion of f(x) up to and including the term in x^2.

c) Find the range of values of x for which your answer to part b) is valid.

a) Convert f(x) into partial fractions:

$$\frac{x-1}{(3+x)(1-5x)} \equiv \frac{A}{(3+x)} + \frac{B}{(1-5x)} \Rightarrow x-1 \equiv A(1-5x) + B(3+x)$$

Let $x = -3$, then $-3 - 1 = A(1-(-15)) \Rightarrow -4 = 16A \Rightarrow A = -\frac{1}{4}$

Let $x = \frac{1}{5}$, then $\frac{1}{5} - 1 = B\left(3 + \frac{1}{5}\right) \Rightarrow -\frac{4}{5} = \frac{16}{5}B \Rightarrow B = -\frac{1}{4}$

See C4 Section 1 if you need a reminder about how to do partial fractions.

b) Start by rewriting the partial fractions in $(a + bx)^n$ form: $f(x) = -\frac{1}{4}(3+x)^{-1} - \frac{1}{4}(1-5x)^{-1}$

Now do the two binomial expansions:

$$\begin{aligned}(3+x)^{-1} &= \left(3\left(1+\tfrac{1}{3}x\right)\right)^{-1}\\ &= \tfrac{1}{3}\left(1+\tfrac{1}{3}x\right)^{-1}\\ &= \tfrac{1}{3}\left(1 + (-1)\left(\tfrac{1}{3}x\right) + \tfrac{(-1)(-2)}{2}\left(\tfrac{1}{3}x\right)^2 + \ldots\right)\\ &= \tfrac{1}{3}\left(1 - \tfrac{1}{3}x + \tfrac{1}{9}x^2 + \ldots\right)\\ &= \tfrac{1}{3} - \tfrac{1}{9}x + \tfrac{1}{27}x^2 + \ldots\end{aligned}$$

$$\begin{aligned}(1-5x)^{-1} &= 1 + (-1)(-5x) + \tfrac{(-1)(-2)}{2}(-5x)^2 + \ldots\\ &= 1 + 5x + 25x^2 + \ldots\end{aligned}$$

And put everything together:

$$\begin{aligned}f(x) = -\tfrac{1}{4}(3+x)^{-1} - \tfrac{1}{4}(1-5x)^{-1} &\approx -\tfrac{1}{4}\left(\tfrac{1}{3} - \tfrac{1}{9}x + \tfrac{1}{27}x^2\right) - \tfrac{1}{4}(1 + 5x + 25x^2)\\ &= -\tfrac{1}{12} + \tfrac{1}{36}x - \tfrac{1}{108}x^2 - \tfrac{1}{4} - \tfrac{5}{4}x - \tfrac{25}{4}x^2\\ &= -\tfrac{1}{3} - \tfrac{11}{9}x - \tfrac{169}{27}x^2\end{aligned}$$

c) Each of the two expansions from part b) is valid for different values of x.
The combined expansion of f(x) is valid where these two ranges overlap, i.e. over the narrower of the two ranges.

The expansion of $(3+x)^{-1}$ is valid when $\left|\frac{x}{3}\right| < 1 \Rightarrow \frac{|x|}{|3|} < 1 \Rightarrow |x| < 3$.

The expansion of $(1-5x)^{-1}$ is valid when $|-5x| < 1 \Rightarrow |-5||x| < 1 \Rightarrow |x| < \frac{1}{5}$.

The expansion of f(x) is valid for values of x in both ranges, so the expansion of f(x) is valid for $|x| < \frac{1}{5}$.

Remember — the expansion of $(p + qx)^n$ is valid when $\left|\frac{qx}{p}\right| < 1$.

Don't mess with me — I'm a partial arts expert...

Here's where it all comes together. This example looks pretty impressive, but if you know your stuff you'll sail through questions like this. I think that's all I've got to say for this page... hmm, looks like I've still got another line to fill... So, going anywhere nice on your holidays this year? Read any good books lately? (Answer: Yes, this one.)

C4 Section 3 — Practice Questions

Ah, here we are on another of these soothing green pages. Relax... this is your happy place... nothing to worry about here... enjoy this tranquil blue pool of shimmering warm-up questions.

Warm-up Questions

1) Give the binomial expansion of:

   a) $(1 + 2x)^3$ b) $(1 - x)^4$ c) $(1 - 4x)^4$

2) For what values of n does the binomial expansion of $(1 + x)^n$ result in a finite expression?

3) Find the binomial expansion of each of the following, up to and including the term in x^3:

   a) $\frac{1}{(1+x)^4}$ b) $\frac{1}{(1-3x)^3}$ c) $\sqrt{1-5x}$

4) a) If the full binomial expansion of $(c + dx)^n$ is an infinite series, what values of x is the expansion valid for?

   b) What values of x are the expansions from question 3 valid for?

5) Give the binomial expansions of the following, up to and including the term in x^2. State which values of x each expansion is valid for.

   a) $\frac{1}{(3+2x)^2}$ b) $\sqrt[3]{8-x}$

By now all your cares should have floated away on the binomial breeze. Time for a bracing dip in an ice-cool bath of exam questions.

Exam Questions

1 $$f(x) = \frac{1}{\sqrt{(9-4x)}}, \text{ for } |x| < \frac{9}{4}.$$

a) Find the binomial expansion of f(x) up to and including the term in x^3. *(5 marks)*

b) Hence find the first three terms in the expansion of $\frac{2-x}{\sqrt{(9-4x)}}$. *(4 marks)*

2 $$f(x) = \frac{36x^2 + 3x - 10}{(4+3x)(1-3x)^2}$$

a) Given that f(x) can be expressed in the form

$$f(x) = \frac{A}{(4+3x)} + \frac{B}{(1-3x)} + \frac{C}{(1-3x)^2}$$

find the values of A, B and C. *(4 marks)*

b) Find the binomial expansion of f(x), up to and including the term in x^2. *(6 marks)*

c) Find the range of values of x for which the binomial expansion of f(x) is valid. *(2 marks)*

C4 Section 3 — Practice Questions

Congratulations, you've almost achieved C4 Sequences and Series nirvana.
Just a few more exam question steps and you'll be there...

3 a) Find the binomial expansion of $(16 + 3x)^{\frac{1}{4}}$, for $|x| < \frac{16}{3}$, up to and including the term in x^2. *(5 marks)*

b) (i) Estimate $\sqrt[4]{12.4}$ by substituting a suitable value of x into your expansion from part (a). Give your answer to 6 decimal places. *(2 marks)*

(ii) What is the percentage error in this estimate? Give your answer to 3 s.f. *(2 marks)*

4 a) Find the binomial expansion of $\left(1 - \frac{4}{3}x\right)^{-\frac{1}{2}}$, up to and including the term in x^3. *(4 marks)*

b) Hence find the values of integer constants a, b and c, such that

$$\sqrt{\frac{27}{(3 - 4x)}} \approx a + bx + cx^2,$$

and state the range of values of x for which this approximation is valid. *(3 marks)*

5 a) (i) Show that $\sqrt{\frac{1 + 2x}{1 - 3x}} \approx 1 + \frac{5}{2}x + \frac{35}{8}x^2$. *(5 marks)*

(ii) For what values of x is your expansion valid? *(2 marks)*

b) Using the above expansion with $x = \frac{2}{15}$, show that $\sqrt{19} \approx \frac{127}{30}$. *(2 marks)*

6 a) Find the values of A and B such that $\frac{13x - 17}{(5 - 3x)(2x - 1)} \equiv \frac{A}{(5 - 3x)} + \frac{B}{(2x - 1)}$. *(3 marks)*

b) (i) Find the binomial expansion of $(2x - 1)^{-1}$, up to and including the term in x^2. *(2 marks)*

(ii) Show that $\frac{1}{(5 - 3x)} \approx \frac{1}{5} + \frac{3}{25}x + \frac{9}{125}x^2$, for $|x| < \frac{5}{3}$. *(5 marks)*

c) Using your answers to parts (a) and (b), find the first three terms of the binomial expansion of $\frac{13x - 17}{(5 - 3x)(2x - 1)}$. *(2 marks)*

Differentiation with Parametric Equations

Another shiny new section, and it starts with the return of an old friend. If you've forgotten what parametric equations are already, go back to Section 2. Go on, I'll wait for you... ... ...OK, are you back now? Ready? Right, on we go...

*Differentiating **Parametric Equations** is a lot **Simpler** than you might expect*

Just suppose you've got a curve defined by two parametric equations, with the parameter t: $y = f(t)$ and $x = g(t)$.

If you can't find the Cartesian equation, it seems like it would be a bit tricky to find the gradient, $\frac{dy}{dx}$.

Luckily the chain rule (see p26) is on hand to help out:

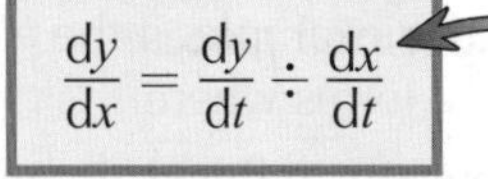

$$\frac{dy}{dx} = \frac{dy}{dt} \div \frac{dx}{dt}$$

This is exactly the same as on p26, except we've replaced '$\times \frac{dt}{dx}$' with '$\div \frac{dx}{dt}$'

EXAMPLE The curve C is defined by the parametric equations $y = t^3 - 2t + 4$ and $x = t^2 - 1$.
Find: a) $\frac{dy}{dx}$ in terms of t, b) the gradient of C when $t = -1$.

Start by differentiating the two parametric equations with respect to t:

a) $\frac{dy}{dt} = 3t^2 - 2, \; \frac{dx}{dt} = 2t$

Now use the chain rule to combine them:

$$\frac{dy}{dx} = \frac{dy}{dt} \div \frac{dx}{dt} = \frac{3t^2 - 2}{2t}$$

Use the answer to a) to find the gradient for a specific value of t:

b) When $t = -1$, $\frac{dy}{dx} = \frac{3(-1)^2 - 2}{2(-1)} = \frac{3-2}{-2} = -\frac{1}{2}$

*Use the **Gradient** to find **Tangents** and **Normals***

Of course, it's rarely as straightforward as just finding the gradient. A lot of the time, you'll then have to use it in the equation of a tangent or normal to the parametric curve.

EXAMPLE For the curve C in the example above, find:
a) the equation of the tangent to the curve when $t = 2$,
b) the equation of the normal to the curve when $t = 2$.

First you need the coordinates of the point where $t = 2$:

a) When $t = 2$, $x = (2)^2 - 1 = 3$ and $y = (2)^3 - 2(2) + 4 = 8 - 4 + 4 = 8$.

You also need the gradient at that point:

When $t = 2$, $\frac{dy}{dx} = \frac{3(2)^2 - 2}{2(2)} = \frac{10}{4} = \frac{5}{2}$

Now use that information to find the equation of the tangent:

The tangent to C at (3, 8) has an equation of the form $y = mx + c$.

So $8 = \frac{5}{2}(3) + c \Rightarrow c = \frac{1}{2}$.

The tangent to curve C when $t = 2$ is $y = \frac{5}{2}x + \frac{1}{2}$.

You could also use $y - y_1 = m(x - x_1)$ to get the equation.

You can find the normal in a similar way:

b) The normal to C at (3, 8) has gradient $-\frac{1}{\left(\frac{5}{2}\right)} = -\frac{2}{5}$.

So $8 = -\frac{2}{5}(3) + c \Rightarrow c = \frac{46}{5}$.

The normal to curve C when $t = 2$ is $y = -\frac{2}{5}x + \frac{46}{5}$.

If you're not quite following all this tangents and normals business, take a look back at C1 to refresh your memory.

And now, yet another chocolate biscuit reference...

To an examiner, adding a 'find the tangent' or 'find the normal' part to a parametric equations question is like adding chocolate to a digestive biscuit — it makes it at least 4 times better. In other words: this is very likely to show up in your C4 exam, so be ready for it. And in case you were wondering, tangent = milk chocolate, normal = dark chocolate.

Implicit Differentiation

This really isn't as complicated as it looks... in fact, I think you'll find that if something's implicit between x and y, it can be ximplicity itself. No, that's not a typo, it's a hilarious joke... 'implicit' between 'x' and 'y'... do you see?...

You need **Implicit Differentiation** if you can't write the **Equation** as $y = f(x)$

1) An 'implicit relation' is the maths name for any equation in x and y that's written in the form $f(x, y) = g(x, y)$ instead of $y = f(x)$.

f(x, y) and g(x, y) don't actually both have to include x and y — one of them could even be a constant.

2) Some implicit relations are either awkward or impossible to rewrite in the form $y = f(x)$. This can happen, for example, if the equation contains a number of different powers of y, or terms where x is multiplied by y.

3) This can make implicit relations tricky to differentiate — the solution is implicit differentiation:

Implicit Differentiation

To find $\frac{dy}{dx}$ for an implicit relation between x and y:

1) **Differentiate terms in x^n only (and constant terms) with respect to x, as normal.**

2) **Use the chain rule to differentiate terms in y^m only:**

$$\frac{d}{dx}f(y) = \frac{d}{dy}f(y)\frac{dy}{dx}$$

In other words, 'differentiate with respect to y, and stick a $\frac{dy}{dx}$ on the end'.

3) **Use the product rule to differentiate terms in both x and y:**

$$\frac{d}{dx}u(x)v(y) = u(x)\frac{d}{dx}v(y) + v(y)\frac{d}{dx}u(x)$$

This version of the product rule is slightly different from the one on p29 — it's got v(y) instead of v(x).

4) **Rearrange the resulting equation in x, y and $\frac{dy}{dx}$ to make $\frac{dy}{dx}$ the subject.**

EXAMPLE Use implicit differentiation to find $\frac{dy}{dx}$ if $2x^2y + y^3 = 6x^2 + 5$.

We need to differentiate each term of the equation with respect to x.

Start by sticking '$\frac{d}{dx}$' in front of each term:

$$\frac{d}{dx}2x^2y + \frac{d}{dx}y^3 = \frac{d}{dx}6x^2 + \frac{d}{dx}5$$

First, deal with the terms in x and constant terms — in this case that's the two terms on the RHS:

$$\Rightarrow \frac{d}{dx}2x^2y + \frac{d}{dx}y^3 = 12x + 0$$

Now use the chain rule on the term in y:

$$\Rightarrow \frac{d}{dx}2x^2y + 3y^2\frac{dy}{dx} = 12x + 0$$

Using the chain rule from the box above, $f(y) = y^3$.

Leave this $\frac{dy}{dx}$ where it is for now.

And use the product rule on the term in x and y:

$$\Rightarrow 2x^2\frac{d}{dx}(y) + y\frac{d}{dx}(2x^2) + 3y^2\frac{dy}{dx} = 12x + 0$$

$$\Rightarrow 2x^2\frac{dy}{dx} + y4x + 3y^2\frac{dy}{dx} = 12x + 0$$

So in terms of the box above, $u(x) = 2x^2$ and $v(y) = y$.

You get a $\frac{dy}{dx}$ term here too (from the '$\frac{d}{dx}v(y)$' bit).

Finally, rearrange to make $\frac{dy}{dx}$ the subject:

$$\Rightarrow \frac{dy}{dx}(2x^2 + 3y^2) = 12x - 4xy$$

$$\Rightarrow \frac{dy}{dx} = \frac{12x - 4xy}{2x^2 + 3y^2}$$

If an imp asks to try your ice lolly, don't let the imp lick it...

Learn the versions of the chain rule and product rule from the box above. All the different bits of the method for implicit differentiation can make it confusing — read the example carefully and make sure you understand every little bit of it.

Implicit Differentiation

If you've gone to all the hard work of differentiating an implicit relation, it would be a shame not to use it. It'd be like a shiny toy that's been kept in its box and never played with. Don't make the maths sad — play with it.

Implicit Differentiation still gives you an expression for the Gradient

Most implicit differentiation questions aren't really that different at heart to any other differentiation question. Once you've got an expression for the gradient, you'll have to use it to do the sort of stuff you'd normally expect.

EXAMPLE Curve A has the equation $x^2 + 2xy - y^2 = 10x + 4y - 21$

a) Show that when $\frac{dy}{dx} = 0$, $y = 5 - x$.

b) Find the coordinates of the stationary points of A.

For starters, we're going to need to find $\frac{dy}{dx}$ by implicit differentiation:

a) $$\frac{d}{dx}x^2 + \frac{d}{dx}2xy - \frac{d}{dx}y^2 = \frac{d}{dx}10x + \frac{d}{dx}4y - \frac{d}{dx}21$$

$$\Rightarrow 2x + \frac{d}{dx}2xy - \frac{d}{dx}y^2 = 10 + \frac{d}{dx}4y - 0$$

Differentiate x^2, $10x$ and 21 with respect to x.

$$\Rightarrow 2x + \frac{d}{dx}2xy - 2y\frac{dy}{dx} = 10 + 4\frac{dy}{dx}$$

Use the chain rule to differentiate y^2 and $4y$.

$$\Rightarrow 2x + 2x\frac{dy}{dx} + y\frac{d}{dx}2x - 2y\frac{dy}{dx} = 10 + 4\frac{dy}{dx}$$

Use the product rule to differentiate $2xy$.

$$\Rightarrow 2x + 2x\frac{dy}{dx} + 2y - 2y\frac{dy}{dx} = 10 + 4\frac{dy}{dx}$$

$$\Rightarrow 2x\frac{dy}{dx} - 2y\frac{dy}{dx} - 4\frac{dy}{dx} = 10 - 2x - 2y$$

Collect '$\frac{dy}{dx}$' terms on one side, and everything else on the other side.

$$\Rightarrow \frac{dy}{dx} = \frac{10 - 2x - 2y}{2x - 2y - 4}$$

So when $\frac{dy}{dx} = 0$, $\frac{10 - 2x - 2y}{2x - 2y - 4} = 0 \Rightarrow 10 - 2x - 2y = 0 \Rightarrow y = 5 - x$

Now we can use the answer to part a) in the equation of the curve to find the points where $\frac{dy}{dx} = 0$.

b) When $\frac{dy}{dx} = 0$, $y = 5 - x$. So at the stationary points,

$$x^2 + 2xy - y^2 = 10x + 4y - 21$$

$$\Rightarrow x^2 + 2x(5 - x) - (5 - x)^2 = 10x + 4(5 - x) - 21$$

Substitute $y = 5 - x$ into the original equation to find the values of x at the stationary points.

$$\Rightarrow x^2 + 10x - 2x^2 - 25 + 10x - x^2 = 10x + 20 - 4x - 21$$

$$\Rightarrow -2x^2 + 20x - 25 = 6x - 1$$

$$\Rightarrow -2x^2 + 14x - 24 = 0$$

$$\Rightarrow x^2 - 7x + 12 = 0$$

$$\Rightarrow (x - 3)(x - 4) = 0$$

$$\Rightarrow x = 3 \text{ or } x = 4$$

$x = 3 \Rightarrow y = 5 - 3 = 2 \quad x = 4 \Rightarrow y = 5 - 4 = 1$

So the stationary points of A are (3, 2) and (4, 1).

Pah, differentiation? They should have called it same-iation...

...you know, cos all the questions basically end up asking for the same thing. Other familiar faces that are likely to show up in implicit differentiation questions include finding tangents and normals to implicitly defined curves. All these differentiation questions set off in different ways to end up asking you the same thing, so make sure you know the basics.

Differentiation of a^x

And so, in our never-ending quest to find yet more stuff to differentiate, we arrive in this peculiar and uncharted corner of maths. Keep your wits about you, and you'll probably make it through this page alive...

Learn the rule for Differentiating a^x

Here's another little rule you need to learn:

For any constant a,

$$\frac{d}{dx}(a^x) = a^x \ln a$$

The rule $\frac{d}{dx}(e^x) = e^x$ (see p27) is actually just a special case of this rule — $\frac{d}{dx}(e^x) = e^x \ln e = e^x \times 1 = e^x$

With a little bit of implicit differentiation, you can prove this rule:

EXAMPLE Show that for any constant a, if $y = a^x$, then $\frac{dy}{dx} = a^x \ln a$.

Take ln of both sides of the equation: $y = a^x \Rightarrow \ln y = \ln a^x$

You can use log laws to rearrange the RHS: $\Rightarrow \ln y = x \ln a$

Now use implicit differentiation on this equation: $\Rightarrow \frac{d}{dx}(\ln y) = \frac{d}{dx}(x \ln a)$

Remember — ln a is a constant.

Use the chain rule to deal with $\frac{d}{dx}(\ln y)$: $\Rightarrow \frac{d}{dy}(\ln y)\frac{dy}{dx} = \ln a$

$\Rightarrow \frac{1}{y}\frac{dy}{dx} = \ln a$

$\frac{d}{dy}\ln y = \frac{1}{y}$ — see p27 if you need a reminder about this.

$\Rightarrow \frac{dy}{dx} = y \ln a$

Use the original equation to get rid of y: $\Rightarrow \frac{dy}{dx} = a^x \ln a$

Differentiate $a^{f(x)}$ using the Chain Rule

Once you've got the basic rule sorted, you can apply it to more complicated examples:

EXAMPLE Find the equation of the tangent to the curve $y = 3^{-2x}$ at the point $\left(\frac{1}{2}, \frac{1}{3}\right)$.

Use the 'normal' chain rule (from p26 — $\frac{dy}{dx} = \frac{dy}{du} \times \frac{du}{dx}$) to find $\frac{dy}{dx}$:

Let $u = -2x$, then $y = 3^u$ and $\frac{dy}{dx} = \frac{d}{du}(3^u)\,\frac{d}{dx}(-2x) = 3^u \ln 3 \times -2 = -2(3^{-2x} \ln 3)$

Now we can find the gradient and y-intercept of the tangent:

So at $\left(\frac{1}{2}, \frac{1}{3}\right)$, $\frac{dy}{dx} = -2(3^{-1} \ln 3) = -\frac{2}{3} \ln 3 = -0.732$ (to 3 s.f.)

So if the equation of the tangent at $\left(\frac{1}{2}, \frac{1}{3}\right)$ has the form $y = mx + c$, then

$\frac{1}{3} = (-\frac{2}{3} \ln 3)\frac{1}{2} + c \Rightarrow c = \frac{1}{3} + \frac{1}{3} \ln 3 = 0.700$ (to 3 s.f.)

So the equation of the tangent to $y = 3^{-2x}$ at $\left(\frac{1}{2}, \frac{1}{3}\right)$ is $y = -0.732x + 0.700$

This is a topic for lumberjacks — it's all about logs and a^xes...

Make sure you understand and learn the method used in the first example on this page. It's a prime candidate for a 'show that' exam question, so if you can regurgitate it at will, it just might net you a couple more precious marks.

Relating Rates of Change

This is one of those topics where the most awkward bit is getting your head round the information in the question. The actual maths is nothing like as bad as the questions usually make it sound. Honest.

The Chain Rule lets you Connect different Rates of Change

1) Some situations have a number of linked variables, like length, surface area and volume, or distance, speed and acceleration.
2) If you know the rate of change of one of these linked variables, and the equations that connect the variables, you can use the chain rule to help you find the rate of change of the other variables.

EXAMPLE A scientist is testing how a new material expands when it is gradually heated. The diagram shows the sample being tested, which is shaped like a triangular prism. After t minutes, the triangle that forms the base of the prism has base length $7x$ cm and height $4x$ cm, and the height of the prism is also $4x$ cm.

If the sample expands at a constant rate, given by $\frac{dx}{dt} = 0.05$ cm min^{-1}, find an expression in terms of x for $\frac{dV}{dt}$, where V is the volume of the prism.

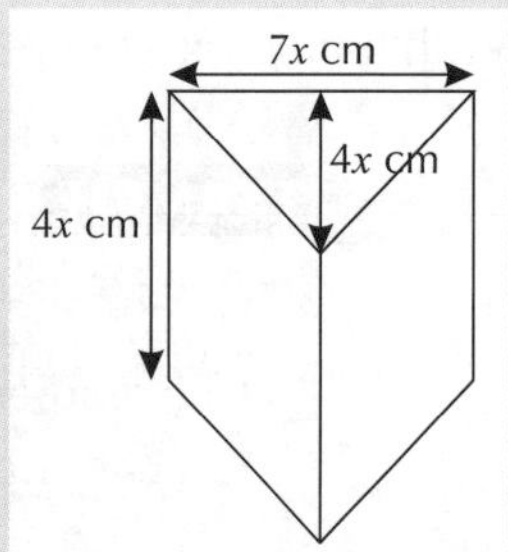

The best way to start this kind of question is to write down what you know. We've got enough information to write an expression for the volume of the prism:

$V = (\frac{1}{2} \times 7x \times 4x) \times 4x = 56x^3$ cm^3

Differentiate this with respect to x:

$\frac{dV}{dx} = 168x^2$

We know that $\frac{dx}{dt} = 0.05$. So we can use the chain rule to find $\frac{dV}{dt}$:

$\frac{dV}{dt} = \frac{dV}{dx} \times \frac{dx}{dt} = 168x^2 \times 0.05 = 8.4x^2$

Watch out for Slightly Trickier questions

1) There are a couple of sneaky tricks in this type of question that could catch you out if you're not prepared for them.
2) In this next example, you have to spot that there's a hidden derivative described in words.
3) You also need to remember the rule $\frac{dy}{dx} = \frac{1}{\left(\frac{dx}{dy}\right)}$ (see p26).

EXAMPLE A giant metal cube from space is cooling after entering the Earth's atmosphere. As it cools, the surface area of the cube decreases at a constant rate of 0.027 m^2 s^{-1}. If the side length of the cube after t seconds is x m, find $\frac{dx}{dt}$ at the point when $x = 15$ m.

Start with what you know:

We use $\frac{d}{dt}$ because it's a rate of time.

The cube has side length x m, so the surface area of the cube is $A = 6x^2 \Rightarrow \frac{dA}{dx} = 12x$

A decreases at a constant rate of 0.027 m^2 s^{-1} — we can write this as $\frac{dA}{dt} = -0.027$

This value is negative because A is decreasing.

Now use the chain rule to find $\frac{dx}{dt}$:

$$\frac{dx}{dt} = \frac{dx}{dA} \times \frac{dA}{dt} = \frac{1}{\left(\frac{dA}{dx}\right)} \times \frac{dA}{dt} = \frac{1}{12x} \times -0.027 = -\frac{0.00225}{x}$$

So when $x = 15$, $\frac{dx}{dt} = -\frac{0.00225}{x} = -\frac{0.00225}{15} = -0.00015$ m s^{-1}

I'd rate this page 10 out of 10 — if I do say so myself...

If you get stuck on a question like this, don't panic. Somewhere in the question there'll be enough information to write at least one equation linking some of the variables. If in doubt, write down any equations you can make, differentiate them all, and then see which of the resulting expressions you can link using the chain rule to make the thing you're looking for.

C4 Section 4 — Practice Questions

If you think that was a lot of differentiation, be thankful you didn't live in Ancient Molgarahenia, where differentiation was the only maths permitted. Try these tasty warm-up questions for an authentic taste of Molgarahenian life.

Warm-up Questions

1) A curve is defined by the parametric equations $x = t^2$, $y = 3t^3 - 4t$.
   (a) Find $\frac{dy}{dx}$ for this curve.
   (b) Find the coordinates of the stationary points of the curve.
2) Use implicit differentiation to find $\frac{dy}{dx}$ for each of the following equations:
   (a) $4x^2 - 2y^2 = 7x^2y$ (b) $3x^4 - 2xy^2 = y$ (c) $\cos x \sin y = xy$
3) Using your answers to question 2, find:
   (a) the gradient of the tangent to the graph of $4x^2 - 2y^2 = 7x^2y$ at $(1, -4)$,
   (b) the gradient of the normal to the graph of $3x^4 - 2xy^2 = y$ at $(1, 1)$.
4) Write down the proof that $\frac{d}{dx}a^x = a^x \ln a$, where a is a constant.
5) A cuboid has length x cm, width $2x$ cm and height $3x$ cm.
   The cuboid is expanding, for some unexplained reason.
   If A is the surface area of the cuboid and V is its volume, find $\frac{dA}{dx}$ and $\frac{dV}{dx}$, and use them to show that if $\frac{dV}{dt} = 3$, then $\frac{dA}{dt} = \frac{22}{3x}$.

It is said that the Great Molgarahenian Plain was carpeted with differentiation as far as the eye could see. The C4 exam won't be quite that bad, but there will be some differentiation in there, so get practising...

Exam Questions

1 The curve C is defined by the parametric equations

$$x = 3\theta - \cos 3\theta, \quad y = 2\sin\theta, \quad -\pi \leq \theta \leq \pi.$$

a) Find an expression for $\frac{dy}{dx}$. *(3 marks)*

b) (i) Show that the gradient of C at the point $(\pi + 1, \sqrt{3})$ is $\frac{1}{3}$. *(3 marks)*

(ii) Find the equation of the normal to C when $\theta = \frac{\pi}{6}$. *(4 marks)*

2 The equation of curve C is $6x^2y - 7 = 5x - 4y^2 - x^2$.

a) The line T has the equation $y = c$ and passes through a point on C where $x = 2$.
Find c, given that $c > 0$. *(2 marks)*

b) T also crosses C at point Q.

(i) Find the coordinates of Q. *(2 marks)*

(ii) Find the gradient of C at Q. *(6 marks)*

C4 Section 4 — Practice Questions

In 272 BC, the famous Molgarahenian philosopher, Bobby the Wise, was put to death for straying from the path of differentiation and doing some simultaneous equations. Don't be like Bobby, stick with these questions (for now)...

3 a) Curve A has the equation $y = 4^x$.
What are the coordinates of the point on A where $\frac{dy}{dx} = \ln 4$? *(2 marks)*

b) Curve B has the equation $y = 4^{(x-4)^3}$. Find the gradient of B at the point $(3, \frac{1}{4})$. *(4 marks)*

4 The curve C has the equation $3e^x + 6y = 2x^2y$.

a) (i) Use implicit differentiation to find an expression for $\frac{dy}{dx}$. *(3 marks)*

(ii) Show that at the stationary points of C, $y = \frac{3e^x}{4x}$. *(2 marks)*

b) Hence find the exact coordinates of the two stationary points of C. *(4 marks)*

5 A curve, C, has parametric equations
$x = t^2 + 2t - 3, \qquad y = 2 - t^3.$

a) The line L is the tangent to C at $y = -6$. Show that the equation of L is $y = -2x + 4$. *(4 marks)*

b) L also meets C at point P.

(i) Find the coordinates of P. *(4 marks)*

(ii) Find the equation of the normal to the curve at P. *(3 marks)*

6

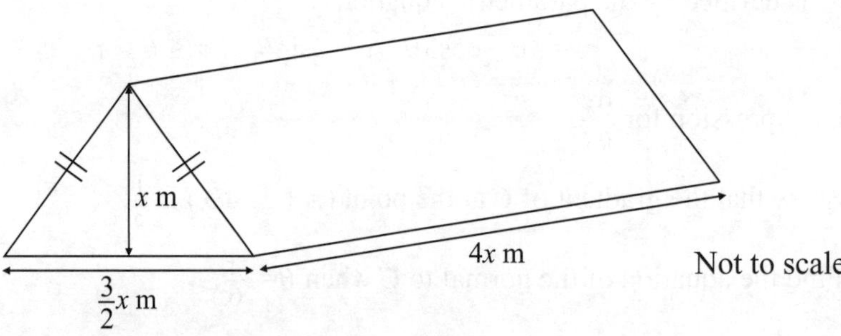

The triangular prism shown in the diagram is expanding.
The dimensions of the prism after t seconds are given in terms of x.
The prism is $4x$ m long, and its cross-section is an isosceles triangle with base $\frac{3}{2}x$ m and height x m.

a) Show that, if the surface area of the prism after t seconds is A m², then $A = \frac{35}{2}x^2$. *(3 marks)*

The surface area of the prism is increasing at a constant rate of 0.07 m² s^{-1}.

b) Find $\frac{dx}{dt}$ when $x = 0.5$. *(3 marks)*

c) If the volume of the prism is V m³, find the rate of change of V when $x = 1.2$. *(4 marks)*

Integration of e^x and 1/x

Although it was many moons ago that you last encountered integration, way back in C2, it's an integral part of C4. It does the opposite of differentiation, so some of this stuff should look familiar to you.

e^x integrates to give e^x (+ C)

As e^x differentiates to give e^x (see p.27), it makes sense that

$$\int e^x dx = e^x + C$$

Don't forget the constant of integration.

Once you're happy with that, you can use it to solve lots of integrations that have an e^x term in them.
If the coefficient of x isn't 1, you need to divide by that coefficient when you integrate — so $\int e^{kx} dx = \frac{1}{k}e^{kx} + C$

EXAMPLES Integrate the following: a) e^{7x} b) $2e^{4-3x}$ c) $e^{\frac{x}{2}}$.

a) $\int e^{7x} dx = \frac{1}{7}e^{7x} + C$

If you differentiated e^{7x} using the chain rule, you'd get $7e^{7x}$. So when you integrate, you need to divide by 7 (the coefficient of x). This is so that if you differentiated your answer you'd get back to e^{7x}.

b) $\int 2e^{4-3x} dx = -\frac{2}{3}e^{4-3x} + C$

This one isn't as bad as it looks — if you differentiated $2e^{4-3x}$, you'd get $-6e^{4-3x}$, so you need to divide by -3 (the coefficient of x) when you integrate. Differentiating your answer gives you $2e^{4-3x}$.

c) $\int e^{\frac{x}{2}} dx = \int e^{\frac{1}{2}x} dx = 2e^{\frac{x}{2}} + C$

If you differentiated this one using the chain rule, you'd get $\frac{1}{2}e^{\frac{x}{2}}$, so you need to multiply by 2 when you integrate.

Whenever you integrate,

ALWAYS DIFFERENTIATE YOUR ANSWER TO CHECK IT WORKS

— you should end up with the thing you integrated in the first place. It's the best way to check that you divided or multiplied by the right number.

1/x integrates to ln |x| (+ C)

When you first came across integration in C1, you couldn't integrate $\frac{1}{x}$ $(= x^{-1})$ by increasing the power by 1 and dividing by it, as you ended up dividing by 0 (which is baaaaad).

However, on p.27, you saw that $\ln x$ differentiates to give $\frac{1}{x}$, so

$$\int \frac{1}{x} dx = \ln|x| + C$$

Don't worry about where the modulus sign (see p.7) comes from — using $|x|$ just means that there isn't a problem when x is negative.

EXAMPLES Integrate the following: a) $\frac{5}{x}$ b) $\frac{1}{3x}$ c) $\frac{1}{4x+5}$.

There are more examples like this one on p.77.

a) $\int \frac{5}{x} dx = 5\int \frac{1}{x} dx = 5\ln|x| + C$

5 is a constant coefficient — you can take it outside the integral if you want.

You could also write $5\ln|x|$ as $\ln|x^5|$.

b) $\int \frac{1}{3x} dx = \frac{1}{3}\int \frac{1}{x} dx = \frac{1}{3}\ln|x| + C$

Be careful with ones like this — 1/3 is just the coefficient, so it goes outside $\ln|x|$. Don't make the mistake of putting $\ln|3x|$ — this would differentiate to give $1/x$ (as $\ln 3x = \ln 3 + \ln x$, so when you differentiate, $\ln 3$ disappears).

c) $\int \frac{1}{4x+5} dx = \frac{1}{4}\ln|4x+5| + C$

However, for this one you have to leave the coefficient (4) inside ln because it's part of the function $4x + 5$. You still have to divide by 4 though (again, try differentiating it to see why).

Integration feels pretty constant to me...

These integrations are pretty easy — the only thing you have to worry about is if x has a coefficient that isn't 1. When this happens, work out what you think the answer will look like (e.g. e^x, $\ln|x|$, etc.), then differentiate to see what you get. Then you might have to adjust your answer, usually by dividing or multiplying by the coefficient, to get back to what you started with.

Integration of Sin and Cos

If you thought you'd killed off the dragon that is trigonometry in C3, you're sadly mistaken. It rears its ugly head again, and now you need to know how to integrate trig functions. Find your most trusty dragon-slaying sword and read on...

Sin and Cos are Easy to integrate

From C3, you know that $\sin x$ differentiates to give $\cos x$, $\cos x$ differentiates to give $-\sin x$ and $\tan x$ differentiates to give $\sec^2 x$ (where the angle x is in radians). So it's pretty obvious that:

$$\int \sin x \, dx = -\cos x + C$$
$$\int \cos x \, dx = \sin x + C$$
$$\int \sec^2 x \, dx = \tan x + C$$

Integrating tan x is a bit different — see p.71.

If x has a coefficient that isn't 1 (e.g. sin $3x$), you just divide by the coefficient when you integrate — just like on the previous page.

EXAMPLE Find $\int \cos 4x - 2\sin 2x + \sec^2 \tfrac{1}{2}x \, dx$.

Integrate each term separately using the results from above:

$\int \cos 4x \, dx = \frac{1}{4}\sin 4x$ $\quad \int -2\sin 2x \, dx = -2\left(-\frac{1}{2}\cos 2x\right) = \cos 2x$ $\quad \int \sec^2 \tfrac{1}{2}x \, dx = \frac{1}{\frac{1}{2}}\tan \tfrac{1}{2}x = 2\tan \tfrac{1}{2}x$

Putting these terms together and adding the constant gives:

$$\int \cos 4x - 2\sin 2x + \sec^2 \tfrac{1}{2}x \, dx = \frac{1}{4}\sin 4x + \cos 2x + 2\tan \tfrac{1}{2}x + C$$

There are some Results you can just Learn

There are a list of trig integrals that you can just learn — you don't need to know where they came from, you can just use them. You've met these ones before — they're the results of differentiating $\text{cosec}\, x$, $\sec x$ and $\cot x$ (see p.31).

There are some more trig integrals on pages 71 and 73.

$$\int \text{cosec}\, x \cot x \, dx = -\text{cosec}\, x + C$$
$$\int \sec x \tan x \, dx = \sec x + C$$
$$\int \text{cosec}^2 x \, dx = -\cot x + C$$

The coefficients of x have to be the same in each term — e.g. you couldn't integrate sec x tan $3x$.

As usual, you need to divide by the coefficient of x when you integrate.

EXAMPLE Find $\int 10\sec 5x \tan 5x + \frac{1}{2}\text{cosec}\, 3x \cot 3x - \text{cosec}^2(6x+1) \, dx$.

This one looks a bit scary, but take it one step at a time. Integrate each bit in turn to get:

1. $\int 10\sec 5x \tan 5x \, dx = \frac{1}{5} \cdot 10\sec 5x$
$= 2\sec 5x$

2. $\int \frac{1}{2}\text{cosec}\, 3x \cot 3x \, dx = -\frac{1}{3} \cdot \frac{1}{2}\text{cosec}\, 3x$
$= -\frac{1}{6}\text{cosec}\, 3x$

3. $\int -\text{cosec}^2(6x+1) \, dx = -\frac{1}{6}(-\cot(6x+1))$
$= \frac{1}{6}\cot(6x+1)$

The + 1 inside the brackets has no effect on the integration — differentiate to see why.

Putting these terms together and adding the constant gives:

$$\int 10\sec 5x \tan 5x + \frac{1}{2}\text{cosec}\, 3x \cot 3x - \text{cosec}^2(6x+1) \, dx = 2\sec 5x - \frac{1}{6}\text{cosec}\, 3x + \frac{1}{6}\cot(6x+1) + C$$

This is starting to grate on me now...

Although you're not given all of these integrals on the formula sheet, some of the trickier ones (e.g. sec x tan x and cosec$^2 x$) are on the list of differentiation formulas for C3. As long as you work backwards (i.e. from $f'(x)$ to $f(x)$) you can just use these results without having to remember them all. Be careful with the coefficients — don't forget to divide by them when you integrate.

Integration of f′(x)/f(x)

Sometimes you get integrals that look really nasty — like fractions. However, there are a couple of clever tricks that can make them easy to integrate.

Some Fractions integrate to ln

If you have a fraction that has a function of x on the numerator and a different function of x on the denominator (e.g. $\frac{x-2}{x^3+1}$), you'll probably struggle to integrate it. However, if you have a fraction where the numerator is the derivative of the denominator (e.g. $\frac{3x^2}{x^3+1}$), it integrates to give ln of whatever the denominator is (in this case, $x^3 + 1$).

In general terms, this is written as:

$$\int \frac{f'(x)}{f(x)}\,dx = \ln|f(x)| + C$$

This is another one that comes from the chain rule (p.26) — if you differentiated $\ln|f(x)|$, you'd end up with the fraction on the left.

The hardest bit about questions like this is recognising that the denominator differentiates to give the numerator. Once you've spotted that, it's dead easy. They might make the numerator a multiple of the denominator just to confuse things, so watch out for that.

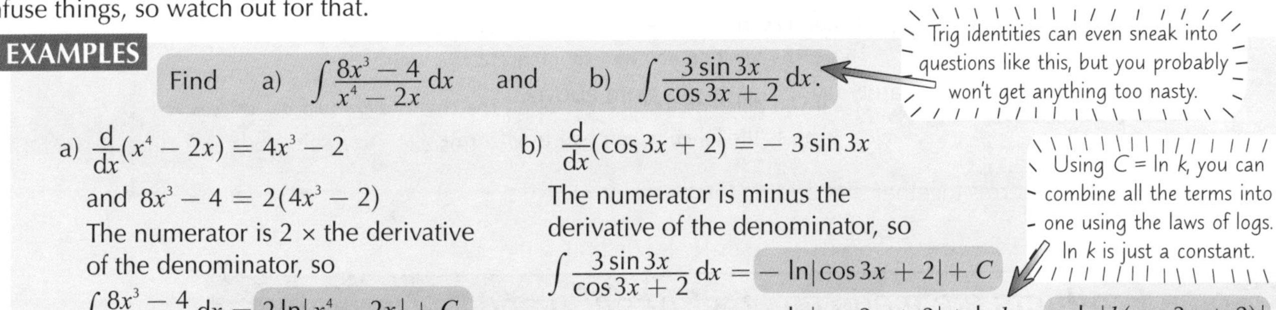

EXAMPLES Find a) $\int \frac{8x^3-4}{x^4-2x}\,dx$ and b) $\int \frac{3\sin 3x}{\cos 3x + 2}\,dx$.

Trig identities can even sneak into questions like this, but you probably won't get anything too nasty.

a) $\frac{d}{dx}(x^4 - 2x) = 4x^3 - 2$

and $8x^3 - 4 = 2(4x^3 - 2)$

The numerator is 2 × the derivative of the denominator, so

$\int \frac{8x^3-4}{x^4-2x}\,dx = 2\ln|x^4 - 2x| + C$

b) $\frac{d}{dx}(\cos 3x + 2) = -3\sin 3x$

The numerator is minus the derivative of the denominator, so

$\int \frac{3\sin 3x}{\cos 3x + 2}\,dx = -\ln|\cos 3x + 2| + C$

$= -\ln|\cos 3x + 2| + \ln k = -\ln|k(\cos 3x + 2)|$

Using $C = \ln k$, you can combine all the terms into one using the laws of logs. $\ln k$ is just a constant.

You can get ln of Trig Functions too

You might have noticed from part (b) above that you can work out the integral of $\tan x$ using this method:

$\tan x = \frac{\sin x}{\cos x}$, and $\frac{d}{dx}(\cos x) = -\sin x$

The numerator is minus the derivative of the denominator, so

$\int \tan x\,dx = \int \frac{\sin x}{\cos x}\,dx = -\ln|\cos x| + C$

$-\ln|\cos x|$ is the same as $\ln|\sec x|$ — this comes from the laws of logs on p.21.

There are some other trig functions that you can integrate in the same way:

$$\int \cot x\,dx = \ln|\sin x| + C$$

$$\int \operatorname{cosec} x\,dx = -\ln|\operatorname{cosec} x + \cot x| + C$$

$$\int \sec x\,dx = \ln|\sec x + \tan x| + C$$

This list is given in the formula booklet — so you don't need to learn them (just be able to use them).

EXAMPLE Find $\int \frac{1}{2}\operatorname{cosec} 2x\,dx$.

You can just use the result above — so all you have to do is work out what happens to the coefficient. The coefficient is 2, so you need to divide by 2 when you integrate:

$\int \frac{1}{2}\operatorname{cosec} 2x\,dx = -\frac{1}{4}\ln|\operatorname{cosec} 2x + \cot 2x| + C$

Check this by differentiating (using the chain rule with $u = \operatorname{cosec} 2x + \cot 2x$).

3 pages in and I've run out of jokes on integration. Please help...

If you come across an integration question with a fraction that doesn't seem to integrate easily, have a quick look and see if one bit is the derivative of the other. If it is, use the rule above and you'll be as happy as Larry (and Larry's always happy).

Integration Using the Chain Rule Backwards

Most integrations aren't as bad as they look — on the previous page, you saw how to integrate special fractions, and now it's time for certain products. There are some things you can look out for when you're integrating...

You can use the **Chain Rule** in **Reverse**

You came across the chain rule in C3 (back on p.26) — it's where you write the thing you're differentiating in terms of u (and u is a function of x). You end up with the product of two derivatives ($\frac{dy}{du}$ and $\frac{du}{dx}$).

When it comes to integrating, if you spot that your integral is a product where one bit is the derivative of part of the other bit, you can use this rule:

$$\int \frac{du}{dx} f'(u)\, dx = f(u) + C$$

where u is a function of x.

EXAMPLE

Find a) $\int 6x^5 e^{x^6}\, dx$ and b) $\int e^{\sin x} \cos x\, dx$.

a) $\int 6x^5 e^{x^6}\, dx = e^{x^6} + C$ If you differentiated $y = e^{x^6}$ using the chain rule, you'd get $6x^5e^{x^6}$. This is the function you had to integrate.

b) $\int e^{\sin x} \cos x\, dx = e^{\sin x} + C$ If you differentiated $y = e^{\sin x}$ using the chain rule, you'd get $e^{\sin x}\cos x$. This is the function you had to integrate.

Some **Products** are made up of a **Function** and its **Derivative**

Similarly, if you spot that part of a product is the derivative of the other part of it (which is raised to a power), you can integrate it using this rule:

$$\int (n+1)f'(x)[f(x)]^n\, dx = [f(x)]^{n+1} + C$$

Remember that the derivative will be a multiple of $n + 1$ (not n) — watch out for any other multiples too. This will probably make more sense if you have a look at an example:

EXAMPLE

Find a) $\int 12x^3(2x^4 - 5)^2\, dx$ and b) $\int 8\,\text{cosec}^2 x \cot^3 x\, dx$.

This one looks pretty horrific, but it isn't too bad once you spot that $-\text{cosec}^2 x$ is the derivative of $\cot x$.

a) Here, $f(x) = 2x^4 - 5$, so differentiating gives $f'(x) = 8x^3$. $n = 2$, so $n + 1 = 3$.
Putting all this into the rule above gives:

$\int 3(8x^3)(2x^4 - 5)^2\, dx = \int 24x^3(2x^4 - 5)^2\, dx = (2x^4 - 5)^3 + C$

Divide everything by 2 to match the original integral:

$\int 12x^3(2x^4 - 5)^2\, dx = \frac{1}{2}(2x^4 - 5)^3 + C.$

b) For this one, $f(x) = \cot x$, so differentiating gives $f'(x) = -\text{cosec}^2 x$. $n = 3$, so $n + 1 = 4$.
Putting all this into the rule gives:

$\int -4\,\text{cosec}^2 x \cot^3 x\, dx = \cot^4 x + C$

Multiply everything by –2 to match the original integral:

$\int 8\,\text{cosec}^2 x \cot^3 x\, dx = -2\cot^4 x + C$

To get rid of hiccups, drink a glass of water backwards...

It seems to me that most of this section is about reversing the things you learnt in C3. I don't know why they ask you to differentiate stuff if you're just going to have to integrate it again and end up where you started. At least it keeps you busy.

Integrating Trig Things Using Trig Identities

Examiners have a nasty habit of expecting you to remember things from previous modules — they just can't let go of the past. In this case, it's the trig identities that popped up in C3 Section 2 (see p.14-18 if you need a reminder).

The Double Angle Formulas are useful for Integration

If you're given a tricky trig function to integrate, see if you can simplify it using one of the double angle formulas. They're especially useful for things like $\cos^2 x$, $\sin^2 x$ and $\sin x \cos x$. Here are the double angle formulas (see p.16):

$$\sin 2x \equiv 2 \sin x \cos x$$

$$\tan 2x \equiv \frac{2 \tan x}{1 - \tan^2 x}$$

$$\cos 2x \equiv \cos^2 x - \sin^2 x$$

$$\cos 2x \equiv 2\cos^2 x - 1$$

$$\cos 2x \equiv 1 - 2\sin^2 x$$

You can rearrange the second two cos $2x$ formulas to get expressions for $\cos^2 x$ and $\sin^2 x$: $\cos^2 x = \frac{1}{2}(\cos 2x + 1)$
$\sin^2 x = \frac{1}{2}(1 - \cos 2x)$

Once you've replaced the original function with one of the double angle formulas, you can just integrate as normal.

EXAMPLE Find a) $\int \sin^2 x \, dx$ b) $\int \cos^2 5x \, dx$ c) $\int \sin x \cos x \, dx$.

Don't forget to double the coefficient of x here. You'll also need to divide by 10 when you integrate.

a) Using the double angle formula above, write $\sin^2 x$ as $\frac{1}{2}(1 - \cos 2x)$, then integrate.

$$\int \sin^2 x \, dx = \int \frac{1}{2}(1 - \cos 2x) dx$$

$$= \frac{1}{2}\left(x - \frac{1}{2}\sin 2x\right) + C = \frac{1}{2}x - \frac{1}{4}\sin 2x + C$$

b) Using the double angle formula above, write $\cos^2 5x$ as $\frac{1}{2}(\cos 10x + 1)$, then integrate.

$$\int \cos^2 5x \, dx = \int \frac{1}{2}(\cos 10x + 1) dx$$

$$= \frac{1}{2}\left(\frac{1}{10}\sin 10x + x\right) + C = \frac{1}{20}\sin 10x + \frac{1}{2}x + C$$

c) Using the double angle formula above, write $\sin x \cos x$ as $\frac{1}{2}\sin 2x$, then integrate.

$$\int \sin x \cos x \, dx = \int \frac{1}{2}\sin 2x \, dx = \frac{1}{2}\left(-\frac{1}{2}\cos 2x\right) + C = -\frac{1}{4}\cos 2x + C$$

Use the Identities to get a function you Know how to Integrate

There are a couple of other identities you can use to simplify trig functions (see p.14):

$$\sec^2\theta \equiv 1 + \tan^2\theta \qquad \text{cosec}^2\theta \equiv 1 + \cot^2\theta$$

These two identities are really useful if you have to integrate $\tan^2 x$ or $\cot^2 x$, as you already know how to integrate $\sec^2 x$ and $\text{cosec}^2 x$ (see p.70). Don't forget the stray 1s flying around — they'll just integrate to x.

EXAMPLE Find a) $\int \tan^2 x - 1 \, dx$ b) $\int \cot^2 3x \, dx$.

a) Rewrite the function in terms of $\sec^2 x$:
$\tan^2 x - 1 \equiv \sec^2 x - 1 - 1 \equiv \sec^2 x - 2$.
Now integrate:

$$\int \sec^2 x - 2 \, dx = \tan x - 2x + C$$

b) Get the function in terms of $\text{cosec}^2 x$:
$\cot^2 3x \equiv \text{cosec}^2 3x - 1$.
Now integrate:

$$\int \text{cosec}^2 3x - 1 \, dx = -\frac{1}{3}\cot 3x - x + C$$

Remember to divide by 3, the coefficient of x, when you integrate.

EXAMPLE Evaluate $\int_0^{\frac{\pi}{3}} 6 \sin 3x \cos 3x + \tan^2 \frac{1}{2}x + 1 \, dx$.

Using the identities, $6 \sin 3x \cos 3x \equiv 3 \sin 6x$ and $\tan^2 \frac{1}{2}x + 1 \equiv \sec^2 \frac{1}{2}x$ gives:

$$\int_0^{\frac{\pi}{3}} 3 \sin 6x + \sec^2 \frac{1}{2}x \, dx = \left[-\frac{3}{6}\cos 6x + 2\tan \frac{1}{2}x\right]_0^{\frac{\pi}{3}}$$

$$= \left[-\frac{1}{2}\cos 6\left(\frac{\pi}{3}\right) + 2\tan\frac{1}{2}\left(\frac{\pi}{3}\right)\right] - \left[-\frac{1}{2}\cos 6(0) + 2\tan\frac{1}{2}(0)\right]$$

$$= \left[-\frac{1}{2}\cos(2\pi) + 2\tan\left(\frac{\pi}{6}\right)\right] - \left[-\frac{1}{2}\cos(0) + 2\tan(0)\right]$$

$$= \left[-\frac{1}{2}(1) + 2\left(\frac{1}{\sqrt{3}}\right)\right] - \left[-\frac{1}{2}(1) + 2(0)\right] = -\frac{1}{2} + \frac{2}{\sqrt{3}} + \frac{1}{2} = \frac{2}{\sqrt{3}}$$

Use the table of common trig angles on p.15 to help you here.

I can't help feeling I've seen these somewhere before...

If you're given a trig function that you don't know how to integrate, play around with these identities and see if you can turn it into something you can integrate. Watch out for coefficients though — they can trip you up if you're not careful.

C4 Section 5 — Practice Questions

That was a fairly small section to ease you into the magical world of integration — and to test your powers, here are some questions for you to have a go at.

Warm-up Questions

1) Find $\int 4e^{2x}\,dx$.

2) Find $\int e^{3x-5}\,dx$.

3) Find $\int \frac{2}{3x}\,dx$.

4) Find $\int \frac{2}{2x+1}\,dx$.

5) Find

a) $\int \cos 4x - \sec^2 7x\,dx$,

b) $\int 6\sec 3x \tan 3x - \operatorname{cosec}^2 \frac{x}{5}\,dx$.

6) Integrate $\int \frac{\cos x}{\sin x}\,dx$.

7) Integrate $\int 3x^2 e^{x^3}\,dx$.

8) Integrate $\int \frac{20x^4 + 12x^2 - 12}{x^5 + x^3 - 3x}\,dx$.

9) Use the appropriate trig identity to find $\int \frac{2\tan 3x}{1 - \tan^2 3x}\,dx$.

10) Use the trig identity $\sec^2 x \equiv 1 + \tan^2 x$ to find $\int 2\tan^2 3x + 2\,dx$.

Most of the exam questions on integration will ask you to do more than simply integrate — there's more on this in the next section. But there are some that are bog-forward, straight-standard, mill-of-the-run questions like the ones below.

Exam Questions

1 Find

a) $\int 3e^{(5-6x)}\,dx$. *(2 marks)*

b) $\int \frac{\operatorname{cosec}^2 x - 2}{\cot x + 2x}\,dx$. *(3 marks)*

2 Use an appropriate identity to find $\int 2\cot^2 x\,dx$. *(3 marks)*

Integration by Substitution

I know, I know — you've already done one integration section, surely there can't be another? Well, I'm afraid there is. And this time, there's nowhere to run...

Use Integration by Substitution on Products of Two Functions

On p.26, you saw how to differentiate functions of functions using the chain rule. Integration by substitution lets you integrate functions of functions by simplifying the integral. Like the chain rule, you have to write part of the function in terms of u, where u is some function of x.

Integration by Substitution

1) **You'll be given an integral that's made up of two functions of x (one is often just x) — e.g. $x(3x + 2)^3$.**
2) **Substitute u for one of the functions of x (to give a function that's easier to integrate) — e.g. $u = 3x + 2$.**
3) **Next, find $\frac{du}{dx}$, and rewrite it so that dx is on its own — e.g. $\frac{du}{dx} = 3$, so $dx = \frac{1}{3}du$.**
4) **Rewrite the original integral in terms of u and du — e.g. $\int x(3x+2)^3\,dx$ becomes $\int \left(\frac{u-2}{3}\right)u^3 \frac{1}{3}du = \int \frac{u^4 - 2u^3}{9}\,du$.**
5) **You should now be left with something that's easier to integrate — just integrate as normal, then at the last step replace u with the original substitution (so for this one, replace u with $3x + 2$).**

$\frac{du}{dx}$ isn't really a fraction, but you can treat it as one for this bit.

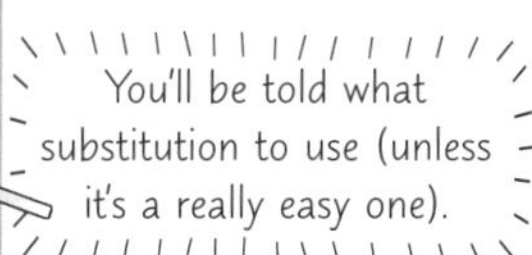

You'll be told what substitution to use (unless it's a really easy one).

EXAMPLE

Use the substitution $u = x^2 - 2$ to find $\int 4x(x^2 - 2)^4\,dx$.

As $u = x^2 - 2$, $\frac{du}{dx} = 2x$, so $dx = \frac{1}{2x}du$.

Substituting gives $\int 4x(x^2-2)^4\,dx = \int 4xu^4 \frac{1}{2x}du = \int 2u^4 du$.

The x's cancel, making it a lot easier to integrate — this often happens.

Integrate... $\int 2u^4 du = \frac{2}{5}u^5 + C$.

...and substitute x back in:

$= \frac{2}{5}(x^2-2)^5 + C$.

For Definite Integrals, you have to Change the Limits

If you're given a definite integral, it's really important that you remember to change the limits to u. Doing it this way means you don't have to put x back in at the last step — just put the numbers into the integration for u.

EXAMPLE

Use the substitution $u = \cos x$ to find $\int_{\frac{\pi}{2}}^{2\pi} -12\sin x\cos^3 x\,dx$.

Trigonometry can pop up here as well.

As $u = \cos x$, $\frac{du}{dx} = -\sin x$, so $dx = -\frac{1}{\sin x}du$.

Find the limits of u:

when $x = \frac{\pi}{2}$, $u = \cos\frac{\pi}{2} = 0$,

when $x = 2\pi$, $u = \cos 2\pi = 1$.

So the limits of u are 0 and 1.

Substituting all this gives:

$$\int_{\frac{\pi}{2}}^{2\pi} -12\sin x\cos^3 x\,dx = \int_0^1 -12\sin x\, u^3 \frac{-1}{\sin x}du = \int_0^1 12u^3 du$$

Integrating and putting in the values of the limits gives:

$[3u^4]_0^1 = [3(1)^4] - [3(0)^4] = 3$

You could also have solved this one using the method on p.72.

Never substitute salt for sugar...

Life is full of limits — age limits, time limits, height limits, limits of how many times I can gaze at my Hugh Jackman poster while still getting my work done... But at least limits of integration will get you exam marks, so it's worth practising them.

Integration by Parts

Just like you can differentiate products using the product rule (see p.29), you can integrate products using the... er... integration by parts. Not quite as catchy I know, but just as thrilling.

Integration by Parts is the Reverse of the Product Rule

If you have to integrate a product but can't use integration by substitution (see previous page), you might be able to use integration by parts. The formula for integrating by parts is:

$$\int u\frac{dv}{dx}\,dx = uv - \int v\frac{du}{dx}\,dx$$

where u and v are both functions of x.

The hardest thing about integration by parts is deciding which bit of your product should be u and which bit should be $\frac{dv}{dx}$. There's no set rule for this — you just have to look at both parts and see which one differentiates to give something nice, then set that one as u. For example, if you have a product that has a single x as one part of it, choose this to be u. It differentiates to 1, which makes integrating $v\frac{du}{dx}$ dead easy.

Find $\int 2xe^x\,dx$.

Let $u = 2x$ and let $\frac{dv}{dx} = e^x$. Then u differentiates to give $\frac{du}{dx} = 2$ and $\frac{dv}{dx}$ integrates to give $v = e^x$.

Putting these into the formula gives: $\int 2xe^x\,dx = 2xe^x - \int 2e^x\,dx$

$= 2xe^x - 2e^x + C$

If you have a product that has ln x as one of its factors, let $u = \ln x$, as ln x is easy to differentiate but quite tricky to integrate (see below).

You can integrate ln x using Integration by Parts

Up till now, you haven't been able to integrate ln x, but all that is about to change. There's a little trick you can use — write ln x as $1\cdot\ln x$ then integrate by parts.

To find $\int \ln x\,dx$, write $\ln x = 1\cdot\ln x$.

Let $u = \ln x$ and let $\frac{dv}{dx} = 1$. Then u differentiates to give $\frac{du}{dx} = \frac{1}{x}$ and $\frac{dv}{dx}$ integrates to give $v = x$.

$$\int \ln x\,dx = x\ln x - \int x\frac{1}{x}dx = x\ln x - \int 1\,dx = x\ln x - x + C$$

You might have to integrate by parts More Than Once

If you have an integral that doesn't produce a nice, easy-to-integrate function for $v\frac{du}{dx}$, you might have to carry out integration by parts more than once.

EXAMPLE Find $\int x^2\sin x\,dx$.

Let $u = x^2$ and let $\frac{dv}{dx} = \sin x$.

Then u differentiates to give $\frac{du}{dx} = 2x$ and $\frac{dv}{dx}$ integrates to give $v = -\cos x$.

Putting these into the formula gives:

$$\int x^2\sin x\,dx = -x^2\cos x - \int -2x\cos x\,dx$$
$$= -x^2\cos x + \int 2x\cos x\,dx$$

$2x\cos x$ isn't very easy to integrate, so integrate by parts again (the $-x^2\cos x$ at the front just stays as it is):

Let $u = 2x$ and let $\frac{dv}{dx} = \cos x$. Then u differentiates to give $\frac{du}{dx} = 2$ and $\frac{dv}{dx}$ integrates to give $v = \sin x$.

Putting these into the formula gives:

$$\int 2x\cos x\,dx = 2x\sin x - \int 2\sin x\,dx = 2x\sin x + 2\cos x$$

So $\int x^2\sin x\,dx = -x^2\cos x + 2x\sin x + 2\cos x + C$.

Every now and then I fall apart...

After you've had a go at some examples, you'll probably realise that integrals with e^x, sin x or cos x in them are actually quite easy, as all three are really easy to integrate and differentiate. Fingers crossed you get one of them in the exam.

Tough Integrals

With a name like 'Tough Integrals', it doesn't sound like it's going to be a very nice page. However, names can be deceiving. Maybe not in this case, but they can be.

You can integrate Partial Fractions

In Section 1 (pages 46-47), you saw how to break down a scary-looking algebraic fraction into partial fractions. This comes in pretty handy when you're integrating — you could try integration by parts on the original fraction, but it would get messy and probably end in tears. Fortunately, once you've split it up into partial fractions, it's much easier to integrate, using the methods on p.69 and p.71.

EXAMPLE

Find $\int \frac{9x^2+x+16}{(x+2)(2x-1)(x-3)}\,dx$.

This is the example from p.46, and it can be written as partial fractions like this: $\frac{2}{(x+2)} - \frac{3}{(2x-1)} + \frac{4}{(x-3)}$

Don't forget the coefficients here. Have a look back at p.69 if you can't remember how to do this.

Integrating the partial fractions is much easier: $\int \frac{2}{(x+2)} - \frac{3}{(2x-1)} + \frac{4}{(x-3)}\,dx = 2\ln|x+2| - \frac{3}{2}\ln|2x-1| + 4\ln|x-3| + C$

$$= \ln\left|\frac{(x+2)^2(x-3)^4}{(2x-1)^{\frac{3}{2}}}\right| + C$$

EXAMPLE

Find $\int \frac{x^2+17x+16}{(x+2)^2(3x-1)}\,dx$.

This is the example from p.47. It's a bit trickier because it has a repeated factor. Written in partial fractions, it looks like this: $\frac{2}{(x+2)^2} - \frac{1}{(x+2)} + \frac{4}{(3x-1)}$

You might find it easiest to use integration by substitution (p.75) on the first fraction: Let $u = x + 2$, then $\frac{du}{dx} = 1$, so $du = dx$. Substituting gives:

$$\int \frac{2}{(x+2)^2}\,dx = \int \frac{2}{u^2}\,du = -\frac{2}{u} = -\frac{2}{(x+2)}$$

Putting it all together: $\int \frac{2}{(x+2)^2} - \frac{1}{(x+2)} + \frac{4}{(3x-1)}\,dx = -\frac{2}{x+2} - \ln|x+2| + \frac{4}{3}\ln|3x-1| + C$

$$= -\frac{2}{x+2} + \ln\left|\frac{(3x-1)^{\frac{4}{3}}}{x+2}\right| + C$$

Some Trig Integrals can be really Nasty

Unfortunately, the vast range of trig identities and formulas you've seen, as well as lots of different rules for integration, mean that there's no end of evil integration questions they can ask you. Here's a particularly nasty example:

EXAMPLE

Use the substitution $u = \tan x$ to find $\int \frac{\sec^4 x}{\sqrt{\tan x}}\,dx$.

First, work out what all the substitutions will be:
If $u = \tan x$, then $\frac{du}{dx} = \sec^2 x$, so $dx = \frac{du}{\sec^2 x}$.
This will leave $\sec^2 x$ on the numerator — you need to find this in terms of u:
From the identity $\sec^2 x \equiv 1 + \tan^2 x$, you get $\sec^2 x \equiv 1 + u^2$,

Then substitute all these bits into the integral:

$$\int \frac{\sec^4 x}{\sqrt{\tan x}}\,dx = \int \frac{1+u^2}{\sqrt{u}}\,du$$

$$= \int \frac{1}{\sqrt{u}} + \frac{u^2}{\sqrt{u}}\,du = \int u^{-\frac{1}{2}} + u^{\frac{3}{2}}\,du$$

$$= 2u^{\frac{1}{2}} + \frac{2}{5}u^{\frac{5}{2}} + C$$

Remember to stick $u = \tan x$ back into the equation.

$$= 2\sqrt{\tan x} + \frac{2}{5}\sqrt{\tan^5 x} + C$$

I'm partial to a cup of tea...

Partial fractions quite often pop up in a two-part question — for the first part, you'll have to write a tricky fraction in partial fractions, and in the second part you'll have to integrate it. It's a good job you're such a whizz at integrating.

Volumes of Revolution

Volumes of revolution is a really exciting title for a fairly exciting subject. Sadly, it isn't to do with plotting your own revolution, but it does let you calculate the volumes of weird-shaped things.

You have to find the **Volume** of an area **Rotated About the X-Axis**

If you're given a definite integral, the solution you come up with is the area under the graph between the two limits (you did this back in C2). If you now rotate that area 2π radians about the x-axis, you'll come up with a solid — and this is what you want to find the volume of. The formula for finding the volume of revolution is:

$$V = \pi \int_{x=x_1}^{x=x_2} y^2 \, dx$$

where y is a function of x (i.e. $y = f(x)$) and x_1 and x_2 are the limits of x.

If you wanted to rotate an area about the y-axis, you'd use the formula $V = \pi\int_{y_1}^{y_2} x^2 dy$. You don't need this for C4 though.

EXAMPLE Find the volume, V, of the solid formed when the area enclosed by the curve $y = \sqrt{6x^2 - 3x + 2}$, the x-axis and the lines $x = 1$ and $x = 2$ is rotated 2π radians about the x-axis.

If $y = \sqrt{6x^2 - 3x + 2}$, then $y^2 = 6x^2 - 3x + 2$.
Putting this into the formula gives:

$$V = \pi\int_1^2 6x^2 - 3x + 2 \, dx = \pi\left[2x^3 - \tfrac{3}{2}x^2 + 2x\right]_1^2$$
$$= \pi\left(\left[2(2)^3 - \tfrac{3}{2}(2)^2 + 2(2)\right] - \left[2(1)^3 - \tfrac{3}{2}(1)^2 + 2(1)\right]\right)$$
$$= \pi\left([16 - 6 + 4] - \left[2 - \tfrac{3}{2} + 2\right]\right) = \pi\left(14 - 2\tfrac{1}{2}\right) = 11\tfrac{1}{2}\pi$$

Don't forget to square y — you might think it's obvious, but it's easily done.

You can use **Parametric Equations** to find a **Volume**

In Section 2 (pages 49-52), you met curves with parametric equations — where x and y are functions of t. You saw how to differentiate them on p.62, and now it's time to integrate them. Once you know how to integrate them, it's easy to find the volume of revolution.
Here are the formulas you need, for a curve with parametric equations $x = f(t)$ and $y = g(t)$ and limits t_1 and t_2.

To find an area:

$$A = \int_{t=t_1}^{t=t_2} y \frac{dx}{dt} \, dt$$

Don't forget to change the limits from x to t.

To find a volume of revolution:

$$V = \pi \int_{t=t_1}^{t=t_2} y^2 \frac{dx}{dt} \, dt$$

You need the dx/dt to get the whole thing in terms of t.

EXAMPLE A curve is given by the parametric equations $x = 2t$, $y = \sin 3t$. Find:
a) the area bounded by the curve, the x-axis and the lines $x = 0$ and $x = 2\pi$.
b) the volume when this area is rotated 2π radians about the x-axis.

a) First of all, $\frac{dx}{dt} = 2$.
Change the limits: $x = 0$, so $2t = 0 \Rightarrow t = 0$
$x = 2\pi$, so $2t = 2\pi \Rightarrow t = \pi$.
Put the expressions for y and $\frac{dx}{dt}$ and the new limits into the formula:

$$A = \int_0^\pi 2\sin 3t \, dt = \left[-\tfrac{2}{3}\cos 3t\right]_0^\pi$$
$$= \left[-\tfrac{2}{3}\cos 3\pi\right] - \left[-\tfrac{2}{3}\cos 0\right]$$
$$= -\tfrac{2}{3}(-1) + \tfrac{2}{3} = \tfrac{4}{3}$$

b) From part a) you know that $\frac{dx}{dt} = 2$.
Squaring y gives $\sin^2 3t$.
Put these into the formula:

$$V = \pi\int_0^\pi 2\sin^2 3t \, dt = \pi\int_0^\pi 1 - \cos 6t \, dt$$
$$= \pi\left[t - \tfrac{1}{6}\sin 6t\right]_0^\pi$$
$$= \pi\left[\pi - \tfrac{1}{6}\sin 6\pi\right] - \pi\left[0 - \tfrac{1}{6}\sin 0\right]$$
$$= \pi\left[\pi - \tfrac{1}{6}(0)\right] - 0 = \pi^2$$

This bit uses the identity $\cos 2t \equiv 1 - 2\sin^2 t$ — don't forget to double the coefficient of t.

The limits are the same as in part a).

Don't be put off if the parametric equations are written in terms of something other than t (trig equations will sometimes be given in terms of θ) — just change $\frac{dx}{dt}$ to $\frac{dx}{d\theta}$ and dt to $d\theta$ (or to whatever the variable is).

Come the revolution, I will have to kill you all...

Not to be confused with the French Revolution, the Industrial Revolution or the lesser-known CGP Revolution, volumes of revolution is part of A2 Maths. So don't go getting any ideas about overthrowing your teachers and not letting them eat cake.

Differential Equations

Differential equations are tricky little devils that have a lot to do with differentiation as well as integration. They're often about rates of change, so the variable t pops up quite a lot.

Differential Equations have a dy/dx Term

(or $\frac{dP}{dt}$, $\frac{ds}{dt}$, $\frac{dV}{dr}$, etc. — depending on the variables)

1) A differential equation is an equation that includes a derivative term (such as $\frac{dy}{dx}$), as well as other variables (like x and y).
2) Before you even think (or worry) about solving them, you have to be able to set up ('formulate') differential equations.
3) Differential equations tend to involve a rate of change (giving a derivative term) and a proportion relation. Remember — if $a \propto b$, then $a = kb$ for some constant k.

EXAMPLE The number of bacteria in a petri dish is increasing over time, t, at a rate directly proportional to the number of bacteria at a given time, b. Formulate a differential equation that shows this information.

The rate of change, $\frac{db}{dt}$, is proportional to b, so $\frac{db}{dt} \propto b$. This means that $\frac{db}{dt} = kb$ for some constant k, $k > 0$.

EXAMPLE The volume of interdimensional space jelly, V, in a container is decreasing over time, t, at a rate directly proportional to the square of its volume. Show this as a differential equation.

The rate of change, $\frac{dV}{dt}$, is proportional to V^2, so $\frac{dV}{dt} \propto V^2$. $\frac{dV}{dt} = -kV^2$ for some constant k, $k > 0$.

V is decreasing, so don't forget the –.

Solve differential equations by Integrating

Now comes the really juicy bit — solving differential equations. It's not as bad as it looks (honest).

Solving Differential Equations

1) **You can only solve differential equations if they have separable variables — where x and y can be separated into functions f(x) and g(y).**
2) **Write the differential equation in the form $\frac{dy}{dx} = f(x)g(y)$.**
3) **Then rearrange the equation to get all the terms with y on the LHS and all the terms with x on the RHS. It'll look something like this: $\frac{1}{g(y)}dy = f(x)dx$.**
4) **Now integrate both sides: $\int \frac{1}{g(y)}dy = \int f(x)dx$.**
5) **Rearrange your answer to get it in a nice form — you might be asked to find it in the form $y = h(x)$. Don't forget the constant of integration (you only need one — not one on each side). It might be useful to write the constant as $\ln k$ rather than C (see p.71).**
6) **If you're asked for a general solution, leave C (or k) in your answer. If they want a particular solution, they'll give you x and y values for a certain point. All you do is put these values into your equation and use them to find C (or k).**

Remember — it might not be in terms of x and y.

Like in integration by substitution, you can treat dy/dx as a fraction here.

EXAMPLE Find the particular solution of $\frac{dy}{dx} = 2y(1 + x)^2$ when $x = -1$ and $y = 4$.

This equation has separable variables: $f(x) = 2(1 + x)^2$ and $g(y) = y$.

Rearranging this equation gives: $\frac{1}{y}dy = 2(1 + x)^2 dx$

And integrating: $\int \frac{1}{y}dy = \int 2(1 + x)^2 dx$

$\Rightarrow \ln|y| = \frac{2}{3}(1 + x)^3 + C$

If you were asked for a general solution, you could just leave it in this form.

Now put in the values of x and y to find the value of C:

$\ln 4 = \frac{2}{3}(1 + (-1))^3 + C \Rightarrow \ln 4 = C$

so $\ln|y| = \frac{2}{3}(1 + x)^3 + \ln 4$

I will formulate a plan to take over the world...

...starting with Cumbria. I've always liked Cumbria. You're welcome to join my army of minions, but first you'll have to become an expert on solving differential equations. Do that, and I'll give you Grasmere — or name a mountain after you.

Differential Equations

One of the most exciting things about differential equations is that you can apply them to real-life situations. Well, I say exciting, but perhaps I should say 'mildly interesting', or maybe just 'more stuff for you to learn'.

You might be given Extra Information

1) In the exam, you might be given a question that takes a real-life problem and uses differential equations to model it.
2) Population questions come up quite often — the population might be increasing or decreasing, and you have to find and solve differential equations to show it. In cases like this, one of your variables will usually be t, time.
3) You might be given a starting condition — e.g. the initial population. The important thing to remember is that:

the starting condition occurs when $t = 0$.

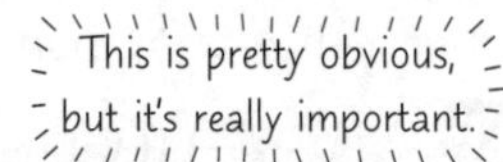

This is pretty obvious,
but it's really important.

4) You might also be given extra information — e.g. the population after a certain number of years (where you have to figure out what t is), or the number of years it takes to reach a certain population (where you have to work out what the population will be). Make sure you always link the numbers you get back to the situation.

Exam Questions are often Broken Down into lots of Parts

Questions like the one below can be a bit overwhelming, but follow it through step by step and it shouldn't be too bad.

EXAMPLE

The population of rabbits in a park is decreasing as winter approaches.
The rate of decrease is directly proportional to the current number of rabbits (P).

a) Formulate a differential equation to model the rate of decrease in terms of the variables P, t (time in days) and k, a positive constant.

b) If the initial population is P_0, solve your differential equation to find P in terms of P_0, k and t.

c) Given that $k = 0.1$, find the time at which the population of rabbits will have halved, to the nearest day.

a) If the rate of decrease is proportional to the number of rabbits, then $\frac{dP}{dt} = -kP$ (it's negative because the population is decreasing).

b) First, solve the differential equation to find the general solution: $\frac{dP}{dt} = -kP \Rightarrow \frac{1}{P}\,dP = -k\,dt$

Integrating this gives: $\int \frac{1}{P}\,dP = \int -k\,dt$

$\Rightarrow \ln P = -kt + C$

You don't need modulus signs for ln P as $P \geq 0$ — you can't have a negative population.

At $t = 0$, $P = P_0$. Putting these values into the equation gives: $\ln P_0 = -k(0) + C$

$\Rightarrow \ln P_0 = C$

So the differential equation becomes: $\ln P = -kt + \ln P_0$

$\Rightarrow P = e^{(-kt + \ln P_0)} = e^{-kt}e^{\ln P_0}$

$\Rightarrow P = P_0 e^{-kt}$

Remember that $e^{\ln x} = x = \ln e^x$.

c) When the population of rabbits has halved, $P = \frac{1}{2}P_0$. You've been told that $k = 0.1$, so substitute these values into the equation above and solve for t:

$\frac{1}{2}P_0 = P_0 e^{-0.1t}$

$\frac{1}{2} = e^{-0.1t}$

$\ln\frac{1}{2} = -0.1t$

$-0.6931 = -0.1t \Rightarrow t = 6.931$

So, to the nearest day, $t = 7$. This means that it will take 7 days for the population of rabbits to halve.

At t = 10, we kill all the bunnies...

These questions can get a bit morbid — just how I like them. They might look a bit scary, as they throw a lot of information at you in one go, but once you know how to solve them, they're a walk in the park. Rabbit traps optional.

Numerical Integration

In the interests of avoiding cruelty to animals, I think it's best to move on. Next up, numerical integration — I promise you it's not as bad as it sounds. Most of it's stuff you've done before — like the Trapezium Rule.

Estimate the area using the *Trapezium Rule*

Here's a quick reminder of the Trapezium Rule — look back over your C2 notes if you can't remember how to do it.

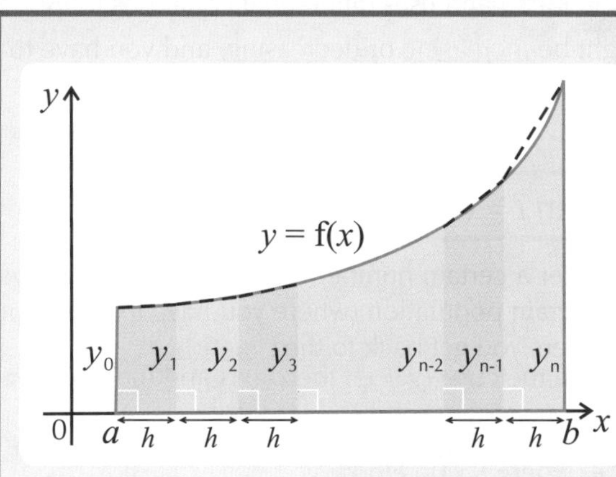

The area of each trapezium is $A_n = \frac{h}{2}(y_n + y_{n+1})$

The area represented by $\int_a^b y\,dx$ is approximately:

$$\int_a^b y\,dx \approx \frac{h}{2}[y_0 + 2(y_1 + y_2 + \dots + y_{n-1}) + y_n]$$

Remember that 5 ordinates is the same as 4 strips.

where n is the number of strips or intervals and h is the width of each strip.

You can find the width of each strip using $h = \frac{(b-a)}{n}$

$y_0, y_1, y_2, \dots, y_n$ are the heights of the sides of the trapeziums — you get these by putting the x-values into the equation of the curve.

Use *More Strips* to get a *More Accurate* answer

Using more strips (i.e. increasing n) gives you a more accurate approximation. You can check how accurate your answer is by working out the percentage error (see below).

EXAMPLE Use the Trapezium Rule to approximate the area of $\int_0^4 \frac{6x^2}{x^3+2}\,dx$, using a) $n = 2$ and b) $n = 4$.

a) For 2 strips, the width of each strip is $h = \frac{4-0}{2} = 2$, so the x-values are 0, 2 and 4.

x	$y = \frac{6x^2}{x^3+2}$
$x_0 = 0$	$y_0 = 0$
$x_1 = 2$	$y_1 = 2.4$
$x_2 = 4$	$y_2 = 1.455$

(3 d.p.)

Putting these values into the formula gives:

$$\int_0^4 \frac{6x^2}{x^3+2}\,dx \approx \frac{2}{2}[0 + 2(2.4) + 1.455] = [4.8 + 1.455] = 6.255$$

(3 d.p.)

b) For 4 strips, the width of each strip is $h = \frac{4-0}{4} = 1$, so the x-values are 0, 1, 2, 3 and 4.

x	$y = \frac{6x^2}{x^3+2}$
$x_0 = 0$	$y_0 = 0$
$x_1 = 1$	$y_1 = 2$
$x_2 = 2$	$y_2 = 2.4$
$x_3 = 3$	$y_3 = 1.862$
$x_4 = 4$	$y_4 = 1.455$

(3 d.p.)

Putting these values into the formula gives:

$$\int_0^4 \frac{6x^2}{x^3+2}\,dx \approx \frac{1}{2}[0 + 2(2 + 2.4 + 1.862) + 1.455] = \frac{1}{2}[12.524 + 1.455] = 6.990$$

(3 d.p.)

You need the *Exact Answer* to work out the *Percentage Error*

To work out the percentage error, calculate or use the exact value of the integral, then use this formula:

$$\%\text{ Error} = \frac{\text{exact value} - \text{approximate value}}{\text{exact value}} \times 100$$

EXAMPLE Calculate the percentage error for a) and b) above to 2 d.p.

This was calculated using the formula on p.71.

First, work out the exact value of the integral: $\int_0^4 \frac{6x^2}{x^3+2}\,dx = [2\ln|x^3+2|]_0^4 = [2\ln 66] - [2\ln 2] = 6.993$ (3 d.p.)

For part a), the percentage error is $\frac{6.993 - 6.255}{6.993} \times 100 = 10.55\%$, and for part b), $\frac{6.993 - 6.990}{6.993} \times 100 = 0.04\%$.

The approximation with more strips has a lower percentage error — so it's a more accurate approximation.

I lost my notes in the Bermuda Trapezium...

The key thing to remember about the Trapezium Rule (well, apart from the rule itself) is that the more strips you have, the more accurate your answer (and so the lower the % error). More strips = more accurate = smaller % error. Got it?

C4 Section 6 — Practice Questions

Phew, that was a whopper of a section. I bet you could do with a break. Well, hold on just a minute — here are some practice questions to do first to check you know your stuff. Let's start with a gentle warm-up.

Warm-up Questions

1) Use the substitution $u = e^x - 1$ to find $\int e^x(e^x + 1)(e^x - 1)^2\,dx$.

2) Find the exact value of $\int_{\frac{\pi}{4}}^{\frac{\pi}{3}} \sec^4 x \tan x\,dx$, using the substitution $u = \sec x$.

3) Use integration by parts to solve $\int 3x^2 \ln x\,dx$.

4) Use integration by parts to solve $\int 4x\cos 4x\,dx$.

5) Use $\dfrac{3x+10}{(2x+3)(x-4)} \equiv \dfrac{A}{2x+3} + \dfrac{B}{x-4}$ to find $\int \dfrac{3x+10}{(2x+3)(x-4)}\,dx$.

6) Find the volume of the solid formed when the area bounded by the curve $y = \frac{1}{x}$, the x-axis and the lines $x = 2$ and $x = 4$ is rotated 2π radians about the x-axis.

7) A curve is given by the parametric equations $x = t^2$ and $y = \frac{1}{t}$, where $t > 0$. Find:

   a) the area bounded by the curve, the x-axis and the lines $x = 4$ and $x = 9$.

   b) the volume formed when this area is rotated 2π radians about the x-axis.

8) Find the general solution to the differential equation $\dfrac{dy}{dx} = \dfrac{1}{y}\cos x$. Give your answer in the form $y^2 = f(x)$.

9) The population of squirrels is increasing suspiciously quickly. The rate of increase is directly proportional to the current number of squirrels, S.

   a) Formulate a differential equation to model the rate of increase in terms of S, t (time in weeks) and k, a positive constant.

   b) The squirrels need a population of 150 to successfully take over the forest. If the initial population is 30 and the value of k is 0.2, how long (to the nearest week) will it take before they can overthrow the evil hedgehogs?

10) Use the Trapezium Rule to estimate the value of $\int_0^6 (6x - 12)(x^2 - 4x + 3)^2\,dx$, first using 4 strips and then again with 6 strips. Calculate the percentage error for each answer.

Unfortunately the exam questions are less likely to be about rebel squirrels, as the examiners tend to be on the hedgehogs' side. If you ever meet an examiner, look closely to make sure he's not a hedgehog in disguise.

Exam Questions

1 Find the volume of the solid formed when the region R, bounded by the curve $y = \operatorname{cosec} x$, the x-axis and the lines $x = \frac{\pi}{4}$ and $x = \frac{\pi}{3}$, is rotated 2π radians about the x-axis.
Give your answer to 3 decimal places.

(3 marks)

C4 Section 6 — Practice Questions

One more page of questions, then you're onto the final section of C4. That's right, the last one.

2 **Figure 1** shows the graph of $y = x \sin x$. The region R is bounded by the curve and the x-axis ($0 \leq x \leq \pi$).

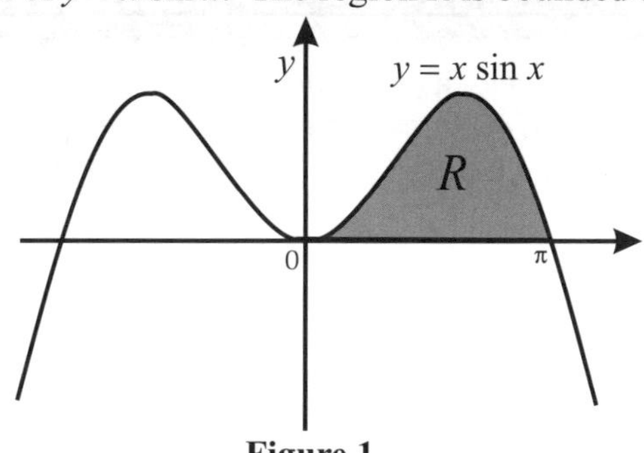

Figure 1

a) Fill in the missing values of y in the table below. Give your answers to 4 decimal places.

x	0	$\frac{\pi}{4}$	$\frac{\pi}{2}$	$\frac{3\pi}{4}$	π
y	0	0.5554			0

(2 marks)

b) Hence find an approximation for the area of R, using the Trapezium Rule.
Give your answer to 3 decimal places. *(4 marks)*

c) Find the exact area of R using integration by parts. *(4 marks)*

d) Hence find the percentage error of the approximation. *(2 marks)*

3 a) Find the general solution to the differential equation

$$\frac{dy}{dx} = \frac{\cos x \cos^2 y}{\sin x}.$$

(4 marks)

b) Given that $y = \pi$ when $x = \frac{\pi}{6}$, solve the differential equation above. *(2 marks)*

4 Find the value of $\int_1^2 \frac{8}{x}(\ln x + 2)^3 \, dx$ using the substitution $u = \ln x$. Give your answer to 4 s.f. *(6 marks)*

5 A company sets up an advertising campaign to increase sales of margarine. After the campaign, the number of tubs of margarine sold each week, m, increases over time, t weeks, at a rate that is directly proportional to the square root of the number of tubs sold.

a) Formulate a differential equation in terms of t, m and a constant k. *(2 marks)*

b) At the start of the campaign, the company was selling 900 tubs of margarine a week.
Use this information to solve the differential equation, giving m in terms of k and t. *(4 marks)*

c) Hence calculate the number of tubs sold in the fifth week after the campaign, given that $k = 2$. *(3 marks)*

Vectors

If you did M1, then you've probably seen some of this vector stuff before. If not, you've got lots to look forward to. In any case, we're going to start with the basics — like what vectors are.

Vectors have Magnitude and Direction — Scalars Don't

1) Vectors have both size and direction — e.g. a velocity of 2 m/s on a bearing of 050°, or a displacement of 3 m north. Scalars are just quantities without a direction, e.g. a speed of 2 m/s, a distance of 3 m.
2) Vectors are drawn as lines with arrowheads on them.
   - The length of the line represents the magnitude (size) of the vector (e.g. the speed component of velocity). Sometimes vectors are drawn to scale.
   - The direction of the arrowhead shows the direction of the vector.

There are two ways of writing vectors:
1) Using a lower case, bold letter. **a**
   When you're handwriting a vector like this, you should underline the letter, i.e. a.
2) Putting an arrow over the endpoints. $\overrightarrow{AB}$

Find the Resultant by Drawing Vectors Nose to Tail

You can add vectors together by drawing the arrows nose to tail.
The single vector that goes from the start to the end of the vectors is called the resultant vector.

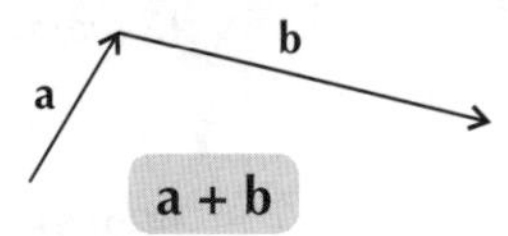

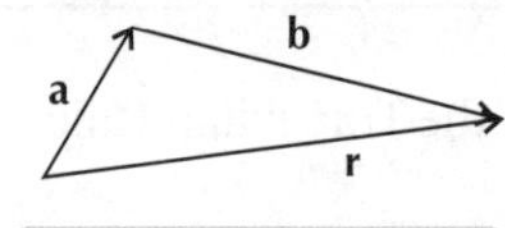

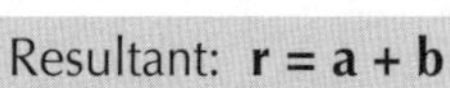

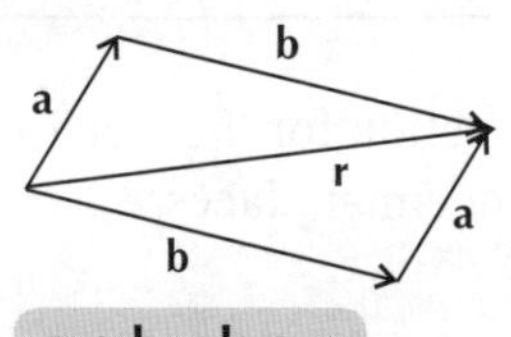

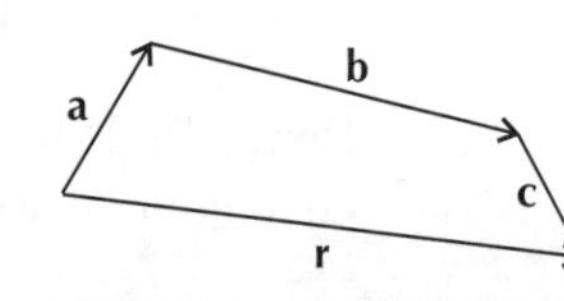

Subtracting a Vector is the Same as Adding a Negative Vector

1) The vector **–a** is in the opposite direction to the vector **a**. They're both exactly the same size.

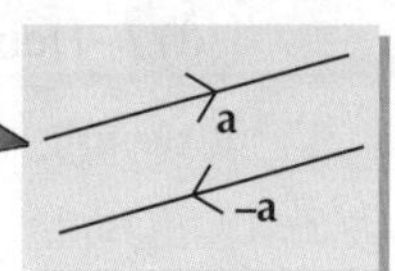

2) So subtracting a vector is the same as adding the negative vector:

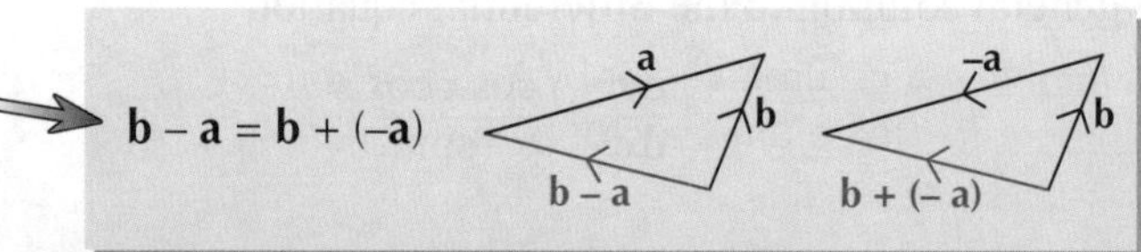

3) You can use the adding and subtracting rules to find a vector in terms of other vectors.

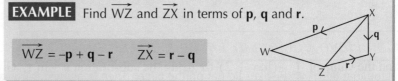

EXAMPLE Find $\overrightarrow{WZ}$ and $\overrightarrow{ZX}$ in terms of **p**, **q** and **r**.

$\overrightarrow{WZ} = -\mathbf{p} + \mathbf{q} - \mathbf{r}$ $\quad \overrightarrow{ZX} = \mathbf{r} - \mathbf{q}$

Vectors a, 2a and 3a are all Parallel

You can multiply a vector by a scalar (just a number, remember) — the length changes but the direction stays the same.

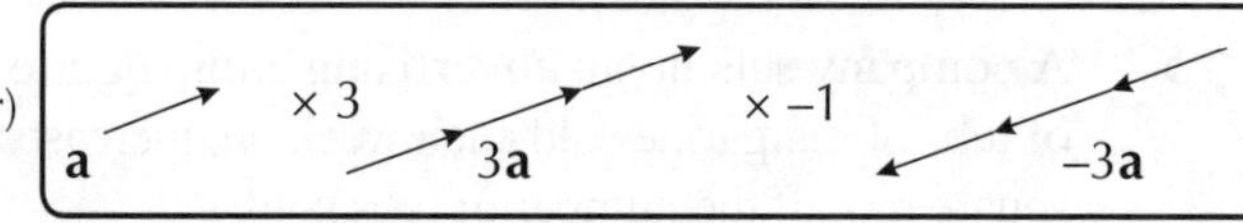

Multiplying a vector by a non-zero scalar always produces a parallel vector.

All these vectors are parallel: $9\mathbf{a} + 15\mathbf{b}$ $\quad 18\mathbf{a} + 30\mathbf{b}$ $\quad 6\mathbf{a} + 10\mathbf{b}$ $\quad 3\mathbf{a} + 5\mathbf{b}$

This is $2(9\mathbf{a} + 15\mathbf{b})$. This is $\frac{2}{3}(9\mathbf{a} + 15\mathbf{b})$. This is $\frac{1}{3}(9\mathbf{a} + 15\mathbf{b})$.

Eating pasta = buying anti-pasta?...

If an exam question asks you to show that two lines are parallel, you just have to show that one vector's a multiple of the other. By the way — exam papers often use λ and μ as scalars in vector questions (so you don't confuse them with vectors).

Vectors

There are a few more ways of representing vectors that you need to know about. Then it's off to the third dimension...

Position Vectors Describe Where a Point Lies

You can use a vector to describe the position of a point, in relation to the origin, O.

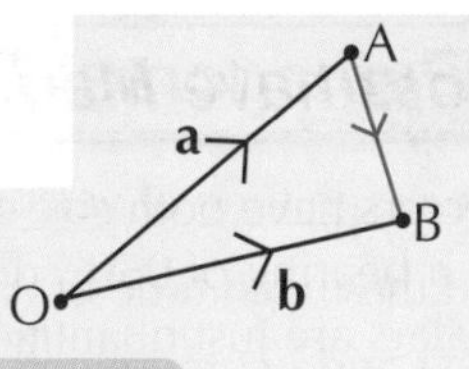

The position vector of point A is $\overrightarrow{OA}$. It's usually called vector **a**.
The position vector of point B is $\overrightarrow{OB}$. It's usually called vector **b**.

You can write other vectors in terms of position vectors: $\overrightarrow{AB} = -\overrightarrow{OA} + \overrightarrow{OB} = \overrightarrow{OB} - \overrightarrow{OA}$
$= -\mathbf{a} + \mathbf{b} = \mathbf{b} - \mathbf{a}$

Vectors can be described using i + j Units

1) A unit vector is any vector with a magnitude of 1 unit. (There's more on unit vectors on the next page.)
2) The vectors **i** + **j** are standard unit vectors. **i** is in the direction of the x-axis, and **j** is in the direction of the y-axis. They each have a magnitude of 1 unit, of course.
3) They're a dead handy way of describing any vector. You use them to say how far horizontally and vertically you have to go to get from the start of the vector to the end.

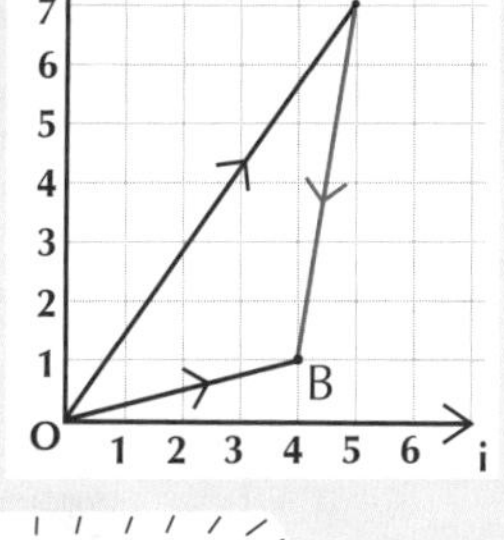

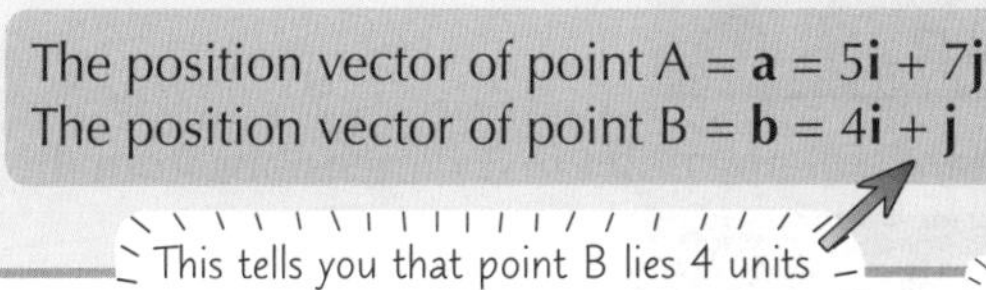

The position vector of point A = $\mathbf{a} = 5\mathbf{i} + 7\mathbf{j}$
The position vector of point B = $\mathbf{b} = 4\mathbf{i} + \mathbf{j}$

This tells you that point B lies 4 units to the right and 1 unit above the origin — it's just like coordinates.

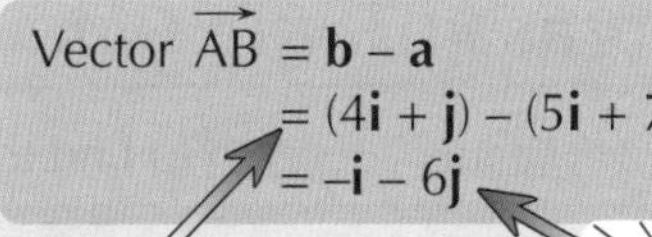

Vector $\overrightarrow{AB} = \mathbf{b} - \mathbf{a}$
$= (4\mathbf{i} + \mathbf{j}) - (5\mathbf{i} + 7\mathbf{j})$
$= -\mathbf{i} - 6\mathbf{j}$

Add/subtract the **i** and **j** components separately.

To go from A to B, you go 1 unit left and 6 units down. It's just like a translation.

And then there are Column Vectors

1) If writing i's and j's gets a bit much for your wrists, you can use column vectors instead. $x\mathbf{i} + y\mathbf{j} = \begin{pmatrix} x \\ y \end{pmatrix}$
2) Calculating with them is a breeze. Just add or subtract the top row, then add or subtract the bottom row separately.
3) When you're multiplying a column vector by a scalar, you multiply each number in the column vector by the scalar.

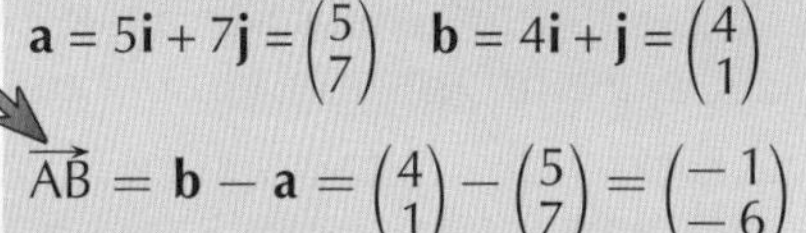

$\mathbf{a} = 5\mathbf{i} + 7\mathbf{j} = \begin{pmatrix} 5 \\ 7 \end{pmatrix}$ $\quad \mathbf{b} = 4\mathbf{i} + \mathbf{j} = \begin{pmatrix} 4 \\ 1 \end{pmatrix}$

$\overrightarrow{AB} = \mathbf{b} - \mathbf{a} = \begin{pmatrix} 4 \\ 1 \end{pmatrix} - \begin{pmatrix} 5 \\ 7 \end{pmatrix} = \begin{pmatrix} -1 \\ -6 \end{pmatrix}$

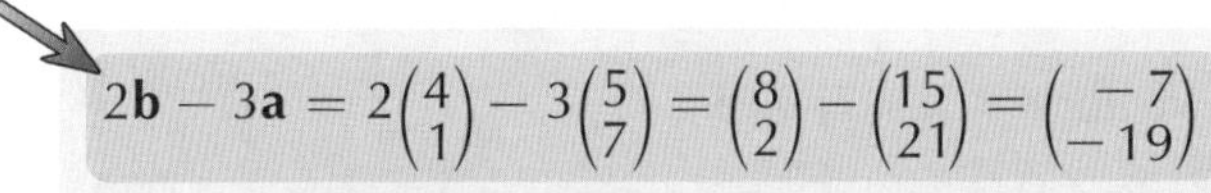

$2\mathbf{b} - 3\mathbf{a} = 2\begin{pmatrix} 4 \\ 1 \end{pmatrix} - 3\begin{pmatrix} 5 \\ 7 \end{pmatrix} = \begin{pmatrix} 8 \\ 2 \end{pmatrix} - \begin{pmatrix} 15 \\ 21 \end{pmatrix} = \begin{pmatrix} -7 \\ -19 \end{pmatrix}$

You Can Have Vectors in Three Dimensions Too

1) Imagine that the x- and y-axes lie flat on the page. Then imagine a third axis sticking straight through the page at right angles to it — this is the z-axis.
2) The points in three dimensions are given (x, y, z) coordinates.
3) When you're talking vectors, **k** is the unit vector in the direction of the z-axis.
4) You can write three-dimensional vectors as column vectors like this:

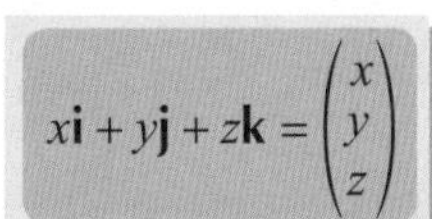

$x\mathbf{i} + y\mathbf{j} + z\mathbf{k} = \begin{pmatrix} x \\ y \\ z \end{pmatrix}$

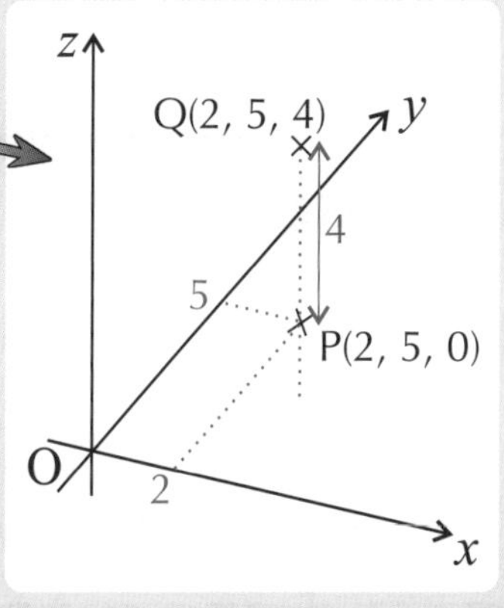

5) So the position vector of point Q is:

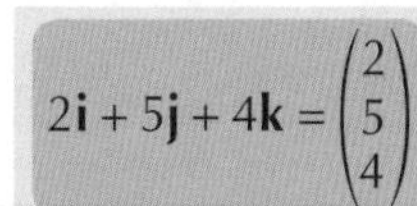

$2\mathbf{i} + 5\mathbf{j} + 4\mathbf{k} = \begin{pmatrix} 2 \\ 5 \\ 4 \end{pmatrix}$

I've got B + Q units in my kitchen...

Three dimensions doesn't really make things much more difficult — it just gives you an extra number to calculate with. You add, subtract and multiply 3D column vectors in the same way as 2D ones — you just have three rows to deal with.

Vectors

Pythagoras pops up all over the place, and here he is again. Fascinating fact — Pythagoras refused to say words containing the Greek equivalent of the letter c. I read it on the internet, so it has to be true.

Use Pythagoras' Theorem to Find Vector Magnitudes

1) The magnitude of vector **a** is written as $|\mathbf{a}|$, and the magnitude of $\overrightarrow{AB}$ is written as $|\overrightarrow{AB}|$.

A vector's magnitude is sometimes called its modulus.

2) The **i** and **j** components of a vector form a convenient right-angled triangle, so just bung them into the Pythagoras formula to find the vector's magnitude.
3) You might be asked to find a unit vector in the direction of a particular vector. Remember — a unit vector has a magnitude of 1 (see the previous page).

EXAMPLE

$\mathbf{a} = 5\mathbf{i} + 3\mathbf{j}$

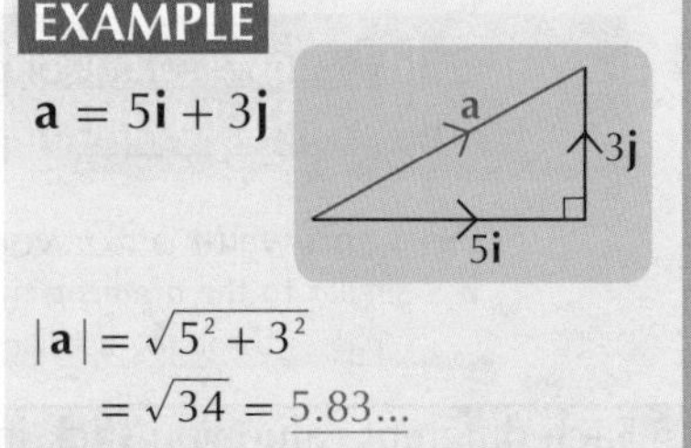

$|\mathbf{a}| = \sqrt{5^2 + 3^2}$
$= \sqrt{34} = 5.83...$

A unit vector in the direction of vector $\mathbf{a} = \frac{\mathbf{a}}{|\mathbf{a}|}$

EXAMPLE If vector **p** has a magnitude of 12 units, find a unit vector parallel to **p**.

$$\frac{\mathbf{p}}{|\mathbf{p}|} = \frac{\mathbf{p}}{12} = \frac{1}{12}\mathbf{p}$$

You Can Use Pythagoras in Three Dimensions Too

1) You can use a variation of Pythagoras' theorem to find the distance of any point in 3 dimensions from the origin, O.

The distance of point (x, y, z) from the origin is $\sqrt{x^2 + y^2 + z^2}$

EXAMPLE 1

Find $|\overrightarrow{OQ}|$.

$|\overrightarrow{OQ}| = \sqrt{x^2 + y^2 + z^2}$
$= \sqrt{2^2 + 5^2 + 4^2}$
$= \sqrt{45}$
$= 6.7$ units

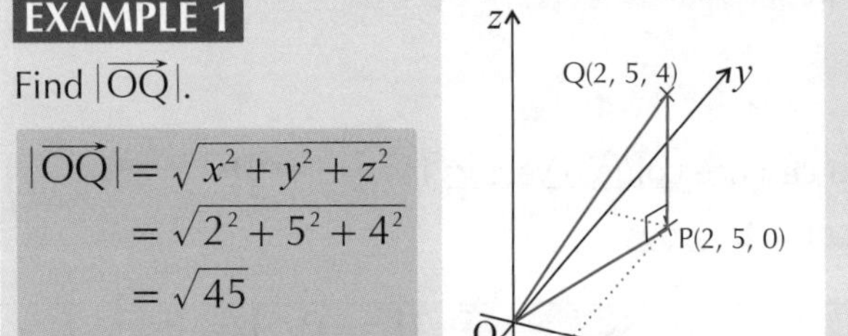

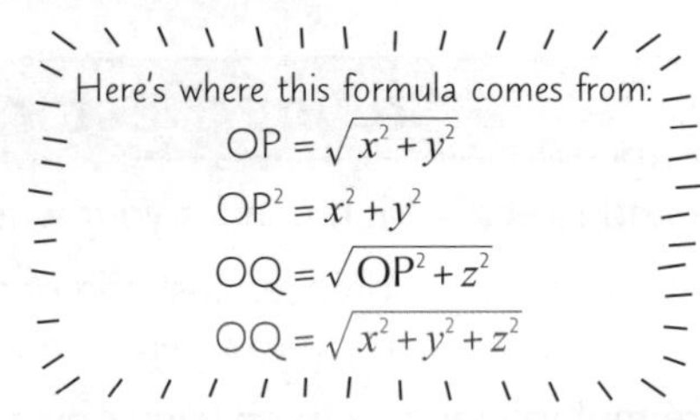

Here's where this formula comes from:
$OP = \sqrt{x^2 + y^2}$
$OP^2 = x^2 + y^2$
$OQ = \sqrt{OP^2 + z^2}$
$OQ = \sqrt{x^2 + y^2 + z^2}$

EXAMPLE 2 Find the magnitude of the vector $\mathbf{r} = 5\mathbf{i} + 7\mathbf{j} + 3\mathbf{k}$.

$|\mathbf{r}| = \sqrt{5^2 + 7^2 + 3^2}$
$= \sqrt{83} = 9.1$ units

2) There's also a Pythagoras-based formula for finding the distance between any two points.

The distance between points (x_1, y_1, z_1) and (x_2, y_2, z_2) is $\sqrt{(x_1 - x_2)^2 + (y_1 - y_2)^2 + (z_1 - z_2)^2}$

EXAMPLE

The position vector of point A is $3\mathbf{i} + 2\mathbf{j} + 4\mathbf{k}$, and the position vector of point B is $2\mathbf{i} + 6\mathbf{j} - 5\mathbf{k}$. Find $|\overrightarrow{AB}|$.

A has the coordinates (3, 2, 4),
B has the coordinates (2, 6, –5).

$|\overrightarrow{AB}| = \sqrt{(x_1 - x_2)^2 + (y_1 - y_2)^2 + (z_1 - z_2)^2}$
$= \sqrt{(3-2)^2 + (2-6)^2 + (4-(-5))^2}$
$= \sqrt{1 + 16 + 81} = 9.9$ units

You can play Battleships with 3D coordinates too — but you don't have to...

The magnitude is just a scalar, so it doesn't have a direction — the magnitude of $\overrightarrow{AB}$ is the same as the magnitude of $\overrightarrow{BA}$. Squaring the numbers in the formulas gets rid of any minus signs, so you don't have to worry about which way round you subtract the coordinates (phew). There's not a lot new on this page, in fact, it's mostly just good old Pythagoras.

Vector Equations of Lines

At first glance, vector equations of straight lines don't look much like normal straight-line equations. But they're pretty similar if you look closely. In any case, just learn the formulas really well and you'll be fine.

Learn the Equation of the Line Through a Point and Parallel to Another Vector

A straight line which goes through point A, and is parallel to vector **b**, has the vector equation: $\mathbf{r} = \mathbf{a} + t\mathbf{b}$

a = position vector of point A
r = position vector of a point on the line, and t = a scalar.

A is a fixed point.

This is pretty much a 3D version of the old $y = mx + c$ equation. **b** is similar to the gradient, m, and **a** gives a point that the line passes through, just like c gives the y-axis intercept.

Each different value you stick in for t in the vector equation gives you the position vector, **r**, of a different point on the line.

EXAMPLE A straight line is parallel to the vector $\mathbf{i} + 3\mathbf{j} - 2\mathbf{k}$. It passes through a point with the position vector $3\mathbf{i} + 2\mathbf{j} + 6\mathbf{k}$. Find its vector equation.

$$\mathbf{r} = \mathbf{a} + t\mathbf{b} = (3\mathbf{i} + 2\mathbf{j} + 6\mathbf{k}) + t(\mathbf{i} + 3\mathbf{j} - 2\mathbf{k})$$

Alternative ways of writing this are: $\mathbf{r} = (3 + t)\mathbf{i} + (2 + 3t)\mathbf{j} + (6 - 2t)\mathbf{k}$,

$$\mathbf{r} = \begin{pmatrix}3\\2\\6\end{pmatrix} + t\begin{pmatrix}1\\3\\-2\end{pmatrix} \text{ and } \mathbf{r} = \begin{pmatrix}3+t\\2+3t\\6-2t\end{pmatrix}$$

And the Equation of the Line Passing Through Two Known Points

A straight line through points C and D, with position vectors **c** and **d**, has the vector equation:

$$\mathbf{r} = \mathbf{c} + t(\mathbf{d} - \mathbf{c})$$

r = position vector of a point on the line, t = a scalar.

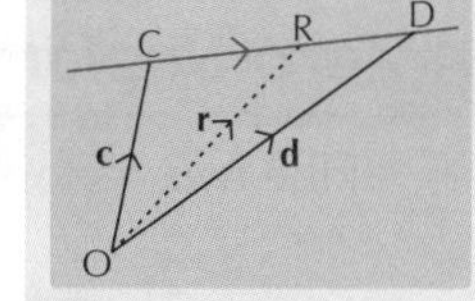

This is basically the same as the vector equation above. You just have to find a vector in the direction of CD first (i.e. $\mathbf{d} - \mathbf{c}$).

EXAMPLE
A line passes through points with the coordinates (3, 2, 4) and (–1, 3, 0). Find a vector equation for this line.

If $\mathbf{c} = \begin{pmatrix}3\\2\\4\end{pmatrix}$, and $\mathbf{d} = \begin{pmatrix}-1\\3\\0\end{pmatrix}$, then $\mathbf{r} = \begin{pmatrix}3\\2\\4\end{pmatrix} + t\left(\begin{pmatrix}-1\\3\\0\end{pmatrix} - \begin{pmatrix}3\\2\\4\end{pmatrix}\right) \Rightarrow \mathbf{r} = \begin{pmatrix}3\\2\\4\end{pmatrix} + t\begin{pmatrix}-4\\1\\-4\end{pmatrix}$

Find the Point of Intersection of two Lines with Simultaneous Equations

If Line 1, $\mathbf{r} = \begin{pmatrix}5\\2\\-1\end{pmatrix} + \mu\begin{pmatrix}1\\-2\\-3\end{pmatrix}$, and Line 2, $\mathbf{r} = \begin{pmatrix}2\\0\\4\end{pmatrix} + \lambda\begin{pmatrix}1\\2\\-1\end{pmatrix}$, intersect, there'll be a value for μ and a value for λ that result in the same point for both lines. This is the point of intersection.

EXAMPLE Determine whether Line 1 and Line 2 (above) intersect. If they do, find the point of intersection.

At the point of intersection, $\begin{pmatrix}5\\2\\-1\end{pmatrix} + \mu\begin{pmatrix}1\\-2\\-3\end{pmatrix} = \begin{pmatrix}2\\0\\4\end{pmatrix} + \lambda\begin{pmatrix}1\\2\\-1\end{pmatrix}$. You can get 3 equations from this:
① $5 + \mu = 2 + \lambda$
② $2 - 2\mu = 0 + 2\lambda$
③ $-1 - 3\mu = 4 - \lambda$

Solve the first two simultaneously: 2 × ①: $10 + 2\mu = 4 + 2\lambda$ ④
④ – ②: $8 + 4\mu = 4 \Rightarrow \mu = -1$
sub. in ②: $2 - 2(-1) = 0 + 2\lambda \Rightarrow \lambda = 2$

Substitute the values for μ and λ into equation ③. If they make the equation true, then the lines do intersect:
$-1 - (3 \times -1) = 4 - 2 \Rightarrow 2 = 2$ — True, so they do intersect.

Now find the intersection point: $\mathbf{r} = \begin{pmatrix}5\\2\\-1\end{pmatrix} + \mu\begin{pmatrix}1\\-2\\-3\end{pmatrix} = \begin{pmatrix}5\\2\\-1\end{pmatrix} - 1\begin{pmatrix}1\\-2\\-3\end{pmatrix} \Rightarrow \mathbf{r} = \begin{pmatrix}4\\4\\2\end{pmatrix} = 4\mathbf{i} + 4\mathbf{j} + 2\mathbf{k}$

This is the position vector of the intersection point. The coordinates are (4, 4, 2).

Stardate 45283.5, position vector 20076i + 23485j + 48267k...

You might be given vector equations in **i**, **j**, **k** form or in column form, so practise these examples using each vector form.

Scalar Product

The scalar product of two vectors is kind of what it says on the tin — two vectors multiplied together to give a scalar result. But this is A2, so it's going to be trickier than simple multiplying. It even involves a bit of cos-ing.

Learn the Definition of the **Scalar Product of Two Vectors**

Scalar Product of Two Vectors

$$\mathbf{a}.\mathbf{b} = |\mathbf{a}||\mathbf{b}|\cos\theta$$

θ is the angle between position vectors **a** and **b**.

Both vectors have to be directed away from the intersection point.

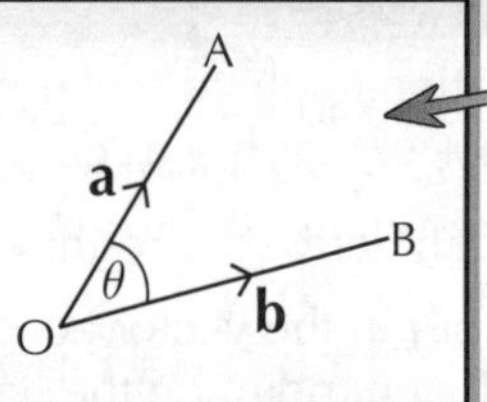

Watch out — the correct angle might not always be obvious.

θ is the angle in the definition.

Here you have to continue **b** on so that it's also directed away from the intersection point.

1) The scalar product of two vectors is always a scalar quantity — it's never a vector.
2) The scalar product can be used to calculate the angle between two lines (see the next page) — $\mathbf{a}.\mathbf{b} = |\mathbf{a}||\mathbf{b}|\cos\theta$ rearranges to $\cos\theta = \dfrac{\mathbf{a}.\mathbf{b}}{|\mathbf{a}||\mathbf{b}|}$.
3) The scalar product **a . b** is read '**a** dot **b**'. It's really, really important to put the dot in, as it shows you mean the scalar product (rather than a different sort of vector product that you don't have to worry about in C4).

A **Zero Scalar Product** Means the Vectors are **Perpendicular**

1) If the two vectors are perpendicular, they're at 90° to each other.
2) Cos 90° = 0, so the scalar product of the two vectors is 0.

Scalar Product of Two Perpendicular Vectors

$$\mathbf{a}.\mathbf{b} = |\mathbf{a}||\mathbf{b}|\cos 90^\circ = 0$$

3) The unit vectors **i**, **j** and **k** are all perpendicular to each other.

So, $\mathbf{i}.\mathbf{j} = 1 \times 1 \times 0 = 0$ and $3\mathbf{j}.4\mathbf{k} = 3 \times 4 \times 0 = 0$

4) This all assumes that the vectors are non-zero. Because if either vector was 0, you'd always get a scalar product of 0, regardless of the angle between them.

The Scalar Product of **Parallel Vectors** is just the **Product of the Magnitudes**

1) If two vectors are parallel, the angle between them is 0°. And cos 0° = 1, so...

Scalar Product of Two Parallel Vectors

$$\mathbf{a}.\mathbf{b} = |\mathbf{a}||\mathbf{b}|\cos 0^\circ = |\mathbf{a}||\mathbf{b}|$$

2) Two **i** unit vectors are parallel to each other (as are two **j**s or two **k**s).

So, $\mathbf{j}.\mathbf{j} = 1 \times 1 \times 1 = 1$ and $3\mathbf{k}.4\mathbf{k} = 3 \times 4 \times 1 = 12$

3) Again, this all assumes that the vectors are non-zero.

Scaley product — a lizard-skin handbag...

The fact that two perpendicular vectors have a zero scalar product is the key to loads of vector exam questions. E.g. you might be asked to show two vectors are perpendicular, or told that two vectors are perpendicular and asked to find a missing vector. Whatever they ask, you'll definitely have to multiply the two vectors — and you're about to learn how.

Scalar Product

Finding the scalar product of two vectors is super quick and easy once you know how to do it.

*Learn This Result for the **Scalar Product***

1) You can use this result to find the scalar product of two known vectors:

If $\mathbf{a} = a_1\mathbf{i} + a_2\mathbf{j} + a_3\mathbf{k}$, and $\mathbf{b} = b_1\mathbf{i} + b_2\mathbf{j} + b_3\mathbf{k}$, then $\mathbf{a.b} = a_1b_1 + a_2b_2 + a_3b_3$

2) The normal laws of multiplication apply to scalar products too — e.g. the commutative law ($\mathbf{a} . \mathbf{b} = \mathbf{b} . \mathbf{a}$) and the distributive law ($\mathbf{a} . (\mathbf{b} + \mathbf{c}) = \mathbf{a} . \mathbf{b} + \mathbf{a} . \mathbf{c}$).

3) By applying these laws, you can derive the result above...

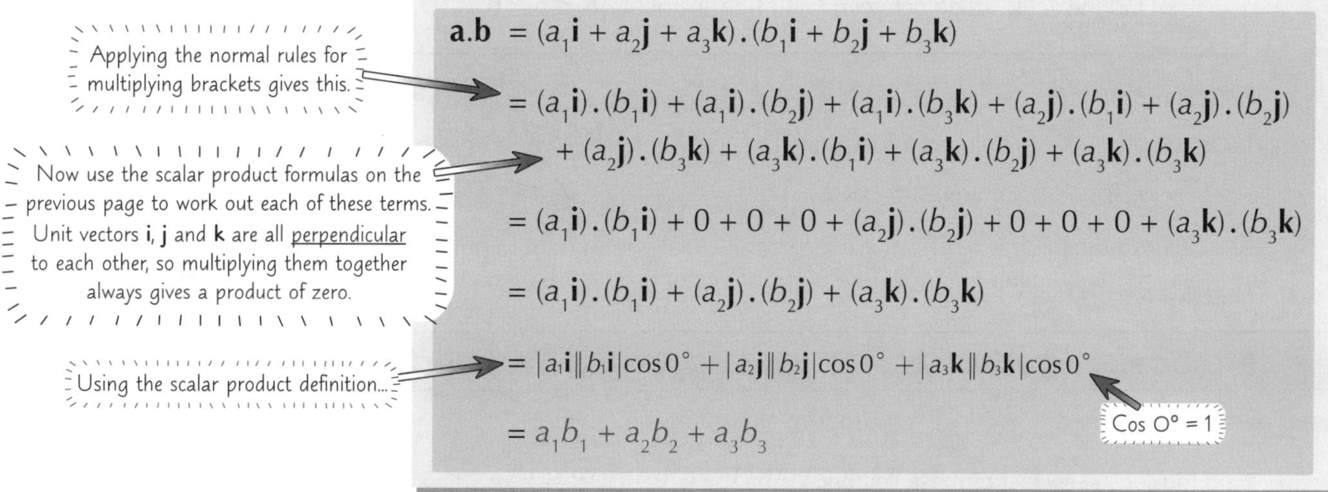

$\mathbf{a.b} = (a_1\mathbf{i} + a_2\mathbf{j} + a_3\mathbf{k}).(b_1\mathbf{i} + b_2\mathbf{j} + b_3\mathbf{k})$
Applying the normal rules for multiplying brackets gives this.
$= (a_1\mathbf{i}).(b_1\mathbf{i}) + (a_1\mathbf{i}).(b_2\mathbf{j}) + (a_1\mathbf{i}).(b_3\mathbf{k}) + (a_2\mathbf{j}).(b_1\mathbf{i}) + (a_2\mathbf{j}).(b_2\mathbf{j})$
$+ (a_2\mathbf{j}).(b_3\mathbf{k}) + (a_3\mathbf{k}).(b_1\mathbf{i}) + (a_3\mathbf{k}).(b_2\mathbf{j}) + (a_3\mathbf{k}).(b_3\mathbf{k})$
Now use the scalar product formulas on the previous page to work out each of these terms. Unit vectors **i**, **j** and **k** are all perpendicular to each other, so multiplying them together always gives a product of zero.
$= (a_1\mathbf{i}).(b_1\mathbf{i}) + 0 + 0 + 0 + (a_2\mathbf{j}).(b_2\mathbf{j}) + 0 + 0 + 0 + (a_3\mathbf{k}).(b_3\mathbf{k})$
$= (a_1\mathbf{i}).(b_1\mathbf{i}) + (a_2\mathbf{j}).(b_2\mathbf{j}) + (a_3\mathbf{k}).(b_3\mathbf{k})$
Using the scalar product definition...
$= |a_1\mathbf{i}||b_1\mathbf{i}|\cos 0° + |a_2\mathbf{j}||b_2\mathbf{j}|\cos 0° + |a_3\mathbf{k}||b_3\mathbf{k}|\cos 0°$
Cos 0° = 1
$= a_1b_1 + a_2b_2 + a_3b_3$

*Use the **Scalar Product** to Find the **Angle** Between Two Vectors*

Finding the angle between two vectors often crops up in vector exam questions.
It's just a matter of using the above result to find the scalar product of the two vectors, then popping it into the scalar product definition, $\cos\theta = \frac{\mathbf{a.b}}{|\mathbf{a}||\mathbf{b}|}$, to find the angle.

EXAMPLE Find the angle between the vectors $-\mathbf{i} - 6\mathbf{j}$ and $4\mathbf{i} + 2\mathbf{j} + 8\mathbf{k}$.

$\cos\theta = \frac{\mathbf{a.b}}{|\mathbf{a}||\mathbf{b}|}$. Let $\mathbf{a} = -\mathbf{i} - 6\mathbf{j}$ and $\mathbf{b} = 4\mathbf{i} + 2\mathbf{j} + 8\mathbf{k}$.

1) Find the scalar product of the vectors.

$\mathbf{a.b} = (-1 \times 4) + (-6 \times 2) + (0 \times 8) = -4 - 12 + 0 = -16$ — This uses the result above.

2) Find the magnitude of each vector (see page 86).

$|\mathbf{a}| = \sqrt{(-1)^2 + (-6)^2 + (0)^2} = \sqrt{37}$ $|\mathbf{b}| = \sqrt{(4)^2 + (2)^2 + (8)^2} = \sqrt{84}$

3) Now plug these values into the equation and find the angle.

$\cos\theta = \frac{\mathbf{a.b}}{|\mathbf{a}||\mathbf{b}|} = \frac{-16}{\sqrt{37}\sqrt{84}} \Rightarrow \theta = 106.7°$

Scalar product — Ooops. I best stop eating chips every day...

So when you scalar multiply two vectors, you basically multiply the **i** components together, multiply the **j** components together, multiply the **k** components together, then add up all the products. You end up with just a number, with no **i**s, **j**s or **k**s attached to it. You'll see this more in the examples on the next page, so don't worry if it seems a bit strange at the mo.

Scalar Product

Right, you've learnt the definitions and the facts. Now it's time to put them to good use.

You Might have to Find the Angle from **Vector Equations** or from **Two Points**

1) If you're given the vector equations for lines that you're finding the angle between, it's important to use the correct bits of the vector equations.
2) You use the **b** bit in **r** = **a** + *t***b** (the 'parallel to' or the 'direction' bit).

EXAMPLE Line l has the equation $\mathbf{r} = \begin{pmatrix} 2 \\ 0 \\ 4 \end{pmatrix} + \lambda\begin{pmatrix} 1 \\ 2 \\ -1 \end{pmatrix}$.

Point A and point B have the coordinates (4, 4, 2) and (1, 0, 3) respectively. Point A lies on l. Find the acute angle between l and line segment AB.

1) First draw a diagram — it'll make everything clearer.

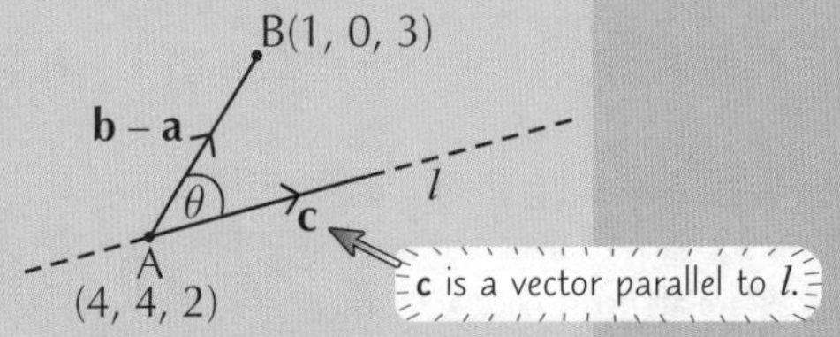

2) Find the vectors that you want to know the angle between.

$\overrightarrow{AB} = \mathbf{b} - \mathbf{a} = \begin{pmatrix} 1 \\ 0 \\ 3 \end{pmatrix} - \begin{pmatrix} 4 \\ 4 \\ 2 \end{pmatrix} = \begin{pmatrix} -3 \\ -4 \\ 1 \end{pmatrix}$ and the 'parallel to' bit of l (which we've called **c**): $\mathbf{c} = \begin{pmatrix} 1 \\ 2 \\ -1 \end{pmatrix}$

3) Find the scalar product of these vectors. $\overrightarrow{AB} \cdot \mathbf{c} = (-3 \times 1) + (-4 \times 2) + (1 \times -1) = -3 - 8 - 1 = -12$

4) Find the magnitude of each vector.

$|\overrightarrow{AB}| = \sqrt{(-3)^2 + (-4)^2 + (1)^2} = \sqrt{26}$ $\quad |\mathbf{c}| = \sqrt{(1)^2 + (2)^2 + (-1)^2} = \sqrt{6}$

5) Now plug these values into the equation and find the angle. $\cos\theta = \dfrac{\overrightarrow{AB}.\mathbf{c}}{|\overrightarrow{AB}||\mathbf{c}|} = \dfrac{-12}{\sqrt{26}\sqrt{6}} \Rightarrow \theta = 164°\ (3\text{ s.f.})$

6) Whoops. The formula gives the non-acute angle — the situation must have been more like this:

B b – a θ x A c l

Remember — the vectors diverge on each side of the angle given by the formula.

Don't panic — just subtract this angle from 180° to get the acute angle, x, between the lines.

180° – 164° = 16°

Prove Lines are **Perpendicular** by Showing that the **Scalar Product = 0**

EXAMPLE Show that the lines $\mathbf{r}_1 = (\mathbf{i} + 6\mathbf{j} + 2\mathbf{k}) + \lambda(\mathbf{i} + 2\mathbf{j} + 2\mathbf{k})$ and $\mathbf{r}_2 = (3\mathbf{i} - \mathbf{j} + \mathbf{k}) + \mu(4\mathbf{i} - 3\mathbf{j} + \mathbf{k})$ are perpendicular.

1) Make sure you've got the right bit of each vector equation — it's the direction you're interested in, so it's **b** in **r** = **a** + *t***b**. $\quad \mathbf{i} + 2\mathbf{j} + 2\mathbf{k}$ and $4\mathbf{i} - 3\mathbf{j} + \mathbf{k}$

2) Find the scalar product of the vectors. $\quad (\mathbf{i} + 2\mathbf{j} + 2\mathbf{k}).(4\mathbf{i} - 3\mathbf{j} + \mathbf{k}) = 4 - 6 + 2 = 0$

3) Draw the correct conclusion. The scalar product is 0, so the vectors are perpendicular.

P...P...P... — prove perpendicularity using products...

They'll word these questions in a zillion different ways. Drawing a diagram can often help you figure out what's what.

C4 Section 7 — Practice Questions

Vectors might cause some mild vexation. It's not the simplest of topics, but practising does help. Try these warm-up questions and see if you can remember what you've just read.

Warm-up Questions

1) Give two vectors that are parallel to each of the following: a) $2\mathbf{a}$ b) $3\mathbf{i} + 4\mathbf{j} - 2\mathbf{k}$ c) $\begin{pmatrix} 1 \\ 2 \\ -1 \end{pmatrix}$

2) Find these vectors in terms of vectors **a**, **b** and **c**.

a) $\overrightarrow{AB}$ b) $\overrightarrow{BA}$ c) $\overrightarrow{CB}$ d) $\overrightarrow{AC}$

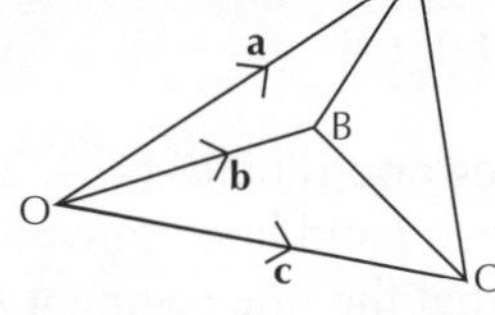

3) Give the position vector of point P, which has the coordinates (2, –4, 5). Give your answer in unit vector form.

4) Find the magnitudes of these vectors:

a) $3\mathbf{i} + 4\mathbf{j} - 2\mathbf{k}$ b) $\begin{pmatrix} 1 \\ 2 \\ -1 \end{pmatrix}$

5) If A(1, 2, 3) and B(3, –1, –2), find: a) $|\overrightarrow{AB}|$ b) $|\overrightarrow{OA}|$ c) $|\overrightarrow{OB}|$

6) Find vector equations for the following lines. Give your answer in **i**, **j**, **k** form and in column vector form.

a) a straight line through (4, 1, 2), parallel to vector $3\mathbf{i} + \mathbf{j} - \mathbf{k}$.

b) a straight line through (2, –1, 1) and (0, 2, 3).

7) Find three points that lie on the line with vector equation $\mathbf{r} = \begin{pmatrix} 3 \\ 2 \\ 4 \end{pmatrix} + t\begin{pmatrix} -1 \\ 3 \\ 0 \end{pmatrix}$.

8) Find **a.b** if: a) $\mathbf{a} = 3\mathbf{i} + 4\mathbf{j}$ and $\mathbf{b} = \mathbf{i} - 2\mathbf{j} + 3\mathbf{k}$ b) $\mathbf{a} = \begin{pmatrix} 4 \\ 2 \\ 1 \end{pmatrix}$ and $\mathbf{b} = \begin{pmatrix} 3 \\ -4 \\ -3 \end{pmatrix}$

9) $\mathbf{r}_1 = \begin{pmatrix} 2 \\ -1 \\ 2 \end{pmatrix} + t\begin{pmatrix} -4 \\ 6 \\ -2 \end{pmatrix}$ and $\mathbf{r}_2 = \begin{pmatrix} 3 \\ 2 \\ 4 \end{pmatrix} + u\begin{pmatrix} -1 \\ 3 \\ 0 \end{pmatrix}$

a) Show that these lines intersect and find the position vector of their intersection point.

b) Find the angle between these lines.

10) Find a vector that is perpendicular to $3\mathbf{i} + 4\mathbf{j} - 2\mathbf{k}$.

You might look at an exam question and think that it's complete gobbledegook. But chances are, when you look at it carefully, you can use what you know to solve it. If you don't know what you need to, you can peek back while doing these questions. You won't be able to in the proper exam, so all the more reason to practise on these.

Exam Questions

1 The quadrilateral ABCD has vertices A(1, 5, 9), B(3, 2, 1), C(–2, 4, 3) and D(5, –1, –7).

a) Find the vector $\overrightarrow{AB}$.
(2 marks)

b) C and D lie on line l_1. Using the parameter μ, find the vector equation of l_1.
(2 marks)

c) Find the coordinates of the intersection point of l_1 and the line that passes through AB.
(5 marks)

d) (i) Find the acute angle between l_1 and AB. Give your answer to 1 decimal place.
(4 marks)

(ii) Find the shortest distance from point A to l_1.
(4 marks)

C4 Section 7 — Practice Questions

And there's more, as Jimmy Cricket (not to be confused with Jiminy Cricket) used to say.

2 The lines l_1 and l_2 are given by the vector equations:

l_1: $\mathbf{r} = (3\mathbf{i} - 3\mathbf{j} - 2\mathbf{k}) + \mu(\mathbf{i} - 4\mathbf{j} + 2\mathbf{k})$

l_2: $\mathbf{r} = (10\mathbf{i} - 21\mathbf{j} + 11\mathbf{k}) + \lambda(-3\mathbf{i} + 12\mathbf{j} - 6\mathbf{k})$

a) Show that l_1 and l_2 are parallel. *(1 mark)*

b) Show that point A(2, 1, –4) lies on l_1. *(2 marks)*

c) Point B lies on l_2 and is such that the line segment AB is perpendicular to l_1 and l_2. Find the position vector of point B. *(6 marks)*

d) Find $|\overrightarrow{AB}|$. *(2 marks)*

3 The lines l_1 and l_2 are given by the equations: $l_1 : \mathbf{r} = \begin{pmatrix} 3 \\ 0 \\ -2 \end{pmatrix} + \lambda \begin{pmatrix} 1 \\ 3 \\ -2 \end{pmatrix}$ $l_2 : \mathbf{r} = \begin{pmatrix} 0 \\ 2 \\ 1 \end{pmatrix} + \mu \begin{pmatrix} 2 \\ -5 \\ -3 \end{pmatrix}$

a) Show that l_1 and l_2 do not intersect. *(4 marks)*

b) Point P has position vector $\begin{pmatrix} 5 \\ 8 \\ -3 \end{pmatrix}$. Point Q is the image of point P after reflection in line l_1.

Point P and Q both lie on the line with equation $\mathbf{r} = \begin{pmatrix} 5 \\ 4 \\ -9 \end{pmatrix} + t \begin{pmatrix} 0 \\ 2 \\ 3 \end{pmatrix}$.

(i) Find the intersection point of line segment PQ and line l_1. *(4 marks)*

(ii) Show that the line segment PQ and line l_1 are perpendicular. *(2 marks)*

(iii) Find the position vector of point Q. *(3 marks)*

4 Point A has the position vector $3\mathbf{i} + 2\mathbf{j} + \mathbf{k}$ and point B has position vector $3\mathbf{i} - 4\mathbf{j} - \mathbf{k}$.

a) Show that AOB is a right-angled triangle. *(3 marks)*

b) Find angle ABO in the triangle using the scalar product definition. *(5 marks)*

c) (i) Point C has the position vector $3\mathbf{i} - \mathbf{j}$. Show that triangle OAC is isosceles. *(3 marks)*

(ii) Calculate the area of triangle OAC. *(4 marks)*

d) (i) Find the vector equation for line l, which passes through points A and B. *(2 marks)*

(ii) The point D lies on line l and has the position vector $a\mathbf{i} + b\mathbf{j} + \mathbf{k}$. Find a and b. *(3 marks)*

General Certificate of Education
Advanced Subsidiary (AS) and Advanced Level

Core Mathematics C4 — Practice Exam One

Time Allowed: 1 hour 30 min

Calculators may be used for this exam (except those with facilities for symbolic algebra, differentiation or integration).

Give any non-exact numerical answers to an appropriate degree of accuracy.

There are 75 marks available for this paper.

1 The graph below shows the curve $y = \sqrt{\sin x}$, $0 \leq x \leq \pi$. The region R is bounded by the curve and the x-axis.

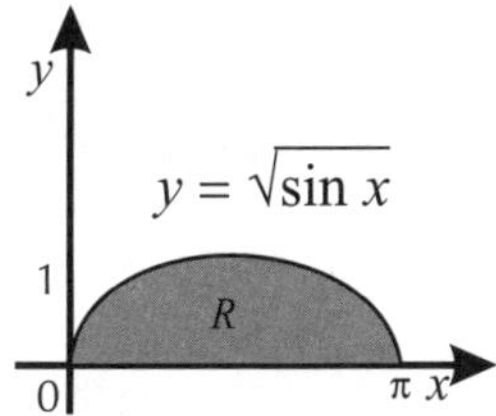

Find the volume of the solid formed when R is rotated 2π radians about the x-axis.

(4 marks)

2 The graph below shows the curve $y = \frac{3\ln x}{x^2}$, $x \geq 0$. The shaded region R is bounded by the curve, the x-axis and the line $x = 3$.

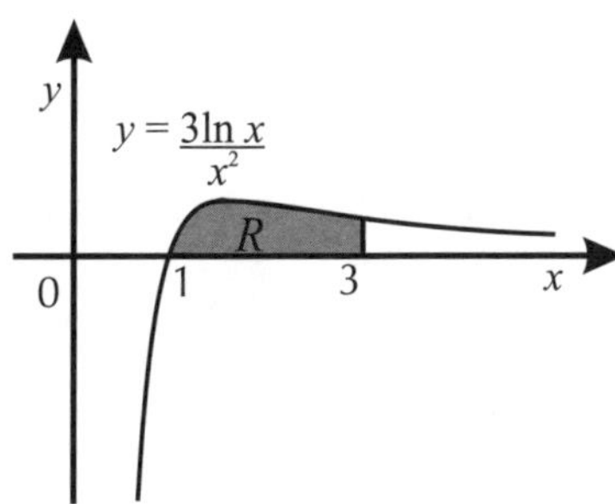

a) Complete the table for the missing y-values. Give your answers to 5 decimal places.

x	1	1.5	2	2.5	3
y	0		0.51986	0.43982	

(2 marks)

b) Find an approximation for the area of R, using the Trapezium Rule and all the values in the table.

(3 marks)

c) Find the value of the integral $\int_1^3 \frac{3\ln x}{x^2}\, dx$ using integration by parts. Give your answer to 5 decimal places.

(5 marks)

3 Find the exact value of

$$\int_0^{\frac{1}{2}} \frac{x}{1-x^2}\,dx$$

using the substitution $x = \sin\theta$. *(6 marks)*

4 The curve C is defined by the parametric equations $x = \frac{\sin\theta}{2} - 3$, $y = 5 - \cos 2\theta$.

a) (i) Find an expression for $\frac{dy}{dx}$ in terms of θ. *(3 marks)*

(ii) Hence find the equation of the tangent to C at the point where $\theta = \frac{\pi}{6}$. *(3 marks)*

b) Find a Cartesian equation for C in the form $y = f(x)$. *(3 marks)*

5 a) Find integers A and B, such that $\frac{5x+4}{(2-x)(1+3x)} \equiv \frac{A}{(2-x)} + \frac{B}{(1+3x)}$. *(5 marks)*

b) Hence find the binomial expansion of $\frac{5x+4}{(2-x)(1+3x)}$, up to and including the term in x^3. *(6 marks)*

c) Find the range of values for which your answer to part b) is valid. *(2 marks)*

6 A curve has the equation $x^3 + x^2y = y^2 - 1$.

a) Use implicit differentiation to find an expression for $\frac{dy}{dx}$. *(4 marks)*

The points P and Q lie on the curve. P has coordinates $(1, a)$ and Q has coordinates $(1, b)$.

b) (i) Find the values of a and b, given that $a > b$. *(2 marks)*

(ii) Find the equation of the normal to the curve at Q. *(3 marks)*

7 Line L_1 has vector equation: $\mathbf{r} = \begin{pmatrix} -1 \\ 0 \\ 3 \end{pmatrix} + \lambda \begin{pmatrix} 2 \\ 2 \\ 1 \end{pmatrix}$.

a) Show that the line passing through points $P(-2, -2, -1)$ and $Q(-5, -4, 1)$ intersects with L_1 and find the point at which they meet. *(5 marks)*

b) Given that $\overrightarrow{OT} = 3\overrightarrow{OP}$, show that the distance between Q and T is $\sqrt{21}$. *(3 marks)*

c) $\overrightarrow{PV}$ is perpendicular to L_1. If the coordinates of V are $(0, f, g)$, show that $2f + g = -9$. *(3 marks)*

d) The line L_2 is parallel to the vector $\begin{pmatrix} 1 \\ 1 \\ 1 \end{pmatrix}$. Find the acute angle between L_1 and L_2. *(3 marks)*

8 a) An ecologist is monitoring the population of newts in a colony. The rate of increase of the population is directly proportional to the square root of the current number of newts in the colony. When there were 36 newts in the colony, the rate of change was calculated to be 0.36.

Formulate a differential equation to model the rate of change, in terms of the variables N (number of newts), t (time in weeks). *(4 marks)*

b) After more research, the ecologist decides that the differential equation

$$\frac{dN}{dt} = \frac{kN}{\sqrt{t}},$$

for a positive constant k, is a better model for the population.
When the ecologist began the survey, the initial population of newts in the colony was 25.

(i) Solve the differential equation, leaving your answer in terms of k and t. *(3 marks)*

(ii) Given that the value of k is 0.05, calculate how long (to the nearest week) it will take for the population to double. *(3 marks)*

General Certificate of Education
Advanced Subsidiary (AS) and Advanced Level

Core Mathematics C4 — Practice Exam Two

Time Allowed: 1 hour 30 min

Calculators may be used for this exam (except those with facilities for symbolic algebra, differentiation or integration).

Give any non-exact numerical answers to an appropriate degree of accuracy.

There are 75 marks available for this paper.

1 a) Express $\dfrac{5x^2 + 10x - 13}{(2-x)^2(1+4x)}$ in partial fractions of the form $\dfrac{A}{(2-x)} + \dfrac{B}{(2-x)^2} + \dfrac{C}{(1+4x)}$, where A, B and C are constants to be found. *(5 marks)*

b) Hence find $\displaystyle\int \frac{5x^2 + 10x - 13}{(2-x)^2(1+4x)}\,dx$. *(4 marks)*

2 a) Find the binomial expansion of $(1-x)^{-\frac{1}{2}}$, up to and including the term in x^3. *(2 marks)*

b) (i) Hence show that $(25-4x)^{-\frac{1}{2}} \approx \frac{1}{5} + \frac{2}{125}x + \frac{6}{3125}x^2 + \frac{4}{15625}x^3$ for small values of x. *(4 marks)*

(ii) State the range of values of x for which the expansion from part (i) is valid. *(1 mark)*

c) Use your expansion from b) with a suitable value of x to show that $\dfrac{1}{\sqrt{20}} \approx \dfrac{447}{2000}$. *(3 marks)*

3 a) Use integration by parts to find $\int 4xe^{-2x}\,dx$. *(4 marks)*

b) Find $\displaystyle\int_1^2 \left(\frac{\ln x}{\sqrt{x}}\right)^2 dx$, using the substitution $u = \ln x$. Give your answer to 3 significant figures. *(5 marks)*

4 The curve C is given by the parametric equations

$$x = \tan\theta, \qquad y = \sin\theta, \qquad 0 < \theta < \frac{\pi}{2}.$$

The region R is bounded by C, the x-axis and the lines $x = \frac{1}{\sqrt{3}}$ and $x = 1$.

a) Show that the volume generated when the region R is rotated 2π radians about the x-axis is given by the integral

$$\pi\int_{\frac{\pi}{6}}^{\frac{\pi}{4}} \sec^2\theta - 1\,\mathrm{d}\theta.$$

(5 marks)

b) Hence find the volume of the solid formed. Give your answer to 3 significant figures. *(3 marks)*

5 The diagram shows a container in the shape of a hollow regular tetrahedron, which is inverted so that the vertex P is at the bottom. The container is being filled with water.

After t minutes, the distance from P to the surface of the water is x cm, and the volume of water in the container is V cm³.

A regular tetrahedron with edge length a and vertical height h has volume $\frac{\sqrt{2}}{12}a^3$, and $h = \sqrt{\frac{2}{3}}a$.

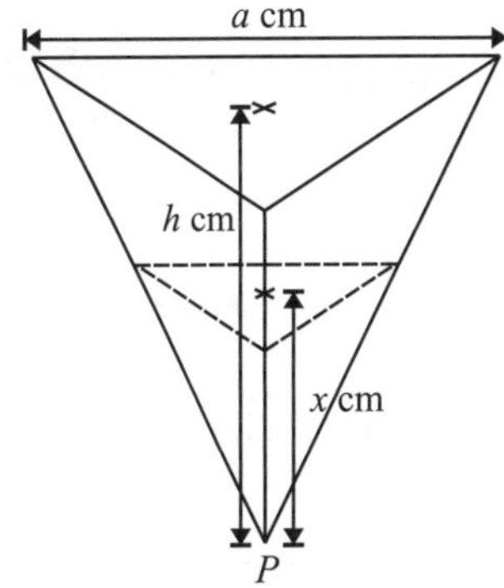

a) Given that the water in the container forms a smaller tetrahedron similar to the container, find expressions in terms of x for:

(i) The edge length of this smaller tetrahedron after t minutes, *(1 mark)*

(ii) The volume of water in the container after t minutes, V. *(1 mark)*

Water is being poured into the container at a constant rate of 240 cm³ min⁻¹.

b) Find $\frac{\mathrm{d}x}{\mathrm{d}t}$ when the depth of the water in the container is 8 cm. *(5 marks)*

The value of $\frac{\mathrm{d}x}{\mathrm{d}t}$ is measured when $x = 12$, and found to be $\frac{32}{9\sqrt{3}}$.
This is less than the value expected if $\frac{\mathrm{d}V}{\mathrm{d}t} = 240$ cm³ min⁻¹.

It is discovered that water has been flowing out of the container through a leak at P at a constant rate of r cm³ min⁻¹ since the container first started being filled.

c) (i) Find $\frac{\mathrm{d}V}{\mathrm{d}t}$ if $\frac{\mathrm{d}x}{\mathrm{d}t} = \frac{32}{9\sqrt{3}}$ when $x = 12$. *(3 marks)*

(ii) Hence find r. *(1 mark)*

6 a) Find the general solution to the differential equation

$$\frac{e^{2x} + x^2}{e^{2x} + x}\frac{dy}{dx} = 2y, \quad x, y \geq 0.$$

(7 marks)

b) (i) Given that $y = 3$ when $x = 0$, find the particular solution to the differential equation above.

(2 marks)

(ii) Hence find the exact value of y for this particular solution when $x = 3$.

(2 marks)

7 A curve is given by the implicit equation $\sin \pi x - \cos\left(\frac{\pi y}{2}\right) = 0.5$, for $0 \leq x \leq 2$, $0 \leq y \leq 2$.

a) Show that $\frac{dy}{dx} = -\frac{2\cos \pi x}{\sin \frac{\pi y}{2}}$.

(2 marks)

b) Hence find:

(i) the coordinates of the stationary point of the curve,

(4 marks)

(ii) the gradient of the tangent to the curve when $x = \frac{1}{6}$.

(3 marks)

8 Vector $\mathbf{x}$ is perpendicular to both vector $\mathbf{y}$ and vector $\mathbf{z}$.

$\mathbf{x} = p\mathbf{i} + \frac{3}{5}\mathbf{j} + q\mathbf{k}$

$\mathbf{y} = 15\mathbf{i} - 20\mathbf{j} + 3\mathbf{k}$

$\mathbf{z} = \frac{3}{2}\mathbf{i} - 2\mathbf{j} + 4\mathbf{k}$

a) (i) Find the values of p and q.

(3 marks)

(ii) Find a unit vector in the direction of $\mathbf{y}$.

(2 marks)

b) Given that the scalar product of $\mathbf{y}$ and $\mathbf{z}$ is 74.5, show that the angle between these vectors is 51° to the nearest degree.

(3 marks)

Binomial Coefficients

Welcome to Statistics 2.
It's a bit of a gentle introduction, to be honest, because this page is basically about counting things.

n Different Objects can be Arranged in *n!* Different Ways...

There are $n!$ ("n factorial") ways of arranging n different objects, where $n! = n \times (n-1) \times (n-2) \times ... \times 3 \times 2 \times 1$.

EXAMPLE a) In how many ways can 4 different ornaments be arranged on a shelf?
b) In how many ways can 8 different objects be arranged?

a) You have 4 choices for the first ornament, 3 choices for the second ornament, 2 choices for the third ornament, and 1 choice for the last ornament. So there are $4! = 4 \times 3 \times 2 \times 1 = 24$ arrangements.

b) There are $8! = 40\,320$ arrangements.

...but Divide by *r!* if *r* of These Objects are the Same

If r of your n objects are identical, then the total number of possible arrangements is $n! \div r!$.

EXAMPLE a) In how many different ways can 5 objects be arranged if 2 of those objects are identical?
b) In how many different ways can 7 objects be arranged if 4 of those objects are identical?

a) Imagine those 2 identical objects were different. Then there would be $5! = 120$ possible arrangements. But because those 2 objects are actually identical, you can always swap them round without making a different arrangement. So there are really only $120 \div 2 = 60$ different ways to arrange the objects.

b) There are $\frac{n!}{r!} = \frac{7!}{4!} = \frac{5040}{24} = 210$ different ways to arrange the objects.

Use Binomial Coefficients if There are Only Two Types of Object

See p55 for more about binomial coefficients.

Binomial Coefficients

$$\binom{n}{r} = {}^nC_r = \frac{n!}{r!(n-r)!}$$

${}^nC_r$ and $\binom{n}{r}$ both mean $\frac{n!}{r!(n-r)!}$

EXAMPLE a) In how many different ways can n objects of two types be arranged if r are of the first type?
b) How many ways are there to select 11 players from a squad of 16?
c) How many ways are there to pick 6 lottery numbers from 49?

a) If the objects were all different, there would be $n!$ ways to arrange them. But r of the objects are of the same type and could be swapped around, so divide by $r!$. Since there are only two types, the other $(n-r)$ could also be swapped around — so divide by $(n-r)!$. This means there are $\frac{n!}{r!(n-r)!}$ arrangements.

b) This is basically a 'number of different arrangements' problem. Imagine the 16 players are lined up — then you could 'pick' or 'not pick' players by giving each of them a sign marked with a tick or a cross. So just find the number of ways to arrange 11 ticks and 5 crosses — this is $\binom{16}{11} = \frac{16!}{11!5!} = 4368$.

c) Again, numbers are either 'picked' or 'unpicked', so there are $\binom{49}{6} = \frac{49!}{6!43!} = 13\,983\,816$ possibilities.

You can use your fingers and toes for counting up to 5! ÷ 3!...

So there you go — your first taste of S2 and hopefully it didn't seem too bad. But statistics (like maths generally) is one of those subjects where everything builds on what you've just learnt. So you need to make really sure you commit all this to memory, and (preferably) understand why it's true too — which is what the three part a)'s are about in the above examples.

The Binomial Probability Function

Being able to count the number of different arrangements of things is a big help when it comes to finding probabilities. This is because the probability of something depends on the number of different ways things could turn out.

Use Binomial Coefficients to Count Arrangements of 'Successes' and 'Failures'

Ages ago, you probably learnt that if p = P(something happens), then $1 - p$ = P(that thing doesn't happen). You'll need that fact now.

EXAMPLE I toss a fair coin 5 times. Find the probability of: a) 0 heads, b) 1 head, c) 2 heads.

First, note that each coin toss is independent of the others. That means you can multiply individual probabilities together.

a) P(0 heads) = P(tails) × P(tails) × P(tails) × P(tails) × P(tails) = $0.5^5 = 0.03125$

P(tails) = P(heads) = 0.5.

b) P(1 head) = P(heads) × P(tails) × P(tails) × P(tails) × P(tails)
+ P(tails) × P(heads) × P(tails) × P(tails) × P(tails)
+ P(tails) × P(tails) × P(heads) × P(tails) × P(tails)
+ P(tails) × P(tails) × P(tails) × P(heads) × P(tails)
+ P(tails) × P(tails) × P(tails) × P(tails) × P(heads)

These are the $\binom{5}{1} = 5$ ways to arrange 1 head and 4 tails.

So $\text{P(1 head)} = 0.5 \times (0.5)^4 \times \binom{5}{1} = 0.03125 \times \frac{5!}{1!4!} = 0.15625$

= P(heads) × $[\text{P(tails)}]^4$ × ways to arrange 1 head and 4 tails.

c) P(2 heads) = $[\text{P(heads)}]^2 \times [\text{P(tails)}]^3$ × ways to arrange 2 heads and 3 tails = $(0.5)^2 \times (0.5)^3 \times \binom{5}{2} = 0.3125$

The Binomial Probability Function gives P(r successes out of n trials)

The previous example really just shows why this thing in a box must be true.

Binomial Probability Function

$$\text{P}(r \text{ successes in } n \text{ trials}) = \binom{n}{r} \times [\text{P(success)}]^r \times [\text{P(failure)}]^{n-r}$$

This is the probability function for a binomial distribution — see next page for more info.

EXAMPLE I roll a fair dice 5 times. Find the probability of rolling: a) 2 sixes, b) 3 sixes, c) 4 numbers less than 3.

Again, note that each roll of a dice is independent of the other rolls.

a) For this part, call "roll a 6" a success, and "roll anything other than a 6" a failure.

Then $\text{P(roll 2 sixes)} = \binom{5}{2} \times \left(\frac{1}{6}\right)^2 \times \left(\frac{5}{6}\right)^3 = \frac{5!}{2!3!} \times \frac{1}{36} \times \frac{125}{216} = 0.161$ (to 3 d.p.).

b) Again, call "roll a 6" a success, and "roll anything other than a 6" a failure.

Then $\text{P(roll 3 sixes)} = \binom{5}{3} \times \left(\frac{1}{6}\right)^3 \times \left(\frac{5}{6}\right)^2 = \frac{5!}{3!2!} \times \frac{1}{216} \times \frac{25}{36} = 0.032$ (to 3 d.p.).

Notice how $\binom{5}{2} = \binom{5}{3}$. In fact, $\binom{n}{r} = \binom{n}{n-r}$.

c) This time, success means "roll a 1 or a 2", while failure is now "roll a 3, 4, 5 or 6".

Then $\text{P(roll 4 numbers less than 3)} = \binom{5}{4} \times \left(\frac{1}{3}\right)^4 \times \left(\frac{2}{3}\right) = \frac{5!}{4!1!} \times \frac{1}{81} \times \frac{2}{3} = 0.041$ (to 3 d.p.).

Let this formula for success go to your head — and then keep it there...

This page is all about finding the probabilities of different numbers of successes in n trials. Now then... if you carry out n trials, there are $n + 1$ possibilities for the number of successes (0, 1, 2, ..., n). This 'family' of possible results along with their probabilities is sounding suspiciously like a probability distribution. Oh rats... I've given away what's on the next page.

The Binomial Distribution

Remember the fun you had in S1 when you learnt all about random variables... well, happy days are here again. This page is about random variables following a binomial distribution (whose probability function you saw on p100).

There are 5 Conditions for a Binomial Distribution

Binomial Distribution: B(n, p)

A random variable X follows a Binomial Distribution as long as these 5 conditions are satisfied:

1) There is a fixed number (n) of trials.
2) Each trial involves either "success" or "failure".
3) All the trials are independent.
4) The probability of "success" (p) is the same in each trial.
5) The variable is the total number of successes in the n trials.

In this case, $P(X = x) = \binom{n}{x} \times p^x \times (1-p)^{n-x}$ for $x = 0, 1, 2,..., n$, and you can write $X \sim B(n, p)$.

Binomial random variables are discrete, since they only take values 0, 1, 2... n.

n and p are the two parameters of the binomial distribution. (Or n is sometimes called the 'index'.)

EXAMPLE: Which of the random variables described below would follow a binomial distribution? For those that do, state the distribution's parameters.

a) **The number of faulty items (T) produced in a factory per day, if the probability of each item being faulty is 0.01 and there are 10 000 items produced every day.**
Binomial — there's a fixed number (10 000) of trials with two possible results ('faulty' or 'not faulty'), a constant probability of 'success', and T is the total number of 'faulty' items.
So (as long as faulty items occur independently) $T \sim B(10\,000, 0.01)$.

b) **The number of red cards (R) drawn from a standard 52-card deck in 10 picks, not replacing the cards each time.**
Not binomial, since the probability of 'success' changes each time (as I'm not replacing the cards).

c) **The number of red cards (R) drawn from a standard 52-card deck in 10 picks, replacing the cards each time.**
Binomial — there's a fixed number (10) of independent trials with two possible results ('red' or 'black/not red'), a constant probability of success (I'm replacing the cards), and R is the number of red cards drawn. $R \sim B(10, 0.5)$.

d) **The number of times (T) I have to toss a coin before I get heads.**
Not binomial, since the number of trials isn't fixed.

e) **The number of left-handed people (L) in a sample of 500 randomly chosen people, if the fraction of left-handed people in the population as a whole is 0.13.**
Binomial — there's a fixed number (500) of independent trials with two possible results ('left-handed' or 'not left-handed'), a constant probability of success (0.13), and L is the number of left-handers. $L \sim B(500, 0.13)$.

EXAMPLE: When I toss a grape in the air and try to catch it in my mouth, my probability of success is always 0.8. The number of grapes I catch in 10 throws is described by the discrete random variable X.

a) How is X distributed? Name the type of distribution, and give the values of any parameters.
b) Find the probability of me catching at least 9 grapes.

a) There's a fixed number (10) of independent trials with two possible results ('catch' and 'not catch'), a constant probability of success (0.8), and X is the total number of catches.
Therefore X follows a binomial distribution, $X \sim B(10, 0.8)$.

b) P(at least 9 catches)

$$= P(9 \text{ catches}) + P(10 \text{ catches})$$
$$= \left\{\binom{10}{9} \times 0.8^9 \times 0.2^1\right\} + \left\{\binom{10}{10} \times 0.8^{10} \times 0.2^0\right\}$$
$$= 0.268435... + 0.107374... = 0.376 \text{ (to 3 d.p.)}.$$

Binomial distributions come with 5 strings attached...

There's a big, boring box at the top of the page with a list of 5 conditions in — and you do need to know it, unfortunately. There's only one way to learn it — keep trying to write down the 5 conditions until you can do it in your sleep.

Using Binomial Tables

Your life is just about to be made a whole lot <u>easier</u>. So smile sweetly and admit that statistics isn't <u>all</u> bad.

*Look up Probabilities in **Binomial Tables***

EXAMPLE I have an unfair coin. When I toss this coin, the probability of getting heads is 0.35. Find the probability that it will land on heads fewer than 3 times when I toss it 12 times in total.

If the random variable X represents the number of heads I get in 12 tosses, then $X \sim B(12, 0.35)$. You need to find $P(X \leq 2)$.

① You <u>could</u> work this out 'manually'...

$$P(0 \text{ heads}) + P(1 \text{ head}) + P(2 \text{ heads}) = \left\{\binom{12}{0} \times 0.35^0 \times 0.65^{12}\right\} + \left\{\binom{12}{1} \times 0.35^1 \times 0.65^{11}\right\} + \left\{\binom{12}{2} \times 0.35^2 \times 0.65^{10}\right\}$$

$$= 0.0057 + 0.0368 + 0.1088 = 0.1513$$

② But it's much quicker to use tables of the <u>binomial cumulative distribution function</u> (c.d.f.).

These show $P(X \leq x)$, for $X \sim B(n, p)$.

- First find the table for the <u>correct values of n and p</u>. Then the table gives you a value for $P(X \leq x)$.
- So here, $n = 12$ and $p = 0.35$, and you need $P(X \leq 2)$. The table tells you this is 0.1513.

See p149 for more binomial tables.

Binomial Cumulative Distribution Function

Values show $P(X \leq x)$, where $X \sim B(n, p)$

	p =	0.05	0.10	0.15	0.20	0.25	0.30	0.35	0.40	0.45	0.50
$n = 12$	x = 0	0.5404	0.2824	0.1422	0.0687	0.0317	0.0138	0.0057	0.0022	0.0008	0.0002
	1	0.8816	0.6590	0.4435	0.2749	0.1584	0.0850	0.0424	0.0196	0.0083	0.0032
	2	0.9804	0.8891	0.7358	0.5583	0.3907	0.2528	0.1513	0.0834	0.0421	0.0193
	3	0.9978	0.9744	0.9078	0.7946	0.6488	0.4925	0.3467	0.2253	0.1345	0.0730
	4	0.9998	0.9957	0.9761	0.9274	0.8424	0.7237	0.5833	0.4382	0.3044	0.1938
	5	1.0000	0.9995	0.9954	0.9806	0.9456	0.8822	0.7873	0.6652	0.5269	0.3872
	6	1.0000	0.9999	0.9993	0.9961	0.9857	0.9614	0.9154	0.8418	0.7393	0.6128
	7	1.0000	1.0000	0.9999	0.9994	0.9972	0.9905	0.9745	0.9427	0.8883	0.8062
	8	1.0000	1.0000	1.0000	0.9999	0.9996	0.9983	0.9944	0.9847	0.9644	0.9270
	9	1.0000	1.0000	1.0000	1.0000	1.0000	0.9998	0.9992	0.9972	0.9921	0.9807
	10	1.0000	1.0000	1.0000	1.0000	1.0000	1.0000	0.9999	0.9997	0.9989	0.9968
	11	1.0000	1.0000	1.0000	1.0000	1.0000	1.0000	1.0000	1.0000	0.9999	0.9998

*Binomial Tables Tell You **More** Than You Might Think*

With a bit of <u>cunning</u>, you can get binomial tables to tell you <u>anything</u> you want to know...

EXAMPLE I have a different unfair coin. When I toss this coin, the probability of getting tails is 0.6. The random variable X represents the number of tails in 12 tosses, so $X \sim B(12, 0.6)$.

If I toss this coin 12 times, use the table above to find the probability that:

a) it will land on tails more than 8 times,
b) it will land on heads at least 6 times,
c) it will land on heads exactly 9 times,
d) it will land on heads more than 3 but fewer than 6 times.

a) The above table only goes up to $p = 0.5$.
So <u>switch things round</u>... if P(tails) = 0.6, then P(heads) = 1 – 0.6 = <u>0.4</u> (and $p = 0.4$ is in the table).
So define a <u>new</u> random variable, Y, representing the number of <u>heads</u> in 12 throws — then $Y \sim B(12, 0.4)$.
This means $P(X > 8) = P(Y \leq 3) = 0.2253$

b) $P(Y \geq 6) = 1 - P(Y < 6) = 1 - P(Y \leq 5) = 1 - 0.6652 = 0.3348$

1) P(event happens) = 1 – P(event doesn't happen),
2) $P(Y < 6) = P(Y \leq 5)$, as Y takes whole number values.

c) $P(Y = 9) = P(Y \leq 9) - P(Y \leq 8) = 0.9972 - 0.9847 = 0.0125$

Use P(A or B) = P(A) + P(B) with the mutually exclusive events "$Y \leq 8$" and "$Y = 9$" to get $P(Y \leq 9) = P(Y \leq 8) + P(Y = 9)$.
Or you can think of it as "subtracting $P(Y \leq 8)$ from $P(Y \leq 9)$ leaves just $P(Y = 9)$".

d) $P(3 < Y < 6) = P(Y \leq 5) - P(Y \leq 3) = 0.6652 - 0.2253 = 0.4399$

Statistical tables are the original labour-saving device...

...as long as you know what you're doing. Careful, though — it's easy to trip yourself up. Basically, as long as you can find the right value of n and p (or $1 - p$, if necessary) in a table, you can use those tables to work out <u>anything</u> you might need. Work through those last examples *really slowly* and make sure you can follow them — they're pretty vital.

Mean and Variance of B(n, p)

You know from S1 what the mean (or expected value) and variance of a random variable are.
And you also know what the binomial distribution is. Put those things together, and you get this page.

For a Binomial Distribution: Mean = np

This formula will be in your formula booklet, but it's worth committing to memory anyway.

Mean of a Binomial Distribution

If $X \sim B(n, p)$, then:

Mean (or Expected Value) = $\mu = E(X) = np$

Greek letters (e.g. μ) often show something based purely on theory rather than experimental results.

Remember... the expected value is the value you'd expect the random variable to take on average if you took loads and loads of readings. It's a "theoretical mean" — the mean of experimental results is unlikely to match it exactly.

EXAMPLE If $X \sim B(20, 0.2)$, what is $E(X)$?

Just use the formula: $E(X) = np = 20 \times 0.2 = 4$

EXAMPLE What's the expected number of sixes when I roll a fair dice 30 times? Interpret your answer.

If the random variable X represents the number of sixes in 30 rolls, then $X \sim B(30, \frac{1}{6})$.

So the expected value of X is $E(X) = 30 \times \frac{1}{6} = 5$

If I were to repeatedly throw the dice 30 times, and find the average number of sixes in each set of 30 throws, then I would expect it to end up pretty close to 5.
And the more sets of 30 throws I did, the closer to 5 I'd expect the average to be.

Notice that the probability of getting exactly 5 sixes on my next set of 30 throws = $\binom{30}{5} \times \left(\frac{1}{6}\right)^5 \times \left(\frac{5}{6}\right)^{25} = 0.192$
So I'm much more likely not to get exactly 5 sixes ($= 1 - 0.192 = 0.808$).
This is why it only makes sense to talk about the mean as a "long-term average", and not as "what I expect to happen next".

For a Binomial Distribution: Variance = npq

Variance of a Binomial Distribution

If $X \sim B(n, p)$, then:

Variance = $Var(X) = \sigma^2 = np(1-p) = npq$

Standard Deviation = $\sigma = \sqrt{np(1-p)} = \sqrt{npq}$

For a binomial distribution, P(success) is usually called p, and P(failure) is sometimes called q ($= 1 - p$).

EXAMPLE If $X \sim B(20, 0.2)$, what is $Var(X)$?

Just use the formula: $Var(X) = np(1-p) = 20 \times 0.2 \times 0.8 = 3.2$

EXAMPLE If $X \sim B(25, 0.2)$, find: a) $P(X \leq \mu)$, b) $P(X \leq \mu - \sigma)$, c) $P(X \leq \mu - 2\sigma)$

$E(X) = \mu = 25 \times 0.2 = 5$, and $Var(X) = \sigma^2 = 25 \times 0.2 \times (1 - 0.2) = 4$, which gives $\sigma = 2$.

So, using tables (for $n = 25$ and $p = 0.2$): a) $P(X \leq \mu) = P(X \leq 5) = 0.6167$

b) $P(X \leq \mu - \sigma) = P(X \leq 3) = 0.2340$

c) $P(X \leq \mu - 2\sigma) = P(X \leq 1) = 0.0274$

See page 149.

For B(n, p) — the variance is always less than the mean...

Nothing too fancy there really. A couple of easy-to-remember formulas, and some stuff about how to interpret these figures which you've seen before anyway. So learn the formulas, put the kettle on, and have a cup of tea while the going's good.

Binomial Distribution Problems

That's everything you need to know about binomial distributions (for now).
So it's time to put it all together and have a look at the kind of thing you might get asked in the exam.

EXAMPLE 1: Selling Double Glazing

A double-glazing salesman is handing out leaflets in a busy shopping centre. He knows that the probability of each passing person taking a leaflet is always 0.3. During a randomly chosen one-minute interval, 30 people passed him.

a) Suggest a suitable model to describe the number of people (X) who take a leaflet.
b) What is the probability that more than 10 people take a leaflet?
c) How many people would the salesman expect to take a leaflet?
d) Find the variance and standard deviation of X.

a) During this one-minute interval, there's a fixed number (30) of independent trials with two possible results ("take a leaflet" and "do not take a leaflet"), a constant probability of success (0.3), and X is the total number of people taking leaflets. So $X \sim B(30, 0.3)$.

b) $P(X > 10) = 1 - P(X \leq 10) = 1 - 0.7304 = 0.2696$

Use binomial tables for this — see p149.

c) The number of people the salesman could expect to take a leaflet is $E(X) = np = 30 \times 0.3 = 9$

d) Variance $= np(1 - p) = 30 \times 0.3 \times (1 - 0.3) = 6.3$ Standard deviation $= \sqrt{6.3} = 2.51$ (to 2 d.p.)

EXAMPLE 2: Multiple-Choice Guessing

A student has to take a 50-question multiple-choice exam, where each question has five possible answers of which only one is correct. He believes he can pass the exam by guessing answers at random.

a) How many questions could the student be expected to guess correctly?
b) If the pass mark is 15, what is the probability that the student will pass the exam?
c) The examiner decides to set the pass mark so that it is at least 3 standard deviations above the expected number of correct guesses. What should the minimum pass mark be?

Let X be the number of correct guesses over the 50 questions. Then $X \sim B(50, 0.2)$.

Define your random variable first, and say how it will be distributed.

a) $E(X) = np = 50 \times 0.2 = 10$

b) $P(X \geq 15) = 1 - P(X < 15) = 1 - P(X \leq 14) = 1 - 0.9393 = 0.0607$

c) $\text{Var}(X) = np(1 - p) = 50 \times 0.2 \times 0.8 = 8$ — so the standard deviation $= \sqrt{8} = 2.828$ (to 3 d.p.).
So the pass mark needs to be at least $10 + (3 \times 2.828) \approx 18.5$ — i.e. the minimum pass mark should be 19.

EXAMPLE 3: An unfair coin (again)

I am spinning a coin that I know is three times as likely to land on heads as it is on tails.

a) What is the probability that it lands on tails for the first time on the third spin?
b) What is the probability that in 10 spins, it lands on heads at least 7 times?

You know that P(heads) = 3 × P(tails), and that P(heads) + P(tails) = 1.
This means that P(heads) = 0.75 and P(tails) = 0.25.

Careful... this doesn't need you to use one of the binomial formulas.

a) P(lands on tails for the first time on the third spin) $= 0.75 \times 0.75 \times 0.25 = 0.141$ (to 3 d.p.).

b) If X represents the number of heads in 10 spins, then $X \sim B(10, 0.75)$.
This means the number of tails in 10 spins can be described by the random variable Y, where $Y \sim B(10, 0.25)$.
$P(X \geq 7) = P(Y \leq 3) = 0.7759$

$p = 0.75$ isn't in your tables, so define a new binomial random variable Y with probability of success $p = 0.25$.

Proof that you shouldn't send a monkey to take your multi-choice exams...

You can see now how useful a working knowledge of statistics is. Ever since you first started using CGP books, I've been banging on about how hard it is to pass an exam without revising. Well, now you can prove I was correct using a bit of knowledge and binomial tables. Yup... statistics can help out with some of those tricky situations you face in life.

S2 Section 1 — Practice Questions

Hopefully, everything you've just read will already be stuck in your brain. But if you need a bit of help to wedge it in place, then try these questions. Actually... I reckon you'd best try them anyway — a little suffering is good for the soul.

Warm-up Questions

1) In how many different orders can the following be arranged?
   a) 15 identical red balls, plus 6 other balls, all of different colours.
   b) 4 red counters, 4 blue counters, 4 yellow counters and 4 green counters.

2) What is the probability of the following?
   a) Getting exactly 5 heads when you spin a fair coin 10 times.
   b) Getting exactly 9 heads when you spin a fair coin 10 times.

3) Which of the following would follow a binomial distribution? Explain your answers.
   a) The number of prime numbers you throw in 30 throws of a standard dice.
   b) The number of people in a particular class at a school who get 'heads' when they flip a coin.
   c) The number of aces in a 7-card hand dealt from a standard deck of 52 cards.
   d) The number of shots I have to take before I score from the free-throw line in basketball.

4) What is the probability of the following?
   a) Getting at least 5 heads when you spin a fair coin 10 times.
   b) Getting at least 9 heads when you spin a fair coin 10 times.

5) If $X \sim B(14, 0.27)$, find:
   a) $P(X = 4)$ b) $P(X < 2)$ c) $P(5 < X \leq 8)$

6) If $X \sim B(25, 0.15)$ and $Y \sim B(15, 0.65)$ find:
   a) $P(X \leq 3)$ b) $P(X \leq 7)$
   c) $P(X \leq 15)$ d) $P(Y \leq 3)$
   e) $P(Y \leq 7)$ f) $P(Y \leq 15)$

7) Find the required probability for each of the following binomial distributions.
   a) $P(X \leq 15)$ if $X \sim B(20, 0.4)$ b) $P(X < 4)$ if $X \sim B(40, 0.15)$
   c) $P(X > 7)$ if $X \sim B(25, 0.45)$ d) $P(X \geq 40)$ if $X \sim B(50, 0.8)$
   e) $P(X = 20)$ if $X \sim B(30, 0.7)$ f) $P(X = 7)$ if $X \sim B(10, 0.75)$

8) Find the mean and variance of the following random variables.
   a) $X \sim B(20, 0.4)$ b) $X \sim B(40, 0.15)$
   c) $X \sim B(25, 0.45)$ d) $X \sim B(50, 0.8)$
   e) $X \sim B(30, 0.7)$ f) $X \sim B(45, 0.012)$

S2 Section 1 — Practice Questions

Right then... you're nearly at the end of the section, and with any luck your tail is up, the wind is in your sails and the going is good. But the real test of whether you're ready for the exam is some exam questions. And as luck would have it, there are some right here. So give them a go and test your mettle, see if you can walk the walk... and so on.

Exam Questions

1 a) The random variable X follows the binomial distribution B(12, 0.6). Find:

(i) $P(X < 8)$,

(2 marks)

(ii) $P(X = 5)$,

(2 marks)

(iii) $P(3 < X \leq 7)$.

(3 marks)

b) If $Y \sim B(11, 0.8)$, find:

(i) $P(Y = 4)$,

(2 marks)

(ii) $E(Y)$,

(1 mark)

(iii) $Var(Y)$.

(1 mark)

2 The probability of an apple containing a maggot is 0.15.

a) Find the probability that in a random sample of 40 apples there are:

(i) fewer than 6 apples containing maggots,

(2 marks)

(ii) more than 2 apples containing maggots,

(2 marks)

(iii) exactly 12 apples containing maggots.

(2 marks)

b) These apples are sold in crates of 40. Ed buys 3 crates.
Find the probability that more than 1 crate contains more than 2 apples with maggots.

(3 marks)

3 Simon tries to solve the crossword puzzle in his newspaper every day for two weeks.
He either succeeds in solving the puzzle, or he fails to solve it.

a) Simon believes that this situation can be modelled by a random variable following a binomial distribution.

(i) State two conditions needed for a binomial distribution to arise here.

(2 marks)

(ii) State which quantity would follow a binomial distribution (assuming the above conditions are satisfied).

(1 mark)

b) Simon believes a random variable X follows the distribution $B(18, p)$.
If $P(X = 4) = P(X = 5)$, find p.

(5 marks)

The Poisson Distribution

It's Section 2, and it's the Poisson distribution. If you speak French, you'll know that Poisson means fish. I think.

A Poisson Distribution has Only One Parameter

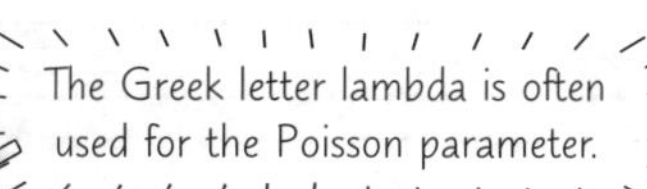

The Greek letter lambda is often used for the Poisson parameter.

A Poisson Distribution has just one parameter: λ.
If the random variable X follows a Poisson distribution, then you can write $X \sim \text{Po}(\lambda)$.

Poisson Probability Distribution Po(λ)

If $X \sim \text{Po}(\lambda)$, then X can take values 0, 1, 2, 3... with probability:

$$P(X = x) = \frac{e^{-\lambda}\lambda^x}{x!}$$

Random variables following a Poisson distribution are discrete — there are 'gaps' between the possible values.

EXAMPLE If $X \sim \text{Po}(2.8)$, find:

a) $P(X = 0)$, b) $P(X = 1)$, c) $P(X = 2)$, d) $P(X < 3)$, e) $P(X \geq 3)$

Use the formula:

a) $P(X = 0) = \frac{e^{-2.8} \times 2.8^0}{0!} = e^{-2.8} = 0.061$ (to 3 d.p.). — Remember... 0! = 1.

b) $P(X = 1) = \frac{e^{-2.8} \times 2.8^1}{1!} = e^{-2.8} \times 2.8 = 0.170$ (to 3 d.p.).

c) $P(X = 2) = \frac{e^{-2.8} \times 2.8^2}{2!} = \frac{e^{-2.8} \times 2.8^2}{2 \times 1} = 0.238$ (to 3 d.p.).

If X ~ Po(λ), then it can only take whole number values, so P(X < 3) is the same as P(X ≤ 2).

d) $P(X < 3) = P(X \leq 2) = P(X = 0) + P(X = 1) + P(X = 2) = 0.061 + 0.170 + 0.238 = 0.469$.

e) $P(X \geq 3) = 1 - P(X < 3) = 1 - 0.469 = 0.531$. — All the normal probability rules apply.

For a Poisson Distribution: Mean = Variance

For a Poisson distribution, the mean and the variance are the same — and they both equal λ, the Poisson parameter. Remember that and you've probably learnt the most important Poisson fact. Ever.

Poisson Mean and Variance

If $X \sim \text{Po}(\lambda)$: **Mean ($\mu$) of X = E(X) = λ**

Variance (σ^2) of X = Var(X) = λ

So the standard deviation is: $\sigma = \sqrt{\lambda}$

EXAMPLE If $X \sim \text{Po}(7)$, find: a) E(X), b) Var(X).

It's Poisson, so $E(X) = \text{Var}(X) = \lambda = 7$.

This is the easiest question ever. So enjoy it while it lasts.

EXAMPLE If $X \sim \text{Po}(1)$, find: a) $P(X \leq \mu)$, b) $P(X \leq \mu - \sigma)$

$E(X) = \mu = 1$, and $\text{Var}(X) = \sigma^2 = 1$, and so $\sigma = 1$.

a) $P(X \leq \mu) = P(X \leq 1) = P(0) + P(1) = \frac{e^{-1} \times 1^0}{0!} + \frac{e^{-1} \times 1^1}{1!} = 0.736$ (to 3 d.p.).

b) $P(X \leq \mu - \sigma) = P(X \leq 0) = P(0) = \frac{e^{-1} \times 1^0}{0!} = 0.368$ (to 3 d.p.).

The Poisson Distribution is named after its inventor...

...the great French mathematician Monsieur Siméon-Denis Distribution. Boom boom. I always tell that joke at parties (which probably explains why I don't get to go to many parties these days). Most important thing here is that bit about the mean and variance being equal... so if you ever come across a distribution where $\mu = \sigma^2$, think 'Poisson' immediately.

The Poisson Parameter

I know what you're thinking... if only everything could be as accommodating as the Poisson distribution, with only one parameter and most things of interest being equal to it, then life would be so much easier. (Sigh.)

The Poisson Parameter is a **Rate**

The number of events/things that occur/are present in a particular period often follows a Poisson distribution. It could be a period of: time (e.g. minute/hour etc.), or space (e.g. litre/kilometre etc.).

Poisson Probability Distribution: Po(λ)

If X represents the number of events that occur in a particular space or time, then X will follow a Poisson distribution as long as:

1) The events occur randomly, and are all independent of each other.
2) The events happen singly (i.e. "one at a time").
3) The events happen (on average) at a constant rate (either in space or time).

So the expected number of events that occur is proportional to the length of the period.

The Poisson parameter λ is then the average rate at which these events occur (i.e. the average number of events in a given interval of space or time).

EXAMPLE The random variable X represents the number of a certain type of cell in a particular volume of a blood sample. Assuming that the blood sample has been stirred, and that a given volume of blood always contains the same number of cells, show that X follows a Poisson distribution.

The sample has been stirred, so that should mean the cells of interest aren't all clustered together. This should ensure the 'events' (i.e. the cells you're interested in) occur randomly and singly. And since the total number of cells in a given volume is constant, the cells of interest should occur (on average) at a constant rate. Since X is the total number of 'events' in a given volume, X must follow a Poisson distribution.

The Poisson Parameter is **Additive**

Additive Property of the Poisson Distribution

- If X represents the number of events in 1 unit of time/space (e.g. 1 minute / hour / m^2 / m^3), and $X \sim \text{Po}(\lambda)$, then the number of events in x units of time/space follows the distribution $\text{Po}(x\lambda)$.
- If $X \sim \text{Po}(\lambda)$ and $Y \sim \text{Po}(\kappa)$, then $X + Y \sim \text{Po}(\lambda + \kappa)$.

EXAMPLE Sunflowers grow singly and randomly in a field with an average of 10 sunflowers per square metre. What is the probability that a randomly chosen area of 0.25 m^2 contains no sunflowers?

The number of sunflowers in 1 m^2 follows the distribution Po(10).

So the number of sunflowers in 0.25 m^2 must follow the distribution Po(2.5).

This means $\text{P(no sunflowers)} = \frac{e^{-2.5} \times 2.5^0}{0!} = e^{-2.5} = 0.082$ (to 3 d.p.).

EXAMPLE The number of radioactive atoms that decay per second follows the Poisson distribution Po(5). If the probability of no atoms decaying in t seconds is 0.5, verify that $t = 0.1386$.

If the random variable X represents the number of radioactive atoms that decay in t seconds, then $X \sim \text{Po}(5t)$.

This means $P(X = 0) = \frac{e^{-5t}(5t)^0}{0!} = e^{-5t} = 0.5$.

This equation is satisfied by $t = 0.1386$, since $e^{-5 \times 0.1386} = e^{-0.693} = 0.500$ (to 3 d.p.).

If events happen randomly, singly and at a constant rate, it's Poisson...

Lots of things follow a Poisson distribution — e.g. the number of radioactive atoms that decay in a given time, the number of sixes in 5 minutes of dice-throwing, the number of raindrops per minute that hit a bit of your tongue as you stare open-mouthed at the sky on a rainy day. Think of a few others... make sure events happen randomly, singly and at a constant rate.

Using Poisson Tables

You've seen statistical tables before — for example, on p102 you saw how you can use tables to quickly work out probabilities for the binomial distribution. If you were paying attention then, this page will seem eerily familiar.

Look up Probabilities in Poisson Tables

Going back to the sunflowers example near the bottom of the previous page...

EXAMPLE Sunflowers grow singly and randomly in a field with an average of 10 sunflowers per square metre. Find the probability that a randomly chosen square metre contains no more than 8 sunflowers.

If the random variable X represents the number of sunflowers in 1 m², then $X \sim \text{Po}(10)$.
You need to find $P(X \leq 8)$.

① You could do this 'manually': $P(X = 0) + P(X = 1) + \ldots + P(X = 8) = \frac{e^{-10} \times 10^0}{0!} + \frac{e^{-10} \times 10^1}{1!} + \ldots + \frac{e^{-10} \times 10^8}{8!}$

② But it's much quicker and easier to use tables of the Poisson cumulative distribution function (c.d.f.).

These show $P(X \leq x)$ if $X \sim \text{Po}(\lambda)$.

Here's a bit of a Poisson table:

- Find your value of λ (here, 10), and the value of x (here, 8).
- You can quickly see that $P(X \leq 8) = 0.3328$.

Poisson Cumulative Distribution Function
Values show $P(X \leqslant x)$, where $X \sim \text{Po}(\lambda)$

λ =	5.5	6.0	6.5	7.0	7.5	8.0	8.5	9.0	9.5	10.0
x = 0	0.0041	0.0025	0.0015	0.0009	0.0006	0.0003	0.0002	0.0001	0.0001	0.0000
1	0.0266	0.0174	0.0113	0.0073	0.0047	0.0030	0.0019	0.0012	0.0008	0.0005
2	0.0884	0.0620	0.0430	0.0296	0.0203	0.0138	0.0093	0.0062	0.0042	0.0028
3	0.2017	0.1512	0.1118	0.0818	0.0591	0.0424	0.0301	0.0212	0.0149	0.0103
4	0.3575	0.2851	0.2237	0.1730	0.1321	0.0996	0.0744	0.0550	0.0403	0.0293
5	0.5289	0.4457	0.3690	0.3007	0.2414	0.1912	0.1496	0.1157	0.0885	0.0671
6	0.6860	0.6063	0.5265	0.4497	0.3782	0.3134	0.2562	0.2068	0.1649	0.1301
7	0.8095	0.7440	0.6728	0.5987	0.5246	0.4530	0.3856	0.3239	0.2687	0.2202
8	0.8944	0.8472	0.7916	0.7291	0.6620	0.5925	0.5231	0.4557	0.3918	0.3328
9	0.9462	0.9161	0.8774	0.8305	0.7764	0.7166	0.6530	0.5874	0.5218	0.4579
10	0.9747	0.9574	0.9332	0.9015	0.8622	0.8159	0.7634	0.7060	0.6453	0.5830
11	0.9890	0.9799	0.9661	0.9467	0.9208	0.8881	0.8487	0.8030	0.7520	0.6968

You Need to Use Poisson Tables with a Bit of Cunning

See p154 for the full set of Poisson tables.

This is exactly the same as you've already seen for binomial tables.

EXAMPLE When cloth is manufactured, faults occur randomly in the cloth at a rate of 8 faults per square metre. Use the above Poisson table to find:

a) The probability of 7 or fewer faults in a square metre of cloth.
b) The probability of more than 4 faults in a square metre of cloth.
c) The probability of exactly 10 faults in a square metre of cloth.
d) The probability of at least 9 faults in a square metre of cloth.
e) The probability of exactly 4 faults in 0.75 m² of cloth.

The faults occur randomly, singly and at a constant rate (= 8 faults per square metre).
So if X represents the number of faults in a square metre, then $X \sim \text{Po}(8)$.

So use the column showing λ = 8.

a) $P(X \leq 7) = 0.4530$

b) $P(X > 4) = 1 - P(X \leq 4) = 1 - 0.0996 = 0.9004$

c) $P(X = 10) = P(X \leq 10) - P(X \leq 9) = 0.8159 - 0.7166 = 0.0993$

d) $P(X \geq 9) = 1 - P(X < 9) = 1 - P(X \leq 8) = 1 - 0.5925 = 0.4075$

e) Let the random variable Y represent the number of faults in 0.75 m² of cloth.
If the number of faults in 1 m² of cloth ~ Po(8), then $Y \sim \text{Po}(0.75 \times 8) = \text{Po}(6)$.

Now use the column showing λ = 6.

So P(exactly 4 faults in 0.75 m² of cloth) $= P(Y \leq 4) - P(Y \leq 3) = 0.2851 - 0.1512 = 0.1339$

Poisson tables — the best thing since binomial tables...

Learn the ways of the Poisson tables, and you shall prove your wisdom. In the exam, you'll be given a big booklet of fun containing all the statistical tables you could ever want. You need to think carefully about how to use them though — e.g. you might have to subtract one figure from another, or subtract one of the figures from 1. Or something else similar.

Po(λ) as an Approximation to B(n, p)

This page is a bit like a buy-one-get-one-free offer — it's in the section about Poisson distributions, but it's actually about binomial distributions. This really is your lucky day...

For Big n and Small p — Po(np) Approximates a Binomial Distribution

Sometimes, a Poisson distribution can be used as an approximation to a binomial distribution.

Po(np) as an Approximation to B(n, p)

If $X \sim B(n, p)$, and: 1) **n is large**, 2) **p is small**,

then X can be approximated by **Po(np)**.

The mean of the binomial distribution is np, so use that as the mean of your Poisson approximation.

EXAMPLE In a school of 1825 students, what is the probability that at least 6 of them were born on June 21st? Use a suitable approximation to find your answer.
(You may assume that all birthdays are independent, and are distributed evenly throughout the year.)

If X represents the number of children in the school born on June 21st, then $X \sim B(1825, \frac{1}{365})$.
You need to find $P(X \geq 6)$.

So far so good. However, your binomial tables don't go past n = 50. And working this out 'by hand' isn't easy. But look at those values of n and p...

Since n is large and p is small, $B(1825, \frac{1}{365})$ can be approximated by $Po(1825 \times \frac{1}{365}) = Po(5)$.

So $P(X \geq 6) = 1 - P(X < 6) = 1 - P(X \leq 5) = 1 - 0.6160 = 0.3840$

From Poisson tables — see p154.

If you work it out using $B(1825, \frac{1}{365})$, you also get 0.3840 — so this is a very good approximation.

The Smaller the Value of p, the Better

1) To use the Poisson approximation to $B(n, p)$, you ideally want n "as large as possible" and p "as small as possible". The bigger n is and the smaller p is, the better the approximation will be.
2) It's important p is small because then the mean and the variance of $B(n, p)$ are approximately equal — something you need if $Po(np)$ is going to be a good approximation.

   If $X \sim B(n, p)$, then $E(X) = np$.
   And if p is small, $(1 - p) \approx 1$ — this means $Var(X) = np(1 - p) \approx np \times 1 = np$.
3) In your exam, you'll usually be told when to use an approximation.

EXAMPLES:

① Factory A forgets to add icing to its chocolate cakes with a uniform probability of 0.02. Use a suitable approximation to find the probability that fewer than 6 of the next 100 cakes made will not be iced.

If X represents the number of "un-iced" cakes, then $X \sim B(100, 0.02)$.
Since n is quite large and p is quite small, $X \sim Po(100 \times 0.02) = Po(2)$.
So $P(X < 6) = P(X \leq 5) = 0.9834$

If you work it out using B(100, 0.02), you get 0.9845.

Sometimes you can still use the approximation if p is very close to 1.

② Factory B adds icing to its chocolate cakes with a uniform probability of 0.99. Use a suitable approximation to find the probability that more than 95 of the next 100 cakes made will be iced.

- If Y represents the number of iced cakes produced by Factory B, then $Y \sim B(100, 0.99)$.
  Here, n is quite large, but p is not small.
- However, if you let W represent the number of "un-iced" cakes made, then $W \sim B(100, 0.01)$.
  Now you can use a Poisson approximation: $W \sim Po(100 \times 0.01) = Po(1)$.
  So $P(Y > 95) = P(W < 5) = P(W \leq 4) = 0.9963$

  Using B(100, 0.01), you get 0.9966.

Remember — you need a small p...

This approximation only works if p is very small (although in the right circumstances, you can also get it to work if p is very close to 1). On a practical note... your Poisson tables only go up to 10 — so if $np > 10$, don't try and use the approximation.

Worked Problems

Make sure you understand what's going on in these examples.

EXAMPLE 1: A breaking-down car

A car randomly breaks down twice a week on average.
The random variable X represents the number of times the car will break down next week.

a) What probability distribution could be used to model X? Explain your answer.
b) Find the probability that the car breaks down fewer than 3 times next week.
c) Find the probability that the car breaks down more than 4 times next week.
d) Find the probability that the car breaks down exactly 6 times in the next fortnight.

a) Since the breakdowns occur randomly, singly and (on average) at a constant rate, and X is the total number of breakdowns in one week, X follows a Poisson distribution: $X \sim \text{Po}(2)$

b) Using tables for $\lambda = 2$: $P(X < 3) = P(X \leq 2) = 0.6767$

c) Again, using tables for $\lambda = 2$: $P(X > 4) = 1 - P(X \leq 4) = 1 - 0.9473 = 0.0527$

d) If the random variable Y represents the number of breakdowns in the next fortnight, then $Y \sim \text{Po}(2 \times 2) = \text{Po}(4)$.
So using tables for $\lambda = 4$: $P(Y = 6) = P(Y \leq 6) - P(Y \leq 5) = 0.8893 - 0.7851 = 0.1042$

EXAMPLE 2: Bad apples

A restaurant owner needs to buy several crates of apples, so she visits a farm that sells apples by the crate. Each crate contains 150 apples. On average 1.5% of the apples are bad, and these bad apples are randomly distributed between the crates. The restaurant owner opens a random crate and inspects each apple.

- If there are no bad apples in this crate, then the restaurant owner will buy the apples she needs from this farm.
- If more than 2 apples in this first crate are bad, then the restaurant owner will not buy from this farm.
- If only 1 or 2 apples in the first crate are bad, then a second crate is opened.
  The restaurant owner will then only buy from this farm if the second crate contains at most 1 bad apple.

a) Find the probability that none of the apples in the first crate are bad.
b) Find the probability that more than 2 apples in the first crate are bad.
c) Find the probability that a second crate is opened.
d) What is the probability of the restaurant owner buying the apples she needs from this farm?

a) The average number of bad apples in each crate is $150 \times 0.015 = 2.25$.
So if X represents the number of bad apples in each crate, then $X \sim \text{Po}(2.25)$.

$$P(X = 0) = \frac{e^{-2.25} \times 2.25^0}{0!} = e^{-2.25} = 0.1054 \text{ (to 4 d.p.)}.$$

Definitely Poisson.

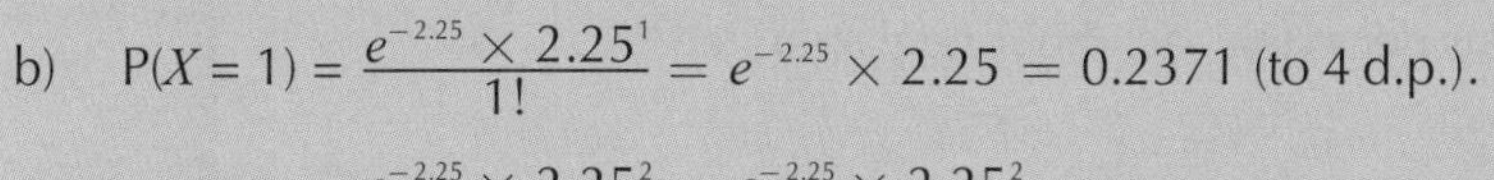

b) $$P(X = 1) = \frac{e^{-2.25} \times 2.25^1}{1!} = e^{-2.25} \times 2.25 = 0.2371 \text{ (to 4 d.p.)}.$$

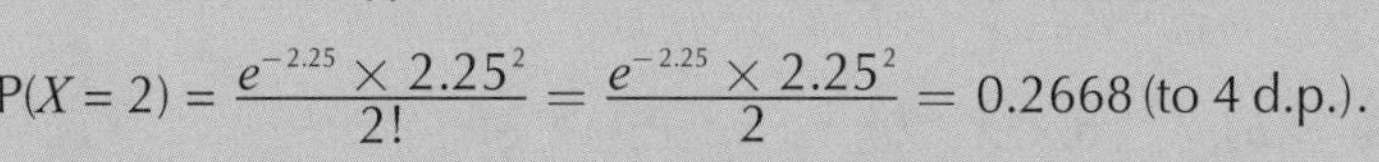

$$P(X = 2) = \frac{e^{-2.25} \times 2.25^2}{2!} = \frac{e^{-2.25} \times 2.25^2}{2} = 0.2668 \text{ (to 4 d.p.)}.$$

So $P(X > 2) = 1 - P(X = 0) - P(X = 1) - P(X = 2) = 1 - 0.1054 - 0.2371 - 0.2668 = 0.3907$

c) A second crate is opened if $X = 1$ or $X = 2$. $P(X = 1 \text{ OR } X = 2) = 0.2371 + 0.2668 = 0.5039$

d) There are two ways the owner will buy apples from this farm:
- Either the first crate will contain no bad apples (probability = 0.1054),
- Or the first crate will contain 1 or 2 bad apples AND the second crate will contain 0 or 1 bad apples.

P(1st crate has 1 or 2 bad AND 2nd crate has 0 or 1 bad) = $0.5039 \times (0.1054 + 0.2371) = 0.1726$

So P(restaurant owner buys from this farm) = $0.1054 + 0.1726 = 0.278$

All it takes is one bad apple question and everything starts to go wrong...

I admit that apple question looks a nightmare at first... but just hold your nerve and take things nice and slowly. For example, in that last part, ask yourself: "What individual things need to happen before the restaurant owner will buy from this farm?" Work out the individual probabilities, add or multiply them as necessary, and Bob's your uncle.

S2 Section 2 — Practice Questions

Well, that's another section completed, which is as good a reason as most to celebrate. But wait... put that celebratory cup of tea on ice for a few minutes more, because you've still got some questions to answer to prove that you really do know everything. So try the questions... and if you get any wrong, do some more revision and try them again.

Warm-up Questions

1) If $X \sim \text{Po}(3.1)$, find (correct to 4 decimal places):
   a) $P(X = 2)$, b) $P(X = 1)$, c) $P(X = 0)$, d) $P(X < 3)$, e) $P(X \geq 3)$

2) If $X \sim \text{Po}(8.7)$, find (correct to 4 decimal places):
   a) $P(X = 2)$, b) $P(X = 1)$, c) $P(X = 0)$, d) $P(X < 3)$, e) $P(X \geq 3)$

3) For the following distributions, find: (i) $E(X)$, (ii) $\text{Var}(X)$, and (iii) the standard deviation of X.
   a) Po(8), b) Po(12.11) c) Po(84.2227)

4) For the following distributions, find: (i) $P(X \leq \mu)$, (ii) $P(X \leq \mu - \sigma)$
   a) Po(9), b) Po(4)

5) Which of the following would follow a Poisson distribution? Explain your answers.
   a) The number of defective products coming off a factory's production line in one day if defective products occur at random at an average of 25 per week.
   b) The number of heads thrown using a coin in 25 tosses if the probability of getting a head is always 0.5.
   c) The number of people joining a post-office queue each minute during lunchtime if people arrive at an average rate of 3 every five minutes.
   d) The total number of spelling mistakes in a document if mistakes are randomly made at an average rate of 3 per page.

6) In a radioactive sample, atoms decay at an average rate of 2000 per hour.
   State how the following quantities are distributed, giving as much detail as possible.
   a) The number of atoms decaying per minute.
   b) The number of atoms decaying per day.

7) Atoms in one radioactive sample decay at an average rate of 60 per minute, while in another they decay at an average rate of 90 per minute.
   a) How would the total number of atoms decaying each minute be distributed?
   b) How would the total number of atoms decaying each hour be distributed?

8) If $X \sim \text{Po}(8)$, use Poisson tables to find:
   a) $P(X \leq 2)$, b) $P(X \leq 7)$, c) $P(X \leq 5)$, d) $P(X < 9)$, e) $P(X \geq 8)$
   f) $P(X > 1)$, g) $P(X > 7)$, h) $P(X = 6)$, i) $P(X = 4)$, j) $P(X = 3)$

9) Which of the following random variables could be approximated by a Poisson distribution? Where it is possible, state the Poisson distribution that could be used.
   a) $X \sim B(4, 0.4)$, b) $Y \sim B(700, 0.01)$, c) $W \sim B(850, 0.34)$
   d) $X \sim B(8, 0.1)$, e) $W \sim B(10\ 000, 0.00001)$, f) $Y \sim B(80, 0.9)$ *(harder)*

10) A gaggle of 100 geese is randomly scattered throughout a field measuring 10 m × 10m. What is the probability that in a randomly selected square metre of field, I find:
   a) no geese? b) 1 goose? c) 2 geese? d) more than 2 geese?

S2 Section 2 — Practice Questions

Nearly there — just... one... more... page...

Exam Questions

1 a) State two conditions needed for a Poisson distribution to be a suitable model for a quantity.

(2 marks)

b) A birdwatcher knows that the number of chaffinches visiting a particular observation spot per hour follows a Poisson distribution with mean 7.

Find the probability that in a randomly chosen hour during the day:

(i) fewer than 4 chaffinches visit the observation spot,

(2 marks)

(ii) at least 7 chaffinches visit the observation spot,

(2 marks)

(iii) exactly 9 chaffinches visit the observation spot.

(2 marks)

c) The number of birds <u>other than</u> chaffinches visiting the same observation spot per hour can be modelled by the Poisson distribution Po(22).

Find the probability that exactly 3 birds (of any species) visit the observation spot in a random 15-minute period.

(4 marks)

2 The number of calls received at a call centre each hour can be modelled by a Poisson distribution with mean 20.

a) Find the probability that in a random 30-minute period:

(i) exactly 8 calls are received,

(3 marks)

(ii) more than 8 calls are received.

(2 marks)

b) For a Poisson distribution to be a suitable model, events have to occur independently. What is meant by "independently" in this context?

(1 mark)

3 When a particular engineer is called out to fix a fault, the probability of him being unable to fix the fault is always 0.02.

a) The engineer's work is assessed after every 400 call-outs. The random variable X represents the number of faults the engineer is unable to fix over those 400 call-outs. Specify the statistical distribution that X will follow, stating the values of any parameters.

(2 marks)

b) (i) Under what conditions can a binomial distribution be approximated by a Poisson distribution?

(2 marks)

(ii) Write down a Poisson distribution that could be used to approximate X.

(1 mark)

(iii) Write down the mean and variance of your Poisson distribution.

(1 mark)

(iv) Using your Poisson approximation, calculate the probability that the engineer will be unable to fix fewer than 10 faults over a period of 400 call-outs.

(2 marks)

Probability Density Functions

A lot of this section will probably look kinda familiar, but at the same time slightly different.
That's because this section covers the same sorts of things as in earlier sections, only with continuous random variables.

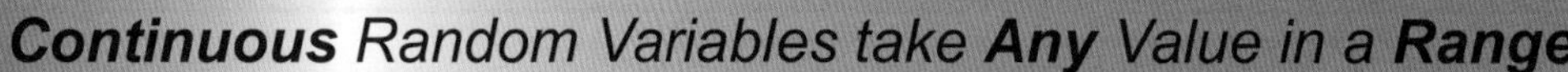

Continuous Random Variables take Any Value in a Range

1) With discrete random variables (like the ones in Sections 1 and 2), there are 'gaps' between the possible values the random variable can take. The random variable's probability function tells you the probability of each of these values occurring.

   For example, if $X \sim B(3, 0.4)$, then you know that X can only take the values 0, 1, 2 or 3, and you could work out the probability of each of these values using the formula on p100. You could even draw a graph of what this probability function looks like.

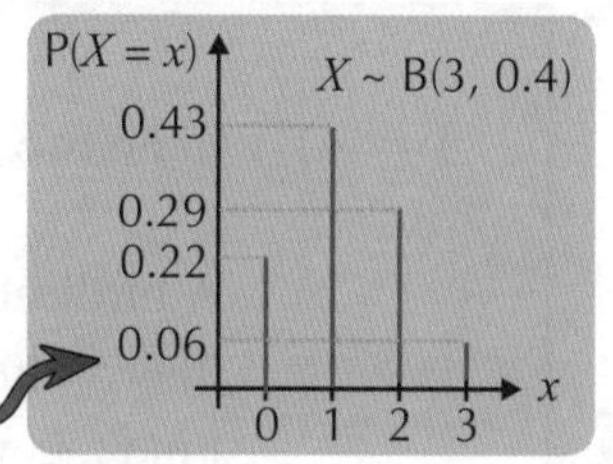

2) Continuous random variables are similar, but they can take any value within a certain range (e.g. they represent things like length, height, weight, etc.).

   So a continuous random variable X might be able to take any value between 0 and 4, for example. You can still draw a graph showing how likely X is to take values within this range. But instead of a series of bars, it would be a continuous line.

3) These graphs that show how likely continuous random variables are to take various values are called probability density functions (or p.d.f.s). Here, f(x) is a p.d.f.

4) It's actually the area under a p.d.f. that shows probability. For example, the shaded area shows the probability that this continuous random variable will take a value between 1 and 2.

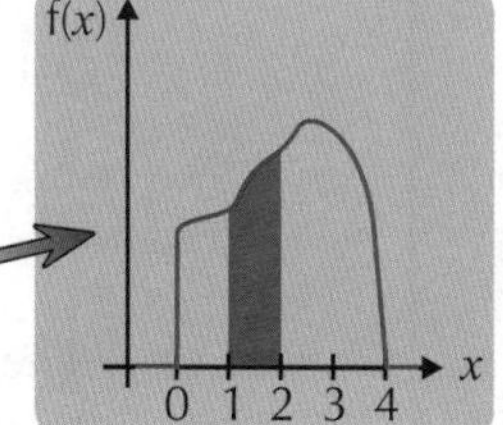

The Total Area under a p.d.f. is 1

Remember... it's the area under a p.d.f. that shows probability, and you find the area under a curve by integrating.

EXAMPLE a) Explain why a p.d.f. can never take negative values.
b) Explain why the total area under any p.d.f. must equal 1.

a) A p.d.f. can never be negative, since probabilities can never be negative.
b) The total area under a p.d.f. must always equal 1 since that's just the total probability of the random variable taking one of its possible values.

In maths-speak, this means $f(x) \geq 0$ for all x, and $\int_{-\infty}^{\infty} f(x)dx = 1$.

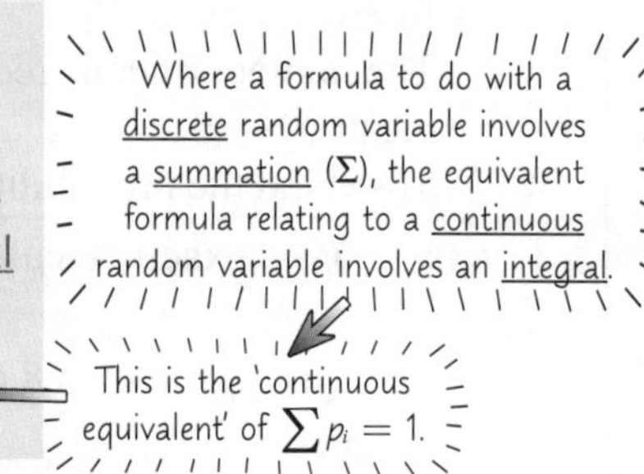

Where a formula to do with a discrete random variable involves a summation (Σ), the equivalent formula relating to a continuous random variable involves an integral.
This is the 'continuous equivalent' of $\sum p_i = 1$.

Find Probabilities by Calculating Areas

Some of the p.d.f.s you'll come across are defined "piecewise" (bit by bit). Don't let that faze you.

EXAMPLE The continuous random variable X has the probability density function below.

$$f(x) = \begin{cases} kx & \text{for } 0 < x < 4 \\ 0 & \text{otherwise} \end{cases}$$

This is a piecewise definition — it's in 2 bits.

a) Find the value of k. b) Find $P(2 < X \leq 3)$. c) Find $P(X = 2.5)$.

a) The total area under the p.d.f. must equal 1.
Using a sketch of f(x), you can tell that $8k = 1$, or $k = 0.125$.

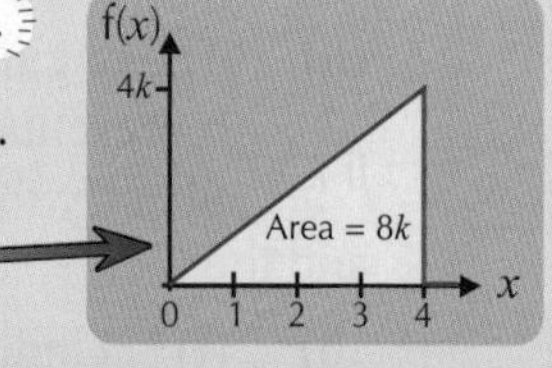

b) You need to find the area under the graph between $x = 2$ and $x = 3$.
Using the formula for the area of a trapezium, $P(2 < X \leq 3) = 0.3125$.

c) The area under a graph at a single point is zero (since it would be the area of a trapezium with zero width). So $P(X = 2.5) = 0$.

The probability of a continuous random variable equalling any single value is always zero — it only makes sense to find the probability of it taking a value within a particular range.
It also means that for a continuous random variable, $P(X < k) = P(X \leq k)$, for any k.

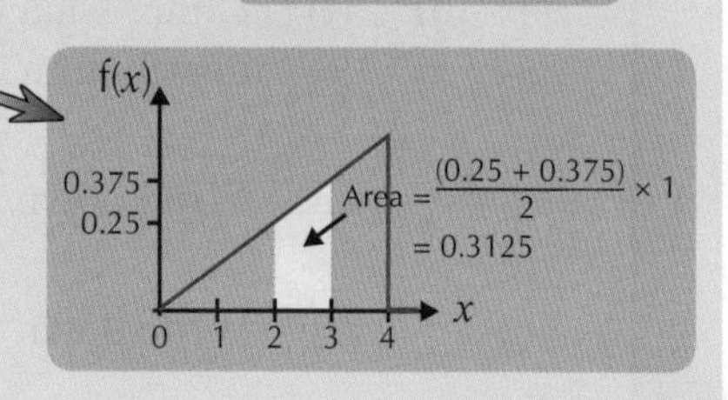

Sometimes, statistics all seems a little bit odd...

That thing about $P(X = x) = 0$ always seems weird to me. I mean... X has to take some value, so it seems peculiar that the probability of it taking any particular value equals zero. But that's the way it is. It makes a bit more sense if you remember that probabilities are represented by areas under a graph. Not many calculations here, but learn the ideas carefully.

Probability Density Functions

It's time to put on your best integrating trousers, because you'll be finding more "areas under curves" on this page.

Some Probabilities Need to be Found by *Integrating*

Remember — probabilities are represented by areas, so if X has p.d.f. f(x):

$$P(a < X \leq b) = \int_a^b f(x)dx$$

EXAMPLE The continuous random variable X has the probability density function below.

$$f(x) = \begin{cases} x^2 + a & \text{for } 0 \leq x \leq 1 \\ 0 & \text{otherwise} \end{cases}$$

a) Sketch f(x), and find the value of a.

b) Find $P(X > \frac{1}{2})$.

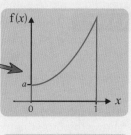

a) The non-zero bit of the p.d.f. is a quadratic function, and so f(x) looks like this:
The area under the graph must equal 1, so integrate.

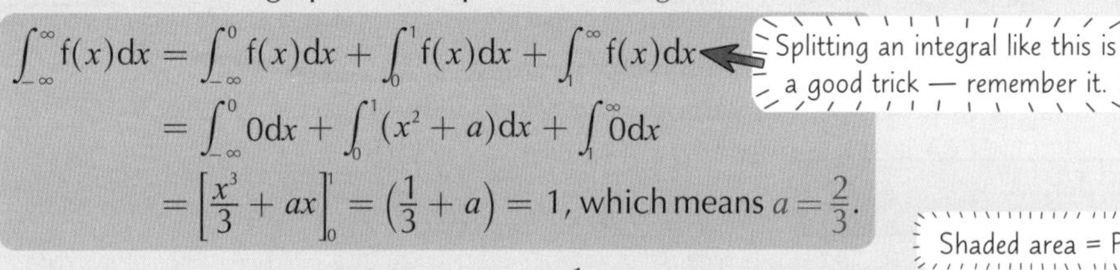

$$\int_{-\infty}^{\infty} f(x)dx = \int_{-\infty}^{0} f(x)dx + \int_0^1 f(x)dx + \int_1^{\infty} f(x)dx$$
$$= \int_{-\infty}^{0} 0dx + \int_0^1 (x^2 + a)dx + \int_1^{\infty} 0dx$$
$$= \left[\frac{x^3}{3} + ax\right]_0^1 = \left(\frac{1}{3} + a\right) = 1, \text{ which means } a = \frac{2}{3}.$$

Splitting an integral like this is a good trick — remember it.

b) Integrate again — this time between $x = \frac{1}{2}$ and $x = 1$.

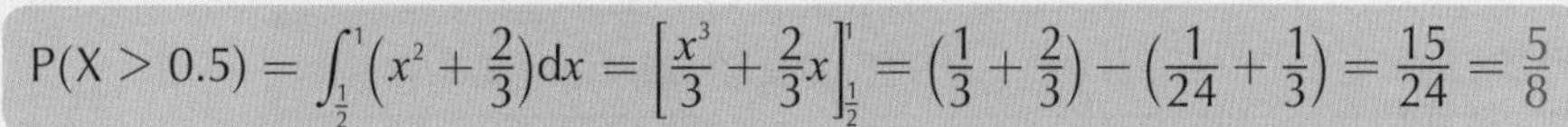

$$P(X > 0.5) = \int_{\frac{1}{2}}^{1} \left(x^2 + \frac{2}{3}\right)dx = \left[\frac{x^3}{3} + \frac{2}{3}x\right]_{\frac{1}{2}}^{1} = \left(\frac{1}{3} + \frac{2}{3}\right) - \left(\frac{1}{24} + \frac{1}{3}\right) = \frac{15}{24} = \frac{5}{8}$$

Shaded area = P(X > 0.5).

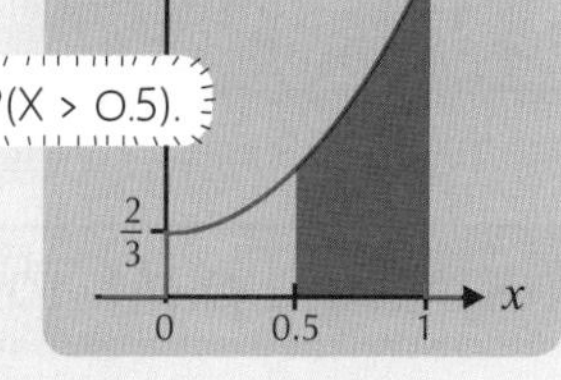

You Might Need to Spot a Function that's *NOT* a p.d.f.

EXAMPLE Which of the following could be probability density functions?

a) $f(x) = \begin{cases} 3x & \text{for } -1 \leq x \leq 1 \\ 0 & \text{otherwise} \end{cases}$ b) $g(x) = \begin{cases} kx & \text{for } 2 \leq x \leq 4 \\ 0 & \text{otherwise} \end{cases}$ c) $h(x) = \begin{cases} kx & \text{for } -2 \leq x \leq 2 \\ 0 & \text{otherwise} \end{cases}$

a) The graph of f(x) looks like this:
But a p.d.f. can never take negative values, so this cannot be a probability density function.

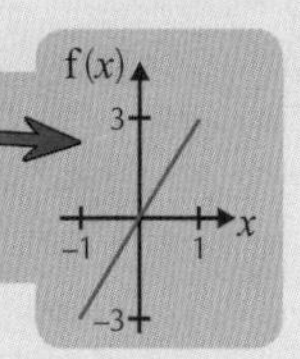

b) Since a p.d.f. can never take a negative value, k cannot be negative.

If k is positive, then the graph of g(x) looks like this,

and the total area under the graph is $\dfrac{2k + 4k}{2} \times 2 = 6k$.

So g(x) could be a p.d.f. as long as $k = \frac{1}{6}$.

The yellow area must equal 1 for g(x) to be a p.d.f.

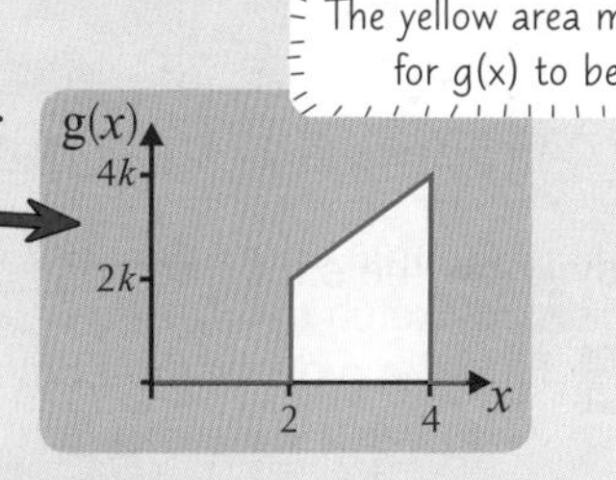

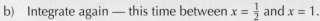

c) If k is positive, then h(x) is negative for $-2 \leq x < 0$, so k cannot be positive.
If k is negative, then h(x) is negative for $0 < x \leq 2$, so k cannot be negative.

If $k = 0$, then $\int_{-\infty}^{\infty} h(x)dx = \int_{-\infty}^{\infty} 0dx = 0$, so h($x$) cannot be a p.d.f.

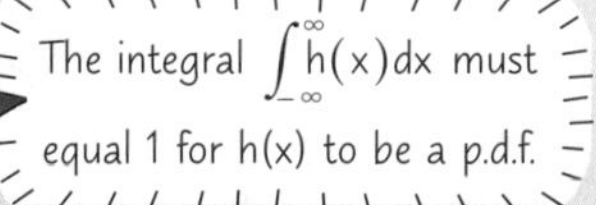

The integral $\int_{-\infty}^{\infty} h(x)dx$ must equal 1 for h(x) to be a p.d.f.

Three things you should definitely know about a p.d.f...

There's not really heaps to say about probability density functions. They can't be negative, the total area under a p.d.f. must equal 1, and you can find probabilities by finding areas under the p.d.f. between different limits. If you remember just those facts and can do a bit of integration, then you'll be well on the way to earning a few easy marks come exam time.

Cumulative Distribution Functions

Now it's time for cumulative distribution functions (c.d.f.s). "Cumulative distribution function" sounds pretty complicated, but all it means is "the area under a p.d.f. up to a certain point".

A *Cumulative Distribution Function* shows $P(X \leq x)$

Cumulative Distribution Functions

If X is a continuous random variable with p.d.f. f(x), then its cumulative distribution function (c.d.f.) F(x) is given by:

$$F(x_0) = P(X \leq x_0) = \int_{-\infty}^{x_0} f(x)dx$$

Cumulative distribution functions are usually labelled with capital letters, e.g. **F(x)** — unlike p.d.f.s, which are usually labelled with lower case letters, e.g. **f(x)**.

EXAMPLE A continuous random variable X has probability density function f(x), where

$$f(x) = \begin{cases} 3x^2 & \text{for } 0 \leq x \leq 1 \\ 0 & \text{otherwise} \end{cases}$$

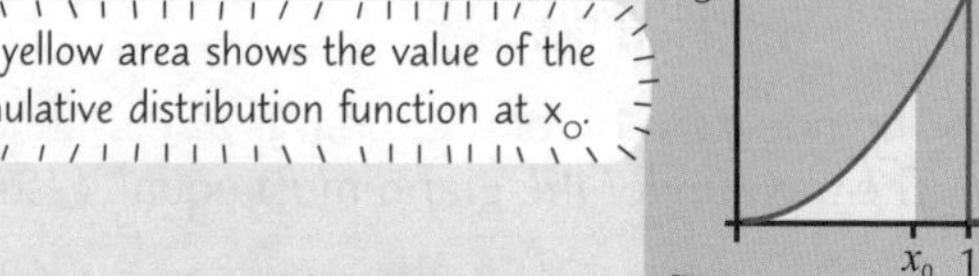
The yellow area shows the value of the cumulative distribution function at x_0.
f(x)
3
x_0
1

Find F(x_0) for some number x_0, where $0 \leq x_0 \leq 1$.

The graph of the p.d.f. is shown on the right.

To find F(x_0), you need to integrate between $-\infty$ and x_0:

$$F(x_0) = \int_{-\infty}^{x_0} f(x)dx = \int_{-\infty}^{0} f(x)dx + \int_{0}^{x_0} f(x)dx$$
$$= \int_{-\infty}^{0} 0dx + \int_{0}^{x_0} 3x^2dx = 0 + [x^3]_0^{x_0} = x_0^3$$

Integrate a p.d.f. to Find a *Cumulative Distribution Function*

The example above involved finding F(x) at a particular point. Now it's time to define F(x) everywhere.

EXAMPLE A continuous random variable X has probability density function f(x), where

$$f(x) = \begin{cases} 2x - 2 & \text{for } 1 \leq x \leq 2 \\ 0 & \text{otherwise} \end{cases}$$

Find the cumulative distribution function of X.

To find F(x), you need to integrate between $-\infty$ and x (so x actually needs to be the upper limit of your integral). To avoid having x as the limit of the integral and the variable you're integrating with respect to, it helps to use a different variable (e.g. 't') inside the integral. The t then disappears when you put in the limits.

$$F(x) = \int_{-\infty}^{1} f(t)dt + \int_{1}^{x} f(t)dt = \int_{-\infty}^{1} 0dt + \int_{1}^{x} (2t - 2)dt$$

For $1 \leq x \leq 2$.

$$= [t^2 - 2t]_1^x = x^2 - 2x - (1 - 2) = x^2 - 2x + 1$$

So $$F(x) = \begin{cases} 0 & \text{for } x < 1 \\ x^2 - 2x + 1 & \text{for } 1 \leq x \leq 2 \\ 1 & \text{for } x > 2 \end{cases}$$

You must define F(x) for all possible values of x. And the 'pieces' should join together with 'no jumps' — the value of the c.d.f. at the end of one 'piece' must equal the value of the c.d.f. at the start of the next 'piece'. Here, F(1) = 0 using both the first and second 'pieces', and F(2) = 1 using both the second and third.

If you already know the c.d.f., then differentiate to find the p.d.f.

EXAMPLE Find the p.d.f. of the continuous random variable X if its cumulative distribution function F(x) is

$$F(x) = \begin{cases} 0 & \text{for } x < 0 \\ \frac{1}{2}(3x - x^3) & \text{for } 0 \leq x \leq 1 \\ 1 & \text{for } x > 1 \end{cases}$$

Differentiate the c.d.f. F(x) to find the p.d.f. f(x):

$$f(x) = \frac{dF(x)}{dx} = \begin{cases} \frac{3}{2} - \frac{3}{2}x^2 & \text{for } 0 \leq x \leq 1 \\ 0 & \text{otherwise} \end{cases}$$

OMG — too many three-letter abbreviations...

Well that wasn't too bad. That bit about using t instead of x looks odd at first but notice how the t disappears once you've done the integration and put in the limits. And don't forget to define F(x) and f(x) for all x between $-\infty$ and ∞.

Cumulative Distribution Functions

Be Extra Careful if the p.d.f. is in 'Pieces'

If a p.d.f. is defined piecewise, then you have to be careful with the c.d.f. where the 'pieces' join.

EXAMPLE Find the cumulative distribution function of X, whose probability density function is

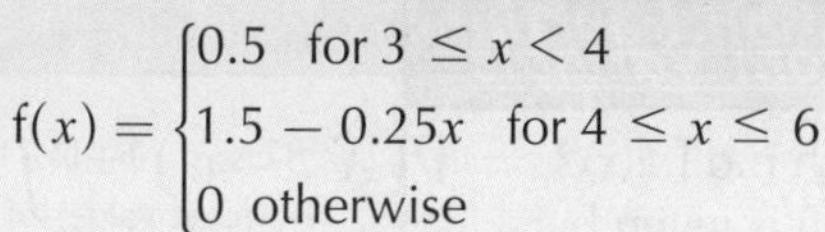

$$f(x) = \begin{cases} 0.5 & \text{for } 3 \le x < 4 \\ 1.5 - 0.25x & \text{for } 4 \le x \le 6 \\ 0 & \text{otherwise} \end{cases}$$

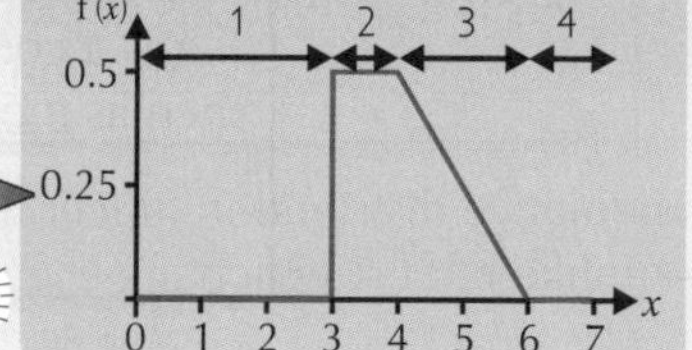

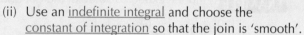

The graph of this p.d.f. is on the right. There'll be 4 pieces to your c.d.f.

- For $x < 3$, $P(X \le x) = 0$ — i.e. $F(x) = 0$. ⟸ So to join on from this smoothly, $F(3) = 0$.
- Then there are two ways to make sure the next piece joins on smoothly.

(i) Always start your integral at $-\infty$:

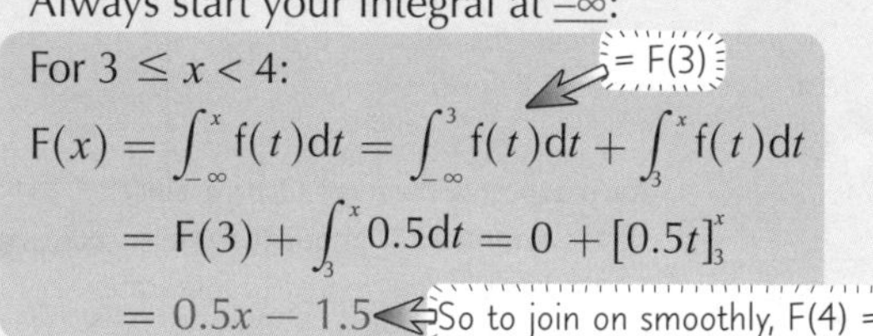

For $3 \le x < 4$:

$$F(x) = \int_{-\infty}^{x} f(t)dt = \int_{-\infty}^{3} f(t)dt + \int_{3}^{x} f(t)dt$$

(= F(3))

$$= F(3) + \int_{3}^{x} 0.5dt = 0 + [0.5t]_3^x$$

$$= 0.5x - 1.5$$ ⟸ So to join on smoothly, $F(4) = 0.5$.

For $4 \le x \le 6$:

$$F(x) = \int_{-\infty}^{4} f(t)dt + \int_{4}^{x} f(t)dt = F(4) + \int_{4}^{x} f(t)dt$$

(= F(4))

$$= 0.5 + \int_{4}^{x} (1.5 - 0.25t)dt$$

$$= 0.5 + [1.5t - 0.125t^2]_4^x$$

$$= 0.5 + (1.5x - 0.125x^2) - (6 - 2)$$

$$= 1.5x - 0.125x^2 - 3.5$$

(ii) Use an indefinite integral and choose the constant of integration so that the join is 'smooth'.

For $3 \le x < 4$: (Use x rather than t in this integral — since there are no limits, the t wouldn't disappear (see p116).)

$$F(x) = \int f(x)dx = \int 0.5dx = 0.5x + k_1$$

But $F(3) = 0$ (to join the first piece of c.d.f. smoothly).
So $k_1 = -1.5$, which gives $F(x) = 0.5x - 1.5$.

For $4 \le x \le 6$:

$$F(x) = \int f(x)dx = \int (1.5 - 0.25x)dx$$
$$= 1.5x - 0.125x^2 + k_2$$

But $F(4) = 0.5$ (using the previous part of the c.d.f.).
So $k_2 = -3.5$, giving $F(x) = 1.5x - 0.125x^2 - 3.5$.

- For $x > 6$, $F(x) = F(6) = 1$. ⟸ A c.d.f. always ends up at 1, but double-check that this makes a smooth join with the previous part of the c.d.f.

Put the bits together to get:

$$F(x) = \begin{cases} 0 & \text{for } x < 3 \\ 0.5x - 1.5 & \text{for } 3 \le x < 4 \\ 1.5x - 0.125x^2 - 3.5 & \text{for } 4 \le x \le 6 \\ 1 & \text{for } x > 6 \end{cases}$$

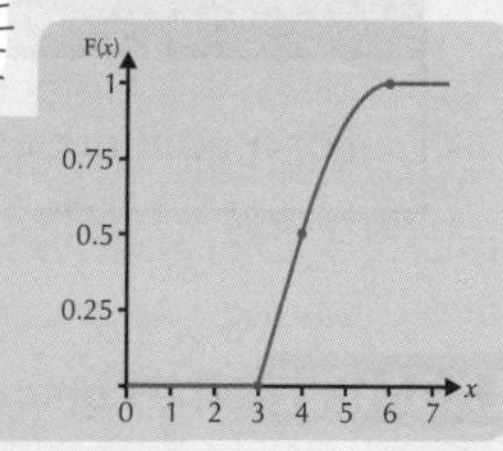

Find All Sorts of Probabilities Using a c.d.f.

You can use a c.d.f. to find the probability of a continuous random variable taking a value within a certain range.

EXAMPLE The cumulative distribution function $F(x)$ of the continuous random variable X is given below.

$$F(x) = \begin{cases} 0 & \text{for } x < 0 \\ 0.5(3x - x^3) & \text{for } 0 \le x \le 1 \\ 1 & \text{for } x > 1 \end{cases}$$

Find: a) $P(X \le 0.5)$, b) $P(X > 0.25)$, c) $P(0.1 \le X \le 0.2)$, d) $P(X < 0.5)$

a) $P(X \le 0.5) = F(0.5) = 0.5 \times (3 \times 0.5 - 0.5^3) = 0.6875$.

b) $P(X > 0.25) = 1 - P(X \le 0.25) = 1 - F(0.25) = 1 - 0.5 \times (3 \times 0.25 - 0.25^3) = 1 - 0.3672 = 0.633$ (to 3 d.p.).

c) $P(0.1 \le X \le 0.2) = P(X \le 0.2) - P(X \le 0.1) = F(0.2) - F(0.1) = 0.296 - 0.1495 = 0.1465$.

d) $P(X < 0.5) = P(X \le 0.5) = 0.6875$. ⟸ For a continuous random variable, $P(X \le k) = P(X < k)$ — since $P(X = k) = 0$.

Don't fall to pieces now — you've done the hardest bit...

Using a c.d.f. to find the probability of X falling within a particular range is similar to what you saw on p102 and p109 with the binomial and Poisson tables — you can work out anything you need, as long as you're prepared to think a bit.

Mean of a Continuous Random Variable

You've seen something a bit like this already (in S1) — except there, the random variables were discrete and the formulas involved a summation (Σ). Here, the random variables are continuous, and you're going to need to integrate.

Integrate to Find the Mean of a Continuous Random Variable

Mean of a Continuous Random Variable

If X is a continuous random variable with p.d.f. f(x), then its mean (μ) or expected value (E(X)) is given by:

$$\mu = \mathrm{E}(X) = \int_{-\infty}^{\infty} x\mathrm{f}(x)\mathrm{d}x$$

This is a bit like the formula for the mean (expected value) of a discrete random variable you saw in S1 — except the sigma (Σ) has been replaced with an integral sign, and p_i with f(x)dx.

EXAMPLE Find the expected value of the continuous random variable X with p.d.f. f (x) given below.

$$\mathrm{f}(x) = \begin{cases} \frac{3}{32}(4 - x^2) & \text{for } -2 \le x \le 2 \\ 0 & \text{otherwise} \end{cases}$$

$$\mathrm{E}(X) = \int_{-\infty}^{\infty} x\mathrm{f}(x)\mathrm{d}x = \int_{-2}^{2} x \cdot \frac{3}{32}(4 - x^2)\mathrm{d}x$$

$$= \int_{-2}^{2}\left(\frac{3}{8}x - \frac{3x^3}{32}\right)\mathrm{d}x = \left[\frac{3x^2}{16} - \frac{3x^4}{128}\right]_{-2}^{2}$$

$$= \left(\frac{3 \times 2^2}{16} - \frac{3 \times 2^4}{128}\right) - \left(\frac{3 \times (-2)^2}{16} - \frac{3 \times (-2)^4}{128}\right) = 0$$

You'd expect a mean of 0 here, since f(x) is symmetrical about the y-axis. So you didn't actually need to integrate.

E(aX + b) = "Just What You'd Expect"

Expected Value of (aX + b)

For a continuous random variable X with p.d.f. f(x): $\mathrm{E}(aX + b) = a\mathrm{E}(X) + b$

EXAMPLE The continuous random variable X has p.d.f. f (x), where $\mathrm{f}(x) = \begin{cases} \frac{3}{37}x^2 & \text{for } 3 \le x \le 4 \\ 0 & \text{otherwise} \end{cases}$

Find: a) the expected value, μ,
b) E(3X + 2),
c) P($X < \mu$).

This p.d.f. isn't symmetrical in the interval [3, 4], so you have to integrate this time.

a) $\mu = \mathrm{E}(X) = \int_{-\infty}^{\infty} x\mathrm{f}(x)\mathrm{d}x = \int_{3}^{4} x \cdot \frac{3}{37}x^2\mathrm{d}x$

$$= \int_{3}^{4} \frac{3}{37}x^3\mathrm{d}x = \frac{3}{37}\left[\frac{x^4}{4}\right]_3^4 = \frac{3}{37 \times 4}(4^4 - 3^4) = \frac{3 \times (256 - 81)}{148} = \frac{525}{148}$$

Always check your mean looks sensible. Here, you'd expect the mean to be somewhere between 3 and 4 (so 525 ÷ 148 = 3.547... seems 'about right').

b) $\mathrm{E}(3X + 2) = 3\mathrm{E}(X) + 2 = 3 \times \frac{525}{148} + 2 = \frac{1575 + 296}{148} = \frac{1871}{148}$

c) $\mathrm{P}(X < \mu) = \int_{-\infty}^{\mu} \mathrm{f}(x)\mathrm{d}x = \int_{3}^{\frac{525}{148}} \frac{3}{37}x^2\mathrm{d}x$

$$= \frac{3}{37}\left[\frac{x^3}{3}\right]_3^{\frac{525}{148}} = \frac{3}{37 \times 3}\left(\left(\frac{525}{148}\right)^3 - 3^3\right) = 0.477 \text{ (to 3 d.p.)}.$$

Variance of a Continuous Random Variable

More integrating, I'm afraid. But stick with it — it'll soon be over.

Integrate to Find the Variance of a Continuous Random Variable

Variance of a Continuous Random Variable

If X is a continuous random variable with p.d.f. f(x), then its variance is given by:

$$\text{Var}(X) = \text{E}(X^2) - [\text{E}(X)]^2 = \text{E}(X^2) - \mu^2$$

$$= \int_{-\infty}^{\infty} x^2 \text{f}(x)\text{d}x - \mu^2$$

This is exactly the same formula that you saw in S1 for discrete random variables.

EXAMPLE The continuous random variable X has p.d.f. f(x) given below, and a mean of 0. Find the variance of X.

$$\text{f}(x) = \begin{cases} \frac{3}{32}(4 - x^2) & \text{for } -2 \le x \le 2 \\ 0 & \text{otherwise} \end{cases}$$

You saw on page 118 that the mean of this p.d.f. is 0.

$$\text{Var}(X) = \text{E}(X^2) - \mu^2 = \int_{-\infty}^{\infty} x^2\text{f}(x)\text{d}x - \mu^2 = \int_{-2}^{2} x^2 \cdot \frac{3}{32}(4 - x^2)\text{d}x - 0^2$$

$$= \int_{-2}^{2}\left(\frac{3x^2}{8} - \frac{3x^4}{32}\right)\text{d}x = \left[\frac{x^3}{8} - \frac{3x^5}{160}\right]_{-2}^{2}$$

$$= \left(\frac{2^3}{8} - \frac{3 \times 2^5}{160}\right) - \left(\frac{(-2)^3}{8} - \frac{3 \times (-2)^5}{160}\right) = 0.8.$$

Find Var(aX + b) by Squaring a and Getting Rid of b

This is the same formula you saw in S1 for discrete random variables.

Variance of (aX + b)

For a continuous random variable X with p.d.f. f(x): $\text{Var}(aX + b) = a^2\text{Var}(X)$

EXAMPLE The continuous random variable X has p.d.f. f (x), where $\text{f}(x) = \begin{cases} \frac{3}{37}x^2 & \text{for } 3 \le x \le 4 \\ 0 & \text{otherwise} \end{cases}$

If $\text{E}(X) = \frac{525}{148}$, find: a) the variance,
b) Var($3X + 2$).

See page 118 for the calculation of the mean of this p.d.f.

a) $$\text{Var}(X) = \text{E}(X^2) - \mu^2 = \int_{-\infty}^{\infty} x^2\text{f}(x)\text{d}x - \left(\frac{525}{148}\right)^2 = \int_{3}^{4} x^2 \cdot \frac{3}{37}x^2\text{d}x - \left(\frac{525}{148}\right)^2$$

$$= \frac{3}{37}\left[\frac{x^5}{5}\right]_3^4 - \left(\frac{525}{148}\right)^2 = \frac{3}{185}(4^5 - 3^5) - \left(\frac{525}{148}\right)^2 = 0.0815467... = 0.0815 \text{ (to 4 d.p.)}$$

b) $\text{Var}(3X + 2) = 3^2 \times \text{Var}(X) = 9 \times 0.0815467... = 0.734$ (to 3 d.p.).

Don't be fooled by the easy-looking formulas above...

...there are a couple of traps lurking here for the unwary:

1) Remember what goes inside the integral when you're calculating the variance... it's $x^2\text{f}(x)$.
2) Don't obsess so much about getting that integral right that you forget to subtract the square of the mean.

Mode, Median and Quartiles

Mode = Maximum Value of a p.d.f.

Mode of a Continuous Random Variable

If X is a continuous random variable with p.d.f. f(x), then its mode is the value of x where f(x) reaches its maximum.

EXAMPLE Find the modes of the continuous random variables whose p.d.f.s are given below.

a) X with p.d.f. $f(x) = \begin{cases} \frac{3}{16}(x^3 - 7x^2 + 10x) & \text{for } 0 \le x \le 2 \\ 0 & \text{otherwise} \end{cases}$ b) Y with p.d.f. $g(y) = \begin{cases} 2y - 2 & \text{for } 1 \le y \le 2 \\ 0 & \text{otherwise} \end{cases}$

a) As always, it's best to start with a sketch of the p.d.f.:

Since $x^3 - 7x^2 + 10x = x(x^2 - 7x + 10) = x(x - 5)(x - 2)$, f($x$) looks like this:

y = x³ – 7x² + 10x is in grey. The p.d.f. f(x) is in red.

Now differentiate to find the maximum of f(x) in the range $0 \le x \le 2$.

$$\frac{d}{dx}\left(\frac{3}{16}(x^3 - 7x^2 + 10x)\right) = \frac{3}{16}(3x^2 - 14x + 10)$$

This equals zero when $x = \frac{14 \pm \sqrt{14^2 - 4 \times 3 \times 10}}{6} = \frac{14 \pm \sqrt{76}}{6}$.

So the mode of X is $x = \frac{14 - \sqrt{76}}{6} = 0.880$ (to 3 d.p.).

$\frac{14 + \sqrt{76}}{6} > 2$, so is too big.

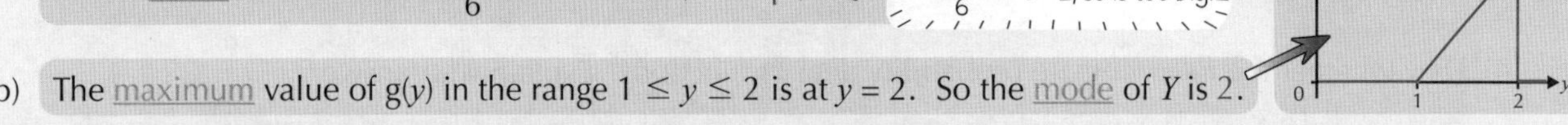

b) The maximum value of g(y) in the range $1 \le y \le 2$ is at $y = 2$. So the mode of Y is 2.

Find the Median and Quartiles using the c.d.f.

Median and Quartiles of a Continuous Random Variable

If X is a continuous random variable with cumulative distribution function F(x), then:

- The median (Q_2) of X is given by $F(Q_2) = 0.5$.
- The lower quartile (Q_1) of X is given by $F(Q_1) = 0.25$.
- The upper quartile (Q_3) of X is given by $F(Q_3) = 0.75$.

EXAMPLE The continuous random variable X has p.d.f. f(x), where $f(x) = \begin{cases} 0.4 & \text{for } 1 \le x < 2 \\ 0.4(x - 1) & \text{for } 2 \le x \le 3 \\ 0 & \text{otherwise} \end{cases}$

Find the interquartile range, $Q_3 - Q_1$.

Integrate to find the c.d.f., making sure the joins are smooth — I used the 'constants of integration' method (p117).

$$F(x) = \begin{cases} 0 & \text{for } x < 1 \\ 0.4x + k_1 & \text{for } 1 \le x < 2 \\ 0.2x^2 - 0.4x + k_2 & \text{for } 2 \le x \le 3 \\ 1 & \text{for } x > 3 \end{cases}$$

Choose k_1 and k_2 to give 'smooth joins'.

$$F(x) = \begin{cases} 0 & \text{for } x < 1 \\ 0.4x - 0.4 & \text{for } 1 \le x < 2 \\ 0.2x^2 - 0.4x + 0.4 & \text{for } 2 \le x \le 3 \\ 1 & \text{for } x > 3 \end{cases}$$

- The lower quartile (Q_1) is given by $F(Q_1) = 0.25$ — and you know Q_1 must be less than 2 (since $F(2) = 0.4$). So solve $0.4Q_1 - 0.4 = 0.25$, which gives $Q_1 = 1.625$.

Find the value of F(x) where the second and third pieces join to work out which piece contains each quartile.

- The upper quartile (Q_3) is given by $F(Q_3) = 0.75$ — and you know x must be greater than 2 (again, as $F(2) = 0.4$). So solve $0.2Q_3^2 - 0.4Q_3 + 0.4 = 0.75$, which gives $Q_3 = \frac{0.4 + \sqrt{0.44}}{0.4} = 1 + \frac{\sqrt{0.44}}{0.4}$ (using the quadratic formula).
- This means the interquartile range $= Q_3 - Q_1 = 1 + \frac{\sqrt{0.44}}{0.4} - 1.625 = 1.033$ (to 3 d.p.).

Mode, median — hmmm, that rings a vague bell from S1...

All sorts of mathematical bits and bobs are being used here — the quadratic formula, differentiation to find the maximum of a curve, and so on. That could happen in the exam, so if necessary, refresh your memory from earlier units.

S2 Section 3 — Practice Questions

It's the end of Section 3, and I'm going to assume that you know what you're supposed to do by now. And if you get any wrong, well... I'll say no more.

Warm-up Questions

1) Find the value of k for each of the probability density functions below.

a) $f(x) = \begin{cases} kx & \text{for } 1 \leq x \leq 10 \\ 0 & \text{otherwise} \end{cases}$ b) $g(x) = \begin{cases} 0.2x + k & \text{for } 0 \leq x \leq 1 \\ 0 & \text{otherwise} \end{cases}$

2) For each of the probability density functions below, find: (i) $P(X < 1)$, (ii) $P(2 \leq X \leq 5)$, (iii) $P(X = 4)$.

a) $f(x) = \begin{cases} 0.08x & \text{for } 0 \leq x \leq 5 \\ 0 & \text{otherwise} \end{cases}$ b) $g(x) = \begin{cases} 0.02(10 - x) & \text{for } 0 \leq x \leq 10 \\ 0 & \text{otherwise} \end{cases}$

3) Find the exact value of k for each of the probability density functions below. Then for each p.d.f., find $P(X < 1)$.

a) $f(x) = \begin{cases} kx^2 & \text{for } 0 \leq x \leq 5 \\ 0 & \text{otherwise} \end{cases}$ b) $g(x) = \begin{cases} 0.1x^2 + kx & \text{for } 0 \leq x \leq 2 \\ 0 & \text{otherwise} \end{cases}$

4) Say whether the following are probability density functions. Explain your answers.

a) $f(x) = \begin{cases} 0.1x^2 + 0.2 & \text{for } 0 \leq x \leq 2 \\ 0 & \text{otherwise} \end{cases}$ b) $g(x) = \begin{cases} x & \text{for } -1 \leq x \leq 1 \\ 0 & \text{otherwise} \end{cases}$

5) Find the cumulative distribution function (c.d.f.) for each of the following p.d.f.s.

a) $f(x) = \begin{cases} 0.08x & \text{for } 0 \leq x \leq 5 \\ 0 & \text{otherwise} \end{cases}$ b) $g(x) = \begin{cases} 0.02(10 - x) & \text{for } 0 \leq x \leq 10 \\ 0 & \text{otherwise} \end{cases}$

c) $h(x) = \begin{cases} 2x & \text{for } 0 \leq x \leq 0.5 \\ 1 & \text{for } 0.5 \leq x \leq 1 \\ 3 - 2x & \text{for } 1 \leq x \leq 1.5 \\ 0 & \text{otherwise} \end{cases}$ d) $m(x) = \begin{cases} 0.5 - 0.1x & \text{for } 2 \leq x \leq 4 \\ 0.1 & \text{for } 4 \leq x \leq 10 \\ 0 & \text{otherwise} \end{cases}$

6) Find the probability density function (p.d.f.) for each of the following c.d.f.s.

a) $F(x) = \begin{cases} 0 & \text{for } x < 0 \\ x^4 & \text{for } 0 \leq x \leq 1 \\ 1 & \text{for } x > 1 \end{cases}$ b) $G(x) = \begin{cases} 0 & \text{for } x < 1 \\ \frac{1}{100}(x - 1)^2 & \text{for } 1 \leq x < 6 \\ \frac{3}{8}x - 2 & \text{for } 6 \leq x \leq 8 \\ 1 & \text{for } x > 8 \end{cases}$

7) The random variables X and Y have p.d.f.s. $f(x)$ and $g(y)$ respectively, where

$f(x) = \begin{cases} 0.08x & \text{for } 0 \leq x \leq 5 \\ 0 & \text{otherwise} \end{cases}$ and $g(y) = \begin{cases} 0.02(10 - y) & \text{for } 0 \leq y \leq 10 \\ 0 & \text{otherwise} \end{cases}$

a) Find the mean and variance of X and Y.

b) Find the mean and variance of $4X + 2$ and $3Y - 4$.

c) Find the mode and median of X.

d) Find the interquartile range of X.

S2 Section 3 — Practice Questions

Think of this page as a game. To win the game, you have to get all the answers to the questions right.
I know what you're thinking... it's a terrible game. In fact, it's not a game at all, but a shameless fib.

Exam Questions

1 The continuous random variable X has probability density function f(x), as defined below.

$$f(x) = \begin{cases} \frac{1}{k}(x+4) & \text{for } 0 \leq x \leq 2 \\ 0 & \text{otherwise} \end{cases}$$

a) Find the value of k. *(3 marks)*

b) Find the cumulative distribution function of X, F(x). *(5 marks)*

c) Calculate E(X). *(3 marks)*

d) Calculate the variance of:

(i) X *(3 marks)*

(ii) $4X - 2$ *(2 marks)*

e) Find the median of X. *(4 marks)*

f) Write down the mode of X. *(1 mark)*

g) Describe the skew of X. *(1 mark)*

2 The continuous random variable X has cumulative distribution function F(x), as defined below.

$$F(x) = \begin{cases} 0 & \text{for } x < 1 \\ k(x-1) & \text{for } 1 \leq x < 3 \\ 0.5(x-2) & \text{for } 3 \leq x \leq 4 \\ 1 & \text{for } x > 4 \end{cases}$$

a) Calculate the value of k. *(2 marks)*

b) Calculate the interquartile range of X. *(5 marks)*

c) (i) Specify the probability density function of X, f(x). *(3 marks)*

(ii) Sketch the graph of f(x). *(1 mark)*

d) (i) Find the mean (μ) of X. *(3 marks)*

(ii) Find the variance (σ^2) of X. *(3 marks)*

(iii) Find $P(X < \mu - \sigma)$. *(2 marks)*

Continuous Uniform Distributions

Continuous distributions don't have 'gaps' between possible values of the random variable.
But they do have probability density functions (p.d.f.s). See Section 3 if either of those facts took you by surprise.

A Continuous **Uniform** Distribution is '**Rectangular**'

A random variable with a continuous uniform distribution can take any value in a particular range, and its value is equally likely to be anywhere in the range.

EXAMPLE The continuous random variable X has a uniform distribution and can take any value from 1 to 5.

a) Sketch the graph of $f(x)$, the probability density function (p.d.f.) of X.

b) Define $f(x)$.

a) It's a uniform distribution, so within its range of possible values, $f(x)$ is constant. Since the total area under the p.d.f. must equal 1 and the width of the rectangle is $5 - 1 = 4$, its height must be $1 \div 4 = 0.25$.

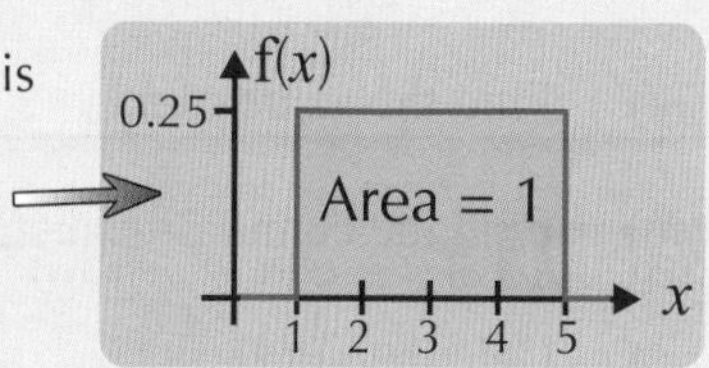

b) So $f(x)$ is given by: $f(x) = \begin{cases} 0.25 & \text{for } 1 \leq x \leq 5 \\ 0 & \text{otherwise} \end{cases}$

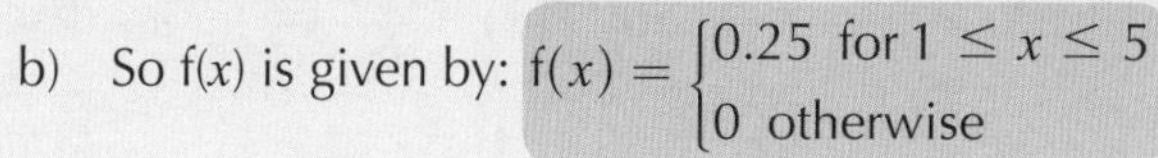

You can go through the same process to work out the p.d.f. of any continuous uniform distribution.
But here's the general formula in a big box.

Continuous Uniform Distribution

If X is a random variable with a continuous uniform distribution, then the p.d.f. of X is:

$$f(x) = \begin{cases} \dfrac{1}{b-a} & \text{for } a \leq x \leq b \\ 0 & \text{otherwise} \end{cases} \qquad \text{for constants } a \text{ and } b.$$

You can write: $X \sim U[a, b]$.

Remember... **Probability = Area Under a p.d.f.**

EXAMPLE If $X \sim U[8, 18]$, find:

a) $P(10 < X < 14.1)$, b) $P(X \leq 14)$, c) $P(X < 14)$, d) $P(X \geq 10.5)$.

It's best to start off by drawing a sketch of the p.d.f.
You know the area of the rectangle (= 1) and its width (= 18 – 8 = 10), so its height must be 1 ÷ 10 = 0.1.

a) $P(10 < X < 14.1)$ = the area under the p.d.f. between $x = 10$ and $x = 14.1$.
This is $(14.1 - 10) \times 0.1 = 4.1 \times 0.1 = 0.41$

b) $P(X \leq 14)$ = the area under the p.d.f. for $x \leq 14$.
This is $(14 - 8) \times 0.1 = 6 \times 0.1 = 0.6$

c) For a continuous distribution, $P(X \leq k) = P(X < k)$ — so $P(X < 14) = P(X \leq 14) = 0.6$

d) $P(X \geq 10.5)$ = the area under the p.d.f. for $x \geq 10.5$.
This is $(18 - 10.5) \times 0.1 = 7.5 \times 0.1 = 0.75$

EXAMPLE If $X \sim U[4, 7]$ and $Y = 8X - 3$, write down the distribution of Y.

$Y \sim U[(8 \times 4 - 3), (8 \times 7 - 3)] = U[29, 53]$

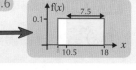

Y will also follow a uniform distribution. Just put the limits of X in the formula for Y.

Working out the areas of rectangles — this page really is the limit...

Well, who'd have thought... a page on working out the areas of rectangles in S2. (Best enjoy it while the going's easy, mind.) There's not much more to say about this page really. So I'll keep my mouth shut and let you get on with the next page.

Continuous Uniform Distributions

You'll be working out expected values and variances of continuous random variables on this page — so you can expect a bit of integration. See pages 118-119 for a bit more info if you don't remember why.

You *Might* be Asked to *Prove* these Formulas for E(X), Var(X) and F(x)

You could be asked to show why any of these formulas are true, so read this page very carefully.

Continuous Uniform Distributions

If $X \sim \mathrm{U}[a, b]$, then:

(i) $\mathrm{E}(X) = \dfrac{a+b}{2}$ (ii) $\mathrm{Var}(X) = \dfrac{(b-a)^2}{12}$ (iii) $\mathrm{F}(x) = \begin{cases} 0 & \text{for } x < a \\ \dfrac{x-a}{b-a} & \text{for } a \le x \le b \\ 1 & \text{for } x > b \end{cases}$

The cumulative distribution function (c.d.f.) — see p116.

EXAMPLE If $X \sim \mathrm{U}[a, b]$, show: (i) $\mathrm{E}(X) = \dfrac{a+b}{2}$, (ii) $\mathrm{Var}(X) = \dfrac{(b-a)^2}{12}$, (iii) $\mathrm{F}(x) = \dfrac{x-a}{b-a}$ for $a < x < b$

(i) From the symmetry of the p.d.f., the expected value of X must be $\dfrac{a+b}{2}$.

Or you can show this by integrating — see page 130, Q4.

(ii) $\mathrm{Var}(X) = \int_{-\infty}^{\infty} x^2 \mathrm{f}(x)\mathrm{d}x - \mu^2 = \int_{-\infty}^{\infty} x^2 \mathrm{f}(x)\mathrm{d}x - \left(\dfrac{a+b}{2}\right)^2$ See p119.

But $\int_{-\infty}^{\infty} x^2 \mathrm{f}(x)\mathrm{d}x = \int_a^b x^2\left(\dfrac{1}{b-a}\right)\mathrm{d}x = \dfrac{1}{b-a}\int_a^b x^2 \mathrm{d}x = \dfrac{1}{b-a}\left[\dfrac{x^3}{3}\right]_a^b = \dfrac{b^3 - a^3}{3(b-a)} = \dfrac{b^2 + ab + a^2}{3}$

$b^3 - a^3 = (b - a)(b^2 + ab + a^2)$

So $\mathrm{Var}(X) = \dfrac{b^2 + ab + a^2}{3} - \left(\dfrac{a+b}{2}\right)^2 = \dfrac{4b^2 + 4ab + 4a^2 - 3a^2 - 6ab - 3b^2}{12}$

$= \dfrac{b^2 - 2ab + a^2}{12} = \dfrac{(b-a)^2}{12}$

(iii) $\mathrm{F}(x) = \int_{-\infty}^{x} \mathrm{f}(t)\mathrm{d}t = \int_a^x \dfrac{1}{b-a}\mathrm{d}t = \dfrac{1}{b-a}\int_a^x 1\,\mathrm{d}t = \dfrac{1}{b-a}[t]_a^x = \dfrac{x-a}{b-a}$

You *Will* be Asked to *Use* the Formulas for E(X), Var(X) and F(x)

EXAMPLE If $X \sim \mathrm{U}[-7, 22]$, find: (i) $\mathrm{E}(X)$, (ii) $\mathrm{Var}(X)$, (iii) $\mathrm{F}(x)$, (iv) $\mathrm{F}(4)$.

(i) $\mathrm{E}(X) = \dfrac{a+b}{2} = \dfrac{-7+22}{2} = 7.5$

(ii) $\mathrm{Var}(X) = \dfrac{(b-a)^2}{12} = \dfrac{(22-(-7))^2}{12} = \dfrac{29^2}{12} = 70.083$ (to 3 d.p.).

(iii) $\mathrm{F}(x) = \begin{cases} 0 & \text{for } x < -7 \\ \dfrac{x+7}{29} & \text{for } -7 \le x \le 22 \\ 1 & \text{for } x > 22 \end{cases}$

You need to write down all of this.

(iv) $\mathrm{F}(4) = \dfrac{4+7}{29} = \dfrac{11}{29}$

EXAMPLE If $X \sim \mathrm{U}[a, b]$, and $\mathrm{E}(X) = \mathrm{Var}(X) = 1$, find a and b.

$\mathrm{E}(X) = \dfrac{a+b}{2} = 1$, so $a = 2 - b$

$\mathrm{Var}(X) = \dfrac{(b-a)^2}{12} = 1$, so $b^2 - 2ab + a^2 = 12$, or $b^2 - 2b(2-b) + (2-b)^2 = 12$.

This gives $4b^2 - 8b + 4 = 12$, or $b^2 - 2b - 2 = 0$.

Solving with the quadratic formula gives $b = 1 + \sqrt{3}$, and then $a = 1 - \sqrt{3}$.

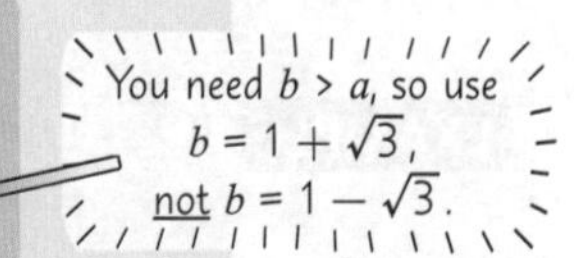

You need b > a, so use
b = 1 + √3,
not b = 1 − √3.

Continuous, Uniform — not the most exciting sounding topic, is it...

The formula for F(x) won't be in your formula booklet, so you'll need to learn it. And you could be asked to show why any of the formulas on this page are true. That means you'll need to be able to write down all the working in the purple box.

Applications of U[a, b]

Continuous uniform distributions describe things that are equally likely to take any value within an interval. So they're good for describing things that are completely random.

Use a Uniform Distribution When All Values are Equally Likely

EXAMPLE A runner's time over 100 m is measured as 12.3 seconds, to the nearest 0.1 second. Describe the distribution of the errors in the timing.

If the time was measured to the nearest 0.1 s, then the error could be anything up to 0.05 s above or below the recorded time. These errors are random — there's no reason to think they're likely to be high, low or in the middle. So if the random variable X represents the errors in the timing, then $X \sim U[-0.05, 0.05]$.

All the Usual Probability Rules Still Apply with Uniform Distributions

EXAMPLE If $X \sim U[4, 7]$ and $Y = 8X - 3$, find $E(Y)$ and $Var(Y)$.

$$E(X) = \frac{a+b}{2} = \frac{4+7}{2} = 5.5$$
$$E(Y) = E(8X - 3) = 8E(X) - 3 = 8 \times 5.5 - 3 = 41$$

See page 118 for more info.

$$Var(X) = \frac{(b-a)^2}{12} = \frac{(7-4)^2}{12} = \frac{9}{12} = 0.75$$
$$Var(Y) = Var(8X - 3) = 8^2 \times Var(X) = 64 \times 0.75 = 48$$

EXAMPLE X and Y are independent random variables, with $X \sim U[1, 3]$ and $Y \sim U[0, 5]$. Find the probability that both X and Y take values greater than 1.2.

X and Y are independent, so $P(X > 1.2 \text{ and } Y > 1.2) = P(X > 1.2) \times P(Y > 1.2)$.

You could find each of these probabilities by integrating — but it's easier to sketch the p.d.f.s of X and Y, and take it from there.

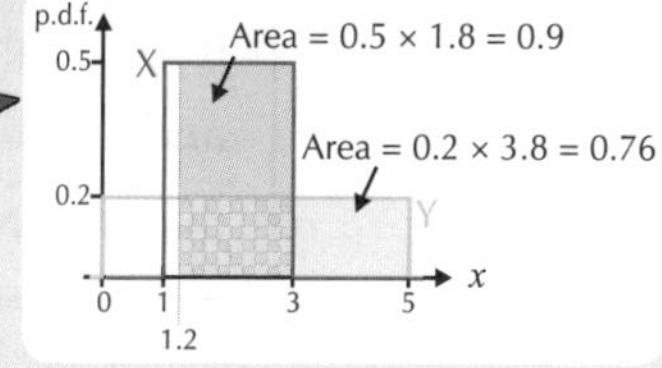

$P(X > 1.2) = 0.5 \times 1.8 = 0.9$ and $P(Y > 1.2) = 0.2 \times 3.8 = 0.76$

So $P(X > 1.2 \text{ and } Y > 1.2) = 0.9 \times 0.76 = 0.684$.

EXAMPLE $X \sim U[3, 12]$.

(a) Sketch the probability density function of X.

(b) Find $E(X^2)$.

(a) It's a continuous uniform distribution, so the p.d.f. is a rectangle with an area of 1.

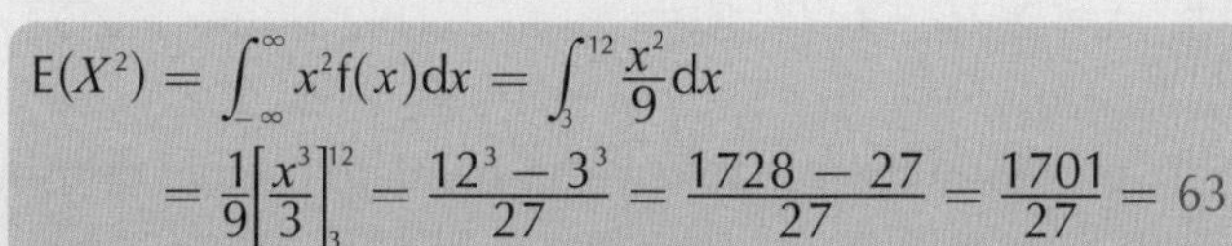

(b) You need to integrate to find $E(X^2)$.

$$E(X^2) = \int_{-\infty}^{\infty} x^2 f(x)\,dx = \int_3^{12} \frac{x^2}{9}\,dx$$
$$= \frac{1}{9}\left[\frac{x^3}{3}\right]_3^{12} = \frac{12^3 - 3^3}{27} = \frac{1728 - 27}{27} = \frac{1701}{27} = 63$$

When I just can't do a question, I use X — where X ~ U[–500, 500]...

Questions on uniform distributions probably won't involve any really tricky maths, and they won't involve you using any of those awkward, fiddly tables. So they're potentially slightly easier marks... as long as you know what you're doing. So learn the stuff above, think carefully before you start pressing loads of buttons on your calculator, and Bob should be your uncle.

Normal Approximation to B(n, p)

If n is big, a binomial distribution (B(n, p)) can be tricky to work with. You saw the Poisson approximation on p110, but sometimes a normal distribution (remember those... you met them in S1) is a better approximation. But there's a snag.

Use a **Continuity Correction** to Approximate a Binomial with a Normal

The binomial distribution is discrete but the normal distribution is continuous. To allow for this you need to use a continuity correction. Like a lot of this stuff, it sounds more complicated than it is.

- A binomially-distributed variable X is discrete, so you can work out $P(X = 0)$, $P(X = 1)$, etc.
- A normally-distributed variable is continuous, and so $P(X = 0) = P(X = 1) = 0$, etc. (see page 114).

So what you do is assume that the 'binomial 1' is spread out over the interval 0.5 - 1.5.

0 ⟸1⟹⟸2⟹⟸3⟹⟸4⟹
0.5 1.5 2.5 3.5 4.5

Then to approximate the binomial $P(X = 1)$, you find the normal $P(0.5 < X < 1.5)$.

Similarly, the 'binomial 2' is spread out over the interval 1.5 - 2.5, and so on.

Learn these **Continuity Corrections**

The interval you need to use with your normal distribution depends on the binomial probability you're trying to find out.

The general principle is the same, though — each binomial value b covers the interval from $b - \frac{1}{2}$ up to $b + \frac{1}{2}$.

Binomial	Normal	
$P(X = b)$	$P(b - \frac{1}{2} < X < b + \frac{1}{2})$	
$P(X \leq b)$	$P(X < b + \frac{1}{2})$	...to include b
$P(X < b)$	$P(X < b - \frac{1}{2})$	...to exclude b
$P(X \geq b)$	$P(X > b - \frac{1}{2})$	...to include b
$P(X > b)$	$P(X > b + \frac{1}{2})$	...to exclude b

The **Normal Approximation** Only Works Well under **Certain Conditions**

Normal Approximation to the Binomial

Suppose the random variable X follows a binomial distribution, i.e. $X \sim \mathbf{B}(n, p)$.

If (i) $p \approx \frac{1}{2}$,

and (ii) n is large,

then $X \sim \mathbf{N}(np, npq)$ (approximately), where $q = 1 - p$.

Since for a binomial distribution, $\mu = np$ and $\sigma^2 = npq$ (see page 103).

Even if p isn't all that close to 0.5, this approximation usually works fine as long as np and nq are both bigger than about 5.

EXAMPLE If $X \sim B(80, 0.4)$, use a suitable approximation to find: (i) $P(X < 45)$ and (ii) $P(X \geq 40)$.

You need to make sure first that the normal approximation is suitable...

n is fairly large, and p is not far from $\frac{1}{2}$, so the normal approximation is valid.

Next, work out np and npq: $np = 80 \times 0.4 = 32$ and $npq = 80 \times 0.4 \times (1 - 0.4) = 19.2$

$q = 1 - p$

So the approximation you need is: $X \sim N(32, 19.2)$

So the standard deviation is $\sqrt{19.2}$.

Now apply a continuity correction, transform the variable to the standard normal distribution (Z), and use tables.

(i) You need $P(X < 45)$ — so with the continuity correction this is $P(X < 44.5)$.

$$P(X < 44.5) = P\left(\frac{X - 32}{\sqrt{19.2}} < \frac{44.5 - 32}{\sqrt{19.2}}\right) = P(Z < 2.85) = 0.9978$$

See page 148 for the normal distribution tables.

(ii) Now you need $P(X \geq 40)$ — with the continuity correction this is $P(X > 39.5)$.

$$P(X > 39.5) = P\left(\frac{X - 32}{\sqrt{19.2}} > \frac{39.5 - 32}{\sqrt{19.2}}\right) = P(Z > 1.71) = 1 - P(Z \leq 1.71) = 1 - 0.9564 = 0.0436$$

Normal Approximation to B(n, p)

I know what you're thinking — you want to know just how good a normal approximation actually is. Well, let's see...

EXAMPLE: Newborn babies

The average number of births per year in a hospital is 228. If each baby is equally likely to be a boy or a girl, then use a suitable approximation to find the probability that next year:

(i) there will be more boys born than girls,

(ii) exactly 100 boys will be born.

Mean = $np = 228 \times 0.5 = 114$
Variance = $npq = 228 \times 0.5 \times 0.5 = 57$

If X represents the number of boys born next year, then you can assume that $X \sim B(228, 0.5)$.
Since n is large, and p is 0.5, then you can use a normal approximation: $X \sim N(114, 57)$.

(i) You need to find $P(X > 114)$. With a continuity correction, this is $P(X > 114.5)$.
It's a normal distribution, so transform this to Z, the standard normal distribution.

$$P(X > 114.5) = P\left(\frac{X-114}{\sqrt{57}} > \frac{114.5-114}{\sqrt{57}}\right) = P(Z > 0.07)$$
$$= 1 - P(Z \leq 0.07) = 1 - 0.5279 = 0.4721$$

Using B(228, 0.5) instead of the normal approximation, you get 0.4736 — so this is a really good approximation.

It'd be even better if you didn't have to round your z value up to 0.07 — if you could look up $0.5/\sqrt{57} = 0.0662...$ in the normal tables, you'd get 0.4736.

(ii) With a continuity correction, you need to find $P(99.5 < X < 100.5)$.

$$P(99.5 < X < 100.5) = P(X < 100.5) - P(X < 99.5)$$
$$= P\left(\frac{X-114}{\sqrt{57}} < \frac{100.5-114}{\sqrt{57}}\right) - P\left(\frac{X-114}{\sqrt{57}} < \frac{99.5-114}{\sqrt{57}}\right)$$
$$= P(Z < -1.79) - P(Z < -1.92)$$
$$= (1 - P(Z < 1.79)) - (1 - P(Z < 1.92))$$
$$= 1 - 0.9633 - 1 + 0.9726 = 0.0093$$

Using B(228, 0.5) instead of the normal approximation, you get 0.0095.

EXAMPLE: Survival rates

a) On average, only 23% of the young of a particular species of bird survive to adulthood. If 80 chicks of this species are randomly selected, use a suitable approximation to find the probability that at least 30% of them survive.

b) If the survival rate were instead 18%, find the probability that more than three-quarters of the 80 chicks would die.

If X represents the number of survivors, then $X \sim B(80, 0.23)$.
Here, p isn't particularly close to 0.5, but n is quite large, so calculate np and nq:
$np = 80 \times 0.23 = 18.4$ and $nq = 80 \times (1 - 0.23) = 61.6$.
Both np and nq are much greater than 5, so a normal approximation should be okay to use — $N(18.4, 14.2)$.
30% of 80 = 24, so with a continuity correction, you need to find $P(X > 23.5)$.

Mean = $np = 80 \times 0.23 = 18.4$
Variance = $npq = 80 \times 0.23 \times 0.77$
= 14.2 (approximately).

$$P(X > 23.5) = P\left(Z > \frac{23.5-18.4}{\sqrt{14.2}}\right) = P(Z > 1.35) = 1 - P(Z \leq 1.35)$$
$$= 1 - 0.9115 = 0.0885$$

Using the original binomial distribution gives an answer of 0.0904, so this is a fairly good approximation.

b) This time, $X \sim B(80, 0.18)$, which means $np = 80 \times 0.18 = 14.4$ and $nq = 80 \times (1 - 0.18) = 65.6$.
So even though p is now quite far from 0.5, try the normal approximation — $N(14.4, 11.8)$.
If more than three-quarters do not survive, that means $X < 20$, so you need to find $P(X < 19.5)$.

$$P(X < 19.5) = P\left(Z < \frac{19.5-14.4}{\sqrt{11.8}}\right) = P(Z < 1.48) = 0.9306$$

Using the original binomial distribution gives an answer of 0.9270, so this is another pretty good approximation.

Admit it — the normal distribution is the most amazing thing ever...

So the normal approximation works pretty well, even when p isn't really all that close to 0.5. But even so, you should always show that your approximation is 'suitable'. In fact, the question will usually tell you to use a 'suitable approximation', so part of your answer should be to show that you've made sure that it is actually okay. Remember that.

Normal Approximation to Po(λ)

More approximations, I'm afraid. But on the bright side, Mr Poisson is back. Good old Mr Poisson.

The Normal Approximation to Po(λ) Works Best if λ is Big

Normal Approximation to the Poisson Distribution

Suppose the random variable X follows a Poisson distribution, i.e. $X \sim \text{Po}(\lambda)$.
If λ is large, then (approximately) $X \sim \text{N}(\lambda, \lambda)$.

Since for a Poisson distribution, mean = variance = λ (see page 107).

Ideally, you want λ 'as large as possible' — but in practice as long as $\lambda > 10$, then you're fine.

Use a Continuity Correction to Approximate a Poisson with a Normal

Since a Poisson distribution is discrete (it can only take values 0, 1, 2...) but a normal distribution is continuous, you need to use a continuity correction. (See p126 for more about continuity corrections.)

EXAMPLE If $X \sim \text{Po}(49)$, find: a) $P(X < 50)$, b) $P(X \geq 45)$, c) $P(X = 60)$.

Since λ is large (it's greater than 10), you can use a normal approximation — $X \sim \text{N}(49, 49)$.

a) The continuity correction means you need to find $P(X < 49.5)$.

Transform to Z and use tables: $P(X < 49.5) = P\left(\frac{X-49}{7} < \frac{49.5-49}{7}\right) = P(Z < 0.07) = 0.5279$

b) This time you need to find $P(X > 44.5)$: $P(X > 44.5) = P\left(Z > \frac{44.5-49}{7}\right) = P(Z > -0.64)$
$= 1 - P(Z \leq -0.64) = P(Z \leq 0.64) = 0.7389$

c) $P(X = 60) = P(59.5 < X < 60.5) = P(X < 60.5) - P(X < 59.5)$
$= P\left(Z < \frac{60.5-49}{7}\right) - P\left(Z < \frac{59.5-49}{7}\right) = P(Z < 1.64) - P(Z < 1.5)$
$= 0.9495 - 0.9332 = 0.0163$

EXAMPLE A sloppy publishing company produces books containing an average of 25 random errors per page.
Use a suitable approximation to find the probability of: a) fewer than 20 errors on a particular page,
b) exactly 25 errors on a particular page.

The errors happen randomly, singly and (on average) at a constant rate, and so the number of errors that occur on a single page (X) will follow a Poisson distribution. Since there's an average of 25 errors per page, $X \sim \text{Po}(25)$.

a) Since λ is large (greater than 10), you can use a normal approximation — i.e. $X \sim \text{N}(25, 25)$.
You need to use a continuity correction here, so P(fewer than 20 errors) ≈ $P(X < 19.5)$.

Transform to Z and use tables: $P(X < 19.5) = P\left(\frac{X-25}{5} < \frac{19.5-25}{5}\right) = P(Z < -1.1)$
$= 1 - P(Z < 1.1)$
$= 1 - 0.8643 = 0.1357$

b) P(exactly 25 errors on a page) ≈ $P(24.5 < X < 25.5) = P(X < 25.5) - P(X < 24.5)$.

Transform to Z and use tables: $P(X < 25.5) - P(X < 24.5) = P\left(Z < \frac{25.5-25}{5}\right) - P\left(Z < \frac{24.5-25}{5}\right)$
$= P(Z < 0.1) - P(Z < -0.1)$
$= P(Z < 0.1) - (1 - P(Z < 0.1)) = 0.5398 - (1 - 0.5398) = 0.0796$

The abnormal approximation — guess wildly then say 'Close enough'...

Lordy, lordy... the number of times you've had to read 'transform something to Z and use tables'. But that's the thing... if you can find probabilities from a normal distribution, then it's bound to be worth marks in the exam. On a different note, continuity corrections are fairly easy to use — it's remembering to use one in the first place that can be a bit tricky.

More About Approximations

You need to know a few different approximations for S2 — and to be honest, it can all get a bit confusing. But although the picture below looks like a complex wiring diagram, it's actually an easy-to-use flowchart to sum up your options.

Approximate if You're **Told to**, or if Your **Tables** 'Don't Go High Enough'

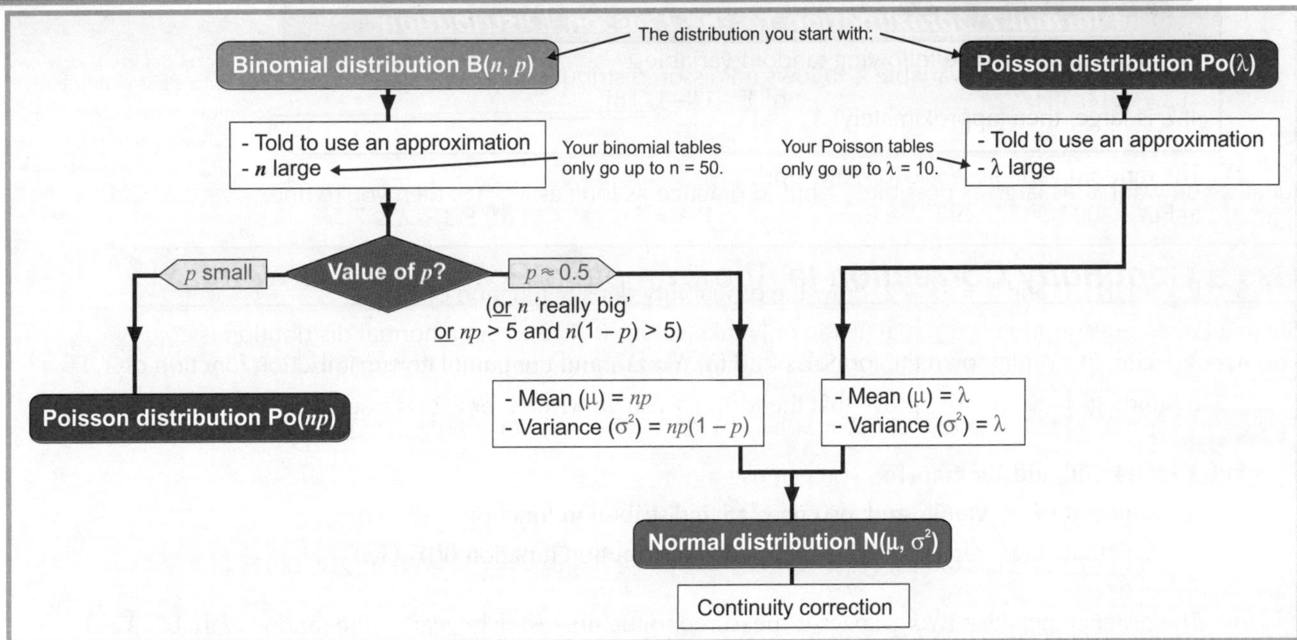

EXAMPLE:

A supermarket gives a customer a free bag when that customer can fit no more items into their existing bags. The number of bags given away was counted. It was found that 62% of customers needed at least one free bag, 2% of customers needed more than 5 free bags, and an average of 8 bags were given away each minute.

If the supermarket has 400 customers one particular morning, use suitable approximations to find:

a) the probability that more than 250 customers take at least one bag,

b) the probability that fewer than 10 customers take more than 5 bags,

c) the probability that more than 500 bags are given away in the first hour after the store opens.

a) Let X represent how many of the 400 customers take at least one bag.
Then $X \sim B(400, 0.62)$, and you need to find $P(X > 250)$.
Here, n is large and p is not too far from 0.5 — so approximate X with $N(248, 94.24)$.

$$P(X > 250) \approx P(X > 250.5) = P\left(\frac{X - 248}{\sqrt{94.24}} > \frac{250.5 - 248}{\sqrt{94.24}}\right) = P(Z > 0.26) = 1 - P(Z \le 0.26) = 0.3974$$

b) Let M represent the total number of customers taking more than 5 bags.
Then $M \sim B(400, 0.02)$, and you need to find $P(M < 10)$.
Here, n is large and p is very small — so use a Poisson approximation: $Po(8)$

$$P(M < 10) = P(M \le 9) = 0.7166$$

Bags given away per minute ~ Po(8).
So bags per hour ~ Po(8 × 60).

c) Let R represent the number of bags given away in the first hour. This is not a fixed number of trials, so it's not a binomial distribution. But the period is fixed (1 hour), so it's Poisson — in fact, $R \sim Po(480)$.
You need to find $P(R > 500)$. Approximate R with $N(480, 480)$.

$$P(R > 500) \approx P(R > 500.5) = P\left(\frac{R - 480}{\sqrt{480}} > \frac{500.5 - 480}{\sqrt{480}}\right) = P(Z > 0.94) = 1 - 0.8264 = 0.1736$$

Check your p — then decide what to do...

The trickiest decision you face when approximating is whether to approximate $B(n, p)$ with a Poisson or a normal distribution — and it all depends on p really. So once you've made that decision, you should be off and running. But don't forget that continuity correction if you're using the normal approximation. You have been warned.

S2 Section 4 — Practice Questions

You've come this far... don't give up now... only two more pages to go. And they're only questions — so it's not like there's loads more you're going to need to cram into your already crowded head. Loins girded? Good, here we go...

Warm-up Questions

1) Sketch the p.d.f.s of the following random variables:
   a) $X \sim \text{U}[7, 11]$, b) $Y \sim \text{U}[-4, 18]$.

2) The random variable $X \sim \text{U}[0, 10]$. Find:
   a) $\text{P}(X < 4)$, b) $\text{P}(X \geq 8)$, c) $\text{P}(X = 5)$, d) $\text{P}(3 < X \leq 7)$.

3) If $X \sim \text{U}[1, 4]$ and $Y = 5X + 2$, draw the probability density function of Y.

4) $X \sim \text{U}[a, b]$. Write down the formulas for $\text{E}(X)$, $\text{Var}(X)$, and the cumulative distribution function of X, $\text{F}(x)$.
   By finding $\int_{-\infty}^{\infty} x \cdot \text{f}(x)\text{d}x$, prove that the formula you've written for $\text{E}(X)$ is true.

5) $X \sim \text{U}[4, 19]$ and $Y = 6X - 3$.
   a) Calculate $\text{E}(X)$, $\text{Var}(X)$, and the cumulative distribution function of X, $\text{F}(x)$.
   b) Calculate $\text{E}(Y)$, $\text{Var}(Y)$, and the cumulative distribution function of Y, $\text{G}(x)$.

6) The distance between two galaxies is measured to the nearest light year. If the random variable X represents the experimental error (in light years), write down the probability distribution of X.

7) X and Y are independent random variables with $X \sim \text{U}[4, 8]$ and $Y \sim \text{U}[-8, 12]$. Find:
   a) $\text{P}(X < 6 \text{ and } Y > 0)$, b) $\text{P}(X < 6 \text{ or } Y > 0)$.

8) I travel by train to work five days per week.
   My morning train is randomly delayed every morning by anything up to 12 minutes.
   If the delay is any greater than 8 minutes, I arrive late for work.
   a) Find the probability that I am late for work on a randomly chosen day during a particular week.
   b) Find the probability that I arrive on time every day during a particular week.
   c) Find the probability that I am late for work more than once during a single week.

9) The random variable X follows a binomial distribution: $X \sim \text{B}(100, 0.45)$.
   Using a normal approximation and continuity corrections, find:
   a) $\text{P}(X > 50)$, b) $\text{P}(X \leq 45)$, c) $\text{P}(40 < X \leq 47)$.

10) The random variable X follows a Poisson distribution: $X \sim \text{Po}(25)$.
    Using a normal approximation and continuity corrections, find:
    a) $\text{P}(X \leq 20)$, b) $\text{P}(X > 15)$, c) $\text{P}(20 \leq X < 30)$.

11) I need a new car, because the number of times my current car breaks down per week follows the distribution Po(50). My current record number of breakdowns in a single week is 55.
    Find the probability that I set a new record next week.

12) Seven people on average join the queue in the local post office every 15 minutes during the 7 hours it is open. The number of people working in the post office is constantly adjusted depending on how busy it is, with the result that there is a constant probability of 0.7 of any person being served within 1 minute.
    a) Find the probability of more than 200 people joining the queue in the post office on a particular day.
    b) If exactly 200 people come to the post office on a particular day, what is the probability that less than 70% of them are seen within a minute?

S2 Section 4 — Practice Questions

One last hurdle before you can consider yourself fully up to speed with continuous distributions.
If you get any of these questions wrong, then go over the hurdle again.

Exam Questions

1 The random variable X is binomially distributed with $X \sim B(100, 0.6)$.

a) (i) State the conditions needed for X to be well approximated by a normal distribution. *(2 marks)*

(ii) Explain why a continuity correction is necessary in these circumstances. *(2 marks)*

b) Using a suitable approximation, find:

(i) $P(X \geq 65)$ *(4 marks)*

(ii) $P(50 < X < 62)$ *(3 marks)*

2 A 40 cm length of ribbon is cut in two at a random point.
The random variable X represents the length of the shorter piece of ribbon in cm.

a) Specify the probability distribution of X. *(2 marks)*

b) Sketch the probability density function of X. *(1 mark)*

c) Calculate $E(X)$ and $Var(X)$. *(3 marks)*

d) Find:

(i) $P(X > 5)$, *(1 mark)*

(ii) $P(X = 2)$. *(1 mark)*

3 The random variable X follows a binomial distribution: $X \sim B(n, p)$.
X is approximated by the normally distributed random variable Y.
Using this normal approximation, $P(X \leq 151) = 0.8944$ and $P(X > 127) = 0.9970$.

a) Find the mean and standard deviation of the normal approximation. *(8 marks)*

b) Use your results from a) to find n and p. *(4 marks)*

4 A factory has the capacity to increase its output by 50 items per week. A potential new customer has said it could sign a contract to order an average of 40 items per week, although the exact number of items needed each week will vary according to a Poisson distribution.

a) Specify a distribution that could be used to model the number of extra items that will be ordered per week if the new contract is signed. *(1 mark)*

b) Using a suitable approximation, find the probability that the number of items the potential new customer will order in a given week will exceed the factory's spare capacity. *(3 marks)*

c) The contract says that if the factory does not meet the new customer's order in two consecutive weeks, the factory must pay compensation. The factory's manager decides that he will only sign the contract if the probability of having to pay compensation is less than 0.01. Should the factory's manager sign the contract? Explain your answer. *(1 mark)*

Populations and Samples

No time for any small talk, I'm afraid. It's straight on with the business of populations and how to find out about them.

A Population is a Group of people or items

For any statistical investigation, there will be a group of people or items that you want to find out about. This group is called the population.

This could be:

- All the students in a maths class
- All the penguins in Antarctica
- All the chocolate puddings produced by a company in a year

1) Populations are said to be finite if it's possible for someone to count how many members there are. E.g. all the students in a maths class would be a finite population.
2) If it's impossible to know exactly how many members there are, the population is said to be infinite.

A population might have a finite number of members in theory, but if it's impossible to count them all in practice, the population is infinite.

E.g. all the blades of grass in a field would be an infinite population (even though you could count them all in theory).

To collect information about your population, you can carry out a survey. This means questioning the people or examining the items.

A Census surveys the Whole Population

When you collect information from every member of a population, it's called a census.

To do this, your population needs to be finite. It also helps if it's fairly small and easily accessible — so that getting information from every member is a straightforward task.

You need to know the advantages and disadvantages of doing a census, so here they are:

Census — Advantages

1) You get accurate information about the population, because every member has been surveyed.
2) It's a true representation of the population — it's unbiased.

See the next page for more on bias.

Census — Disadvantages

1) For large populations, it takes a lot of time and effort to carry out.
2) This makes it expensive to do.
3) It can be difficult to make sure all members are surveyed. If some are missed, bias can creep in.
4) If the tested items are used up or damaged in some way, a census is impractical.

Watch out for anything that might make doing a census a silly idea.

A Sample is Part of a Population

If doing a census is impossible or impractical, you can find out about a population by questioning or examining just a selection of the people or items. This selected group is called a sample.

Before selecting your sample, you need to identify the sampling units — these are the individual members of the population. A full list of all the sampling units is called a sampling frame. This list must give a unique name or number to each sampling unit, and is used to represent the population when selecting a random sample (see the next page).

EXAMPLE A company produces 100 chocolate puddings every day, and each pudding is labelled with a unique product number. Every day, a sample of 5 puddings is eaten as part of a quality control test.

a) Why is it necessary for the company to take a sample rather than carry out a census?

If they ate all the puddings, there would be none left to sell.

b) Identify the sampling units.

The individual puddings

c) Suggest a sampling frame.

A list of all one hundred unique product numbers.

A sampling frame can only be produced when you know exactly who or what makes up the population.

I wouldn't mind sampling some chocolate puddings...

A slow start to the section, I'll grant you that. But just because there aren't any sums to do doesn't mean you can skim over this stuff. It's the basis of what's to come. And they like to ask you to identify sampling frames and units in exam questions.

Sampling

This page is about the three Rs — Representative samples, Random sampling, and Racoons...

A Sample needs to be Representative of its Population

Data collected from a sample is used to draw conclusions about the whole population (see p.134). So, it's vital that the sample is as much like the population as possible. A biased sample is one which doesn't fairly represent the population.

To Avoid Sampling Bias:

1. Select from the correct population and make sure none of the population is excluded — that means drawing up an accurate sampling frame and sticking to it. E.g. if you want to find out the views of residents from a particular street, your sample should only include residents from that street and should be chosen from a full list of the residents.
2. Select your sample at random — see below. Non-random sampling methods include things like the sampler just asking their friends — who might all give similar answers, or asking for volunteers — meaning they only get people with strong views on a subject.
3. Make sure all your sample members respond — otherwise the results could be biased. E.g. if some of your sampled residents are out when you go to interview them, it's important that you go back and get their views another time.

In Random Sampling, all Sampling Units are Equally Likely to be selected

In a Simple Random Sample...

- Every person or item in the population has an equal chance of being in the sample.
- Each selection is independent of every other selection.

Every single possible sample is equally likely.

1) To get a truly random sample, you need a complete list of the population — an accurate sampling frame.
2) To choose the sample, give every sampling unit a number. Then generate a list of random numbers and match them to the sampling units to select your sample.

Use a computer, calculator, dice or random number tables...

EXAMPLE A zoo has 80 racoons. Describe how the random number table opposite could be used to select a sample of three of them, for a study on tail lengths.

8330	3992	1840
0330	1290	3237
9165	4815	0766

A list of all 80 racoons.

1) First, draw up a sampling frame, giving each racoon a two-digit number between 01 and 80.
2) Then, find the first three numbers between 01 and 80 from the table, (30, 39 and 18), and select the racoons with the matching numbers.

You need to be able to Justify choosing a Sample over a Census

In most situations, it's more practical to survey a sample rather than carry out a census — make sure you can explain why. But remember, the downside is that your results might not be as reliable, either due to sampling bias, or just the natural variability between samples (see below).

Sampling — Advantages

1) Quicker and cheaper than a census, and easier to get hold of all the required information.
2) It's the only option when surveyed items are used up or damaged.

Sampling — Disadvantages

1) Variability between samples — each possible sample will give different results, so you could just happen to select one which doesn't accurately reflect the population. E.g. you could randomly pick the 3 racoons with the longest tails in one sample and the 3 with the shortest tails in another. One way to reduce the likelihood of large variability is by using a large sample size. The more sampling units that are surveyed, the more reliable the information should be.
2) Samples can easily be affected by sampling bias.

A sample should be a miniature version of the population...

Using simple random sampling should reduce the risk of sampling bias, and so increase the likelihood of reliable results. Random sampling also means that the selected observations are independent random variables with the same distribution as the population. This is an important assumption for the theory in this section, and you'll see more about it on the next page.

Statistics

So, you're pretty hot on sampling, but a sample in itself isn't much use. You need to know what to do with it. Read on.

Statistics are used to Estimate Population Parameters

Parameters are quantities that describe the characteristics of a population — e.g. the mean, variance, or proportion that satisfy certain criteria. Parameters can be estimated from sample data using quantities called statistics.

Statistics

A statistic is a quantity calculated only from the known observations in a sample.
A statistic is a random variable — it takes different values for different samples.

Greek letters, like μ and σ, are often used for parameters, and Latin letters (e.g. m, s) are used for statistics.

If a random sample $X_1, ..., X_n$ is taken from a population with mean μ and variance σ^2:

The sample mean $\overline{X} = \frac{\sum X_i}{n}$ and sample variance $S^2 = \frac{\sum (X_i - \overline{X})^2}{n-1}$ are statistics that can be used to estimate μ and σ^2.

It's important you can recognise what's a statistic and what's not...

EXAMPLE A random sample $X_1, ..., X_{10}$ is taken from a population with unknown mean, μ. State whether or not the following are statistics:

a) $X_{10} - X_1$ b) $\sum X_i$ c) $\sum X_i^2 - \mu$

a) Yes, b) Yes, c) No

c) depends on the unknown value of μ.

Back to what I was saying at the bottom of the last page... The 10 observations are independent random variables, defined as X_1, X_2, etc., and each takes a value from the population. A statistic calculated from these observations is also a random variable — its value depends on the values in the sample.

Every Statistic has a Sampling Distribution

If you took a sample of observations and calculated a particular statistic, then took another sample and calculated the same statistic, then took another sample, etc., you'd end up with lots of values of the same statistic.

The probability distribution of a statistic is called the sampling distribution — it gives all the possible values of the statistic, along with the corresponding probabilities. Finding sampling distributions often comes up in the exam.

EXAMPLES:

A pirate's treasure chest contains a large number of coins. Unfortunately, the pirate has been diddled and the chest only contains 5p and 10p coins. The ratio of 5p to 10p coins is 4:1.

a) A random sample of 2 coins is taken from the chest. List all the possible samples.
b) Let X_i represent the ith coin in the sample. Find the probability distribution of X_i.
c) Find the sampling distribution of the sample mean, $\overline{X}$.

You can use the same general method for other statistics, e.g. the median.

a) The possible samples are: (5, 5), (5, 10), (10, 5), (10, 10)

b) The probability distribution specifies all the possible values X_i could take, and the probabilities of each value:

x_i	5	10
$P(X_i = x_i)$	0.8	0.2

The ratio 4:1 gives P(5) = 4/5 and P(10) = 1/5 — that's 0.8 and 0.2 as decimals.

c) Calculate the mean for each sample — e.g. (5, 5) gives (5 + 5)/2 = 5. Then work out the probabilities:
$P(\overline{X} = 5) = P(5, 5) = 0.8 \times 0.8 = 0.64$ ← You can multiply the probabilities because X_1 and X_2 are independent.
$P(\overline{X} = 7.5) = P(5, 10) \text{ or } P(10, 5) = (0.8 \times 0.2) + (0.2 \times 0.8) = 0.32$
$P(\overline{X} = 10) = P(10, 10) = 0.2 \times 0.2 = 0.04$
So the sampling distribution of $\overline{X}$ is

$\bar{x}$	5	7.5	10
$P(\overline{X} = \bar{x})$	0.64	0.32	0.04

Check that these probabilities add up to 1 — if not, you've made a mistake.

In exam questions, you'll often have to find distributions for binomial or Poisson statistics like this...

A company makes celebrity-themed coat hangers. A constant proportion of the coat hangers they make are rejected for being not quite realistic enough. A random sample of 20 coat hangers is inspected. The random variable X_i is defined as: $X_i = 0$, if coat hanger$_i$ is acceptable and $X_i = 1$, if it's faulty. Write down the sampling distribution of the statistic $Y = \sum X_i$.

See S2 Section 1 for the binomial distribution.

Each coat hanger is an independent trial with constant probability, p, of being faulty, and Y is the number of faulty items. So, $Y \sim B(20, p)$ ← The proportion is unknown, so just call it p.

Null and Alternative Hypotheses

So this is what the section's been building up to — testing theories about a population. The technical waffle on the next two pages might feel a bit hard-going, but don't despair — it's paving the way for a return to some old friends later on.

A Hypothesis is a Statement you want to Test

You could easily be asked to define terms in the exam, so make sure you learn the definitions on the next two pages.

Hypothesis testing is about using sample data to test statements about population parameters. Unfortunately, it comes with a fleet of terms you need to know.

- **Null Hypothesis (H_0)** — a statement about the value of a population parameter. Your data may allow you to reject this hypothesis.
- **Alternative Hypothesis (H_1)** — a statement that describes the value of the population parameter if H_0 is rejected.
- **Hypothesis test** — a statistical test that tests the claim made about a parameter by H_0 against that made by H_1. It tests whether H_0 should be rejected or not, using evidence from sample data.
- **Test Statistic** — a statistic calculated from sample data which is used to decide whether or not to reject H_0.

1) For any hypothesis test, you need to write two hypotheses — a null hypothesis and an alternative hypothesis.
2) You often choose the null hypothesis to be something you actually think is false. This is because hypothesis tests can only show that statements are false — they can't prove that things are true. So, you're aiming to find evidence for what you think is true, by disproving what you think is false.
3) H_0 needs to give a specific value to the parameter, since all your calculations will be based on this value. You assume this value holds true for the test, then see if your data allows you to reject it. H_1 is then a statement that describes how you think the value of the parameter differs from the value given by H_0.
4) The test statistic you choose depends on the parameter you're interested in. It should be a 'summary' of the sample data, and should have a sampling distribution that can be calculated using the parameter value specified by H_0.

EXAMPLE A 4-sided spinner has sides labelled A–D. Jemma thinks that the spinner is biased towards side A. She spins it 20 times and counts the number of times, Y, that she gets side A.

a) Write down a suitable null hypothesis to test Jemma's theory.
b) Write down a suitable alternative hypothesis.
c) Describe the test statistic Jemma should use.

a) If you assume the spinner is unbiased, each side has a probability of 0.25 of being spun. Let p = the probability of spinning side A. Then:

$H_0: p = 0.25$ ← By assuming the spinner is unbiased, the parameter, p, can be given the specific value 0.25. Jemma is then interested in disproving this hypothesis.

b) If the spinner is biased towards side A, then the probability will be greater than 0.25. So: $H_1: p > 0.25$ ← This is what Jemma actually thinks.

c) The test statistic is Y, the number of times she gets side A. ← Assuming H_0 is true, the sampling distribution of Y is B(20, 0.25).

Hypothesis Tests can be One-Tailed or Two-Tailed

The 'tailed' business is to do with the critical region used by the test — see next page.

For H_0: $\theta = a$, where θ is a parameter and a is a number:

1) The test is one-tailed if H_1 is specific about the value of θ compared to a, i.e. H_1: $\theta > a$, or H_1: $\theta < a$.
2) The test is two-tailed if H_1 specifies only that θ doesn't equal a, i.e. H_1: $\theta \neq a$.

Whether you use a one-tailed or a two-tailed test depends on how you define H_1. And that depends on what you want to find out about the parameter and any suspicions you might have about it.

E.g. in the example above, Jemma suspects that the probability of getting side A is greater than 0.25. This is what she wants to test, so it is sensible to define H_1: $p > 0.25$.

If she wants to test for bias, but is unsure if it's towards or against side A, she could define H_1: $p \neq 0.25$.

A statistician's party game — pin two tails on the donkey...

Or should it be one? Anyway, a very important thing to remember is that the results of a hypothesis test are either 'reject H_0', or 'do not reject H_0' — which means you haven't found enough evidence to disprove H_0, and not that you've proved it.

Significance Levels and Critical Regions

You use the value of your test statistic to decide whether or not to reject your null hypothesis. Poor little unloved H_0.

*If your Data is **Significant**, Reject H_0*

1) You would reject H_0 if the observed value of the test statistic is unlikely under the null hypothesis.
2) The significance level of a test (α) determines how unlikely the value needs to be before H_0 is rejected. It also determines the strength of the evidence that the test has provided — the lower the value of α, the stronger the evidence you have for saying H_0 is false. You'll usually be told what level to use — e.g. 1% ($\alpha = 0.01$), 5% ($\alpha = 0.05$), or 10% ($\alpha = 0.1$). α is also the probability of incorrectly rejecting H_0 — i.e. of getting extreme data by chance.
3) To decide whether your result is significant:
   - Define the sampling distribution of the test statistic under the null hypothesis.
   - Calculate the probability of getting a value that's at least as extreme as the observed value from this distribution.
   - If the probability is less than or equal to the significance level, reject H_0 in favour of H_1.

EXAMPLE Javed wants to test at the 5% level whether or not a coin is biased towards tails. He tosses the coin 10 times and records the number of tails, X. He gets 9 tails.

a) Define suitable hypotheses for p, the probability of getting tails.
b) State the condition under which Javed would reject H_0.

P(at least as extreme as 9) means 9 or more.

a) $H_0: p = 0.5$ and $H_1: p > 0.5$.   b) Under H_0, $X \sim B(10, 0.5)$. If $P(X \geq 9) \leq 0.05$, Javed would reject H_0.

Significance level

*The **Critical Region** is the **Set of Significant Values***

1) The critical region (CR) is the set of all values of the test statistic that would cause you to reject H_0. It's chosen so that P(test statistic is in critical region) = α, or is as close to α as possible.
2) One-tailed tests have a single CR, containing the highest or lowest values. For two-tailed tests, the region is split into two — half at the lower end and half at the upper end. Each half has a probability of $\frac{1}{2}\alpha$.
3) To test whether your result is significant, find the critical region and if it contains the observed value, reject H_0.

Returning to the example above...

The table below shows the sampling distribution of X — the number of tails in 10 tosses, under H_0.

x	0	1	2	3	4	5	6	7	8	9	10
$P(X = x)$	0.001	0.010	0.044	0.117	0.205	0.246	0.205	0.117	0.044	0.010	0.001

This is B(10, 0.5).

Find the critical region for the test, at the 5% level.

This is a one-tailed test with $H_1: p > 0.5$, so you're only interested in the upper end of the distribution.

The critical region is the biggest possible set of 'high' values of X with a total probability of ≤ 0.05.

Try the set $X \geq 8$: $P(X \geq 8) = 0.044 + 0.010 + 0.001 = 0.055 > 0.05$
Try the set $X \geq 9$: $P(X \geq 9) = 0.010 + 0.001 = 0.011 < 0.05$

$\Rightarrow$ Critical region is $X \geq 9$

You need to justify your CR by writing down the probabilities.

Careful here: $P(X = x)$ can be $\leq \alpha$ without X being in the CR. E.g. $P(X = 8) = 0.044$, but 8 isn't in the CR because $P(X \geq 8) > \alpha$.

So values of 9 or 10 would cause you to reject $H_0: p = 0.5$.

The actual significance level of a test is the probability of rejecting H_0. This is often quite different from the level of significance originally asked for in the question.

The actual significance level is also the probability of incorrectly rejecting H_0.

E.g. for the above test, the actual significance level is $P(X \geq 9) = 0.011$, which is much lower than 0.05.

Exam questions often ask about the actual significance level — so make sure you understand the difference.

I repeat, X has entered the critical region — we have a significant situation...

Hope you've been following the last two pages closely. Basically, you need two hypotheses and the value of a test statistic calculated from sample data. By assuming H_0 is true, you can find the probabilities of the different values this statistic can take — if the observed value is unlikely enough, then reject H_0. Right, time to put all the different components together...

Hypothesis Tests and Binomial Distributions

OK, it's time to pick your best 'hypothesis testing' foot and put it firmly forward. It's also a good time to reacquaint yourself with binomial distributions, which you met in S2 Section 1. Have a look back there before you go any further.

Use a Hypothesis Test to Find Out about the Population Parameter p

The first step in exam questions is to work out which distribution to use to model the situation — you've a choice of binomial or Poisson. Words like 'proportion', 'percentage' or 'probability' are clues that it's binomial.

Hypothesis tests for the binomial parameter p all follow the same general method — shown in the example below.

EXAMPLE:

In a past census of employees, 20% were in favour of a change to working hours. A later survey is carried out on a random sample of 30 employees, and 2 vote for a change to hours. The manager claims that there has been a decrease in the proportion of employees in favour of a change to working hours.

Stating your hypotheses clearly, test the manager's claim at the 5% level of significance.

1) Start by identifying the population parameter that you're going to test:

   Let p = proportion of employees in favour of change to hours.

2) Write null and alternative hypotheses for p.
   If you assume there's been no change in the proportion: $H_0: p = 0.2$

   The manager's interested in whether the proportion has decreased, so: $H_1: p < 0.2$

   You assume there's been no change in the value of the parameter, so you can give it a value of 0.2. The alternative hypothesis states what the manager actually thinks.

3) State the test statistic X — the number of 'successes', and its sampling distribution under H_0.
   $X \sim B(n, p)$ where n is the number in the sample and p is the probability of 'success' under H_0.

   Let X = number of employees in sample who are in favour of change. Under H_0, $X \sim B(30, 0.2)$.

4) State the significance level of the test. Here it's 5%, so $\alpha = 0.05$.

   The sampling distribution of the test statistic uses the value $p = 0.2$.

5) Test for significance by finding the probability of a value for your test statistic at least as extreme as the observed value. This is a one-tailed test and you're interested in the lower end of the distribution.
   So you want to find the probability of X taking a value less than or equal to 2.

   Using the binomial tables (see p.149): $P(X \leq 2) = 0.0442$, and since $0.0442 < 0.05$, the result is significant.

6) Now write your conclusion. Remember, hypothesis testing is about disproving the null hypothesis, or not disproving it — i.e. rejecting H_0, or not rejecting it. So that's how you need to word your conclusion.
   And don't forget to answer the original question:

   There is evidence at the 5% level of significance to reject H_0 and to support the manager's claim that the proportion in favour of change has decreased.

   Always say "there is evidence to reject H_0", or "there is insufficient evidence to reject H_0". Never talk about "accepting H_0" or "rejecting H_1".

And if you're asked (or prefer) to find a critical region, your test would look the same except for step 5...

5) Test for significance by finding the critical region for a test at this level of significance.
   This is a one-tailed test and you're interested in the lower end of the distribution.
   The critical region is the biggest possible set of 'low' values of X with a total probability of ≤ 0.05.

   Using the binomial tables: Try $X \leq 2$: $P(X \leq 2) = 0.0442 < 0.05$. Now try $X \leq 3$: $P(X \leq 3) = 0.1227 > 0.05$.
   So, CR is $X \leq 2$. These results fall in the CR, so the result is significant.

My hypothesis is — this is very likely to come up in the exam...

There are different sorts of questions that might come up on hypothesis testing. But this is the basic method, so make sure you learn it inside out. Cover the page and outline the six steps. Then work through the example again yourself.

Hypothesis Tests and Binomial Distributions

A couple more examples here of the sorts of questions that might come up in the exam. Aren't I kind.

EXAMPLES:

Exam questions can be a bit more involved than just asking for a straightforward hypothesis test. They want to know about critical regions and actual significance levels, which makes the whole thing a bit more long-winded.

EXAMPLE 1 — USING CRITICAL REGIONS

Records show that the proportion of trees in a wood that suffer from a particular leaf disease is 15%. Chloe thinks that recent weather conditions might have affected this proportion. She examines a random sample of 20 of the trees.

a) Using a 10% level of significance, find the critical region for a two-tailed test of Chloe's theory. The probability of rejection in each tail should be less than 0.05.

b) Find the actual significance level of a test based on your critical region from part a).

Chloe finds that 8 of the sampled trees have the leaf disease.

c) Comment on this finding in relation to your answer to part a) and Chloe's theory.

Read part a) carefully — you could be asked to make the probability in each tail as close as possible to $\frac{1}{2}\alpha$, rather than less than.

a) Let p = proportion of trees with the leaf disease.

$H_0: p = 0.15 \quad H_1: p \neq 0.15$

Let X = number of sampled trees with the disease. Under H_0, $X \sim B(20, 0.15)$.

$\alpha = 0.1$, and since the test is two-tailed, the probability of X falling in each tail should be 0.05, at most.

This is a two-tailed test, so you're interested in both ends of the sampling distribution.
The lower tail is the biggest possible set of 'low' values of X with a total probability of ≤ 0.05.
The upper tail is the biggest possible set of 'high' values of X with a total probability of ≤ 0.05.

Using the tables:

Lower tail:
$P(X \leq 0) = 0.0388 < 0.05$
$P(X \leq 1) = 0.1756 > 0.05$

Upper tail: (Look up $P(X \leq x - 1)$ and subtract from 1.)
$P(X \geq 6) = 1 - P(X \leq 5) = 1 - 0.9327 = 0.0673 > 0.05$
$P(X \geq 7) = 1 - P(X \leq 6) = 1 - 0.9781 = 0.0219 < 0.05$

So, CR is $X = 0$ or $X \geq 7$.

If you wanted the probability to be as close as possible to 0.05 instead of less than, the upper tail would be $X \geq 6$.

b) The actual significance level is $P(X = 0) + P(X \geq 7) = 0.0388 + 0.0219 = 0.0607$. ← You could also give this as 6.07%.

c) The observed value of 8 is in the critical region. So there is evidence at the 10% level of significance to reject H_0 and to support Chloe's theory that there has been a change in the proportion of affected trees.

And if you can't use the tables for your value of p, you have to use the binomial formula to work things out.

EXAMPLE 2 — WITHOUT USING TABLES

The proportion of pupils at a school who support the local football team is found to be $\frac{1}{3}$. Nigel attends a school nearby and claims that there is less support for the same local team at his school. In a random sample of 20 pupils from Nigel's school, 3 support the local team. Use a 5% level of significance to test Nigel's claim.

Let p = proportion of pupils who support the local team.

$H_0: p = \frac{1}{3} \quad H_1: p < \frac{1}{3}$

Let X = number of sampled pupils supporting the team. Under H_0, $X \sim B(20, \frac{1}{3})$. $\alpha = 0.05$.

Now you need to find the probability of getting a value less than or equal to 3. The tables don't have values for $p = \frac{1}{3}$, so you need to work out the probabilities individually and add them up:

See p.100 for the binomial formula. Here you need to use: $\binom{20}{x}(\frac{1}{3})^x(\frac{2}{3})^{20-x}$

$$P(X \leq 3) = P(X = 0) + P(X = 1) + P(X = 2) + P(X = 3)$$
$$= (\tfrac{2}{3})^{20} + 20(\tfrac{1}{3})(\tfrac{2}{3})^{19} + 190(\tfrac{1}{3})^2(\tfrac{2}{3})^{18} + 1140(\tfrac{1}{3})^3(\tfrac{2}{3})^{17} = 0.0604$$

$0.0604 > 0.05$, so the result is not significant. There is insufficient evidence at the 5% level of significance to reject H_0 and to support Nigel's claim that there is less support for the team.

If your value of p isn't in the binomial tables, don't panic...

You won't find $p = 0.2438$ in the tables, or even $p = 0.24$, for that matter. But this isn't a problem as long as you know how to use the binomial formula. And remember, the actual significance level isn't necessarily just α — that would be too easy.

Hypothesis Tests and Poisson Distributions

You can do exactly the same type of test, but for Poisson distributions. The Poisson parameter is λ.

Use a **Hypothesis Test** to **Find Out** about the **Population Parameter** λ

If λ is the rate at which an event occurs in a population and X is the number of those events that occur in a random interval, then X can be used as the test statistic for testing theories on λ.

EXAMPLE A bookshop sells copies of the book *'All you've never wanted to know about the Poisson distribution'* at a (surprisingly high) rate of 10 a week. The shop's manager decides to reduce the price of the book. In one randomly selected week after the price change, 16 copies are sold. Use a 10% level of significance to test whether there is evidence to suggest that sales of the book have increased.

Let λ = the rate at which copies of the book are sold per week.

$H_0: \lambda = 10 \quad H_1: \lambda > 10$

Let X = number of copies sold in a random week. Under H_0, $X \sim \text{Po}(10)$. $\alpha = 0.1$.

The mention of 'rate' tells you that the situation can be modelled by a Poisson distribution.

To find the probability of X taking a value greater than or equal to 16, use the Poisson tables (see p.154):

$P(X \geq 16) = 1 - P(X \leq 15) = 1 - 0.9513 = 0.0487$, and since $0.0487 < 0.1$, the result is significant.

Don't forget the conclusion:

There is evidence at the 10% level of significance to reject H_0 and to suggest that sales have increased.

If the Numbers are **Awkward**, you can use **Approximations**

If $X \sim B(n, p)$ for large n and small p, then X can be approximated by $\text{Po}(np)$.

See p.110 for more on the Poisson approximation.

EXAMPLE May has a crazy, 20-sided dice, which she thinks might be biased towards the number 1. She rolls the dice 100 times and gets 12 ones. Test May's theory at the 1% level of significance.

If the dice is unbiased, $P(1) = 1 \div 20 = 0.05$.

So, $H_0: p = 0.05$ and $H_1: p > 0.05$, where p is the probability of rolling a 1.
Let X = number of ones in 100 rolls. Under H_0, $X \sim B(100, 0.05)$. $\alpha = 0.01$.

You can't look up $n = 100$ in the tables, but n is big and p is quite small, so X can be approximated by Po(5).
So using the Poisson tables:

$P(X \geq 12) = 1 - P(X \leq 11) = 1 - 0.9945 = 0.0055$. $0.0055 < 0.01$, so it's significant at the 1% level. There is very strong evidence to reject H_0 and to support May's claim that the dice is biased towards the number 1.

The evidence provided by this test is much stronger than the evidence provided by the test in the example above, because the value of α is much lower. So you can be more confident that you've correctly rejected H_0.

If $X \sim \text{Po}(\lambda)$ and λ is large, then the approximation $X \sim N(\lambda, \lambda)$ can be used. See p.126-129 for a reminder of normal approximations.

EXAMPLE An automated sewing machine produces faults randomly, at an average of 5 per day. The machine is improved, and in a random five-day period, 20 faults are found. Using a suitable approximation, test at the 5% significance level whether the number of faults has decreased.

$H_0: \lambda = 5$ and $H_1: \lambda < 5$.

Let X = number of faults in 5 days. Under H_0, $X \sim \text{Po}(25) \Rightarrow X \sim N(25, 25)$.

λ is large, so you can approximate by using a normal distribution.

$P(X \leq 20) = P(X < 20.5) = P\left(Z < \frac{20.5 - 25}{\sqrt{25}}\right)$

Don't forget to include the continuity correction — see p.126. Here ≤ 20 becomes < 20.5.

$= P(Z < -0.9) = 1 - P(Z < 0.9) = 1 - 0.8159 = 0.1841$. $0.1841 > 0.05$, so there's insufficient evidence at the 5% level of significance to reject H_0. There is insufficient evidence to say that the number of faults has decreased.

Questions on hypothesis testing in exam papers ~ Po(2)...

The different types of questions on the last page can come up for Poisson too — e.g. working out critical regions, or using the Poisson probability formula (p.107) to calculate probabilities. Go through the first two examples on this page again, but this time carry out the tests by finding the critical region each time. And make sure you know the rules for approximating.

S2 Section 5 — Practice Questions

Phew, that section really did have a bit of everything — you could say it was a smorgasbord of tasty S2 treats. To make sure you've fully digested everything on offer, finish off with these delicious practice questions.

Warm-up Questions

1) The manager of a tennis club wants to know if members are happy with the facilities provided.
   a) Identify the population the manager is interested in.
   b) Identify the sampling units.
   c) Suggest a suitable sampling frame.

2) For each of the following situations, explain whether it would be more sensible to carry out a census or a sample survey:
   a) Marcel is in charge of a packaging department of 8 people. He wants to know the average number of items a person packs per day.
   b) A toy manufacturer produces batches of 500 toys. As part of a safety check, they want to test the toys to work out the strength needed to pull them apart.
   c) Tara has a biased dice. She wants to find the proportion of dice rolls that will result in a 'three'.

3) Why is it a good idea to use simple random sampling to select a sample?

4) The weights of a population of jars of pickled onions have unknown mean μ and standard deviation σ. A random sample of 50 weights (X_1, ..., X_{50}) are recorded. For each of the following, say whether or not it's a statistic:

   a) $\frac{X_{25}+X_{26}}{2}$ b) $\sum X_i - \sigma$ c) $\sum X_i^2 + \mu$ d) $\frac{\sum X_i}{50}$

5) For each of the following, state whether a one-tailed or two-tailed hypothesis test should be used. Define suitable null and alternative hypotheses for each test.
   a) Salma thinks a coin might be biased. She wants to find out about p, the proportion of coin tosses that result in 'heads'.
   b) The number of errors made by a typist every hour follows a Poisson distribution with mean $\lambda = 20$. After receiving some training, the typist wants to test whether he now makes fewer errors.

6) Suggest suitable test statistics for hypothesis tests of:
   a) A binomial parameter, p. b) The mean, λ, of a Poisson distribution.

7) a) Carry out the following tests of the binomial parameter p. Let X represent the number of successes in a random sample of size 20:
   (i) Test H_0: $p = 0.2$ against H_1: $p < 0.2$, at the 5% significance level, using $x = 2$.
   (ii) Test H_0: $p = 0.4$ against H_1: $p > 0.4$, at the 1% significance level, using $x = 15$.

   b) Carry out the following tests of the Poisson parameter λ. Let X represent the number of events in a given interval and λ be the average rate at which they are assumed to occur in intervals of identical size:
   (i) Test H_0: $\lambda = 7$ against H_1: $\lambda < 7$, at the 5% significance level, using $x = 3$.
   (ii) Test H_0: $\lambda = 2.5$ against H_1: $\lambda > 2.5$, at the 10% significance level, using $x = 4$.

8) a) Find the critical region for the following test where $X \sim B(10, p)$: Test H_0: $p = 0.3$ against H_1: $p < 0.3$, at the 5% significance level.
   b) Find the critical region for the following test where $X \sim Po(\lambda)$: Test H_0: $\lambda = 6$ against H_1: $\lambda < 6$, at the 10% significance level

S2 Section 5 — Practice Questions

As the bright lights of S2 slowly fade into the distance, you're about to descend into the murky gloom of some practice exams. To make it out the other side, you'll need all the exam-style practice you can get. And that means doing these questions.

Exam Questions

1 Prize draw tickets are drawn from a container, inside which are large quantities of tickets numbered with '1' or '2'. The tickets correspond to 1 or 2 prizes. 70% have the number 1 and 30% have the number 2.

A random sample of 3 tickets is drawn from the container. Find the sampling distribution for the median, M, of the numbers on the tickets.

(7 marks)

2 Over a long period of time, the chef at an Italian restaurant has found that there is a probability of 0.2 that a customer ordering a dessert on a weekday evening will order tiramisu. He thinks that the proportion of customers ordering desserts on Saturday evenings who order tiramisu is greater than 0.2.

a) State the name of the probability distribution that would be used in a hypothesis test for the value of p, the proportion of Saturday evening dessert eaters ordering tiramisu. *(1 mark)*

A random sample of 20 customers who ordered a dessert on a Saturday evening was taken. 7 of these customers ordered tiramisu.

b) (i) Stating your hypotheses clearly, test the chef's theory at the 5% level of significance.

(ii) Find the minimum number of tiramisu orders needed for the result to be significant.

(7 marks)

3 A tennis player serves a fault on her first serve at an average rate of 4 per service game. The player receives some extra coaching. In a randomly selected set of tennis, she serves 12 first-serve faults in 5 service games. She wants to test whether her average rate of first-serve faults has decreased.

a) Write down the conditions needed for the number of first-serve faults per service game to be modelled by a Poisson distribution. *(2 marks)*

Assume the conditions you stated in part a) hold.

b) Using a suitable approximation, carry out the test at the 5% level of significance. *(6 marks)*

4 The residents of a town are being asked their views on a plan to build a wind farm in the area. Environmental campaigners claim that 10% of the residents are against the plan. A random sample of 50 residents is surveyed.

a) Using a 10% significance level, find the critical region for a two-tailed test of this claim. The probability of rejecting each tail should be as close as possible to 5%. *(5 marks)*

b) State the probability of incorrectly rejecting H_0 using your critical region from part a). *(2 marks)*

It's found that 4 of the sampled residents say they are against the plan.

c) Comment on this finding in relation to the environmental campaigners' claim. *(2 marks)*

General Certificate of Education
Advanced Subsidiary (AS) and Advanced Level

Statistics S2 — Practice Exam One

Time Allowed: 1 hour 30 min

Calculators may be used for this exam (except those with facilities for symbolic algebra, differentiation or integration).

Give any non-exact numerical answers to an appropriate degree of accuracy.

Statistical tables can be found on page 148. Values used from these tables must be quoted in full.

There are 75 marks available for this paper.

1 The number of houses, X, sold each week by an estate agent in a small town can be modelled by a Poisson distribution. The estate agent sells houses at an average rate of 2 per week.

a) Find the probability that in a randomly selected week, the estate agent will sell:

(i) exactly 1 house, *(2 marks)*

(ii) at least 2 houses but no more than 4 houses. *(3 marks)*

b) To qualify for a "monthly bonus", the estate agent needs to sell at least 2 houses each week for 4 consecutive weeks. Find the probability that the estate agent qualifies for the "monthly bonus" over the next 4-week period. *(3 marks)*

c) Find the probability that the estate agent sells at least 2 houses in exactly 30 of the next 52 weeks. *(2 marks)*

d) Use a suitable approximation to find the probability that the estate agent will sell less than 52 houses over the next 26 weeks. *(6 marks)*

2 The continuous random variable X has the probability density function

$$f(x) = \begin{cases} \frac{kx}{2} & \text{for } 0 \leq x < 2 \\ \frac{k}{3}(5 - x) & \text{for } 2 \leq x \leq 5 \\ 0 & \text{otherwise} \end{cases}$$

where k is a positive constant.

a) Sketch the graph of $f(x)$. *(2 marks)*

b) Find the value of k. *(2 marks)*

c) Specify fully the cumulative distribution function, $F(x)$, of X. *(6 marks)*

d) Hence, or otherwise, calculate the median, m, of X. *(3 marks)*

3 An average of 5% of chocolate bars made by a particular manufacturer contain a 'golden ticket'. A student buys 5 chocolate bars every week for 8 weeks. The number of golden tickets he finds is represented by the random variable X.

a) State two necessary conditions for X to follow the binomial distribution B(40, 0.05). *(2 marks)*

b) Assuming that $X \sim \text{B}(40, 0.05)$, find:

(i) $\text{P}(X > 1)$, *(2 marks)*

(ii) $\text{E}(X)$. *(1 mark)*

c) Two other students also buy a total of 40 chocolate bars each. The total number of golden tickets the three students find between them is represented by the random variable Y.

Using a suitable approximation, find the probability that they find a total of at least 3 golden tickets between them. *(3 marks)*

4 Each day, a particular train can arrive at a random time between 2 minutes before its scheduled time and 9 minutes after. The continuous random variable X represents the number of minutes after its scheduled time the train arrives (and will be negative if the train is early).

a) Specify the distribution of X. *(1 mark)*

b) (i) Find the probability that the train is more than 6 minutes late. *(2 marks)*

(ii) Find the probability that the train arrives within 1 minute of its scheduled arrival time (either early or late). *(1 mark)*

c) A commuter catches this same train 5 days a week. If the train is more than 6 minutes late, he will miss a connecting train.

Calculate the probability that the commuter will miss the connecting train at least twice during a particular week. *(4 marks)*

5 A home furnishings manufacturer makes curtains using a particular type of fabric. The fabric has, on average, 10 defects per 10 metre roll, which occur randomly. The company's manager decides that they should buy the fabric from a different supplier, who sells the same type of fabric, but in 5 metre rolls.

The manager examines a randomly selected roll of fabric from the new supplier. It has 3 defects. She claims that the fabric from the new supplier has fewer defects than the fabric from the old supplier.

Stating your hypotheses clearly, use a 10% level of significance to test the manager's claim.

(6 marks)

6 A particular model of car is prone to developing a rattle in the first year after being made. The probability of any particular car developing this rattle is 0.65.

a) In a random sample of 20 cars of this model, find the probability that:

(i) at least 12 but fewer than 15 cars rattle,

(3 marks)

(ii) more than half of the cars rattle.

(1 mark)

b) A further 5 random samples of 20 cars are tested.
Find the probability that more than half of the cars in exactly 3 of these 5 samples rattle.

(3 marks)

c) The manufacturers decide to test a larger sample, consisting of 200 cars.
Use a suitable approximation to find the probability of exactly 140 cars having the rattle.

(5 marks)

7 A student wants to find out what the most popular type of music is amongst all the pupils in her school. She decides to ask a sample of 50 of the 1425 pupils.

a) Identify the population the student is interested in.

(1 mark)

b) Suggest a suitable sampling frame for the student to use.

(1 mark)

Another student says that it would be better to carry out a census, rather than take a sample.

c) Give one reason why they might have said this.

(1 mark)

8 a) Explain what is meant by each of the following:

(i) a two-tailed hypothesis test

(2 marks)

(ii) actual significance level

(1 mark)

Jack runs 'beginners' judo classes. He estimates that one fifth of the people who attend his classes have done judo before. To test this, he plans to question a random sample of 20 of the people who attend his classes.

b) Find the critical region for a two-tailed test of Jack's hypothesis.
The probability in each tail should be less than or equal to 2.5%.

(5 marks)

c) Find the actual significance level of a test based on your critical region from part b).

(1 mark)

General Certificate of Education
Advanced Subsidiary (AS) and Advanced Level

Statistics S2 — Practice Exam Two

Time Allowed: 1 hour 30 min

Calculators may be used for this exam (except those with facilities for symbolic algebra, differentiation or integration).

Give any non-exact numerical answers to an appropriate degree of accuracy.

Statistical tables can be found on page 148.
Values used from these tables must be quoted in full.

There are 75 marks available for this paper.

1 A scientist is testing a household cleaning product. She cleans a tile on which bacteria have been grown, then examines how many bacteria survive. Surviving bacteria are spread randomly on the tile.

a) An average of 6 bacteria per square centimetre are initially assumed to survive.
If the random variable X represents the number of surviving bacteria in a randomly chosen square centimetre of tile, find:

(i) $P(X < 10)$ *(2 marks)*

(ii) $P(5 \leq X \leq 7)$ *(3 marks)*

b) During one test, the scientist counts the total number of surviving bacteria on 15 randomly chosen square centimetres of tile.
The scientist's results can be summarised as: $\Sigma x = 83$ and $\Sigma x^2 = 543$.
Calculate the mean and the variance of the number of surviving bacteria per square centimetre. Give your answers to 2 decimal places. *(3 marks)*

c) Explain why the data in b) support the use of a Poisson distribution to model the number of surviving bacteria per square centimetre. *(1 mark)*

d) Use your mean from b) to find $P(X = 5)$. *(2 marks)*

2 The continuous random variable X has the cumulative distribution function

$$F(x) = \begin{cases} 0 & \text{for } x < 0 \\ 0.5x^4 + 0.2x & \text{for } 0 \leq x \leq 1 \\ 9.2x - 3.5x^2 - k & \text{for } 1 < x \leq 1.2 \\ 1 & \text{for } x > 1.2 \end{cases}$$

for some constant k.

a) Find the value of k. *(2 marks)*

b) Given that the lower quartile (Q_1) of X is 0.688, calculate the interquartile range. Give your answer correct to two decimal places. *(3 marks)*

c) Find the probability density function, $f(x)$, of X. *(3 marks)*

d) Find the mode of X. *(2 marks)*

3 The probability of a randomly selected car having a potentially dangerous fault is 0.07.
A random sample of 100 cars from across the country is tested.
The random variable C represents the total number of cars in the sample having a potentially dangerous fault.

a) Specify fully a suitable distribution that could be used to model C. *(1 mark)*

b) Find $P(5 < C \leq 13)$ using:

(i) a Poisson approximation, *(3 marks)*

(ii) a normal approximation. *(4 marks)*

c) Comment on which of your estimates in b) you would expect to be more accurate. *(1 mark)*

4 A machine tool is set up to produce metal cylinders with a diameter of exactly 42 mm. However, the actual diameters of the finished cylinders differ randomly by as much as 0.5 mm from the intended value.

a) Let the random variable X represent the actual diameter (in mm) of the cylinders produced.

(i) Specify the probability density function, $f(x)$, of X. *(1 mark)*

(ii) Calculate $E(X)$ and $Var(X)$. *(2 marks)*

(iii) Find $F(x)$, the cumulative distribution function of X. *(2 marks)*

(iv) Hence or otherwise find the median, m, of X. *(1 mark)*

b) One of the firm's customers says it can only accept cylinders that are within ±0.3 mm of 42 mm. No alterations are made to the machine tool.

(i) Find the probability that a random cylinder is acceptable to the customer. *(1 mark)*

(ii) The random variable Y represents the number of cylinders in a batch of 200 that are acceptable to the customer. Specify the distribution of Y. *(1 mark)*

(iii) Using a suitable approximation, find the probability that more than 65% of a batch of 200 cylinders will be acceptable to the customer. *(3 marks)*

5 A 'donkey-rides' business hires out donkeys for rides along the beach. The average rate at which customers want to hire a donkey on a weekday during the summer is 2 per hour.

a) Write down a suitable distribution to model the number of customers per hour. *(2 marks)*

b) Find the probability that in one randomly selected hour:

(i) there are fewer than 3 customers *(1 mark)*

(ii) there is exactly 1 customer *(2 marks)*

On Saturdays during the summer, the 'donkey-rides' business is open for 6 hours a day.
On one randomly selected Saturday, there are 25 customers.

c) Using a suitable approximation, test at the 1% level of significance whether there is evidence to suggest that there are more customers per hour on a Saturday than on a weekday. *(6 marks)*

6 Each student in a class has a standard pack of 52 cards, where each pack is made up of the same number of red and black cards and contains 12 picture cards in total.

a) One student picks 3 cards at random from her pack, without replacing the selected cards before the next pick. The random variable X represents the number of picture cards picked. Explain why X does not follow a binomial distribution. *(1 mark)*

b) Another student chooses 3 cards at random, but replaces each of the selected cards before the next pick. The random variable Y represents the number of picture cards picked. Calculate:

(i) the probability that the student chooses exactly two picture cards, *(2 marks)*

(ii) the mean of Y, *(1 mark)*

(ii) the variance of Y. *(1 mark)*

c) All 20 students in the group now choose 4 cards at random from their pack, replacing their selected cards each time. The random variable Q represents the number of students that choose exactly 3 red cards. Find the probability that Q is at least 2 but no greater than 8. *(4 marks)*

7 A random sample $X_1, ..., X_n$ is taken from a population with unknown variance σ^2.

a) For each of the following, say whether or not it's a statistic:

(i) $\frac{X_i - \overline{X}}{\sigma}$ *(1 mark)*

(ii) $\sum_{i=1}^{n} X_i$ *(1 mark)*

b) Describe what is meant by the sampling distribution of the statistic $\overline{X} = \frac{\sum X_i}{n}$. *(1 mark)*

8 Past records suggest that 45% of the members of a gym use the swimming pool. The gym's manager thinks that the popularity of the swimming pool has decreased over recent months.

a) A random sample of 16 gym members is surveyed and it is found that 3 of them use the pool. Using a 5% level of significance, test whether there is evidence to suggest that the popularity of the pool has decreased. *(7 marks)*

b) The manager decides that the same test should be done again, but this time using a larger sample. He surveys a random sample of 50 members and carries out the test. He concludes that at the 5% level of significance there is evidence to suggest that the popularity of the pool has decreased. Find the maximum possible number of gym members in the sample of 50 who use the pool. *(4 marks)*

EDEXCEL S2 — STATISTICAL TABLES

The normal distribution function

The cumulative distribution function $\Phi(z)$ is tabulated below. This is defined as $\Phi(z) = \frac{1}{\sqrt{2\pi}}\int_{-\infty}^{z} e^{-\frac{1}{2}t^2}\,dt$.

z	$\Phi(z)$	z	$\Phi(z)$	z	$\Phi(z)$	z	$\Phi(z)$	z	$\Phi(z)$
0.00	0.5000	0.50	0.6915	1.00	0.8413	1.50	0.9332	2.00	0.9772
0.01	0.5040	0.51	0.6950	1.01	0.8438	1.51	0.9345	2.02	0.9783
0.02	0.5080	0.52	0.6985	1.02	0.8461	1.52	0.9357	2.04	0.9793
0.03	0.5120	0.53	0.7019	1.03	0.8485	1.53	0.9370	2.06	0.9803
0.04	0.5160	0.54	0.7054	1.04	0.8508	1.54	0.9382	2.08	0.9812
0.05	0.5199	0.55	0.7088	1.05	0.8531	1.55	0.9394	2.10	0.9821
0.06	0.5239	0.56	0.7123	1.06	0.8554	1.56	0.9406	2.12	0.9830
0.07	0.5279	0.57	0.7157	1.07	0.8577	1.57	0.9418	2.14	0.9838
0.08	0.5319	0.58	0.7190	1.08	0.8599	1.58	0.9429	2.16	0.9846
0.09	0.5359	0.59	0.7224	1.09	0.8621	1.59	0.9441	2.18	0.9854
0.10	0.5398	0.60	0.7257	1.10	0.8643	1.60	0.9452	2.20	0.9861
0.11	0.5438	0.61	0.7291	1.11	0.8665	1.61	0.9463	2.22	0.9868
0.12	0.5478	0.62	0.7324	1.12	0.8686	1.62	0.9474	2.24	0.9875
0.13	0.5517	0.63	0.7357	1.13	0.8708	1.63	0.9484	2.26	0.9881
0.14	0.5557	0.64	0.7389	1.14	0.8729	1.64	0.9495	2.28	0.9887
0.15	0.5596	0.65	0.7422	1.15	0.8749	1.65	0.9505	2.30	0.9893
0.16	0.5636	0.66	0.7454	1.16	0.8770	1.66	0.9515	2.32	0.9898
0.17	0.5675	0.67	0.7486	1.17	0.8790	1.67	0.9525	2.34	0.9904
0.18	0.5714	0.68	0.7517	1.18	0.8810	1.68	0.9535	2.36	0.9909
0.19	0.5753	0.69	0.7549	1.19	0.8830	1.69	0.9545	2.38	0.9913
0.20	0.5793	0.70	0.7580	1.20	0.8849	1.70	0.9554	2.40	0.9918
0.21	0.5832	0.71	0.7611	1.21	0.8869	1.71	0.9564	2.42	0.9922
0.22	0.5871	0.72	0.7642	1.22	0.8888	1.72	0.9573	2.44	0.9927
0.23	0.5910	0.73	0.7673	1.23	0.8907	1.73	0.9582	2.46	0.9931
0.24	0.5948	0.74	0.7704	1.24	0.8925	1.74	0.9591	2.48	0.9934
0.25	0.5987	0.75	0.7734	1.25	0.8944	1.75	0.9599	2.50	0.9938
0.26	0.6026	0.76	0.7764	1.26	0.8962	1.76	0.9608	2.55	0.9946
0.27	0.6064	0.77	0.7794	1.27	0.8980	1.77	0.9616	2.60	0.9953
0.28	0.6103	0.78	0.7823	1.28	0.8997	1.78	0.9625	2.65	0.9960
0.29	0.6141	0.79	0.7852	1.29	0.9015	1.79	0.9633	2.70	0.9965
0.30	0.6179	0.80	0.7881	1.30	0.9032	1.80	0.9641	2.75	0.9970
0.31	0.6217	0.81	0.7910	1.31	0.9049	1.81	0.9649	2.80	0.9974
0.32	0.6255	0.82	0.7939	1.32	0.9066	1.82	0.9656	2.85	0.9978
0.33	0.6293	0.83	0.7967	1.33	0.9082	1.83	0.9664	2.90	0.9981
0.34	0.6331	0.84	0.7995	1.34	0.9099	1.84	0.9671	2.95	0.9984
0.35	0.6368	0.85	0.8023	1.35	0.9115	1.85	0.9678	3.00	0.9987
0.36	0.6406	0.86	0.8051	1.36	0.9131	1.86	0.9686	3.05	0.9989
0.37	0.6443	0.87	0.8078	1.37	0.9147	1.87	0.9693	3.10	0.9990
0.38	0.6480	0.88	0.8106	1.38	0.9162	1.88	0.9699	3.15	0.9992
0.39	0.6517	0.89	0.8133	1.39	0.9177	1.89	0.9706	3.20	0.9993
0.40	0.6554	0.90	0.8159	1.40	0.9192	1.90	0.9713	3.25	0.9994
0.41	0.6591	0.91	0.8186	1.41	0.9207	1.91	0.9719	3.30	0.9995
0.42	0.6628	0.92	0.8212	1.42	0.9222	1.92	0.9726	3.35	0.9996
0.43	0.6664	0.93	0.8238	1.43	0.9236	1.93	0.9732	3.40	0.9997
0.44	0.6700	0.94	0.8264	1.44	0.9251	1.94	0.9738	3.50	0.9998
0.45	0.6736	0.95	0.8289	1.45	0.9265	1.95	0.9744	3.60	0.9998
0.46	0.6772	0.96	0.8315	1.46	0.9279	1.96	0.9750	3.70	0.9999
0.47	0.6808	0.97	0.8340	1.47	0.9292	1.97	0.9756	3.80	0.9999
0.48	0.6844	0.98	0.8365	1.48	0.9306	1.98	0.9761	3.90	1.0000
0.49	0.6879	0.99	0.8389	1.49	0.9319	1.99	0.9767	4.00	1.0000
0.50	0.6915	1.00	0.8413	1.50	0.9332	2.00	0.9772		

Percentage points of the normal distribution

The z-values in the table are those which a random variable $Z \sim N(0, 1)$ exceeds with probability p, i.e. $P(Z > z) = 1 - \Phi(z) = p$.

p	z	p	z
0.5000	0.0000	0.0500	1.6449
0.4000	0.2533	0.0250	1.9600
0.3000	0.5244	0.0100	2.3263
0.2000	0.8416	0.0050	2.5758
0.1500	1.0364	0.0010	3.0902
0.1000	1.2816	0.0005	3.2905

EDEXCEL S2 — STATISTICAL TABLES

The binomial cumulative distribution function

The values below show $P(X \leq x)$, where $X \sim B(n, p)$.

	$p =$	0.05	0.10	0.15	0.20	0.25	0.30	0.35	0.40	0.45	0.50
$n = 5$	$x =$ 0	0.7738	0.5905	0.4437	0.3277	0.2373	0.1681	0.1160	0.0778	0.0503	0.0313
	1	0.9774	0.9185	0.8352	0.7373	0.6328	0.5282	0.4284	0.3370	0.2562	0.1875
	2	0.9988	0.9914	0.9734	0.9421	0.8965	0.8369	0.7648	0.6826	0.5931	0.5000
	3	1.0000	0.9995	0.9978	0.9933	0.9844	0.9692	0.9460	0.9130	0.8688	0.8125
	4	1.0000	1.0000	0.9999	0.9997	0.9990	0.9976	0.9947	0.9898	0.9815	0.9688
$n = 6$	$x =$ 0	0.7351	0.5314	0.3771	0.2621	0.1780	0.1176	0.0754	0.0467	0.0277	0.0156
	1	0.9672	0.8857	0.7765	0.6554	0.5339	0.4202	0.3191	0.2333	0.1636	0.1094
	2	0.9978	0.9842	0.9527	0.9011	0.8306	0.7443	0.6471	0.5443	0.4415	0.3438
	3	0.9999	0.9987	0.9941	0.9830	0.9624	0.9295	0.8826	0.8208	0.7447	0.6563
	4	1.0000	0.9999	0.9996	0.9984	0.9954	0.9891	0.9777	0.9590	0.9308	0.8906
	5	1.0000	1.0000	1.0000	0.9999	0.9998	0.9993	0.9982	0.9959	0.9917	0.9844
$n = 7$	$x =$ 0	0.6983	0.4783	0.3206	0.2097	0.1335	0.0824	0.0490	0.0280	0.0152	0.0078
	1	0.9556	0.8503	0.7166	0.5767	0.4449	0.3294	0.2338	0.1586	0.1024	0.0625
	2	0.9962	0.9743	0.9262	0.8520	0.7564	0.6471	0.5323	0.4199	0.3164	0.2266
	3	0.9998	0.9973	0.9879	0.9667	0.9294	0.8740	0.8002	0.7102	0.6083	0.5000
	4	1.0000	0.9998	0.9988	0.9953	0.9871	0.9712	0.9444	0.9037	0.8471	0.7734
	5	1.0000	1.0000	0.9999	0.9996	0.9987	0.9962	0.9910	0.9812	0.9643	0.9375
	6	1.0000	1.0000	1.0000	1.0000	0.9999	0.9998	0.9994	0.9984	0.9963	0.9922
$n = 8$	$x =$ 0	0.6634	0.4305	0.2725	0.1678	0.1001	0.0576	0.0319	0.0168	0.0084	0.0039
	1	0.9428	0.8131	0.6572	0.5033	0.3671	0.2553	0.1691	0.1064	0.0632	0.0352
	2	0.9942	0.9619	0.8948	0.7969	0.6785	0.5518	0.4278	0.3154	0.2201	0.1445
	3	0.9996	0.9950	0.9786	0.9437	0.8862	0.8059	0.7064	0.5941	0.4770	0.3633
	4	1.0000	0.9996	0.9971	0.9896	0.9727	0.9420	0.8939	0.8263	0.7396	0.6367
	5	1.0000	1.0000	0.9998	0.9988	0.9958	0.9887	0.9747	0.9502	0.9115	0.8555
	6	1.0000	1.0000	1.0000	0.9999	0.9996	0.9987	0.9964	0.9915	0.9819	0.9648
	7	1.0000	1.0000	1.0000	1.0000	1.0000	0.9999	0.9998	0.9993	0.9983	0.9961
$n = 9$	$x =$ 0	0.6302	0.3874	0.2316	0.1342	0.0751	0.0404	0.0207	0.0101	0.0046	0.0020
	1	0.9288	0.7748	0.5995	0.4362	0.3003	0.1960	0.1211	0.0705	0.0385	0.0195
	2	0.9916	0.9470	0.8591	0.7382	0.6007	0.4628	0.3373	0.2318	0.1495	0.0898
	3	0.9994	0.9917	0.9661	0.9144	0.8343	0.7297	0.6089	0.4826	0.3614	0.2539
	4	1.0000	0.9991	0.9944	0.9804	0.9511	0.9012	0.8283	0.7334	0.6214	0.5000
	5	1.0000	0.9999	0.9994	0.9969	0.9900	0.9747	0.9464	0.9006	0.8342	0.7461
	6	1.0000	1.0000	1.0000	0.9997	0.9987	0.9957	0.9888	0.9750	0.9502	0.9102
	7	1.0000	1.0000	1.0000	1.0000	0.9999	0.9996	0.9986	0.9962	0.9909	0.9805
	8	1.0000	1.0000	1.0000	1.0000	1.0000	1.0000	0.9999	0.9997	0.9992	0.9980
$n = 10$	$x =$ 0	0.5987	0.3487	0.1969	0.1074	0.0563	0.0282	0.0135	0.0060	0.0025	0.0010
	1	0.9139	0.7361	0.5443	0.3758	0.2440	0.1493	0.0860	0.0464	0.0233	0.0107
	2	0.9885	0.9298	0.8202	0.6778	0.5256	0.3828	0.2616	0.1673	0.0996	0.0547
	3	0.9990	0.9872	0.9500	0.8791	0.7759	0.6496	0.5138	0.3823	0.2660	0.1719
	4	0.9999	0.9984	0.9901	0.9672	0.9219	0.8497	0.7515	0.6331	0.5044	0.3770
	5	1.0000	0.9999	0.9986	0.9936	0.9803	0.9527	0.9051	0.8338	0.7384	0.6230
	6	1.0000	1.0000	0.9999	0.9991	0.9965	0.9894	0.9740	0.9452	0.8980	0.8281
	7	1.0000	1.0000	1.0000	0.9999	0.9996	0.9984	0.9952	0.9877	0.9726	0.9453
	8	1.0000	1.0000	1.0000	1.0000	1.0000	0.9999	0.9995	0.9983	0.9955	0.9893
	9	1.0000	1.0000	1.0000	1.0000	1.0000	1.0000	1.0000	0.9999	0.9997	0.9990

The binomial cumulative distribution function (continued)

	p =	0.05	0.10	0.15	0.20	0.25	0.30	0.35	0.40	0.45	0.50
n = 12	x = 0	0.5404	0.2824	0.1422	0.0687	0.0317	0.0138	0.0057	0.0022	0.0008	0.0002
	1	0.8816	0.6590	0.4435	0.2749	0.1584	0.0850	0.0424	0.0196	0.0083	0.0032
	2	0.9804	0.8891	0.7358	0.5583	0.3907	0.2528	0.1513	0.0834	0.0421	0.0193
	3	0.9978	0.9744	0.9078	0.7946	0.6488	0.4925	0.3467	0.2253	0.1345	0.0730
	4	0.9998	0.9957	0.9761	0.9274	0.8424	0.7237	0.5833	0.4382	0.3044	0.1938
	5	1.0000	0.9995	0.9954	0.9806	0.9456	0.8822	0.7873	0.6652	0.5269	0.3872
	6	1.0000	0.9999	0.9993	0.9961	0.9857	0.9614	0.9154	0.8418	0.7393	0.6128
	7	1.0000	1.0000	0.9999	0.9994	0.9972	0.9905	0.9745	0.9427	0.8883	0.8062
	8	1.0000	1.0000	1.0000	0.9999	0.9996	0.9983	0.9944	0.9847	0.9644	0.9270
	9	1.0000	1.0000	1.0000	1.0000	1.0000	0.9998	0.9992	0.9972	0.9921	0.9807
	10	1.0000	1.0000	1.0000	1.0000	1.0000	1.0000	0.9999	0.9997	0.9989	0.9968
	11	1.0000	1.0000	1.0000	1.0000	1.0000	1.0000	1.0000	1.0000	0.9999	0.9998
n = 15	x = 0	0.4633	0.2059	0.0874	0.0352	0.0134	0.0047	0.0016	0.0005	0.0001	0.0000
	1	0.8290	0.5490	0.3186	0.1671	0.0802	0.0353	0.0142	0.0052	0.0017	0.0005
	2	0.9638	0.8159	0.6042	0.3980	0.2361	0.1268	0.0617	0.0271	0.0107	0.0037
	3	0.9945	0.9444	0.8227	0.6482	0.4613	0.2969	0.1727	0.0905	0.0424	0.0176
	4	0.9994	0.9873	0.9383	0.8358	0.6865	0.5155	0.3519	0.2173	0.1204	0.0592
	5	0.9999	0.9978	0.9832	0.9389	0.8516	0.7216	0.5643	0.4032	0.2608	0.1509
	6	1.0000	0.9997	0.9964	0.9819	0.9434	0.8689	0.7548	0.6098	0.4522	0.3036
	7	1.0000	1.0000	0.9994	0.9958	0.9827	0.9500	0.8868	0.7869	0.6535	0.5000
	8	1.0000	1.0000	0.9999	0.9992	0.9958	0.9848	0.9578	0.9050	0.8182	0.6964
	9	1.0000	1.0000	1.0000	0.9999	0.9992	0.9963	0.9876	0.9662	0.9231	0.8491
	10	1.0000	1.0000	1.0000	1.0000	0.9999	0.9993	0.9972	0.9907	0.9745	0.9408
	11	1.0000	1.0000	1.0000	1.0000	1.0000	0.9999	0.9995	0.9981	0.9937	0.9824
	12	1.0000	1.0000	1.0000	1.0000	1.0000	1.0000	0.9999	0.9997	0.9989	0.9963
	13	1.0000	1.0000	1.0000	1.0000	1.0000	1.0000	1.0000	1.0000	0.9999	0.9995
	14	1.0000	1.0000	1.0000	1.0000	1.0000	1.0000	1.0000	1.0000	1.0000	1.0000
n = 20	x = 0	0.3585	0.1216	0.0388	0.0115	0.0032	0.0008	0.0002	0.0000	0.0000	0.0000
	1	0.7358	0.3917	0.1756	0.0692	0.0243	0.0076	0.0021	0.0005	0.0001	0.0000
	2	0.9245	0.6769	0.4049	0.2061	0.0913	0.0355	0.0121	0.0036	0.0009	0.0002
	3	0.9841	0.8670	0.6477	0.4114	0.2252	0.1071	0.0444	0.0160	0.0049	0.0013
	4	0.9974	0.9568	0.8298	0.6296	0.4148	0.2375	0.1182	0.0510	0.0189	0.0059
	5	0.9997	0.9887	0.9327	0.8042	0.6172	0.4164	0.2454	0.1256	0.0553	0.0207
	6	1.0000	0.9976	0.9781	0.9133	0.7858	0.6080	0.4166	0.2500	0.1299	0.0577
	7	1.0000	0.9996	0.9941	0.9679	0.8982	0.7723	0.6010	0.4159	0.2520	0.1316
	8	1.0000	0.9999	0.9987	0.9900	0.9591	0.8867	0.7624	0.5956	0.4143	0.2517
	9	1.0000	1.0000	0.9998	0.9974	0.9861	0.9520	0.8782	0.7553	0.5914	0.4119
	10	1.0000	1.0000	1.0000	0.9994	0.9961	0.9829	0.9468	0.8725	0.7507	0.5881
	11	1.0000	1.0000	1.0000	0.9999	0.9991	0.9949	0.9804	0.9435	0.8692	0.7483
	12	1.0000	1.0000	1.0000	1.0000	0.9998	0.9987	0.9940	0.9790	0.9420	0.8684
	13	1.0000	1.0000	1.0000	1.0000	1.0000	0.9997	0.9985	0.9935	0.9786	0.9423
	14	1.0000	1.0000	1.0000	1.0000	1.0000	1.0000	0.9997	0.9984	0.9936	0.9793
	15	1.0000	1.0000	1.0000	1.0000	1.0000	1.0000	1.0000	0.9997	0.9985	0.9941
	16	1.0000	1.0000	1.0000	1.0000	1.0000	1.0000	1.0000	1.0000	0.9997	0.9987
	17	1.0000	1.0000	1.0000	1.0000	1.0000	1.0000	1.0000	1.0000	1.0000	0.9998
	18	1.0000	1.0000	1.0000	1.0000	1.0000	1.0000	1.0000	1.0000	1.0000	1.0000

The binomial cumulative distribution function (continued)

	p =	0.05	0.10	0.15	0.20	0.25	0.30	0.35	0.40	0.45	0.50
n = 25	x = 0	0.2774	0.0718	0.0172	0.0038	0.0008	0.0001	0.0000	0.0000	0.0000	0.0000
	1	0.6424	0.2712	0.0931	0.0274	0.0070	0.0016	0.0003	0.0001	0.0000	0.0000
	2	0.8729	0.5371	0.2537	0.0982	0.0321	0.0090	0.0021	0.0004	0.0001	0.0000
	3	0.9659	0.7636	0.4711	0.2340	0.0962	0.0332	0.0097	0.0024	0.0005	0.0001
	4	0.9928	0.9020	0.6821	0.4207	0.2137	0.0905	0.0320	0.0095	0.0023	0.0005
	5	0.9988	0.9666	0.8385	0.6167	0.3783	0.1935	0.0826	0.0294	0.0086	0.0020
	6	0.9998	0.9905	0.9305	0.7800	0.5611	0.3407	0.1734	0.0736	0.0258	0.0073
	7	1.0000	0.9977	0.9745	0.8909	0.7265	0.5118	0.3061	0.1536	0.0639	0.0216
	8	1.0000	0.9995	0.9920	0.9532	0.8506	0.6769	0.4668	0.2735	0.1340	0.0539
	9	1.0000	0.9999	0.9979	0.9827	0.9287	0.8106	0.6303	0.4246	0.2424	0.1148
	10	1.0000	1.0000	0.9995	0.9944	0.9703	0.9022	0.7712	0.5858	0.3843	0.2122
	11	1.0000	1.0000	0.9999	0.9985	0.9893	0.9558	0.8746	0.7323	0.5426	0.3450
	12	1.0000	1.0000	1.0000	0.9996	0.9966	0.9825	0.9396	0.8462	0.6937	0.5000
	13	1.0000	1.0000	1.0000	0.9999	0.9991	0.9940	0.9745	0.9222	0.8173	0.6550
	14	1.0000	1.0000	1.0000	1.0000	0.9998	0.9982	0.9907	0.9656	0.9040	0.7878
	15	1.0000	1.0000	1.0000	1.0000	1.0000	0.9995	0.9971	0.9868	0.9560	0.8852
	16	1.0000	1.0000	1.0000	1.0000	1.0000	0.9999	0.9992	0.9957	0.9826	0.9461
	17	1.0000	1.0000	1.0000	1.0000	1.0000	1.0000	0.9998	0.9988	0.9942	0.9784
	18	1.0000	1.0000	1.0000	1.0000	1.0000	1.0000	1.0000	0.9997	0.9984	0.9927
	19	1.0000	1.0000	1.0000	1.0000	1.0000	1.0000	1.0000	0.9999	0.9996	0.9980
	20	1.0000	1.0000	1.0000	1.0000	1.0000	1.0000	1.0000	1.0000	0.9999	0.9995
	21	1.0000	1.0000	1.0000	1.0000	1.0000	1.0000	1.0000	1.0000	1.0000	0.9999
	22	1.0000	1.0000	1.0000	1.0000	1.0000	1.0000	1.0000	1.0000	1.0000	1.0000
n = 30	x = 0	0.2146	0.0424	0.0076	0.0012	0.0002	0.0000	0.0000	0.0000	0.0000	0.0000
	1	0.5535	0.1837	0.0480	0.0105	0.0020	0.0003	0.0000	0.0000	0.0000	0.0000
	2	0.8122	0.4114	0.1514	0.0442	0.0106	0.0021	0.0003	0.0000	0.0000	0.0000
	3	0.9392	0.6474	0.3217	0.1227	0.0374	0.0093	0.0019	0.0003	0.0000	0.0000
	4	0.9844	0.8245	0.5245	0.2552	0.0979	0.0302	0.0075	0.0015	0.0002	0.0000
	5	0.9967	0.9268	0.7106	0.4275	0.2026	0.0766	0.0233	0.0057	0.0011	0.0002
	6	0.9994	0.9742	0.8474	0.6070	0.3481	0.1595	0.0586	0.0172	0.0040	0.0007
	7	0.9999	0.9922	0.9302	0.7608	0.5143	0.2814	0.1238	0.0435	0.0121	0.0026
	8	1.0000	0.9980	0.9722	0.8713	0.6736	0.4315	0.2247	0.0940	0.0312	0.0081
	9	1.0000	0.9995	0.9903	0.9389	0.8034	0.5888	0.3575	0.1763	0.0694	0.0214
	10	1.0000	0.9999	0.9971	0.9744	0.8943	0.7304	0.5078	0.2915	0.1350	0.0494
	11	1.0000	1.0000	0.9992	0.9905	0.9493	0.8407	0.6548	0.4311	0.2327	0.1002
	12	1.0000	1.0000	0.9998	0.9969	0.9784	0.9155	0.7802	0.5785	0.3592	0.1808
	13	1.0000	1.0000	1.0000	0.9991	0.9918	0.9599	0.8737	0.7145	0.5025	0.2923
	14	1.0000	1.0000	1.0000	0.9998	0.9973	0.9831	0.9348	0.8246	0.6448	0.4278
	15	1.0000	1.0000	1.0000	0.9999	0.9992	0.9936	0.9699	0.9029	0.7691	0.5722
	16	1.0000	1.0000	1.0000	1.0000	0.9998	0.9979	0.9876	0.9519	0.8644	0.7077
	17	1.0000	1.0000	1.0000	1.0000	0.9999	0.9994	0.9955	0.9788	0.9286	0.8192
	18	1.0000	1.0000	1.0000	1.0000	1.0000	0.9998	0.9986	0.9917	0.9666	0.8998
	19	1.0000	1.0000	1.0000	1.0000	1.0000	1.0000	0.9996	0.9971	0.9862	0.9506
	20	1.0000	1.0000	1.0000	1.0000	1.0000	1.0000	0.9999	0.9991	0.9950	0.9786
	21	1.0000	1.0000	1.0000	1.0000	1.0000	1.0000	1.0000	0.9998	0.9984	0.9919
	22	1.0000	1.0000	1.0000	1.0000	1.0000	1.0000	1.0000	1.0000	0.9996	0.9974
	23	1.0000	1.0000	1.0000	1.0000	1.0000	1.0000	1.0000	1.0000	0.9999	0.9993
	24	1.0000	1.0000	1.0000	1.0000	1.0000	1.0000	1.0000	1.0000	1.0000	0.9998
	25	1.0000	1.0000	1.0000	1.0000	1.0000	1.0000	1.0000	1.0000	1.0000	1.0000

The binomial cumulative distribution function (continued)

	$p =$	0.05	0.10	0.15	0.20	0.25	0.30	0.35	0.40	0.45	0.50
$n = 40$	$x =$ 0	0.1285	0.0148	0.0015	0.0001	0.0000	0.0000	0.0000	0.0000	0.0000	0.0000
	1	0.3991	0.0805	0.0121	0.0015	0.0001	0.0000	0.0000	0.0000	0.0000	0.0000
	2	0.6767	0.2228	0.0486	0.0079	0.0010	0.0001	0.0000	0.0000	0.0000	0.0000
	3	0.8619	0.4231	0.1302	0.0285	0.0047	0.0006	0.0001	0.0000	0.0000	0.0000
	4	0.9520	0.6290	0.2633	0.0759	0.0160	0.0026	0.0003	0.0000	0.0000	0.0000
	5	0.9861	0.7937	0.4325	0.1613	0.0433	0.0086	0.0013	0.0001	0.0000	0.0000
	6	0.9966	0.9005	0.6067	0.2859	0.0962	0.0238	0.0044	0.0006	0.0001	0.0000
	7	0.9993	0.9581	0.7559	0.4371	0.1820	0.0553	0.0124	0.0021	0.0002	0.0000
	8	0.9999	0.9845	0.8646	0.5931	0.2998	0.1110	0.0303	0.0061	0.0009	0.0001
	9	1.0000	0.9949	0.9328	0.7318	0.4395	0.1959	0.0644	0.0156	0.0027	0.0003
	10	1.0000	0.9985	0.9701	0.8392	0.5839	0.3087	0.1215	0.0352	0.0074	0.0011
	11	1.0000	0.9996	0.9880	0.9125	0.7151	0.4406	0.2053	0.0709	0.0179	0.0032
	12	1.0000	0.9999	0.9957	0.9568	0.8209	0.5772	0.3143	0.1285	0.0386	0.0083
	13	1.0000	1.0000	0.9986	0.9806	0.8968	0.7032	0.4408	0.2112	0.0751	0.0192
	14	1.0000	1.0000	0.9996	0.9921	0.9456	0.8074	0.5721	0.3174	0.1326	0.0403
	15	1.0000	1.0000	0.9999	0.9971	0.9738	0.8849	0.6946	0.4402	0.2142	0.0769
	16	1.0000	1.0000	1.0000	0.9990	0.9884	0.9367	0.7978	0.5681	0.3185	0.1341
	17	1.0000	1.0000	1.0000	0.9997	0.9953	0.9680	0.8761	0.6885	0.4391	0.2148
	18	1.0000	1.0000	1.0000	0.9999	0.9983	0.9852	0.9301	0.7911	0.5651	0.3179
	19	1.0000	1.0000	1.0000	1.0000	0.9994	0.9937	0.9637	0.8702	0.6844	0.4373
	20	1.0000	1.0000	1.0000	1.0000	0.9998	0.9976	0.9827	0.9256	0.7870	0.5627
	21	1.0000	1.0000	1.0000	1.0000	1.0000	0.9991	0.9925	0.9608	0.8669	0.6821
	22	1.0000	1.0000	1.0000	1.0000	1.0000	0.9997	0.9970	0.9811	0.9233	0.7852
	23	1.0000	1.0000	1.0000	1.0000	1.0000	0.9999	0.9989	0.9917	0.9595	0.8659
	24	1.0000	1.0000	1.0000	1.0000	1.0000	1.0000	0.9996	0.9966	0.9804	0.9231
	25	1.0000	1.0000	1.0000	1.0000	1.0000	1.0000	0.9999	0.9988	0.9914	0.9597
	26	1.0000	1.0000	1.0000	1.0000	1.0000	1.0000	1.0000	0.9996	0.9966	0.9808
	27	1.0000	1.0000	1.0000	1.0000	1.0000	1.0000	1.0000	0.9999	0.9988	0.9917
	28	1.0000	1.0000	1.0000	1.0000	1.0000	1.0000	1.0000	1.0000	0.9996	0.9968
	29	1.0000	1.0000	1.0000	1.0000	1.0000	1.0000	1.0000	1.0000	0.9999	0.9989
	30	1.0000	1.0000	1.0000	1.0000	1.0000	1.0000	1.0000	1.0000	1.0000	0.9997
	31	1.0000	1.0000	1.0000	1.0000	1.0000	1.0000	1.0000	1.0000	1.0000	0.9999
	32	1.0000	1.0000	1.0000	1.0000	1.0000	1.0000	1.0000	1.0000	1.0000	1.0000

EDEXCEL S2 — STATISTICAL TABLES

The binomial cumulative distribution function (continued)

	$p =$	0.05	0.10	0.15	0.20	0.25	0.30	0.35	0.40	0.45	0.50
$n = 50$	$x =$ 0	0.0769	0.0052	0.0003	0.0000	0.0000	0.0000	0.0000	0.0000	0.0000	0.0000
	1	0.2794	0.0338	0.0029	0.0002	0.0000	0.0000	0.0000	0.0000	0.0000	0.0000
	2	0.5405	0.1117	0.0142	0.0013	0.0001	0.0000	0.0000	0.0000	0.0000	0.0000
	3	0.7604	0.2503	0.0460	0.0057	0.0005	0.0000	0.0000	0.0000	0.0000	0.0000
	4	0.8964	0.4312	0.1121	0.0185	0.0021	0.0002	0.0000	0.0000	0.0000	0.0000
	5	0.9622	0.6161	0.2194	0.0480	0.0070	0.0007	0.0001	0.0000	0.0000	0.0000
	6	0.9882	0.7702	0.3613	0.1034	0.0194	0.0025	0.0002	0.0000	0.0000	0.0000
	7	0.9968	0.8779	0.5188	0.1904	0.0453	0.0073	0.0008	0.0001	0.0000	0.0000
	8	0.9992	0.9421	0.6681	0.3073	0.0916	0.0183	0.0025	0.0002	0.0000	0.0000
	9	0.9998	0.9755	0.7911	0.4437	0.1637	0.0402	0.0067	0.0008	0.0001	0.0000
	10	1.0000	0.9906	0.8801	0.5836	0.2622	0.0789	0.0160	0.0022	0.0002	0.0000
	11	1.0000	0.9968	0.9372	0.7107	0.3816	0.1390	0.0342	0.0057	0.0006	0.0000
	12	1.0000	0.9990	0.9699	0.8139	0.5110	0.2229	0.0661	0.0133	0.0018	0.0002
	13	1.0000	0.9997	0.9868	0.8894	0.6370	0.3279	0.1163	0.0280	0.0045	0.0005
	14	1.0000	0.9999	0.9947	0.9393	0.7481	0.4468	0.1878	0.0540	0.0104	0.0013
	15	1.0000	1.0000	0.9981	0.9692	0.8369	0.5692	0.2801	0.0955	0.0220	0.0033
	16	1.0000	1.0000	0.9993	0.9856	0.9017	0.6839	0.3889	0.1561	0.0427	0.0077
	17	1.0000	1.0000	0.9998	0.9937	0.9449	0.7822	0.5060	0.2369	0.0765	0.0164
	18	1.0000	1.0000	0.9999	0.9975	0.9713	0.8594	0.6216	0.3356	0.1273	0.0325
	19	1.0000	1.0000	1.0000	0.9991	0.9861	0.9152	0.7264	0.4465	0.1974	0.0595
	20	1.0000	1.0000	1.0000	0.9997	0.9937	0.9522	0.8139	0.5610	0.2862	0.1013
	21	1.0000	1.0000	1.0000	0.9999	0.9974	0.9749	0.8813	0.6701	0.3900	0.1611
	22	1.0000	1.0000	1.0000	1.0000	0.9990	0.9877	0.9290	0.7660	0.5019	0.2399
	23	1.0000	1.0000	1.0000	1.0000	0.9996	0.9944	0.9604	0.8438	0.6134	0.3359
	24	1.0000	1.0000	1.0000	1.0000	0.9999	0.9976	0.9793	0.9022	0.7160	0.4439
	25	1.0000	1.0000	1.0000	1.0000	1.0000	0.9991	0.9900	0.9427	0.8034	0.5561
	26	1.0000	1.0000	1.0000	1.0000	1.0000	0.9997	0.9955	0.9686	0.8721	0.6641
	27	1.0000	1.0000	1.0000	1.0000	1.0000	0.9999	0.9981	0.9840	0.9220	0.7601
	28	1.0000	1.0000	1.0000	1.0000	1.0000	1.0000	0.9993	0.9924	0.9556	0.8389
	29	1.0000	1.0000	1.0000	1.0000	1.0000	1.0000	0.9997	0.9966	0.9765	0.8987
	30	1.0000	1.0000	1.0000	1.0000	1.0000	1.0000	0.9999	0.9986	0.9884	0.9405
	31	1.0000	1.0000	1.0000	1.0000	1.0000	1.0000	1.0000	0.9995	0.9947	0.9675
	32	1.0000	1.0000	1.0000	1.0000	1.0000	1.0000	1.0000	0.9998	0.9978	0.9836
	33	1.0000	1.0000	1.0000	1.0000	1.0000	1.0000	1.0000	0.9999	0.9991	0.9923
	34	1.0000	1.0000	1.0000	1.0000	1.0000	1.0000	1.0000	1.0000	0.9997	0.9967
	35	1.0000	1.0000	1.0000	1.0000	1.0000	1.0000	1.0000	1.0000	0.9999	0.9987
	36	1.0000	1.0000	1.0000	1.0000	1.0000	1.0000	1.0000	1.0000	1.0000	0.9995
	37	1.0000	1.0000	1.0000	1.0000	1.0000	1.0000	1.0000	1.0000	1.0000	0.9998
	38	1.0000	1.0000	1.0000	1.0000	1.0000	1.0000	1.0000	1.0000	1.0000	1.0000

EDEXCEL S2 — STATISTICAL TABLES

The Poisson cumulative distribution function

The values below show $P(X \leq x)$, where $X \sim Po(\lambda)$.

$\lambda =$	0.5	1.0	1.5	2.0	2.5	3.0	3.5	4.0	4.5	5.0
$x =$ 0	0.6065	0.3679	0.2231	0.1353	0.0821	0.0498	0.0302	0.0183	0.0111	0.0067
1	0.9098	0.7358	0.5578	0.4060	0.2873	0.1991	0.1359	0.0916	0.0611	0.0404
2	0.9856	0.9197	0.8088	0.6767	0.5438	0.4232	0.3208	0.2381	0.1736	0.1247
3	0.9982	0.9810	0.9344	0.8571	0.7576	0.6472	0.5366	0.4335	0.3423	0.2650
4	0.9998	0.9963	0.9814	0.9473	0.8912	0.8153	0.7254	0.6288	0.5321	0.4405
5	1.0000	0.9994	0.9955	0.9834	0.9580	0.9161	0.8576	0.7851	0.7029	0.6160
6	1.0000	0.9999	0.9991	0.9955	0.9858	0.9665	0.9347	0.8893	0.8311	0.7622
7	1.0000	1.0000	0.9998	0.9989	0.9958	0.9881	0.9733	0.9489	0.9134	0.8666
8	1.0000	1.0000	1.0000	0.9998	0.9989	0.9962	0.9901	0.9786	0.9597	0.9319
9	1.0000	1.0000	1.0000	1.0000	0.9997	0.9989	0.9967	0.9919	0.9829	0.9682
10	1.0000	1.0000	1.0000	1.0000	0.9999	0.9997	0.9990	0.9972	0.9933	0.9863
11	1.0000	1.0000	1.0000	1.0000	1.0000	0.9999	0.9997	0.9991	0.9976	0.9945
12	1.0000	1.0000	1.0000	1.0000	1.0000	1.0000	0.9999	0.9997	0.9992	0.9980
13	1.0000	1.0000	1.0000	1.0000	1.0000	1.0000	1.0000	0.9999	0.9997	0.9993
14	1.0000	1.0000	1.0000	1.0000	1.0000	1.0000	1.0000	1.0000	0.9999	0.9998
15	1.0000	1.0000	1.0000	1.0000	1.0000	1.0000	1.0000	1.0000	1.0000	0.9999
16	1.0000	1.0000	1.0000	1.0000	1.0000	1.0000	1.0000	1.0000	1.0000	1.0000
17	1.0000	1.0000	1.0000	1.0000	1.0000	1.0000	1.0000	1.0000	1.0000	1.0000
18	1.0000	1.0000	1.0000	1.0000	1.0000	1.0000	1.0000	1.0000	1.0000	1.0000
19	1.0000	1.0000	1.0000	1.0000	1.0000	1.0000	1.0000	1.0000	1.0000	1.0000

$\lambda =$	5.5	6.0	6.5	7.0	7.5	8.0	8.5	9.0	9.5	10.0
$x =$ 0	0.0041	0.0025	0.0015	0.0009	0.0006	0.0003	0.0002	0.0001	0.0001	0.0000
1	0.0266	0.0174	0.0113	0.0073	0.0047	0.0030	0.0019	0.0012	0.0008	0.0005
2	0.0884	0.0620	0.0430	0.0296	0.0203	0.0138	0.0093	0.0062	0.0042	0.0028
3	0.2017	0.1512	0.1118	0.0818	0.0591	0.0424	0.0301	0.0212	0.0149	0.0103
4	0.3575	0.2851	0.2237	0.1730	0.1321	0.0996	0.0744	0.0550	0.0403	0.0293
5	0.5289	0.4457	0.3690	0.3007	0.2414	0.1912	0.1496	0.1157	0.0885	0.0671
6	0.6860	0.6063	0.5265	0.4497	0.3782	0.3134	0.2562	0.2068	0.1649	0.1301
7	0.8095	0.7440	0.6728	0.5987	0.5246	0.4530	0.3856	0.3239	0.2687	0.2202
8	0.8944	0.8472	0.7916	0.7291	0.6620	0.5925	0.5231	0.4557	0.3918	0.3328
9	0.9462	0.9161	0.8774	0.8305	0.7764	0.7166	0.6530	0.5874	0.5218	0.4579
10	0.9747	0.9574	0.9332	0.9015	0.8622	0.8159	0.7634	0.7060	0.6453	0.5830
11	0.9890	0.9799	0.9661	0.9467	0.9208	0.8881	0.8487	0.8030	0.7520	0.6968
12	0.9955	0.9912	0.9840	0.9730	0.9573	0.9362	0.9091	0.8758	0.8364	0.7916
13	0.9983	0.9964	0.9929	0.9872	0.9784	0.9658	0.9486	0.9261	0.8981	0.8645
14	0.9994	0.9986	0.9970	0.9943	0.9897	0.9827	0.9726	0.9585	0.9400	0.9165
15	0.9998	0.9995	0.9988	0.9976	0.9954	0.9918	0.9862	0.9780	0.9665	0.9513
16	0.9999	0.9998	0.9996	0.9990	0.9980	0.9963	0.9934	0.9889	0.9823	0.9730
17	1.0000	0.9999	0.9998	0.9996	0.9992	0.9984	0.9970	0.9947	0.9911	0.9857
18	1.0000	1.0000	0.9999	0.9999	0.9997	0.9993	0.9987	0.9976	0.9957	0.9928
19	1.0000	1.0000	1.0000	1.0000	0.9999	0.9997	0.9995	0.9989	0.9980	0.9965
20	1.0000	1.0000	1.0000	1.0000	1.0000	0.9999	0.9998	0.9996	0.9991	0.9984
21	1.0000	1.0000	1.0000	1.0000	1.0000	1.0000	0.9999	0.9998	0.9996	0.9993
22	1.0000	1.0000	1.0000	1.0000	1.0000	1.0000	1.0000	0.9999	0.9999	0.9997

Projectiles

A 'projectile' is just any old object that's been lobbed through the air. When you're doing projectile questions you'll have to model the motion of particles in two dimensions whilst ignoring air resistance.

Split Velocity of Projection into Two Components

A particle projected with a speed u at an angle α to the horizontal has two components of initial velocity — one horizontal (parallel to the x-axis) and one vertical (parallel to the y-axis).
These are called x and y components, and they make projectile questions dead easy to deal with:

Here's the same information in a diagram:

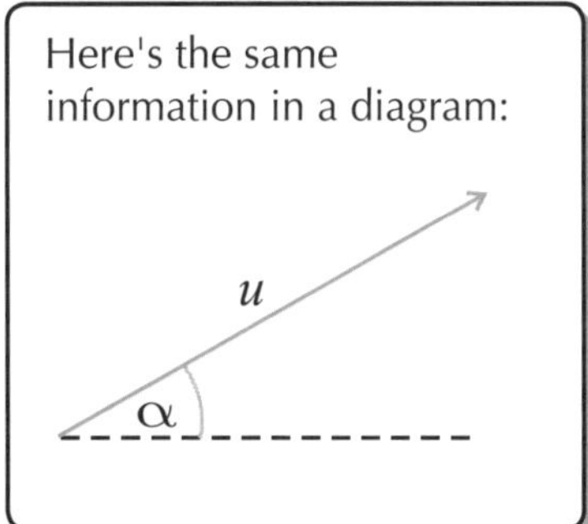

Split the velocity into its x and y components:

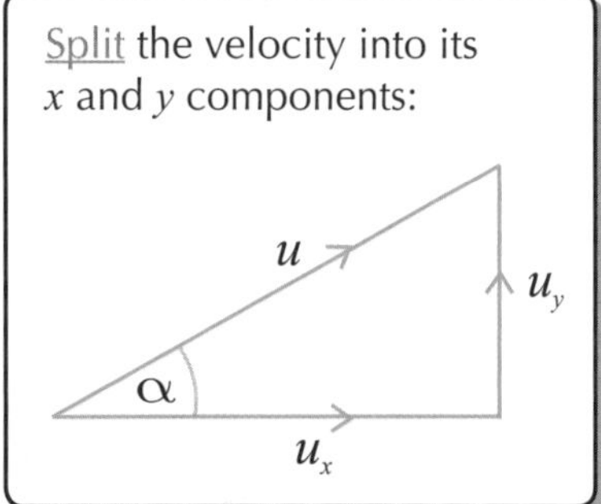

Finally, work out the values of the components using trigonometry:

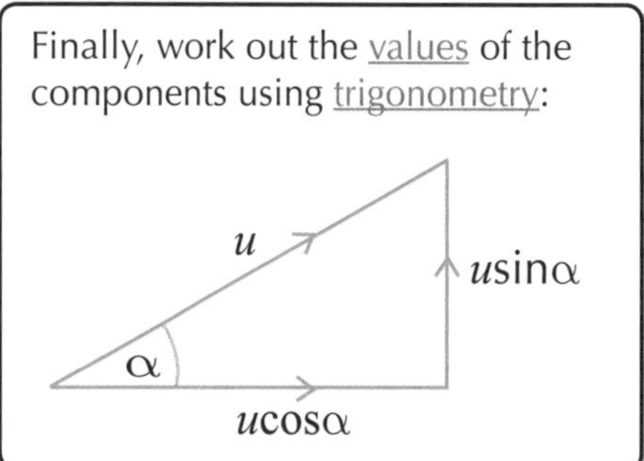

Split the Motion into Horizontal and Vertical Components too

Split everything you know about the motion into horizontal and vertical components too. Then you can deal with them separately using the 'uvast' equations from M1. The only thing that's the same in both directions is time — so this connects the two directions. Remember that the only acceleration is due to gravity — so horizontal acceleration is zero.

EXAMPLE A stone is thrown horizontally with speed 10 ms^{-1} from a height of 2 m above the horizontal ground. Find the time taken for the stone to hit the ground and the horizontal distance travelled before impact. Find also the speed and direction of the stone after 0.5 s.

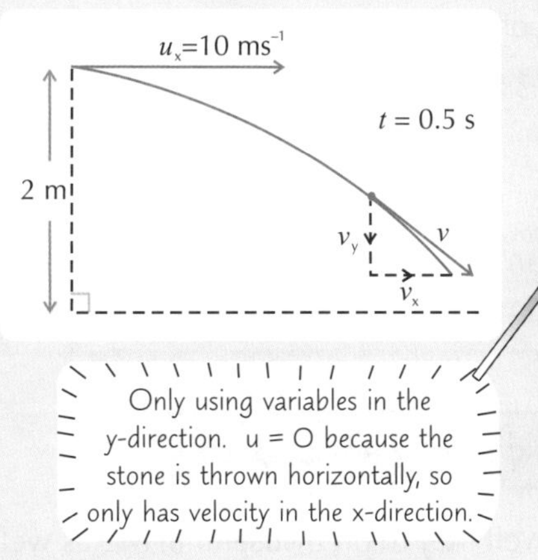

Only using variables in the y-direction. u = 0 because the stone is thrown horizontally, so only has velocity in the x-direction.

Resolving vertically (take down as +ve):

$u = u_y = 0$ $s = 2$
$a = 9.8$ $t = ?$

$s = ut + \frac{1}{2}at^2$

$2 = 0 \times t + \frac{1}{2} \times 9.8 \times t^2$

$t = 0.639$ s (to 3 s.f.)
i.e. the stone lands after 0.639 seconds

Resolving horizontally (take right as +ve):

$u = u_x = 10$ $s = ?$
$a = 0$ $t = 0.6389$

The same as for the vertical motion.

$s = ut + \frac{1}{2}at^2$

$= 10 \times 0.6389 + \frac{1}{2} \times 0 \times 0.6389^2$

$= 6.39$ m

i.e. the stone has gone 6.39 m horizontally when it lands.

Now find the velocity after 0.5 s — again, keep the vertical and horizontal bits separate.

Unless you're told otherwise, always take g = 9.8 ms^{-2}.

$v = u + at$

$v_y = 0 + 9.8 \times 0.5$

$= 4.9$ ms^{-1}

$v = u + at$

$v_x = 10 + 0 \times \frac{1}{2}$

$= 10$ ms^{-1}

v_x is always equal to u_x when there's no horizontal acceleration.

Now you can find the speed and direction...

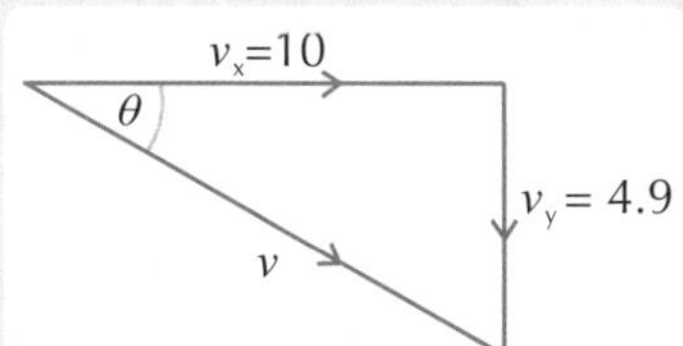

$v = \sqrt{4.9^2 + 10^2} = 11.1$ ms^{-1}

$\tan\theta = \frac{4.9}{10}$

So $\theta = 26.1°$ below horizontal

Projectiles

EXAMPLE A cricket ball is projected with a speed of 30 ms^{-1} at an angle of 25° to the horizontal. Assume the ground is horizontal and the ball is struck from a point 1.5 m above the ground. Find:

a) the maximum height the ball reaches (h),

b) the horizontal distance travelled by the ball before it hits the ground (r),

c) the length of time the ball is at least 5 m above the ground.

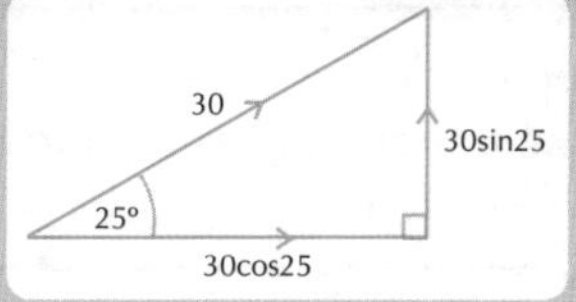

a) **Resolving vertically** (take up as +ve):

$u = 30\sin 25°$ $\quad v = 0$
$a = -9.8$ $\quad s = ?$

The ball will momentarily stop moving vertically when it reaches its maximum height.

$$v^2 = u^2 + 2as$$
$$0 = (30\sin 25°)^2 + 2(-9.8 \times s)$$
$$s = 8.201\text{m}$$
$$\text{h} = 8.201\text{m} + 1.5\text{m} = 9.70\text{m}$$

Don't forget to add the height from which the ball is hit.

b) **Resolving vertically** (take up as +ve):

$s = -1.5$
$a = -9.8$
$u = 30\sin 25°$
$t = ?$

$$s = ut + \frac{1}{2}at^2$$
$$-1.5 = (30\sin 25°)t - \frac{1}{2}(9.8)t^2$$
$$t^2 - 2.587t - 0.306 = 0$$
$$t = -0.11 \text{ or } \boldsymbol{t = 2.70\,\text{s}}$$

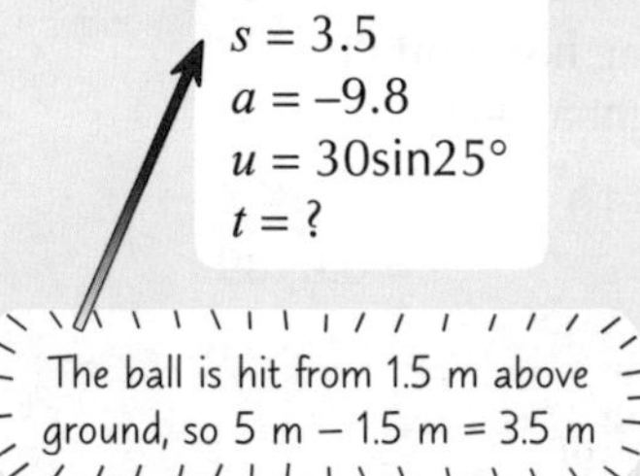

Using the quadratic formula you get two answers, but time can't be negative, so forget about this answer.

Resolving horizontally (take right as +ve)

$s = \text{r}$ $\quad u = 30\cos 25°$
$t = 2.70$ $\quad a = 0$

$$s = ut + \frac{1}{2}at^2$$
$$\text{r} = 30\cos 25° \times 2.70 + \frac{1}{2} \times 0 \times 2.70^2$$
$$= 73.4\,\text{m}$$

c) **Resolving vertically** (take up as +ve):

$s = 3.5$
$a = -9.8$
$u = 30\sin 25°$
$t = ?$

The ball is hit from 1.5 m above ground, so 5 m – 1.5 m = 3.5 m

$$s = ut + \frac{1}{2}at^2$$
$$3.5 = (30\sin 25°)t - \frac{1}{2}(9.8)t^2$$
$$t^2 - 2.587t + 0.714 = 0$$
$$t = 0.31 \text{ or } t = 2.27\,\text{s}$$

These are the two times when the ball is 5 m above the ground.

So, length of time at least 5 m above the ground:

2.27 s – 0.31 s = 1.96 s

The **Components of Velocity** can be described using **i and j Vectors**

Ho ho — **i** and **j** vectors. You'll remember those jokers from M1, no doubt. Well they're pretty useful in M2 as well:

EXAMPLE A stone is thrown from a point 1.2 metres above the horizontal ground. It travels for 4 seconds before landing on the ground. The stone is thrown with velocity ($2q\mathbf{i} + q\mathbf{j}$) ms^{-1}, where **i** and **j** are the horizontal and vertical unit vectors respectively. Find the value of q and the initial speed of the stone.

Resolving vertically (take up as +ve):

$u = q$ $\quad t = 4$
$a = -9.8$ $\quad s = -1.2$

The vertical component of velocity is q, the horizontal component is $2q$. Simples.

$$s = ut + \frac{1}{2}at^2$$
$$-1.2 = 4q - \frac{1}{2}(9.8)4^2$$
$$4q = 77.2$$
$$q = 19.3$$

Now find the initial speed of the stone:

$$u = \sqrt{(2q)^2 + q^2}$$
$$= \sqrt{38.6^2 + 19.3^2} = 43.2\,\text{ms}^{-1}$$

Projectiles

Just one last example of projectile motion. But boy is it a beauty...

EXAMPLE

A golf ball is struck from a point A on a horizontal plane. When the ball has moved a horizontal distance x, its height above the plane is y. The ball is modelled as a particle projected with initial speed u ms^{-1} at an angle α.

a) Show that $y = x\tan\alpha - \frac{gx^2}{2u^2\cos^2\alpha}$.

The ball just passes over the top of a 10 m tall tree, which is 45 m away. Given that $\alpha = 45°$,

b) find the speed of the ball as it passes over the tree.

a) Displacement, acceleration and initial velocity are the only variables in the formula, so use these. Also use time, because that's the variable which connects the two components of motion. The formula includes motion in both directions (x and y), so form two equations and substitute one into the other:

Resolving horizontally (taking right as +ve):

$u_x = u\cos\alpha$ $\quad a = 0$

$s = x$ $\quad t = t$

Using $s = ut + \frac{1}{2}at^2$:

$x = u\cos\alpha \times t$

Rearrange to make t the subject:

$t = \frac{x}{u\cos\alpha}$ — call this **equation 1**

When you're using these variables, this is the obvious equation to use.

t doesn't appear in the final formula, so by making it the subject you can eliminate it.

Resolving vertically (taking up as +ve):

$u_y = u\sin\alpha$ $\quad a = -g$

$s = y$ $\quad t = t$

Using $s = ut + \frac{1}{2}at^2$:

$y = (u\sin\alpha \times t) - \frac{1}{2}gt^2$ — call this **equation 2**

It would be a massive pain to make t the subject here, so do it with the other equation.

t is the same horizontally and vertically, so you can <u>substitute</u> **equation 1** into **equation 2** and eliminate t:

$$y = u\sin\alpha \times \frac{x}{u\cos\alpha} - \frac{1}{2}g\left(\frac{x}{u\cos\alpha}\right)^2 = x\frac{\sin\alpha}{\cos\alpha} - \frac{1}{2}g\left(\frac{x^2}{u^2\cos^2\alpha}\right)$$

$$= x\tan\alpha - \frac{gx^2}{2u^2\cos^2\alpha}$$ — as required.

$\frac{\sin\theta}{\cos\theta} = \tan\theta$

b) Using the result from a), and substituting $x = 45$, $y = 10$ and $\alpha = 45°$:

$$10 = 45\tan 45° - \frac{9.8 \times 45^2}{2u^2 \times \cos^2 45°} = 45 - \frac{19\,845}{u^2}$$

Rearrange to find the speed of projection, u:

$35u^2 = 19\,845 \Rightarrow$ $\boldsymbol{u = 23.81}$ **ms**$^{-1}$

If you need to round part way through a calculation, then round to <u>more</u> s.f. than your final answer will be rounded to. A better idea is not to round at all and use your calculator's memory.

Now resolve to find the components of the ball's velocity as it passes over the tree:

Resolving horizontally (taking right as +ve):

$v_x = u_x = 23.81\cos 45 =$ **16.84 ms**$^{-1}$

Remember — with projectiles there's no horizontal acceleration, so v_x always equals u_x.

Resolving vertically (taking up as +ve):

$u_y = 23.81\sin 45$ $\quad a = -g$

$s = 10$ $\quad v_y = ?$

Using $v^2 = u^2 + 2as$:

$v_y^2 = 283.46 - 2 \times 9.8 \times 10 =$ **87.46**

Don't bother finding the square root, as you need v_y^2 in the next step. Sneaky.

Now you can find the speed: $\quad v = \sqrt{v_x^2 + v_y^2} = 19.3$ ms^{-1} (3 s.f.)

Projectiles — they're all about throwing up. Or across. Or slightly down...

You've used the equations of motion before, in M1, and there isn't much different here. The main thing to remember is that <u>horizontal acceleration is zero</u> — great news because it makes half the calculations as easy as a log-falling beginner's class.

Displacement, Velocity and Acceleration

The "uvast" equations you saw back in M1 are all well and good when you've got a particle with constant acceleration. But when the acceleration of a particle varies with time, you need a few new tricks up your sleeve...

Differentiate to find *Velocity* and *Acceleration* from *Displacement*...

If you've got a particle moving in a straight line with acceleration that varies with time, you need to use calculus to find equations to describe the motion. (Look back at your C1 notes for a reminder about calculus.)

1) To find an equation for velocity, differentiate the equation for displacement with respect to time.
2) To find an equation for acceleration, differentiate the equation for velocity with respect to time. (Or differentiate the equation for displacement with respect to time twice.)

DISPLACEMENT (s) —Differentiate→ **VELOCITY** (v) —Differentiate→ **ACCELERATION** (a)

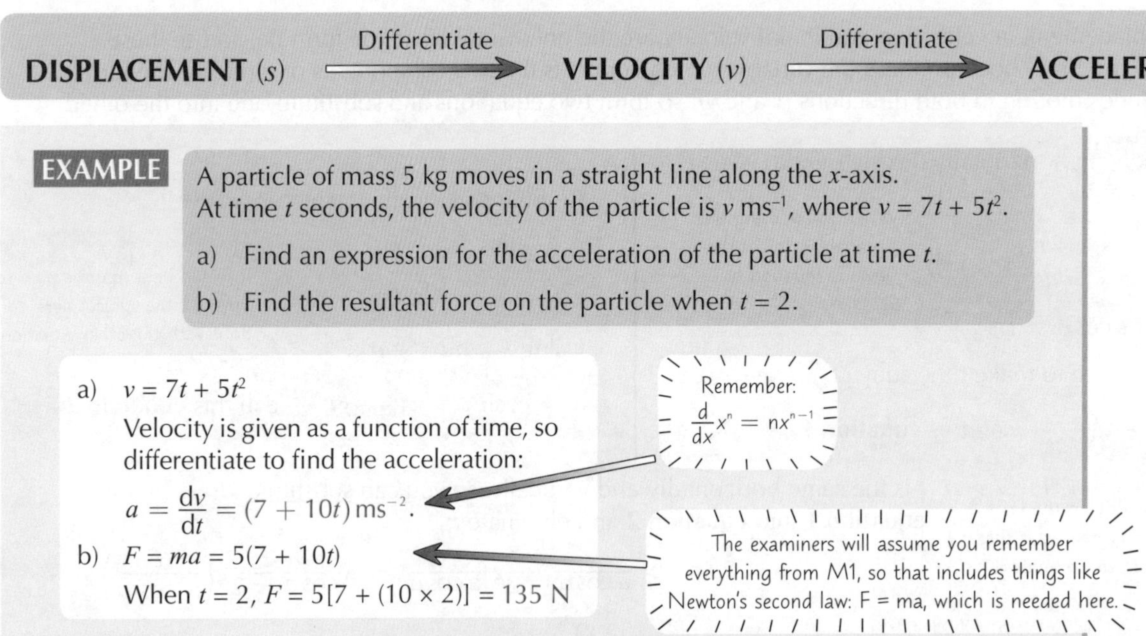

EXAMPLE A particle of mass 5 kg moves in a straight line along the x-axis. At time t seconds, the velocity of the particle is v ms^{-1}, where $v = 7t + 5t^2$.

a) Find an expression for the acceleration of the particle at time t.

b) Find the resultant force on the particle when $t = 2$.

a) $v = 7t + 5t^2$
Velocity is given as a function of time, so differentiate to find the acceleration:
$a = \frac{dv}{dt} = (7 + 10t)\,\text{ms}^{-2}$.

b) $F = ma = 5(7 + 10t)$
When $t = 2$, $F = 5[7 + (10 \times 2)] = 135$ N

Remember: $\frac{d}{dx}x^n = nx^{n-1}$
The examiners will assume you remember everything from M1, so that includes things like Newton's second law: F = ma, which is needed here.

...and *Integrate* to find *Velocity* and *Displacement* from *Acceleration*

It's pretty similar if you're trying to go "back the other way", except you integrate rather than differentiate:

1) To find an equation for velocity, integrate the equation for acceleration with respect to time.
2) To find an equation for displacement, integrate the equation for velocity with respect to time.

DISPLACEMENT (s) ←Integrate— **VELOCITY** (v) ←Integrate— **ACCELERATION** (a)

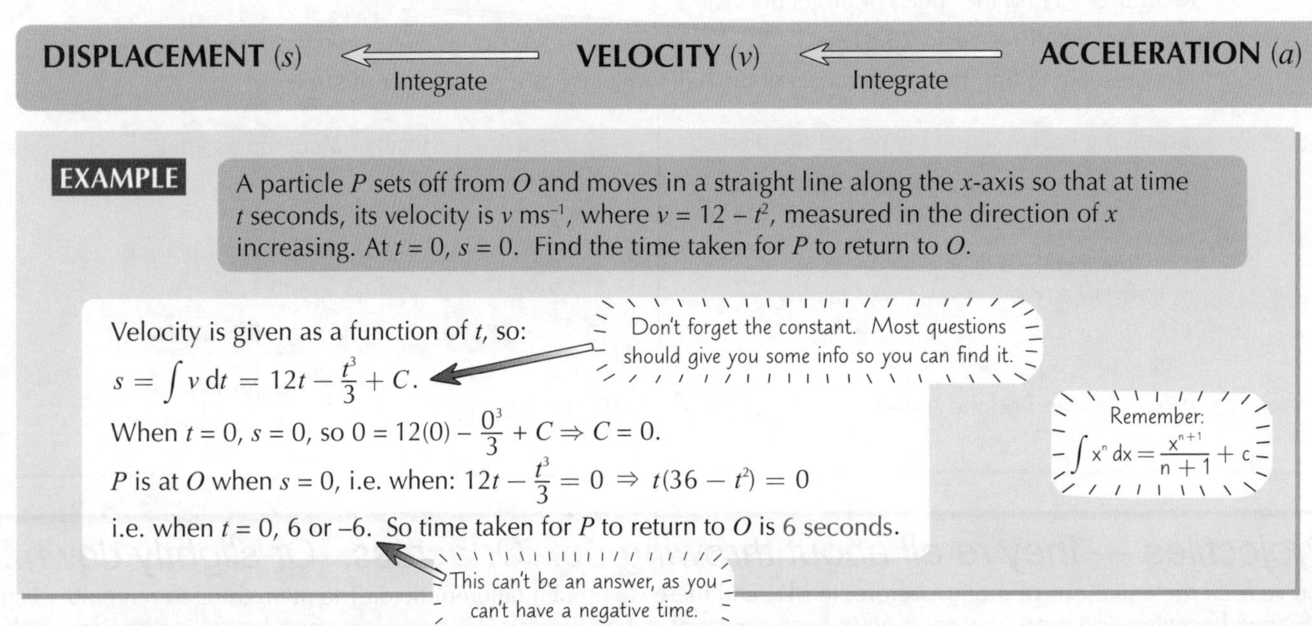

EXAMPLE A particle P sets off from O and moves in a straight line along the x-axis so that at time t seconds, its velocity is v ms^{-1}, where $v = 12 - t^2$, measured in the direction of x increasing. At $t = 0$, $s = 0$. Find the time taken for P to return to O.

Velocity is given as a function of t, so:
$s = \int v\,dt = 12t - \frac{t^3}{3} + C$.
When $t = 0$, $s = 0$, so $0 = 12(0) - \frac{0^3}{3} + C \Rightarrow C = 0$.
P is at O when $s = 0$, i.e. when: $12t - \frac{t^3}{3} = 0 \Rightarrow t(36 - t^2) = 0$
i.e. when $t = 0$, 6 or –6. So time taken for P to return to O is 6 seconds.

Don't forget the constant. Most questions should give you some info so you can find it.
Remember: $\int x^n\,dx = \frac{x^{n+1}}{n+1} + c$
This can't be an answer, as you can't have a negative time.

Displacement, Velocity and Acceleration

Sometimes the **Velocity** is Defined by **More Than One Expression**

The velocity of a particle can sometimes be defined by different expressions for different values of t.
It just means that you have to deal with each time interval separately when you're differentiating and integrating.

These questions are a favourite with examiners — so make sure you understand what's going on in this example:

EXAMPLE

A particle P sets off from the origin at $t = 0$ and moves in a straight line along the x-axis in the direction of x increasing. The velocity of P after t seconds is v ms^{-1}, where v is given by:

$$v = \begin{cases} 2t - \frac{t^2}{4} & 0 \leqslant t \leqslant 6 \\ 21 - 3t & t > 6 \end{cases}$$

Make sure you read the question carefully, so you know which expression for v to use.

a) Find the displacement of P from O when $t = 6$.

At some $t > 6$, P reaches A, the point of maximum positive displacement from O.
From A, P begins to move in a straight line along the x-axis back towards the origin. Find:

b) the distance of A from O,

c) the speed of P when it returns to the origin.

a) Integrate the expression for velocity with respect to time to find displacement:

$s = \int v \, dt = \int \left(2t - \frac{t^2}{4}\right) dt = t^2 - \frac{t^3}{12} + C$ for $0 \leqslant t \leqslant 6$.

When $t = 0$, P is at the origin (i.e. $s = 0$) Use this to find C:

$0 = 0^2 - \frac{0^3}{12} + C \Rightarrow C = 0.$

So, when $t = 6$, $s = 6^2 - \frac{6^3}{12} + 0 = 18$ m

b) Again, integrate the expression for velocity with respect to time to find displacement:

$s = \int v \, dt = \int (21 - 3t) \, dt = 21t - \frac{3t^2}{2} + K$ for $t > 6$

From part a), when $t = 6$, $x = \mathbf{18}$.

Use this as your initial condition to find K, because even though t = 6 isn't in the interval t > 6, it is the lower limit of the interval.

So: $18 = 21 \times 6 - \frac{3 \times 36}{2} + K \Rightarrow \boldsymbol{K = -54}$

P changes direction at A, so will be momentarily at rest (i.e. v will be 0).

You're told this in the question.

The question states that this is for some $t > 6$, so: $v = 0 = 21 - 3t \quad \Rightarrow \quad \boldsymbol{t = 7}$.

Distance of A from O is the distance travelled by P after 7 seconds:

$s = (21 \times 7) - \frac{3(7^2)}{2} - 54 = 19.5$ m

c) Differentiate the expression for velocity with respect to time to find the acceleration:

So, for $t > 6$: $a = \frac{d}{dt}(21 - 3t) = -3$ ms^{-2} (in the direction of x increasing).

So, for motion back *towards* the origin, $a = 3$ ms^{-2}.

From b), the velocity of P at A is 0 and distance from O to A is 19.5 m

So, use $v^2 = u^2 + 2as$:

$v^2 = 0^2 + (2 \times 3 \times 19.5) \quad \Rightarrow v = 10.8$ ms^{-1} (3 s.f.)

The acceleration here is constant, so you can use one of the uvast equations.

CGP driving tips #1 — differentiate velocity from displacement...

Calculus? In Mechanics? What fresh horror is this? Actually, it's really not that bad at all. Just make sure you know when to differentiate and when to integrate and then bang in the numbers you're given in the question to get the answer. Sorted.

Describing Motion Using Vectors

I can tell that you loved the last two pages, but I know what you're thinking: "That's all fair enough mate, but what about when a particle is moving in two dimensions?" Well, you know I can't ignore a question like that, so here you go...

Differentiate and Integrate with Vector Notation for Motion on a Plane

1) When you've got a particle moving in two dimensions (i.e. on a plane), you can describe its position, velocity and acceleration using the unit vectors **i** and **j** (which you should remember from M1). This "**i** and **j**" notation shows the horizontal and vertical components of displacement, velocity or acceleration separately.
2) The relationship between displacement (position), velocity and acceleration from page 158 still applies to particles moving on a plane:

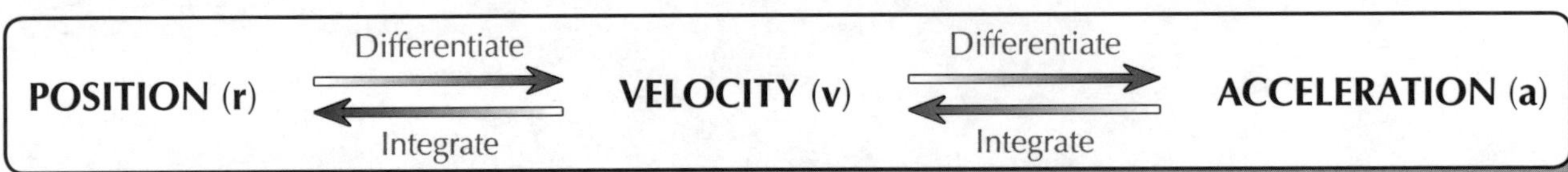

3) This means that you'll have to differentiate and integrate vectors written in i and j notation. Luckily, doing this is as easy as squeezing lemons — all you have to do is differentiate/integrate each component of the vector separately:

So, if $\mathbf{r} = x\mathbf{i} + y\mathbf{j}$ is a position vector, then:

velocity, $\mathbf{v} = \frac{d\mathbf{r}}{dt} = \frac{dx}{dt}\mathbf{i} + \frac{dy}{dt}\mathbf{j}$

The shorthand for $\frac{dr}{dt}$ is $\dot{r}$ (the single dot means differentiate r once with respect to time)...

and acceleration, $\mathbf{a} = \frac{d\mathbf{v}}{dt} = \frac{d^2\mathbf{r}}{dt^2} = \frac{d^2x}{dt^2}\mathbf{i} + \frac{d^2y}{dt^2}\mathbf{j}$.

...and the shorthand for $\frac{d^2r}{dt^2}$ is $\ddot{r}$ (the double dots mean differentiate r twice with respect to time).

It's a similar thing for integration:

If $\mathbf{v} = w\mathbf{i} + z\mathbf{j}$ is a velocity vector, then position, $\mathbf{r} = \int \mathbf{v}\,dt = \int (w\mathbf{i} + z\mathbf{j})\,dt = \left[\int w\,dt\right]\mathbf{i} + \left[\int z\,dt\right]\mathbf{j}$

Unfortunately, there's no snazzy shorthand for integration. Ahh well, easy come, easy go.

EXAMPLE:

A particle is moving on a horizontal plane so that at time t it has velocity v ms^{-1}, where

$$\mathbf{v} = (8 + 2t)\mathbf{i} + (t^3 - 6t)\mathbf{j}$$

At $t = 2$, the particle has a position vector of $(10\mathbf{i} + 3\mathbf{j})$ m with respect to a fixed origin O.

a) Find the acceleration of the particle at time t.

b) Show that the position of the particle relative to O when $t = 4$ is $\mathbf{r} = 38\mathbf{i} + 27\mathbf{j}$.

a) $\mathbf{a} = \dot{\mathbf{v}} = \frac{d\mathbf{v}}{dt}$

$= 2\mathbf{i} + (3t^2 - 6)\mathbf{j}$

Yep, that really is all there is to it.

b) $\mathbf{r} = \int \mathbf{v}\,dt$

$= (8t + t^2)\mathbf{i} + \left(\frac{t^4}{4} - 3t^2\right)\mathbf{j} + \mathbf{C}$

You still need a constant of integration, but it will be a vector with **i** and **j** components.

When $t = 2$, $\mathbf{r} = (10\mathbf{i} + 3\mathbf{j})$, so use this info to find the vector **C**:

$10\mathbf{i} + 3\mathbf{j} = 20\mathbf{i} - 8\mathbf{j} + \mathbf{C}$

$\Rightarrow \mathbf{C} = (10 - 20)\mathbf{i} + (3 - -8)\mathbf{j} = -10\mathbf{i} + 11\mathbf{j}$

Collect **i** and **j** terms and add/subtract to simplify.

So, $\mathbf{r} = (8t + t^2 - 10)\mathbf{i} + \left(\frac{t^4}{4} - 3t^2 + 11\right)\mathbf{j}$.

When $t = 4$, $\mathbf{r} = (32 + 16 - 10)\mathbf{i} + (64 - 48 + 11)\mathbf{j} = 38\mathbf{i} + 27\mathbf{j}$ — as required.

Describing Motion Using Vectors

Watch out for Questions that include **Forces**

When you see "the action of a single force, **F** newtons" in one of these vector questions, you should immediately think **F** = m**a**, because you're almost certainly going to need it. Here are a couple of examples showing the examiners' faves:

EXAMPLE

A particle P is moving under the action of a single force, **F** newtons. The position vector, **r** m, of P after t seconds is given by

$$\mathbf{r} = (2t^3 - 3)\mathbf{i} + \frac{t^4}{2}\mathbf{j}$$

a) Find an expression for the acceleration of P at time t seconds.

b) P has mass 6 kg. Find the magnitude of **F** when $t = 3$.

a) $\mathbf{v} = \dot{\mathbf{r}} = 6t^2\mathbf{i} + 2t^3\mathbf{j}$
$\mathbf{a} = \dot{\mathbf{v}} = 12t\mathbf{i} + 6t^2\mathbf{j}$

b) At $t = 3$, $\mathbf{a} = 36\mathbf{i} + 54\mathbf{j}$

Using $\mathbf{F} = m\mathbf{a}$, substitute $m = 6$:

$\mathbf{F} = (6 \times 36)\mathbf{i} + (6 \times 54)\mathbf{j} = 216\mathbf{i} + 324\mathbf{j}$

$|\mathbf{F}| = \sqrt{216^2 + 324^2} = 389$ N (3 s.f.)

You could find the magnitude of **a** first instead if you wanted, then just multiply by m.

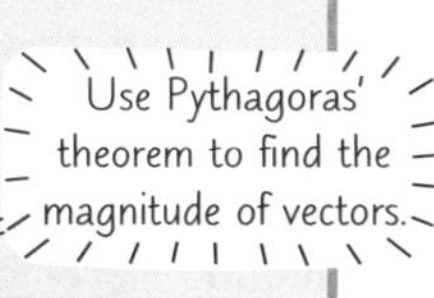

Use Pythagoras' theorem to find the magnitude of vectors.

EXAMPLE

A particle of mass 4 kg moves in a plane under the action of a single force, **F** newtons.

At time t seconds, $\mathbf{F} = (24t\mathbf{i} - 8\mathbf{j})$ N

At time $t = 0$, the velocity of the particle is $(7\mathbf{i} + 22\mathbf{j})$ ms^{-1}.

a) The velocity of the particle at time t is **v** ms^{-1}. Show that

$$\mathbf{v} = (3t^2 + 7)\mathbf{i} + (22 - 2t)\mathbf{j}$$

b) Find the value of t when the particle is moving parallel to the vector **i**.

Here you have to work out the acceleration vector before you can do any integrating.

a) Use $\mathbf{F} = m\mathbf{a}$ to find an expression for the acceleration of the particle at time t:

$(24t\mathbf{i} - 8\mathbf{j}) = 4\mathbf{a} \Rightarrow \mathbf{a} = 6t\mathbf{i} - 2\mathbf{j}$

$\mathbf{v} = \int \mathbf{a}\,dt = \int (6t\mathbf{i} - 2\mathbf{j})\,dt = 3t^2\mathbf{i} - 2t\mathbf{j} + \mathbf{C}$

When $t = 0$, $\mathbf{v} = (7\mathbf{i} + 22\mathbf{j})$ ms^{-1}. Use this information to find **C**:

$7\mathbf{i} + 22\mathbf{j} = 0\mathbf{i} + 0\mathbf{j} + \mathbf{C} \Rightarrow \mathbf{C} = 7\mathbf{i} + 22\mathbf{j}$. So at time t,

$\mathbf{v} = 3t^2\mathbf{i} - 2t\mathbf{j} + 7\mathbf{i} + 22\mathbf{j}$

$= (3t^2 + 7)\mathbf{i} + (22 - 2t)\mathbf{j}$ — as required.

b) When the particle is moving parallel to the vector **i**, the **j** component of **v** is 0, and the **i** component is non-zero, so:

$22 - 2t = 0 \Rightarrow t = 11$

At $t = 11$, the **i** component of velocity is $(3 \times 11^2) + 7 = 370$, i.e. not zero.

So the particle is moving parallel to the vector **i** at 11 s.

Motion in two dimensions — it's plane simple...

Just remember to differentiate and integrate by treating each component separately, and pretty soon you'll be able to differentiate velocity vectors in 11-dimensional hyperspace. Just think how cool that'll look at the next sci-fi convention.

M2 Section 1 — Practice Questions

Well that wasn't such a bad intro to the world of M2. Before you crack on with more mechanical delights, I reckon it's time for some practice questions to make sure you've made sense of everything in this section. And because I'm nice, I'll start you off with some nice easy warm-up questions...

Warm-up Questions

1) A particle is projected with initial velocity u ms^{-1} at an angle α to the horizontal. What is the initial velocity of the particle in the direction parallel to the horizontal in terms of u and α?
2) A rifle fires a bullet horizontally at 120 ms^{-1}. The target is hit at a horizontal distance of 60 m from the end of the rifle. Find how far the target is vertically below the end of the rifle. Take $g = 9.8$ ms^{-2}.
3) A golf ball takes 4 seconds to land after being hit with a golf club from a point on the horizontal ground. If it leaves the club with a speed of 22 ms^{-1}, at an angle of α to the horizontal, find α. Take $g = 9.8$ ms^{-2}.
4) A particle sets off from the origin at $t = 0$ and moves along the x-axis with velocity $v = 8t^2 - 2t$. Find expressions for:
   a) the acceleration of the particle at time t, and b) the displacement of the particle at time t
5) A particle moving in a plane has position vector $\mathbf{r}$, where $\mathbf{r} = x\mathbf{i} + y\mathbf{j}$. What quantities are represented by the vectors $\dot{\mathbf{r}}$ and $\ddot{\mathbf{r}}$?
6) A particle sets off from the origin at $t = 0$ and moves in a plane with velocity $\mathbf{v} = 4t\mathbf{i} + t^2\mathbf{j}$. Find the position vector $\mathbf{r}$ and the acceleration vector $\mathbf{a}$ for the particle at time t.

Right, now you're warmed up and there's absolutely no danger of you pulling a maths muscle, it's time to get down to the serious business of practice exam questions.

Exam Questions

Whenever a numerical value of g is required in the questions below, take $g = 9.8$ ms^{-2}.

1

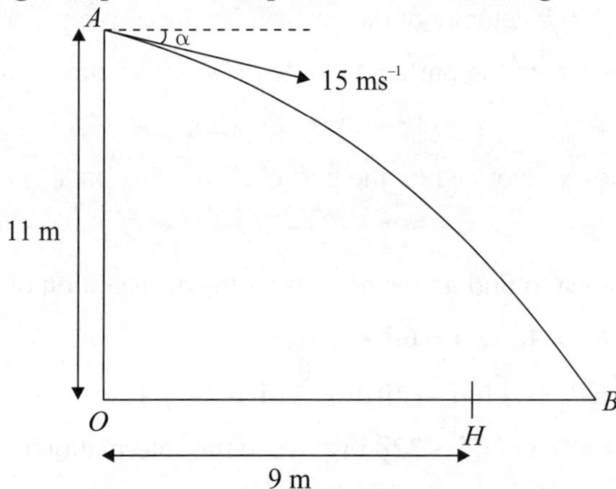

A stone is thrown from point A on the edge of a cliff, towards a point H, which is on horizontal ground. The point O is on the ground, 11 m vertically below the point of projection. The stone is thrown with speed 15 ms^{-1} at an angle α below the horizontal, where $\tan\alpha = \frac{3}{4}$.
The horizontal distance from O to H is 9 m.
The stone misses the point H and hits the ground at point B, as shown above. Find:

a) the time taken by the stone to reach the ground. *(5 marks)*

b) the horizontal distance the stone misses H by. *(3 marks)*

c) the speed of projection which would have ensured that the stone landed at H. *(5 marks)*

M2 Section 1 — Practice Questions

There's more where that came from. Oh yes indeed...

2 A particle P is moving in a horizontal plane under the action of a single force **F** newtons. After t seconds, P has position vector:

$$\mathbf{r} = (2t^3 - 7t^2 + 12)\mathbf{i} + (3t^2 - 4t^3 - 7)\mathbf{j} \text{ m}$$

where the unit vectors **i** and **j** are in the directions of east and north respectively. Find:

a) an expression for the velocity of P after t seconds. *(2 marks)*

b) the speed of P when $t = \frac{1}{2}$, and the direction of motion of P at this time. *(3 marks)*

At $t = 2$, the magnitude of **F** is 170 N. Find:

c) the acceleration of P at $t = 2$, *(3 marks)*

d) the mass of the particle, *(3 marks)*

e) the value of t when **F** is acting due parallel to **j**. *(3 marks)*

3 A stationary football is kicked with a speed of 20 ms^{-1}, at an angle of 30° to the horizontal, towards a goal 30 m away. The crossbar is 2.5 m above the level ground. Assuming the path of the ball is not impeded, determine whether the ball passes above or below the crossbar. What assumptions does your model make? *(6 marks)*

4 A particle sets off from the origin O at $t = 0$ and moves in a straight line along the x-axis. At time t seconds, the velocity of the particle is v ms^{-1} where

$$v = \begin{cases} 9t - 3t^2 & 0 \leqslant t \leqslant 4 \\ \dfrac{-192}{t^2} & t > 4 \end{cases}$$

Find:

a) the maximum speed of the particle in the interval $0 \leqslant t \leqslant 4$. *(4 marks)*

b) the displacement of the particle from O at

(i) $t = 4$ *(3 marks)*

(ii) $t = 6$ *(4 marks)*

5 A golf ball is hit from a tee at point O on the edge of a vertical cliff. Point O is 30 m vertically above A, the base of the cliff. The ball is hit with velocity $(14\mathbf{i} + 35\mathbf{j})$ ms^{-1} towards a hole, H, which lies on the horizontal ground. At time t seconds, the position of the ball is $(x\mathbf{i} + y\mathbf{j})$ m relative to O. **i** and **j** are the horizontal and vertical unit vectors respectively.

a) By writing down expressions for x and y in terms of t, show that $y = \frac{5x}{2} - \frac{x^2}{40}$ *(4 marks)*

The ball lands on the ground at point B, 7 m beyond H, where AHB is a straight horizontal line.

b) Find the horizontal distance AB. *(3 marks)*

c) Find the speed of the ball as it passes through a point vertically above H. *(4 marks)*

Discrete Groups of Particles in 1 Dimension

Welcome to the Centre of Mass. No, not your local Catholic church...

For Particles in a Line — Combine Moments about the Origin

1) The weight of an object is considered to act at its centre of mass. A group of objects also has a centre of mass, which isn't necessarily in the same position as any one of the objects.
2) It's often convenient to model these objects as particles (point masses) since the position of a particle is the position of its centre of mass. If a group of particles all lie in a horizontal line, then the centre of mass of the group will lie somewhere on the same line.

   Modelling systems was covered in M1.
3) The moment (turning effect) of a particle from a fixed point is: weight (mass × gravity) × perpendicular distance from point

   This is mgx if the fixed point and the particle are horizontally aligned (see M1 for more on moments).
4) The moment of a group of particles in a horizontal line about a point in the horizontal line can be found by adding together all the individual moments about the point — Σmgx.
5) This has the same effect as the combined weight (Σmg) acting at the centre of mass of the whole group ($\bar{x}$).

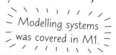

Writing this as a formula:

$\Sigma mgx = \bar{x}\Sigma mg$

e.g. for 3 particles in a horizontal line:

$m_1gx_1 + m_2gx_2 + m_3gx_3 = \bar{x}(m_1g + m_2g + m_3g)$

$\Rightarrow m_1x_1 + m_2x_2 + m_3x_3 = \bar{x}(m_1 + m_2 + m_3)$

$\Rightarrow \Sigma mx = \bar{x}\Sigma m$

The gs cancel out on each side.

Use this simplified formula to find the centre of mass, $\bar{x}$, of a group of objects in a horizontal line.

EXAMPLE Three particles are placed at positions along the x-axis as shown. Find the coordinates of the centre of mass of the group of particles.

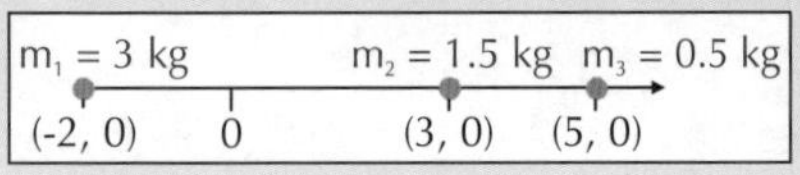

1) Use the formula $\Sigma mx = \bar{x}\Sigma m$ and put in what you know:

   $m_1x_1 + m_2x_2 + m_3x_3 = \bar{x}(m_1 + m_2 + m_3)$

   $\Rightarrow (3 \times -2) + (1.5 \times 3) + (0.5 \times 5) = \bar{x}(3 + 1.5 + 0.5)$

   $\Rightarrow 1 = 5\bar{x} \quad \Rightarrow \quad \bar{x} = 0.2$
2) So the centre of mass of the group has the coordinates (0.2, 0)

Negative coordinates go in the formula just as they are.

Use $\bar{y}$ for Particles in a Vertical Line

It's the same for particles arranged in a vertical line. The centre of mass has the coordinate $(0, \bar{y})$.

$$\Sigma my = \bar{y}\Sigma m$$

EXAMPLE A light vertical rod AB has particles attached at various positions, as shown. At what height is the centre of mass of the rod?

A light rod has length but no width or depth, and no mass (as it's light).

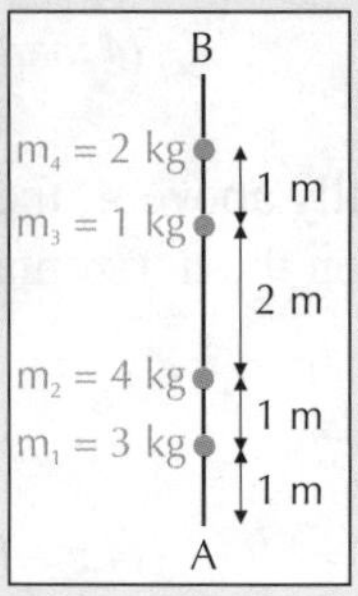

1) First, work out the positions of all the particles relative to a single point or 'origin'. Since you're asked for the vertical height, pick point A at the bottom of the rod:

   $y_1 = 1, y_2 = 2, y_3 = 4, y_4 = 5.$
2) Plug the numbers into the formula:

   $\Sigma my = \bar{y}\Sigma m \quad \Rightarrow \quad m_1y_1 + m_2y_2 + m_3y_3 + m_4y_4 = \bar{y}(m_1 + m_2 + m_3 + m_4)$

   $\Rightarrow (3 \times 1) + (4 \times 2) + (1 \times 4) + (2 \times 5) = \bar{y} \times (3 + 4 + 1 + 2)$

   $\Rightarrow 25 = \bar{y} \times 10 \quad \Rightarrow \quad \bar{y} = 25 \div 10 = 2.5.$
3) Make sure you've answered the question — $\bar{y}$ is the vertical coordinate from the 'origin' which we took as the bottom of the rod. So the vertical height of the centre of mass is 2.5 m.

Take a moment to understand the basics...

Once you've got your head around what's going on with a system of particles, the number crunching is the easy part. You'll often have to tackle wordy problems where you first have to model a situation using rods and particles and things — you should be more than familiar with doing this from M1, and there's more practice to come later in the section.

Discrete Groups of Particles in 2 Dimensions

Let's face it, in the 'real world', you'll rarely come across a group in a perfectly orderly line (think of queuing up in the sales — madness). Luckily, the same principles apply in two dimensions — it's no harder than the stuff on the last page.

Use the *Position Vector* $\bar{\mathbf{r}}$ *for* ***Centre of Mass*** *of a* ***Group*** *on a* ***Plane***

There are two ways to find the centre of mass of a group of particles on a plane (i.e. in 2 dimensions, x and y, rather than just in a line). The quickest way uses position vectors, but I'll show you both methods and you can choose.

EXAMPLE Find the coordinates of the centre of mass of the system of particles shown in the diagram.

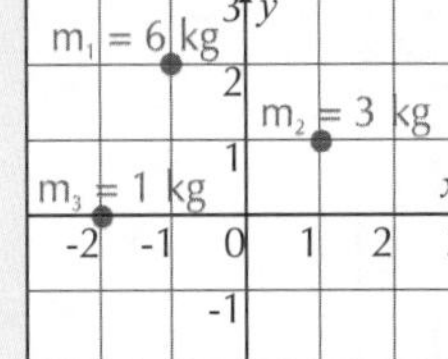

The Long Way — find the x and y coordinates separately:

1) Find the x coordinate of the centre of mass first (pretend they're in a horizontal line...)
   $x_1 = -1$, $x_2 = 1$, $x_3 = -2$, so:
   $m_1x_1 + m_2x_2 + m_3x_3 = \bar{x}(m_1 + m_2 + m_3) \Rightarrow (6 \times -1) + (3 \times 1) + (1 \times -2) = \bar{x}(6 + 3 + 1)$
   $\Rightarrow \bar{x} = -\frac{5}{10} = \underline{-0.5}$.
2) Now find the y coordinate in the same way: $y_1 = 2$, $y_2 = 1$, $y_3 = 0$, so:
   $m_1y_1 + m_2y_2 + m_3y_3 = \bar{y}(m_1 + m_2 + m_3) \Rightarrow (6 \times 2) + (3 \times 1) + (1 \times 0) = \bar{y}(6 + 3 + 1)$
   $\Rightarrow \bar{y} = \frac{15}{10} = \underline{1.5}$.
3) So the centre of mass has the coordinates $\underline{(-0.5, 1.5)}$.

Column position vectors like these are just like coordinates standing upright — $\mathbf{r} = \binom{x}{y}$.

The Short Way — use position vectors:

1) Write out the position vector ($\mathbf{r}$) for each particle: $\mathbf{r}_1 = \binom{-1}{2}$, $\mathbf{r}_2 = \binom{1}{1}$, $\mathbf{r}_3 = \binom{-2}{0}$.
2) Use the formula, but replace the xs and ys with $\mathbf{r}$s: $\Sigma m\mathbf{r} = \bar{\mathbf{r}}\Sigma m \Rightarrow m_1\mathbf{r}_1 + m_2\mathbf{r}_2 + m_3\mathbf{r}_3 = \bar{\mathbf{r}}(m_1 + m_2 + m_3)$

$\Rightarrow 6\binom{-1}{2} + 3\binom{1}{1} + 1\binom{-2}{0} = \bar{\mathbf{r}}(6 + 3 + 1) \Rightarrow \binom{-6}{12} + \binom{3}{3} + \binom{-2}{0} = 10\bar{\mathbf{r}}$

$\Rightarrow \binom{-5}{15} = 10\bar{\mathbf{r}} \Rightarrow \bar{\mathbf{r}} = \binom{-0.5}{1.5}$. So the centre of mass has position vector $\binom{-0.5}{1.5}$, and coordinates $\underline{(-0.5, 1.5)}$.

> Using this method the formula becomes: $\Sigma m\mathbf{r} = \bar{\mathbf{r}}\Sigma m$

The ***Formula*** *works for finding* ***Unknown Masses*** *and* ***Locations***

You won't always be asked to find the centre of mass of a system. You could be given the position of the centre of mass and asked to work out something else, like the mass or coordinates of a particle in the system. Use the same formula:

EXAMPLE The diagram shows the position of the centre of mass (COM) of a system of three particles attached to the corners of a light rectangular lamina. Find m_2.

A lamina is just a flat (2D) shape.

$m_1 = 8$ kg, m_2, COM, 3 m, 3.5 m, 4 m, 6 m, $m_3 = 2$ kg

1) First of all, pick your origin — bottom left looks as good as anywhere — and define all your positions from this point:
   $\mathbf{r}_1 = \binom{0}{4}$, $\mathbf{r}_2 = \binom{6}{4}$, $\mathbf{r}_3 = \binom{6}{0}$. The COM, $\bar{\mathbf{r}}$, is at $\binom{3}{3.5}$.
2) Fill in what you know in the formula:
   $\Sigma m\mathbf{r} = \bar{\mathbf{r}}\Sigma m \Rightarrow m_1\mathbf{r}_1 + m_2\mathbf{r}_2 + m_3\mathbf{r}_3 = \bar{\mathbf{r}}(m_1 + m_2 + m_3)$

   $\Rightarrow 8\binom{0}{4} + m_2\binom{6}{4} + 2\binom{6}{0} = \binom{3}{3.5} \times (8 + m_2 + 2) \Rightarrow \binom{0}{32} + \binom{6m_2}{4m_2} + \binom{12}{0} = \binom{3}{3.5} \times (m_2 + 10)$

   $\Rightarrow \binom{6m_2 + 12}{4m_2 + 32} = \binom{3m_2 + 30}{3.5m_2 + 35}$
3) Pick either the top row or bottom row to solve the equation for m_2 (it should be the same in both), e.g.: Top — $6m_2 + 12 = 3m_2 + 30 \Rightarrow m_2 = \underline{6\text{ kg}}$. Bottom — $4m_2 + 32 = 3.5m_2 + 35 \Rightarrow m_2 = \underline{6\text{ kg}}$.

2D or not 2D — that is the question...

Well actually the question's more likely to be 'Find the centre of mass of the following system of particles...', but then I doubt that would have made Hamlet quite such a gripping tale. Make sure you can do this stuff with your eyes shut because you'll need it again later on, and there's also a new compulsory blindfolded section to the M2 exam this year...

Standard Uniform Laminas

A page full of shapes for you to learn, just like in little school. However, you need to be able to find the centres of mass of these uniform plane laminas, not just colour them in. Even if you can do it neatly inside the lines.

Use Lines of Symmetry with Regular and Standard Shapes

Uniform laminas have evenly spread mass, so the centre of mass is in the centre of the shape, on all the lines of symmetry. So for shapes with more than one line of symmetry, the centre of mass is where the lines of symmetry intersect.

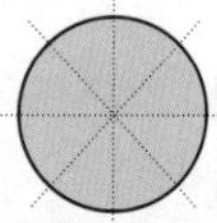
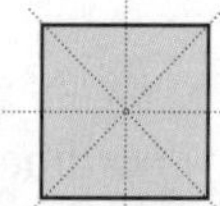
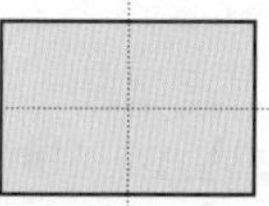

EXAMPLE Find the coordinates of the centre of mass of a uniform rectangular lamina with vertices A(−4, 7), B (2, 7), C(−4, −3) and D(2, −3).

1) A little sketch never goes amiss...

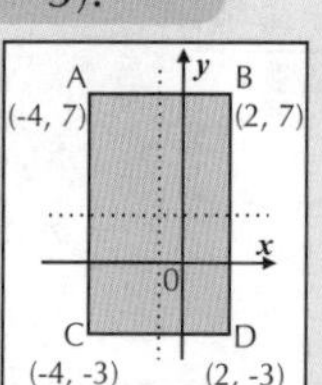

2) $\overline{x}$ is the midpoint of AB (or CD), i.e. (−4 + 2) ÷ 2 = −1.
3) $\overline{y}$ is the midpoint of AC (or BD), i.e. (7 + −3) ÷ 2 = 2.
4) So the centre of mass is at (−1, 2). Easy peasy lemon squeezy*.

The Centre of Mass of a Triangle is the Centroid

1) In any triangle, the lines from each vertex to the midpoint of the opposite side are called medians.

In an equilateral triangle, the medians are lines of symmetry.

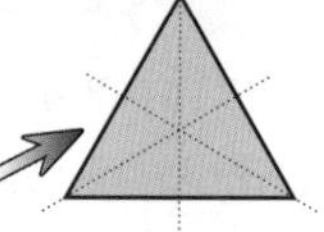

2) If you draw in the medians on any triangle, the point where they meet will be two thirds of the way up each median from each vertex. This point is the centroid, and it's the centre of mass in a uniform triangle.

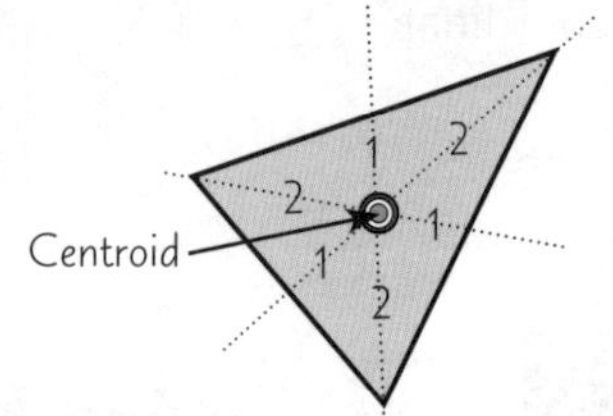

3) There's a formula for finding the coordinates of the centroid:

For a triangle with vertices at (x_1, y_1), (x_2, y_2) and (x_3, y_3):

Centre of Mass $(\overline{x}, \overline{y})$ is at $\left(\frac{x_1 + x_2 + x_3}{3}, \frac{y_1 + y_2 + y_3}{3}\right)$

(i.e. the mean x coordinate and mean y coordinate)

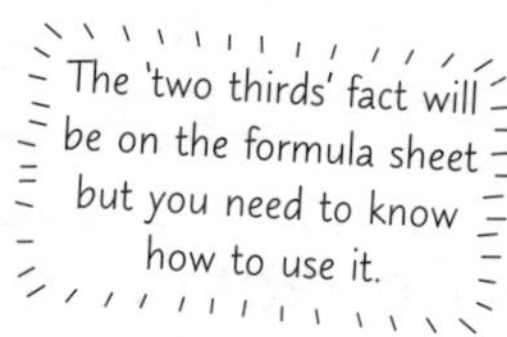

The 'two thirds' fact will be on the formula sheet but you need to know how to use it.

Use the Formula to find the COM of a Sector of a Circle

Finding the centre of mass of a sector of a circle is a bit harder, so the formula is given to you in the exam:

For a uniform circle sector, radius r and angle 2α radians:

Centre of Mass is at $\frac{2r\sin\alpha}{3\alpha}$ from the centre of the circle on the axis of symmetry.

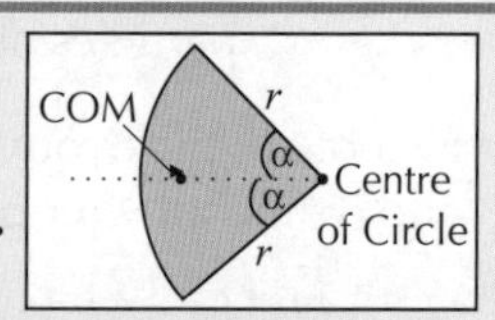

EXAMPLE A sector is cut from a uniform circle of radius 3 cm, centre P. The sector is an eighth of the whole circle. How far along the axis of symmetry is the centre of mass of the sector from P?

1) The angle of the sector is an eighth of the whole circle, so $2\alpha = \frac{2\pi}{8} \Rightarrow \alpha = \frac{\pi}{8}$.
2) Using the formula $\frac{2r\sin\alpha}{3\alpha}$, with r = 3 cm:

Centre of Mass = $\frac{2 \times 3 \times \sin\frac{\pi}{8}}{\frac{3\pi}{8}}$ = 1.9489... = 1.95 cm from P (to 3 s.f.)

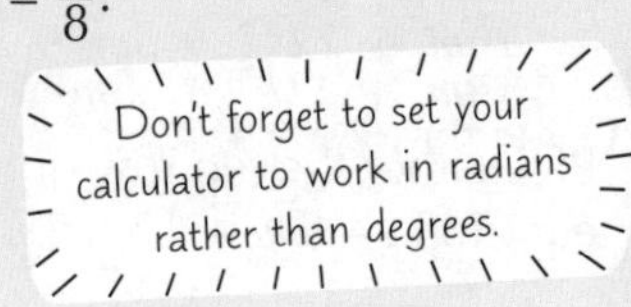

Don't forget to set your calculator to work in radians rather than degrees.

I love a lamina in uniform...

A nice easy page with lots of pretty shapes and colours. Before you start unleashing your inner toddler and demanding sweets and afternoon naps, make sure you fully understand what's been said on this page, because the tough stuff is coming right up. There's plenty of time for sweets and afternoon naps when the exams are over. Trust me...

*Squeezing lemons is actually quite tricky so I'm not sure where this saying comes from.

Composite Shapes

It's time to combine all the things covered so far in the section into one lamina lump. Yay.

For a Composite Shape — Find each COM Individually then Combine

A composite shape is one that can be broken up into standard parts such as triangles, rectangles and circles. Once you've found the COM of a part, imagine replacing it with a particle of the same mass in the position of the COM. Do this for each part, then find the COM of the group of 'particles' — this is the COM of the composite shape.

EXAMPLE A house-shaped lamina is cut from a single piece of card, with dimensions as shown. Find the location of the centre of mass of the shape in relation to the point O.

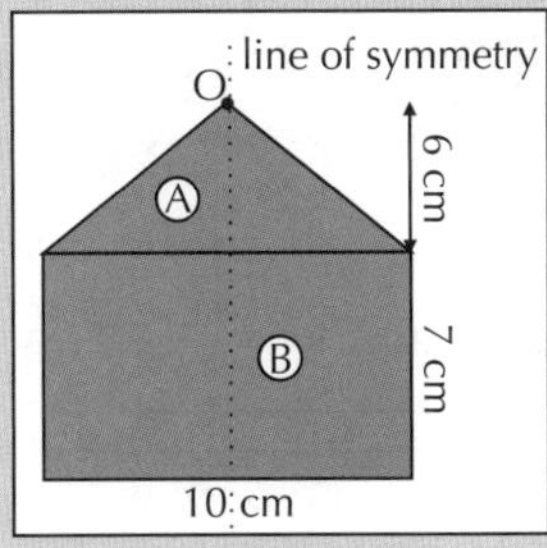

1) First, split up the shape into a triangle (A) and rectangle (B). As both bits are made of the same material, the masses of A and B are in proportion to their areas, so we can say $m_A = \frac{1}{2} \times 10 \times 6 = 30$, and $m_B = 10 \times 7 = 70$.
2) The shape has a line of symmetry, so the centre of mass must be on that line, directly below the point O.
3) Next find the vertical position of the centres of mass of both A and B individually:
   $y_A = \frac{2}{3}$ of the distance down from O $= \frac{2}{3} \times 6$ cm $= 4$ cm from O
   (since A is a triangle and the vertical line of symmetry from O is a median of the triangle — p.166)
   $y_B = 6$ cm $+ (7$ cm $\div 2) = 9.5$ cm from O
   (since B has a horizontal line of symmetry halfway down, but is 6 cm below O to start with)

Use symmetry where you can — but make sure you explain what you've done.

4) Treat the shapes as two particles positioned at the centres of mass of each shape, and use the formula from p.165:
   $\Sigma my = \bar{y}\Sigma m \Rightarrow m_A y_A + m_B y_B = \bar{y}(m_A + m_B)$
   $\Rightarrow (30 \times 4) + (70 \times 9.5) = \bar{y}(30 + 70) \Rightarrow 785 = 100\bar{y} \Rightarrow \bar{y} = 785 \div 100 = 7.85$ cm.
5) Make sure you've answered the question —
   The centre of mass of the whole shape is 7.85 cm vertically below O on the line of symmetry. Job done.

You can use the Removal Method for Some Shapes

You may have a shape that looks like a 'standard' shape with other standard shapes 'removed' rather than stuck together. The removal method is like the one above, except the individual centres of mass are subtracted rather than added.

EXAMPLE Find the coordinates of the centre of mass of the lamina shown — a circle of radius 3 with a quarter sector removed.

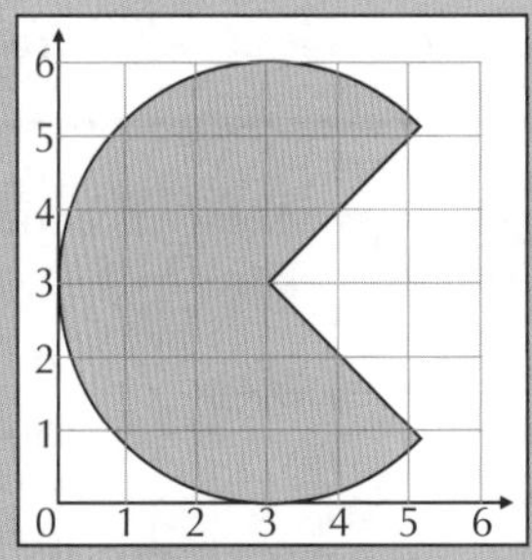

1) Let's call the 'whole' circle A and the sector that's been removed B. Since B is a quarter of A, we can say that the masses are $m_A = 4$ and $m_B = 1$.
2) 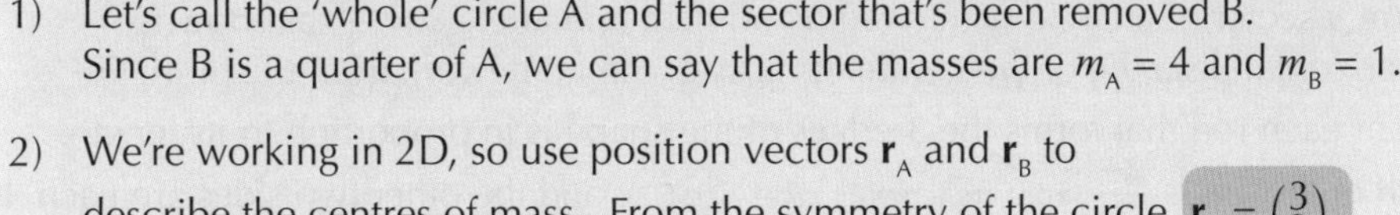
   We're working in 2D, so use position vectors $\mathbf{r}_A$ and $\mathbf{r}_B$ to describe the centres of mass. From the symmetry of the circle, $\mathbf{r}_A = \binom{3}{3}$.
   $\mathbf{r}_B$ can be worked out using the formula on p. 166:
   $y_B = 3$ (from the symmetry of the sector) and $x_B = 3 + \frac{2r\sin\alpha}{3\alpha}$.
   The angle of the sector, $2\alpha = \frac{\pi}{2} \Rightarrow \alpha = \frac{\pi}{4}$, and r = 3,
   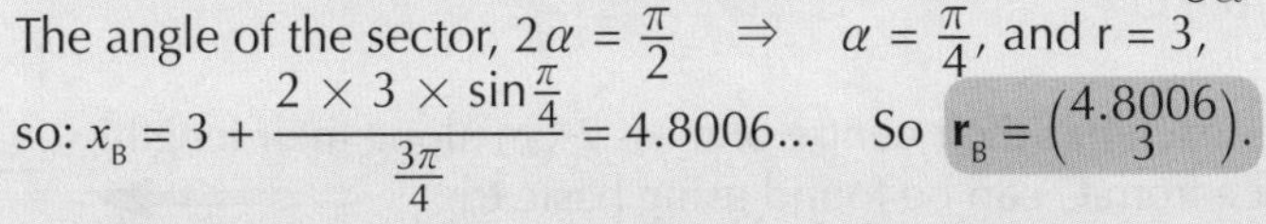
   so: $x_B = 3 + \frac{2 \times 3 \times \sin\frac{\pi}{4}}{\frac{3\pi}{4}} = 4.8006...$ So $\mathbf{r}_B = \binom{4.8006}{3}$.
3) Using the removal method, our formula becomes: $m_A\mathbf{r}_A - m_B\mathbf{r}_B = \bar{\mathbf{r}}(m_A - m_B)$
   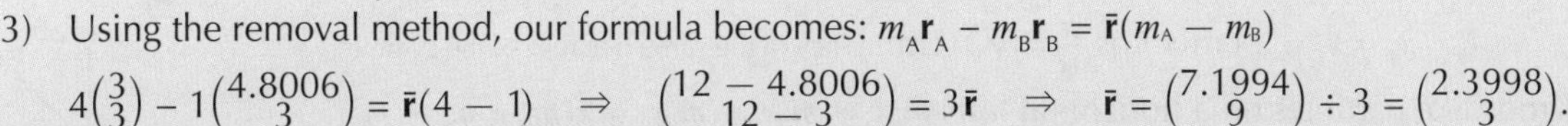
   $4\binom{3}{3} - 1\binom{4.8006}{3} = \bar{\mathbf{r}}(4-1) \Rightarrow \binom{12 - 4.8006}{12 - 3} = 3\bar{\mathbf{r}} \Rightarrow \bar{\mathbf{r}} = \binom{7.1994}{9} \div 3 = \binom{2.3998}{3}$.
4) So the coordinates of the centres of mass of the shape are (2.40, 3).

Waxing is another effective removal method...

Now you've got all you need to find the centre of mass of any lamina shape, so long as you can spot how it breaks up into circles, triangles, etc. Quite arty-farty this. Set out your working neatly though, especially for the more complicated shapes.

Frameworks

More pretty shapes, this time made from rods rather than laminas — imagine bending a wire coathanger into something shapely (and infinitely more useful since wire hangers are rubbish). These shapes are called frameworks.

Treat Each Side as a Rod with its own Centre of Mass

In a framework, there's nothing in the middle, so all the mass is within the rods that make up the shape's edges. If the rods are straight and uniform, the centre of mass of each one is at the midpoint of the rod. Try to imagine each side of the shape as a separate rod, even if it's a single wire bent round into a shape.

EXAMPLES a) Find the coordinates of the centre of mass of the framework shown.

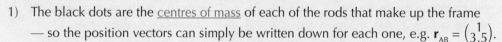

1) The black dots are the centres of mass of each of the rods that make up the frame — so the position vectors can simply be written down for each one, e.g. $\mathbf{r}_{AB} = \begin{pmatrix} 1 \\ 3.5 \end{pmatrix}$.
2) The mass of each rod is proportional to its length, so $m_{AB} = 5$ etc.
3) You've now got the equivalent of a group of 6 particles, so put it all in the formula:

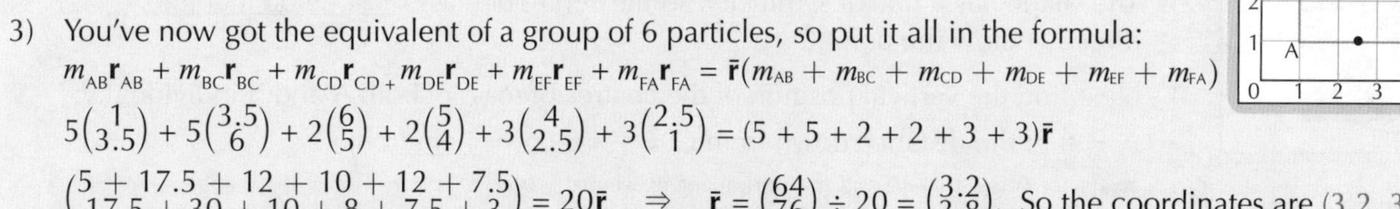

$$m_{AB}\mathbf{r}_{AB} + m_{BC}\mathbf{r}_{BC} + m_{CD}\mathbf{r}_{CD} + m_{DE}\mathbf{r}_{DE} + m_{EF}\mathbf{r}_{EF} + m_{FA}\mathbf{r}_{FA} = \bar{\mathbf{r}}(m_{AB} + m_{BC} + m_{CD} + m_{DE} + m_{EF} + m_{FA})$$

$$5\begin{pmatrix} 1 \\ 3.5 \end{pmatrix} + 5\begin{pmatrix} 3.5 \\ 6 \end{pmatrix} + 2\begin{pmatrix} 6 \\ 5 \end{pmatrix} + 2\begin{pmatrix} 5 \\ 4 \end{pmatrix} + 3\begin{pmatrix} 4 \\ 2.5 \end{pmatrix} + 3\begin{pmatrix} 2.5 \\ 1 \end{pmatrix} = (5 + 5 + 2 + 2 + 3 + 3)\bar{\mathbf{r}}$$

$$\begin{pmatrix} 5 + 17.5 + 12 + 10 + 12 + 7.5 \\ 17.5 + 30 + 10 + 8 + 7.5 + 3 \end{pmatrix} = 20\bar{\mathbf{r}} \Rightarrow \bar{\mathbf{r}} = \begin{pmatrix} 64 \\ 76 \end{pmatrix} \div 20 = \begin{pmatrix} 3.2 \\ 3.8 \end{pmatrix}.$$ So the coordinates are (3.2, 3.8).

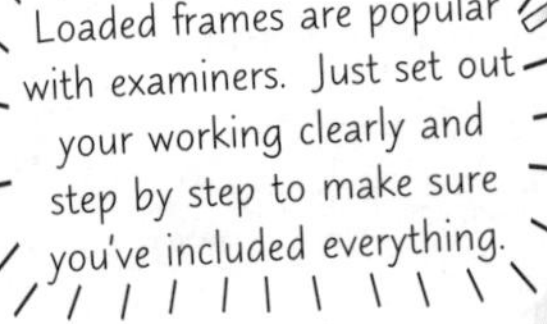

Loaded frames are popular with examiners. Just set out your working clearly and step by step to make sure you've included everything.

b) A particle with the same mass as the whole framework is attached to the frame at A. Find the new centre of mass of the system.

1) The system consists of the framework mass which acts at (3.2, 3.8) (from a)), plus the mass of a particle at (1, 1). As they're the same mass, you can call each mass '1'.
2) $1\mathbf{r}_{Frame} + 1\mathbf{r}_{Particle} = 2\bar{\mathbf{r}} \Rightarrow \begin{pmatrix} 3.2 \\ 3.8 \end{pmatrix} + \begin{pmatrix} 1 \\ 1 \end{pmatrix} = 2\bar{\mathbf{r}} \Rightarrow \bar{\mathbf{r}} = \begin{pmatrix} 4.2 \\ 4.8 \end{pmatrix} \div 2 = \begin{pmatrix} 2.1 \\ 2.4 \end{pmatrix}$.

So the coordinates of the new COM are (2.1, 2.4).

Arcs have their own Formula

Arcs are parts of the edge of a circle, and just like sectors have their own formula to work out their centre of mass:

For a uniform arc of a circle of radius r and angle 2α radians:

Centre of Mass is at $\frac{r\sin\alpha}{\alpha}$ from the centre of the circle on the axis of symmetry.

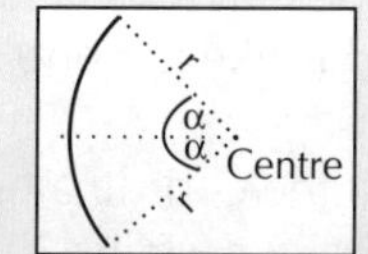

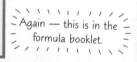

Again — this is in the formula booklet.

EXAMPLE A wire is bent to form a sector of a circle with a radius of 4 cm and angle $\phi = \frac{\pi}{3}$, as shown. Find, to 3 s.f., the horizontal distance of the centre of mass of the framework from the point C.

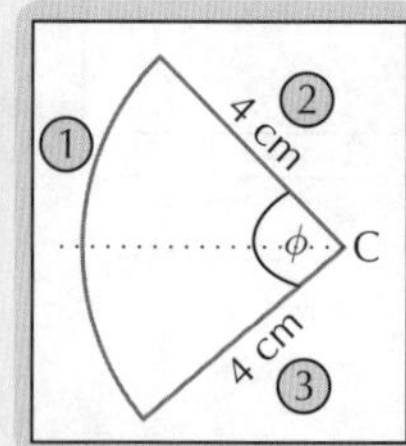

1) The mass of each rod that forms the 3 edges of the shape is in proportion to its length. The length of the arc is $\frac{4\pi}{3}$ (from arc length = $r\theta$ — see C2), and the other two sides are each 4.
2) To find the COM of the arc, use the formula $\frac{r\sin\alpha}{\alpha}$ (where $2\alpha = \frac{\pi}{3}$, so $\alpha = \frac{\pi}{6}$):

$$x_1 = \frac{4 \times \sin\frac{\pi}{6}}{\frac{\pi}{6}} = \frac{12}{\pi} \text{ cm from C.}$$

3) Then for the straight rods: each has their centre of mass 2 cm along their length, and the horizontal distance from C can be found using basic trig:

$x_2 = x_3 = 2 \text{ cm} \times \cos\frac{\pi}{6} = \sqrt{3}$ cm. (They're the same because of the symmetry.)

4) Treat the 3 rods like particles on a horizontal line: $m_1x_1 + m_2x_2 + m_3x_3 = \bar{x}(m_1 + m_2 + m_3)$

$$\left(\frac{4\pi}{3} \times \frac{12}{\pi}\right) + (4 \times \sqrt{3}) + (4 \times \sqrt{3}) = \bar{x}\left(\frac{4\pi}{3} + 4 + 4\right) \Rightarrow 16 + 8\sqrt{3} = \left(8 + \frac{4\pi}{3}\right)\bar{x} \Rightarrow \bar{x} = 2.45 \text{ cm to 3 s.f.}$$

Arc-asm is the lowest form of wit — yet still funnier than this gag...

There's been a lot to take in on the last few pages. You'll notice every 'new' bit needs you to do all the 'old' bits too, and more besides. Maths is kinda like that. Make sure you're astoundingly marvellous at the section so far before you move on.

Laminas in Equilibrium

This is what the whole section's been working up to. The raison d'être for centres of mass, if you'll pardon my French. The position of the centre of mass will tell you what happens when you hang it up or tilt it. Très intéressant, non?

Laminas *Hang* with the Centre of Mass *Directly Below* the *Pivot*

When you suspend a shape, either from a point on its edge or from a pivot point within the shape, it will hang in equilibrium so that the centre of mass is vertically below the suspension point.

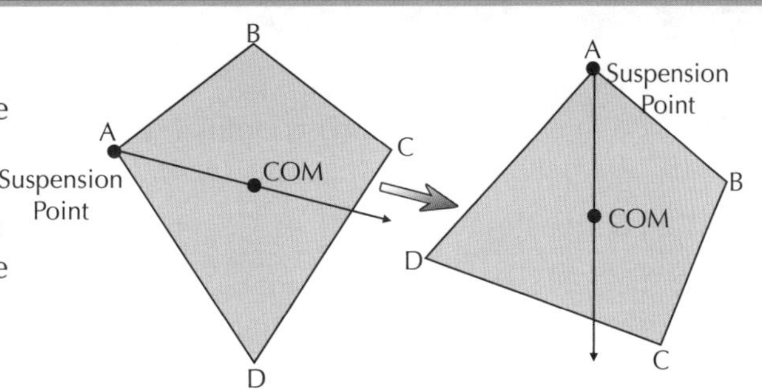

Knowing where the centre of mass lies will let you work out the angle that the shape hangs at.

EXAMPLE In the shape above, A is at (0, 6), C is at (8, 6), and the COM is at (4, 5). Find, in radians to 3 s.f., the angle AC makes with the vertical when the shape is suspended from A.

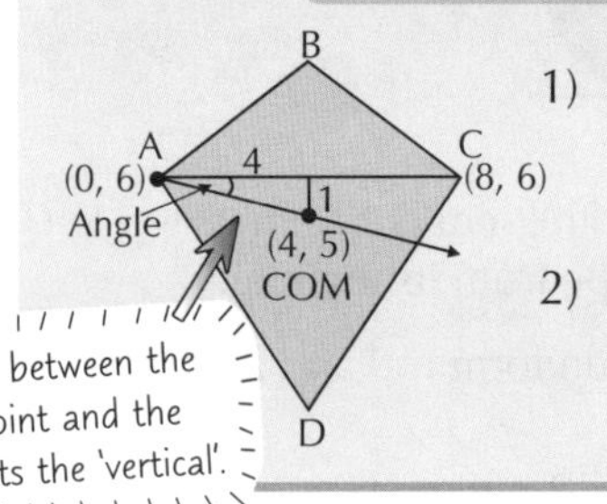

A straight line between the suspension point and the COM represents the 'vertical'.

1) Do a little sketch of the shape showing the lengths you know. Draw in the line representing the vertical from the suspension point to the COM and label the angle you need to find.

2) The angle should now be an easy piece of trig away:
Angle = $\tan^{-1}\frac{1}{4}$ = 0.245 radians to 3 s.f.

In an exam question, you'll usually have to find the position of the centre of mass first and THEN do this bit to finish.

Shapes *Topple* if the COM is not *Directly Above* the *Bottom Edge*

SAFE

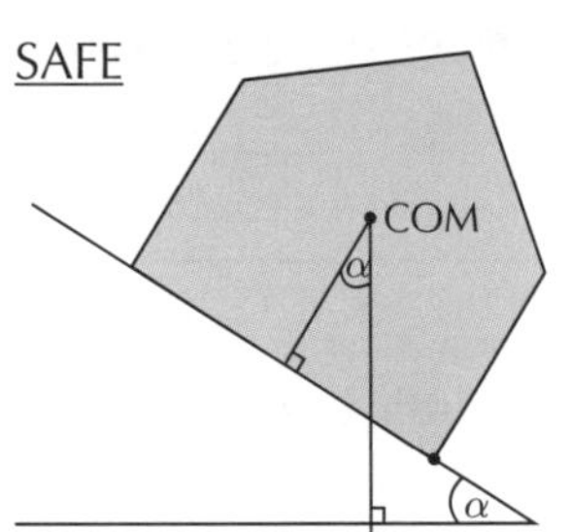

MORTAL PERIL

COM

Tilting a shape on an inclined plane will make it topple over eventually (assuming there's enough friction to stop it sliding).

To make it fall over, you need to incline the plane above an angle, α, where the centre of mass is vertically above the bottom corner or edge of the shape, as shown in the pictures on the left.

EXAMPLE The house-shaped lamina from p. 167 is in equilibrium on a plane inclined at an angle α. Find the value of α at the point where the shape is about to topple (in rads to 3 s.f.).

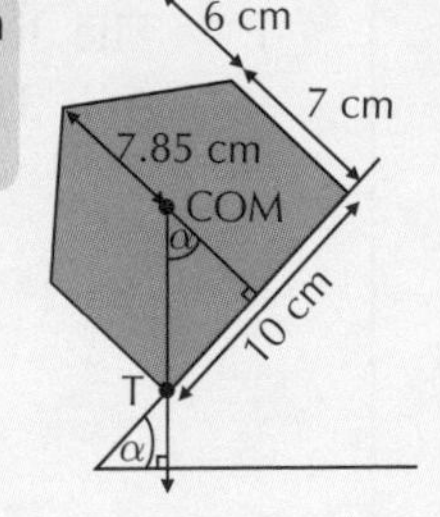

1) Draw in a line between the COM and the corner point (T) of the shape — this line will be vertical at the tipping point.

Use what you know about the position of the COM to draw a right-angled triangle containing α.
Height of COM from bottom edge = 7 + 6 – 7.85 = 5.15 cm.
COM is also halfway along the bottom edge, i.e. 10 ÷ 2 = 5 cm from T.

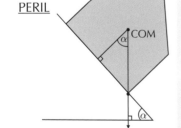

2) Use basic trig to work out the size of the angle:
$\alpha = \tan^{-1}\left(\frac{5}{5.15}\right)$ = 0.771 rads to 3 s.f.

COM
α
5.15 cm
T
5 cm

Don't hang around — get practising or you're heading for a fall...

This page may seem deceptively easy because in both examples it's assumed you've already found the centre of mass (that's what all the other pages were about in case you'd forgotten). In the exam you'll more than likely have to find the COM first and then work out the hanging or toppling angles. Luckily, there's plenty of practice at doing this on the next few pages...

M2 Section 2 — Practice Questions

Hurrah and huzzah — it's time to put your slick Section 2 skills (try saying that in a hurry) to the test. As with all strenuous exercise, you need to warm up properly — and as if by chance, look what we have here...

Warm-up Questions

1) Three particles have mass $m_1 = 1$ kg, $m_2 = 2$ kg, and $m_3 = 3$ kg.
Find the centre of mass of the system of particles if their coordinates are, respectively:
a) (1, 0), (2, 0), (3, 0) b) (0, 3), (0, 2), (0, 1) c) (3, 4), (3, 1), (1, 0)

2) A system of particles located at coordinates A(0, 0), B(0, 4), C(5, 4) and D(5, 0) have masses m kg, $2m$ kg, $3m$ kg and 12 kg respectively. Find m, if the centre of mass of the system is at (3.5, 2).

3) Find the coordinates of the centres of mass of each of the uniform laminas shown below.

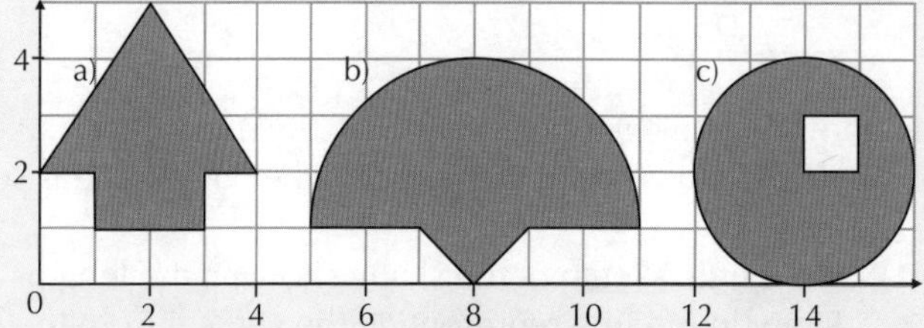

4) A square uniform lamina of width 10 cm has a smaller square of width 2 cm cut from its top left corner. Find the distance of the centre of mass of the remaining shape from its top edge.

5) a) A semicircular framework (radius 5 cm) is modelled as a straight uniform rod and a uniform arc. Find the distance of the centre of mass from the straight edge.
b) The frame is suspended from one of its corners and hangs in equilibrium. Find the angle the straight edge makes with the vertical. Give your answer in radians to 3 d.p.

The universe is full of seemingly unanswerable questions to ponder.
Fortunately for those not particularly inclined towards philosophy there are some perfectly good answerable ones here. Enjoy.

Exam Questions

1 The diagram below shows three particles attached to a light rectangular lamina at coordinates A(1, 3), B(5, 1) and C(4, y).

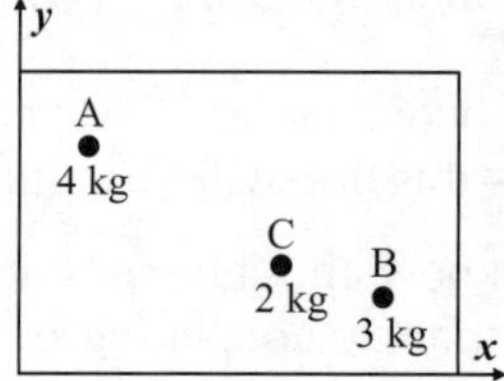

The centre of mass of the system is at $(\bar{x}, 2)$.

(a) Show that $y = 1.5$. *(3 marks)*

(b) Show that $\bar{x} = 3$. *(3 marks)*

The light lamina is replaced with a uniform rectangle PQRS, having a mass of 6 kg and vertices at P(0, 0), Q(0, 5), R(7, 5) and S(7, 0). Particles A, B and C remain at their existing coordinates.

(c) Find the coordinates of the new centre of mass of the whole system. *(6 marks)*

M2 Section 2 — Practice Questions

2 A wire sculpture is modelled as a frame made from two uniform rods, one straight with mass $2m$, and one a semicircular arc with mass πm, with 2 particles of mass $3m$ and $4m$ attached to each corner, as shown:

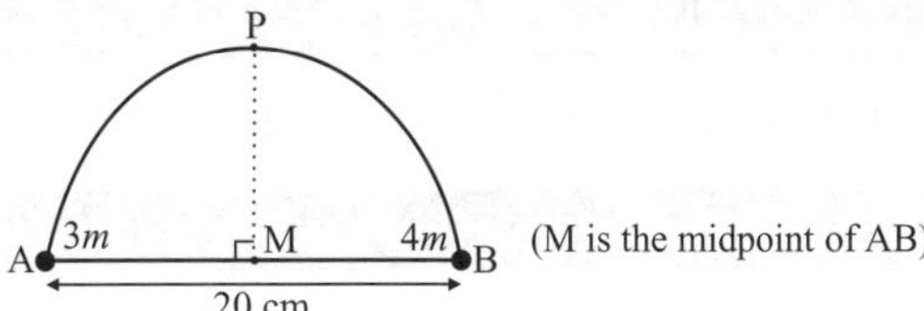

(a) Find, in cm to 4 decimal places, the distance of the centre of mass of the loaded framework from:

(i) MP. *(3 marks)*

(ii) AB. *(3 marks)*

The sculpture is suspended from the point P, and hangs in equilibrium.

(b) Find the angle MP makes with the vertical. Give your answer in radians to 3 s.f. *(3 marks)*

3 A cardboard 'For Sale' sign is modelled as a uniform lamina consisting of two squares and an isosceles triangle. The line of symmetry through the triangle coincides with that of the larger square, as shown.

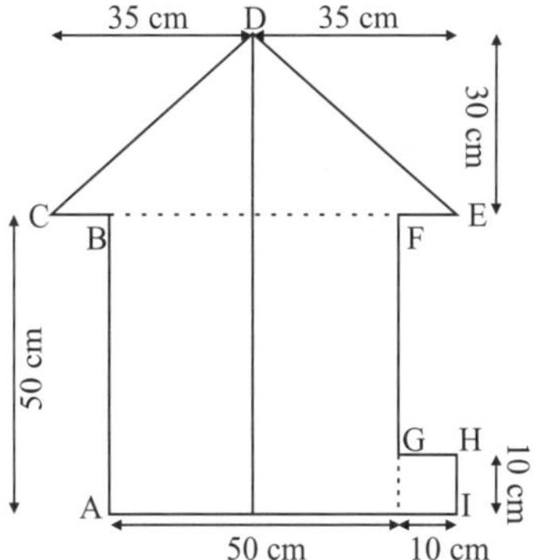

(a) Show that the centre of mass of the sign, to 3 s.f., is 25.8 cm from AB and 34.5 cm from AI. *(6 marks)*

The sign, with a mass of 1 kg, is suspended from the point D, and hangs in equilibrium, at an angle. A small weight, modelled as a particle, is attached at A, so that the sign hangs with AI horizontal.

(b) Find the mass of the particle needed to make the sign hang in this way. Give your answer in kg to 3 s.f.. *(3 marks)*

4 A stencil is made from a uniform sheet of metal by removing a quarter of a circle with centre at the point O.

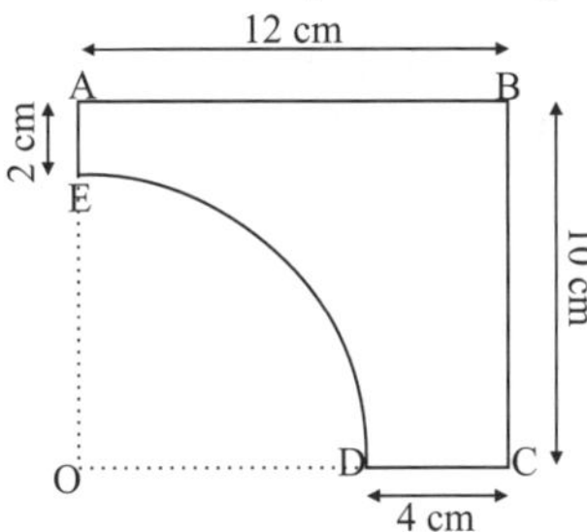

(a) Taking the point O as the origin, find the coordinates of the centre of mass of the stencil, to 3 s.f. Assume the stencil can be modelled as a lamina. *(7 marks)*

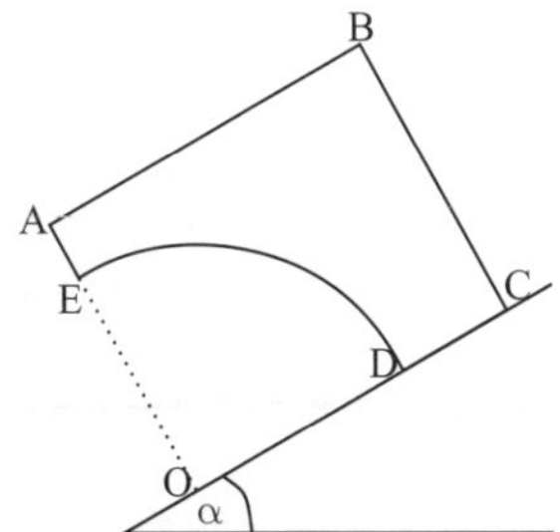

Particles are added to the stencil to adjust the centre of mass so that it now acts at coordinates (9, 6) from O. The stencil rests in equilibrium on a rough inclined plane, as shown. The angle of incline is increased until the shape is just about to fall over, balanced on the point D.

(b) Find the angle of incline above which the shape will topple. Give your answer in radians to 3 s.f. *(3 marks)*

Work Done

Hello, good evening, welcome to Section 3 — where work and energy are tonight's chef's specials...

You Can Find the **Work Done** by a Force Over a Certain **Distance**

When a force is acting on a particle, you can work out the work done by the force using the formula:

Work done = force (F) × distance moved in the direction of the force (s)

For F in Newtons, and s in metres, the unit of work done is joules (J).

E.g. if an object is pushed 4 m across a horizontal floor by a force of magnitude 12 N acting horizontally, the work done by the force will be 12 × 4 = 48 J

EXAMPLE A rock is dragged across horizontal ground by a rope attached to the rock at an angle of 25° to the horizontal. Given that the work done by the force is 470 J and the tension in the rope is 120 N, find the distance the rock is moved.

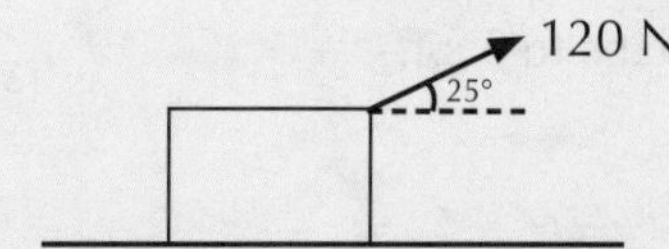

Work = horizontal component of force × s

$470 = 120\cos 25 \times s$

$s = 4.32$ m

Because the force and the distance moved have to be in the same direction.

EXAMPLE A sack of flour of mass m kg is attached to a vertical rope and raised h m at a constant speed. Show that the work done against gravity by the tension in the rope, T, can be expressed as mgh.

T N

mg N

Resolve vertically:
$F = ma$
$T - mg = m \times 0$
$\Rightarrow T = mg$

Work done $= Fs$
$= T \times h$
$= mgh$

Work and gravity

You can always use the formula mgh to find the work done by a force against gravity.

A Particle Moving **Up a Rough Slope** does Work against **Friction and Gravity**

EXAMPLE A block of mass 3 kg is pulled 9 m up a rough plane inclined at an angle of 20° to the horizontal by a force, T. The block moves at a constant speed. The work done by T against friction is 154 J.

Find: a) the work done by T against gravity
b) the coefficient of friction between the block and the plane.

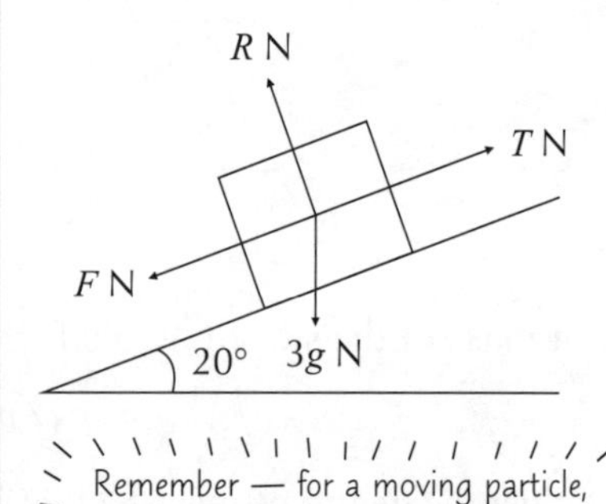

a) Work done against gravity $= mgh$
$= 3g \times 9\sin 20$
$=$ **90.5 J** (3 s.f.)

You need to use the vertical height, because it's only vertically that T does work against gravity.

b) Resolve perpendicular to the slope to find R:
$R - 3g\cos 20 = m \times 0$
$\Rightarrow R = 3g\cos 20$

Particle is moving, so:
$F = \mu R$
$= \mu \times 3g\cos 20$

Remember — for a moving particle, F = μR, where μ is the coefficient of friction and R is the normal reaction.

Work done by T against friction
$= F \times s = 154$

So, $\mu \times 3g\cos 20 \times 9 = 154$
$\mu =$ **0.619** (3 s.f.)

The bit of T that is working against friction must be equal to F as the block is moving with constant speed (i.e. a = 0), so you can just use F here.

My work done = coffee × flapjack...

The really important thing to remember from this page is that the distance moved must be in the same direction as the force. Also, don't forget that a particle moving at constant velocity has no resultant force acting on it — this makes resolving forces easy.

Kinetic and Potential Energy

Here are couple of jokers you might remember from GCSE Science. I know, I know — Science. This means we're skirting dangerously close to the real world here. :| Don't be too afraid though — it's not as scary as you might think...

A Moving Particle Possesses Kinetic Energy

Any particle that is moving has kinetic energy (K.E.). You can find the kinetic energy of a particle using the formula:

$$\text{K.E.} = \frac{1}{2}mv^2$$

You need to learn this formula — you won't be given it in the exam.

If mass, m, is measured in kg and velocity, v, in ms^{-1}, then kinetic energy is measured in joules.

EXAMPLE An ice skater of mass 60 kg is moving at a constant velocity of 8 ms^{-1}. Find the ice skater's kinetic energy.

$$\text{Kinetic energy} = \frac{1}{2}mv^2$$
$$= \frac{1}{2} \times 60 \times 8^2 = 1920 \text{ J}$$

Work Done is related to Kinetic Energy

The work done by a resultant force to change the velocity of a particle moving horizontally is equal to the change in that particle's kinetic energy:

Work done = change in kinetic energy

$$\text{Work done} = \frac{1}{2}mv^2 - \frac{1}{2}mu^2 = \frac{1}{2}m(v^2 - u^2)$$

EXAMPLE A particle P of mass 6 kg is pulled along a rough horizontal plane by a force of 40 N, acting parallel to the plane. The particle travels 4 m in a straight line between two points on the plane, A and B. The coefficient of friction between P and the plane is 0.35.

a) Find the work done against friction in moving P from A to B.

At B, P has a speed of 8 ms^{-1}.

b) Calculate the speed of P at A.

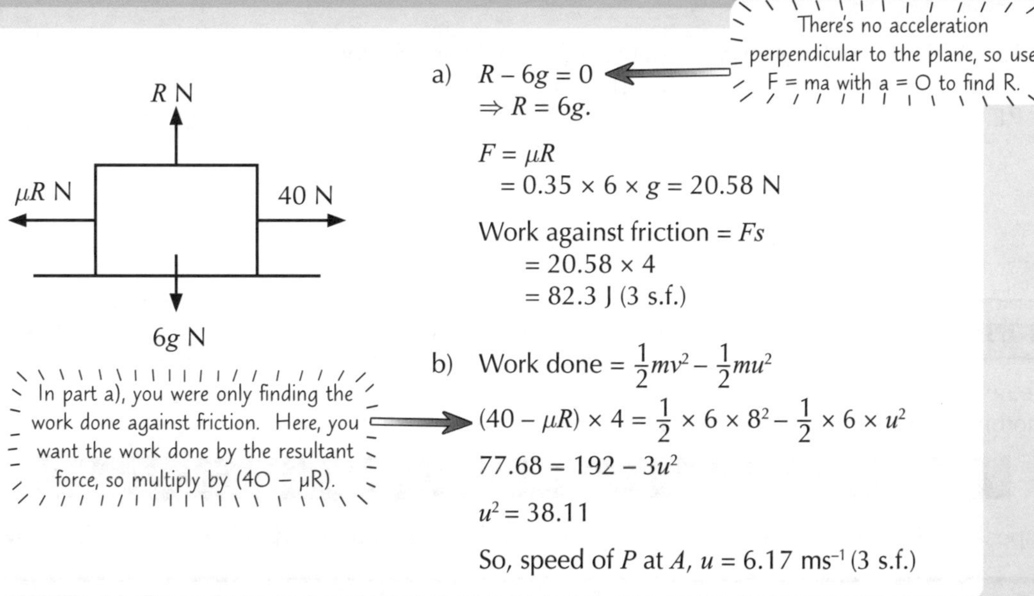

a) $R - 6g = 0$
$\Rightarrow R = 6g$.

There's no acceleration perpendicular to the plane, so use F = ma with a = 0 to find R.

$F = \mu R$
$= 0.35 \times 6 \times g = 20.58$ N

Work against friction $= Fs$
$= 20.58 \times 4$
$= 82.3$ J (3 s.f.)

b) Work done $= \frac{1}{2}mv^2 - \frac{1}{2}mu^2$

$(40 - \mu R) \times 4 = \frac{1}{2} \times 6 \times 8^2 - \frac{1}{2} \times 6 \times u^2$

$77.68 = 192 - 3u^2$

$u^2 = 38.11$

So, speed of P at A, $u = 6.17$ ms^{-1} (3 s.f.)

In part a), you were only finding the work done against friction. Here, you want the work done by the resultant force, so multiply by (40 – μR).

Kinetic and Potential Energy

Potential Energy is all about a Particle's Height

The gravitational potential energy (P.E.) of a particle can be found using the formula:

P.E. = mgh ← You need to learn this formula as well.

If mass (m) is measured in kg, acceleration due to gravity (g) in ms^{-2} and the vertical height above some base level (h) in m, then P.E. is measured in joules.

The greater the height of a particle above the 'base level', the greater that particle's gravitational potential energy.

EXAMPLE

A lift and its occupants have a combined mass of 750 kg. The lift moves vertically from the ground to the first floor of a building, 6.1 m above the ground. After pausing, it moves vertically to the 17th floor, 64.9 m above the ground. Find the gravitational potential energy gained by the lift and its occupants in moving:

a) from the ground floor to the first floor,

b) from the first floor to the 17th floor.

a) P.E. gained $= mg \times$ increase in height
$= 750 \times 9.8 \times 6.1$
$= 44\ 800$ J (3 s.f)

b) P.E. gained $= mg \times$ increase in height
$= 750 \times 9.8 \times (64.9 - 6.1)$
$= 432\ 000$ J (3 s.f.)

Potential Energy Always uses the Vertical Height

When you're working out the potential energy of a particle, the value of h you use should always, always, always be the vertical height above the 'base level'. This means that for a particle moving on a slope, it's only the vertical component of the distance you're interested in:

EXAMPLE A skateboarder and her board have a combined mass of 65 kg. The skateboarder starts from rest at a point X and freewheels down a slope inclined at 15° to the horizontal. She travels 40 m down the line of greatest slope. Find the gravitational potential energy lost by the skateboarder.

The skateboarder has moved a distance of 40 m down the slope, so this is a vertical distance of: 40sin15° m.
P.E. $= mgh$
$= 65 \times 9.8 \times 40\sin 15°$
$= 6590$ J $= 6.59$ kJ (both to 3 s.f.)

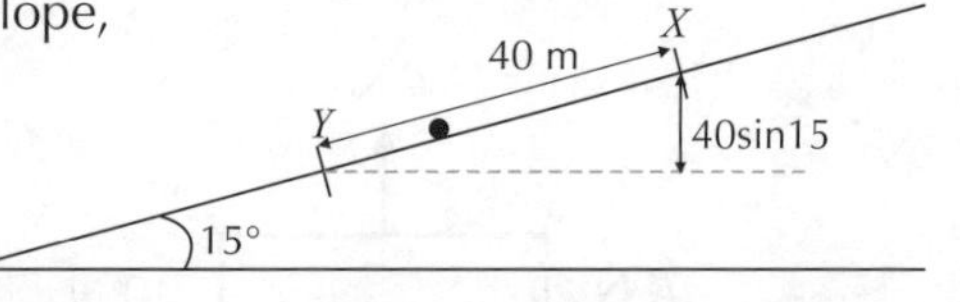

Mechanical Energy is the Sum of a Particle's Kinetic and Potential Energies

Over the next couple of pages, you're going to see a fair bit about 'mechanical energy'.
This is nothing to freak out about — it's just the sum of the kinetic and potential energies of a particle:

Total Mechanical Energy = Kinetic Energy + Gravitational Potential Energy

Strictly speaking, it also includes Elastic Potential Energy, but you don't need to know about that in M2 — hooray!

Particle P has so much potential — if only he could apply himself...

There shouldn't be anything earth-shattering on these two pages — I'd bet my completed 1994-95 Premier League sticker album that you've seen both of these types of energy before*. Still, it's worth refreshing yourself for what comes next.

*I won't though, it's too dear to me. Ahh, shinies...

The Work-Energy Principle

Those pages refreshing your memory on potential and kinetic energy weren't just for fun and giggles. Behold...

Learn the *Principle of Conservation of Mechanical Energy...*

The principle of conservation of mechanical energy says that:

If there are no external forces doing work on an object, the total mechanical energy of the object will remain constant.

An external force is any force other than the weight of the object, e.g. friction, air resistance, tension in a rope, etc. This means that the sum of potential and kinetic energies remains the same throughout an object's motion. This is a pretty useful bit of knowledge:

EXAMPLE

A BASE jumper with mass 88 kg jumps from a ledge on a building, 150 m above the ground. He falls with an initial velocity of 6 ms^{-1} towards the ground. He releases his parachute at a point 60 m above the ground.

a) Find the initial kinetic energy of the jumper in kJ.

b) Use the principle of conservation of mechanical energy to find the jumper's kinetic energy and speed at the point where he releases his parachute.

c) State one assumption you have made in modelling this situation.

a) Initial K.E. $= \frac{1}{2}mu^2 = \frac{1}{2} \times 88 \times (6)^2$
$= 1584 = 1.58$ kJ (3 s.f.)

b) Decrease in P.E. as he falls:
$mgh = 88 \times 9.8 \times (150 - 60)$
$= 77\,616$ J

You can just use the change in height here, as it's the change in P.E. that you're interested in.

Using conservation of mechanical energy: Increase in K.E. = Decrease in P.E.

So, K.E. when parachute released – Initial K.E. = Decrease in P.E.

$\frac{1}{2}mv^2$ = Decrease in P.E. + Initial K.E.
$= 77616 + 1584 = 79.2$ kJ

Rearrange $\frac{1}{2}mv^2 = 79\,200$ to find the speed of the jumper when parachute is released:

$$v = \sqrt{\frac{79\,200}{\frac{1}{2} \times 88}} = 42.4 \text{ ms}^{-1} \text{ (3 s.f.)}$$

If you don't assume this, then you can't use the principle of conservation of energy.

c) That the only force acting on the jumper is his weight.

...and the Work-Energy Principle

1) As you saw above, if there are no external forces doing work on an object, then the total mechanical energy of the object remains constant.
2) So, if there *is* an external force doing work on an object, then the total mechanical energy of the object must change.
3) This leads to the work-energy principle:

The work done on an object by external forces is equal to the change in the total mechanical energy of that object.

4) The work-energy principle is pretty similar to the result on page 173. It's generally more useful though, because you can use it for objects moving in any direction — not just horizontally.

Turn the page for a **HOT** and **SEXY** example...

The Work-Energy Principle

As promised, a lovely example of the work-energy principle...

Example

A particle of mass 3 kg is projected up a rough plane inclined at an angle θ to the horizontal, where $\tan\theta = \frac{5}{12}$. The particle moves through a point A at a speed of 11 ms^{-1}.
The particle continues to move up the line of greatest slope and comes to rest at a point B before sliding back down the plane. The coefficient of friction between the particle and the slope is $\frac{1}{3}$.

a) Use the work-energy principle to find the distance AB.

b) Find the speed of the particle when it returns to A.

a) Call the distance AB x.

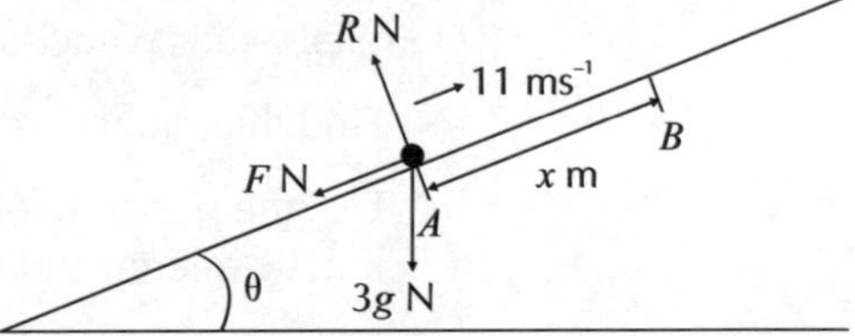

You're told to use the work-energy principle, so first find the change in total mechanical energy:

Change in K.E. of the particle = Final K.E. – Initial K.E.

$= \frac{1}{2}mv^2 - \frac{1}{2}mu^2 = 0 - \left(\frac{1}{2} \times 3 \times 11^2\right) = \mathbf{-181.5\ J}$

Change in P.E. of the particle = mg × (change in height)

$= 3gx\sin\theta = 3gx \times \frac{5}{13} = \mathbf{\frac{15gx}{13}\ J}$ ← $\tan\theta = \frac{5}{12} \Rightarrow \sin\theta = \frac{5}{13}$

So, change in total mechanical energy

$= \mathbf{-181.5 + \frac{15gx}{13}}$

The only external force doing work on the particle is the frictional force, F.
So you need to find the work done by F.

First, resolve perpendicular to slope:

$R - 3g\cos\theta = 0 \Rightarrow R = 3g \times \frac{12}{13} = \frac{36g}{13}$

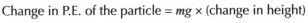

$F = \mu R = \frac{1}{3} \times \frac{36g}{13} = \frac{12g}{13}$ ← $\tan\theta = \frac{5}{12} \Rightarrow \cos\theta = \frac{12}{13}$

Work done by $F = Fs = \frac{12g}{13} \times -x = \mathbf{-\frac{12gx}{13}}$ ← Displacement is negative because the particle is moving in the opposite direction to F.

Using the work-energy principle:
Change in total mechanical energy = Work done by F

So: $-181.5 + \frac{15gx}{13} = -\frac{12gx}{13}$

$\frac{27gx}{13} = 181.5$

$x = \frac{181.5 \times 13}{27g} = 8.92$ m (3 s.f.)

b) The particle moves from A, up to B and back down to A, so overall change in P.E. = 0

So, the change in total mechanical energy between the first and second time the particle is at A is just the change in Kinetic Energy, i.e. Final K.E. – Initial K.E. = $\frac{1}{2}mv^2 - \frac{1}{2}mu^2$

Work done on the particle = $Fs = F \times -2x$ ← The particle has travelled the distance AB twice and is always moving in the opposite direction to the frictional force.

$= \frac{12g}{13} \times -2(8.917) = \mathbf{-161.3}$

Using the work-energy principle:

$\frac{1}{2} \times 3 \times v^2 - \frac{1}{2} \times 3 \times 11^2 = -161.3$ ← u = 11 ms^{-1}, as this is the speed of the particle when it's first at A.

$\frac{3}{2}v^2 = 181.5 - 161.3 \quad \Rightarrow \quad v = 3.67$ ms^{-1} (3 s.f.)

Does this mean we can save energy by doing less work...

There are a few different ways you could tackle part b). You could just look at the motion back down the slope and look at the K.E. gained and the P.E. lost. Or you could resolve parallel to the slope, work out the acceleration and use $v^2 = u^2 + 2as$.
If the question doesn't tell you what method to use, you'll get marks for using any correct method. Correct being the key word.

Power

Right, last page of learnin' in this section. It's a good 'un as well. And just think: after this — practice questions. Get in.

Power is the Rate at which Work is done on an Object

Power is a measure of the rate a force does work on an object.
The unit for power is the watt, where 1 watt (1 W) = 1 joule per second.

So Power = $\frac{\text{Work Done}}{\text{Time}}$

For an engine producing a driving force of F Newtons, and moving a vehicle at a speed of v ms^{-1}, the power in watts can be found using the formula:

Power = $F \times v$

Power = $\frac{\text{Work Done}}{\text{Time}} = \frac{\text{Force} \times \text{Distance}}{\text{Time}}$ = Force × Velocity

This is the formula you'll end up using most of the time — those examiners can't resist a question about engines. But don't forget what power means, just in case they throw you a curveball — it's the rate of doing work.

EXAMPLE

A train of mass 500 000 kg is travelling along a straight horizontal track with a constant speed of 20 ms^{-1}. The train experiences a constant resistance to motion of magnitude 275 000 N.

a) Find the rate at which the train's engine is working. Give your answer in kW.

b) The train now moves up a hill inclined at 2° to the horizontal. If the engine continues to work at the same rate and the magnitude of the non-gravitational resistance to motion remains the same, find the new constant speed of the train.

a) Call the driving force of the train T N and the speed of the train u ms^{-1}.
Resolve horizontally to find T:
$T - 275\,000 = m \times 0$
So $T = 275\,000$ N
Power = $T \times u = 275\,000 \times 20 = 5500$ kW.

b) Call the new driving force T' and resolve parallel to the slope:
$T' - 275\,000 - 500\,000g\sin 2° = m \times 0$
$\Rightarrow T' = 275\,000 + 500\,000g\sin 2°$ N = 446 008 N
Power = $T' \times v$
$5\,500\,000 = 446\,008 \times v \quad \Rightarrow \quad v = \frac{5\,500\,000}{446\,008} = 12.3$ ms^{-1} (3 s.f.)

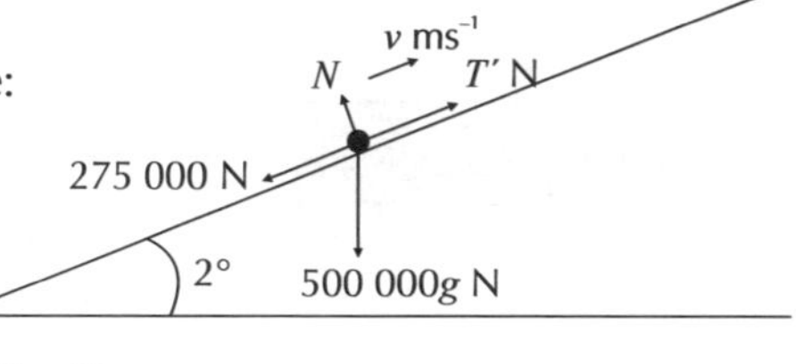

EXAMPLE

A tractor of mass 3000 kg is moving down a hill inclined at an angle of θ to the horizontal, where $\sin\theta = \frac{1}{24}$. The acceleration of the tractor is 1.5 ms^{-2} and its engine is working at a constant rate of 30 kW. Find the magnitude of the non-gravitational resistance to motion at the instant when the tractor is travelling at a speed of 8 ms^{-1}.

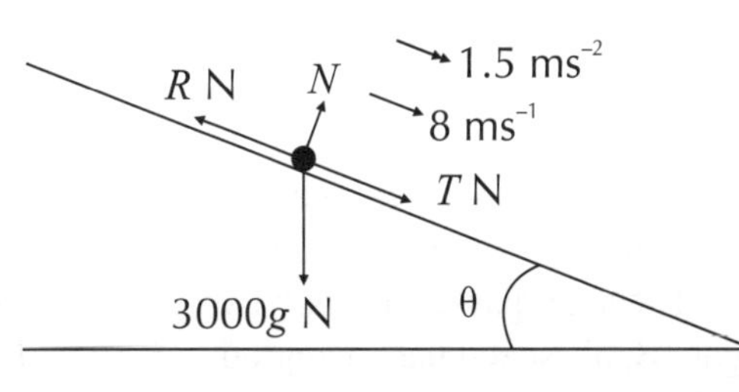

Use Power = $F \times v$ to find T:
$30\,000 = T \times 8 \Rightarrow T = 3750$ N
Resolve parallel to the slope: $T + mg\sin\theta - R = ma$
$3750 + (3000 \times 9.8 \times \frac{1}{24}) - R = 3000 \times 1.5$
$R = 3750 + 1225 - 4500$
$R = 475$ N

Add the component of weight, as the tractor is moving down the slope.

There is acceleration here, so this term doesn't disappear for once.

All together now — Watt's the unit for power...

Well that pretty much wraps up this section on Work and Energy. Plenty of formulas to learn and plenty of fun force diagrams to draw. If you're itching for some practice at all this then turn over and crack on. Even if you're not, do it anyway.

M2 Section 3 — Practice Questions

I don't know about you, but I enjoyed that section. Lots of engines and energy and blocks moving on slopes and GRRRRR look how manly I am as I do work against friction. *Ahem* sorry about that. Right-oh — practice questions...

Warm-up Questions

1) A crate is pushed across a smooth horizontal floor by a force of 250 N, acting in the direction of motion. Find the work done in pushing the crate 3 m.
2) A crane lifts a concrete block 12 m vertically at constant speed. If the crane does 34 kJ of work against gravity, find the mass of the concrete block. Take $g = 9.8$ ms^{-1}.
3) A horse of mass 450 kg is cantering at a speed of 13 ms^{-1}. Find the horse's kinetic energy.
4) An ice skater of mass 65 kg sets off from rest. After travelling 40 m in a straight line across horizontal ice, she has done 800 J of work. Find the speed of the ice skater at this point.
5) A particle of mass 0.5 kg is projected upwards from ground level and reaches a maximum height of 150 m above the ground. Find the increase in the particle's gravitational potential energy. Take $g = 9.8$ ms^{-2}.
6) State the principle of conservation of mechanical energy. Explain why you usually need to model an object as a particle if you are using this principle.
7) A jubilant cowboy throws his hat vertically upwards with a velocity of 5 ms^{-1}. Use conservation of energy to find the maximum height the hat reaches above the point of release. Take $g = 9.8$ ms^{-2}.
8) State the work-energy principle. Explain what is meant by an 'external force'.
9) A car's engine is working at a rate of 350 kW. If the car is moving with speed 22 ms^{-1}, find the driving force of the engine.

Well those warm-up questions should have got your maths juices flowing, and you should now be eager to move on to something a bit more exam-like. It's probably best not to ask what maths juice is.

Exam Questions

Whenever a numerical value of g is required in the questions below, take $g = 9.8$ ms^{-2}.

1

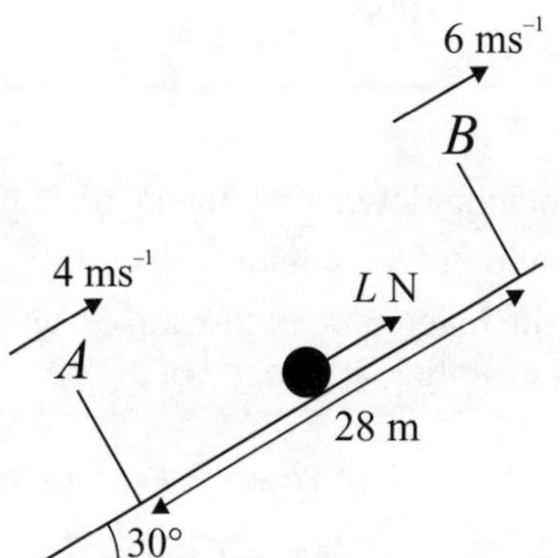

A skier is pulled up a sloping plane by a force, L, acting parallel to the plane which is inclined at an angle of 30° to the horizontal. The skier and his skis have a combined mass of 90 kg and he experiences a constant frictional force of 66 N as he moves up the slope. The skier passes through two gates, A and B, which are 28 m apart. His speed at gate A is 4 ms^{-1}. At gate B, his speed has increased to 6 ms^{-1}. Find:

a) the increase in the skier's total mechanical energy as he moves from gate A to gate B, *(5 marks)*

b) the magnitude of the force, L, pulling the skier up the slope. *(3 marks)*

M2 Section 3 — Practice Questions

I hope you've still got the energy left to power through this last bit of work. I don't want to have to force you...

2 A stone of mass 0.3 kg is dropped down a well. The stone hits the surface of the water in the well with a speed of 20 ms^{-1}.

a) Calculate the kinetic energy of the stone as it hits the water. *(2 marks)*

b) By modelling the stone as a particle and using conservation of energy, find the height above the surface of the water from which the stone was dropped. *(3 marks)*

c) When the stone hits the water, it begins to sink vertically and experiences a constant resistive force of 23 N. Use the work-energy principle to find the depth the stone has sunk to when the speed of the stone is reduced to 1 ms^{-1}. *(5 marks)*

3 A van of mass 2700 kg is travelling at a constant speed of 16 ms^{-1} up a road inclined at an angle of 12° to the horizontal. The non-gravitational resistance to motion is modelled as a single force of magnitude of 800 N.

a) Find the rate of work of the engine. *(4 marks)*

When the van passes a point A, still travelling at 16 ms^{-1}, the engine is switched off and the van comes to rest without braking, a distance x m from A. If all resistance to motion remains constant, find:

b) the distance x, *(4 marks)*

c) the time taken for the van to come to rest. *(4 marks)*

4

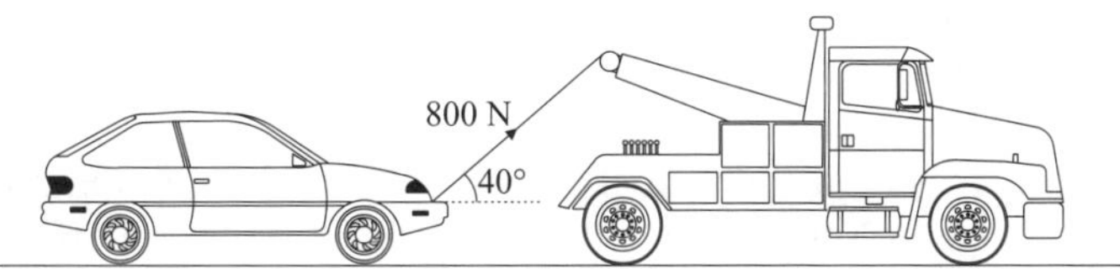

A car of mass 1500 kg is towed 320 m along a straight horizontal road by a rope attached to a pick-up truck. The rope is attached to the car at an angle of 40° to the horizontal and the tension in the rope is 800 N. The car experiences a constant resistance to motion from friction.

a) Find the work done by the towing force. *(3 marks)*

b) Over the 320 m, the car increases in speed from 11 ms^{-1} to 16 ms^{-1}. Assuming that the magnitude of the towing force remains constant at 800 N, find the coefficient of friction between the car and the road. *(4 marks)*

5 A cyclist is riding up a road at a constant speed of 4 ms^{-1}. The road is inclined at an angle α to the horizontal. The cyclist is working at a rate of 250 W and experiences a constant non-gravitational resistance to motion of magnitude 35 N. The cyclist and his bike have a combined mass of 88 kg.

a) Find the angle of the slope, α. *(4 marks)*

b) The cyclist now increases his work rate to 370 W. If all resistances to motion remain unchanged, find the cyclist's acceleration when his speed is 4 ms^{-1}. *(4 marks)*

Momentum and Impulse

To ease you gently into Section 4 here are a couple of pages on two things which should be familiar from M1 — momentum and impulse. The only new thing is an extra dimension — look out for those vectors, we're going 2D...

An Impulse causes a Change in Momentum

All moving objects have momentum (mass (kg) × velocity (ms^{-1})). If an object receives an impulse (I — measured in Newton seconds, or Ns) its momentum will change. The size of the change is the size of the impulse.

Impulse = final momentum – initial momentum

$I = mv - mu$ or $\mathbf{I} = m\mathbf{v} - m\mathbf{u}$ ← This is the vector form.

Since velocity is a vector, momentum and impulse are vectors too.

EXAMPLE A ball (m = 0.1 kg) travels with a velocity of $(5\mathbf{i} + 12\mathbf{j})$ ms^{-1} before receiving an impulse of $\mathbf{I}$ Ns. If the ball's new velocity is $(15\mathbf{i} + 22\mathbf{j})$ ms^{-1}, find $\mathbf{I}$.

1) Don't be put off by the vector notation. Plug the info in the formula as usual: $\mathbf{I} = m\mathbf{v} - m\mathbf{u}$, where $m = 0.1$, $\mathbf{v} = 15\mathbf{i} + 22\mathbf{j}$ and $\mathbf{u} = 5\mathbf{i} + 12\mathbf{j}$.
2) $\mathbf{I} = 0.1(15\mathbf{i} + 22\mathbf{j}) - 0.1(5\mathbf{i} + 12\mathbf{j})$
   $= 1.5\mathbf{i} + 2.2\mathbf{j} - 0.5\mathbf{i} - 1.2\mathbf{j}$
   $= 1\mathbf{i} + 1\mathbf{j} = \mathbf{i} + \mathbf{j}$.
3) So the ball received an impulse of $(\mathbf{i} + \mathbf{j})$ Ns.

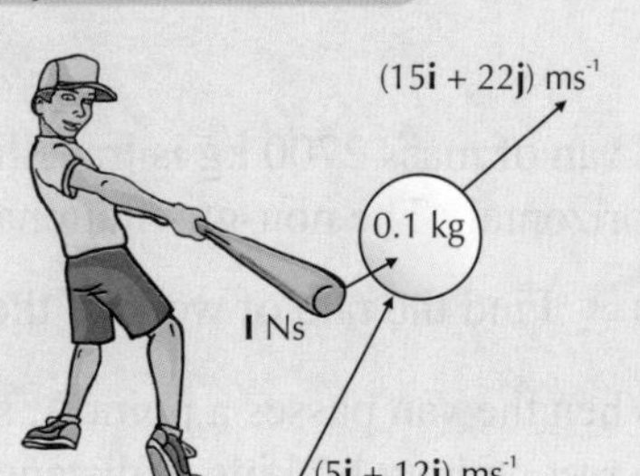

Use Pythagoras and Trig for the Magnitude and Angle of Impulse

With vectors, you can use the horizontal **i** component and the vertical **j** component to form a right-angled triangle. Then simply use basic trig and Pythagoras to find any angles, or the magnitude (scalar size) of impulses or velocities.

EXAMPLE A badminton player smashes a shuttlecock (m = 0.005 kg) with an impulse of $(0.035\mathbf{i} - 0.065\mathbf{j})$ Ns. If the shuttle was initially travelling at $(-3\mathbf{i} + \mathbf{j})$ ms^{-1}, find its speed after the smash, and the angle it makes with the horizontal.

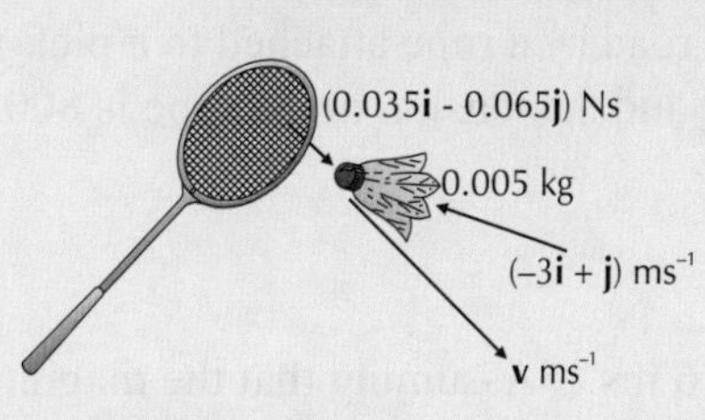

1) Find the final velocity as a vector first, so: $\mathbf{I} = m\mathbf{v} - m\mathbf{u}$, where $\mathbf{I} = 0.035\mathbf{i} - 0.065\mathbf{j}$, $m = 0.005$ and $\mathbf{u} = -3\mathbf{i} + \mathbf{j}$.
   $0.035\mathbf{i} - 0.065\mathbf{j} = 0.005\mathbf{v} - 0.005(-3\mathbf{i} + \mathbf{j})$
   $\Rightarrow 0.035\mathbf{i} - 0.065\mathbf{j} = 0.005\mathbf{v} + 0.015\mathbf{i} - 0.005\mathbf{j}$
   $\Rightarrow 0.005\mathbf{v} = 0.035\mathbf{i} - 0.065\mathbf{j} - 0.015\mathbf{i} + 0.005\mathbf{j}$
   $\Rightarrow 0.005\mathbf{v} = 0.02\mathbf{i} - 0.06\mathbf{j}$
   $\Rightarrow \mathbf{v} = (0.02\mathbf{i} - 0.06\mathbf{j}) \div 0.005 = 4\mathbf{i} - 12\mathbf{j}$.
2) Draw a right-angled triangle of the velocity vector:
3) Use Pythagoras to find the speed (the magnitude of the velocity):
   $|\mathbf{v}| = \sqrt{4^2 + 12^2} = 12.6\ ms^{-1}$ to 3 s.f.
4) Use trig to find the angle of motion with the horizontal:
   $\theta = \tan^{-1}\left(\frac{12}{4}\right) = 71.6°$ to 3 s.f.

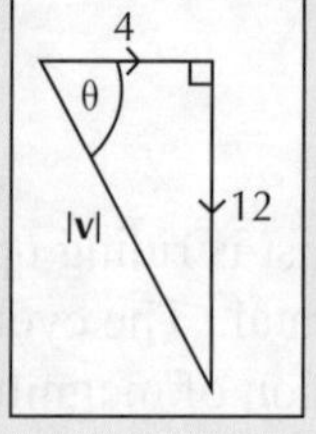

Finding the magnitude of a vector this way should be familiar to you from M1.

The perils of internet shopping — the midnight impulse buy...

I told you I'd ease you in gently. You should know all the bits of maths on this page from M1 — it's just a case of combining them. It often helps to write down all the bits of information you know before you start plugging numbers into formulas, especially when you've got quite a wordy question where some key info mightn't be immediately obvious.

Momentum and Impulse

Back in M1 you learnt about the 'principle of conservation of linear momentum' — a lengthy title that boils down to 'momentum in = momentum out'.

Momentum is Conserved when things are Free to Move

When two things collide that are free to move around, they exert an equal and opposite impulse on each other — these impulses 'cancel out' so there is no impulse for the overall system. No impulse means no change in momentum:

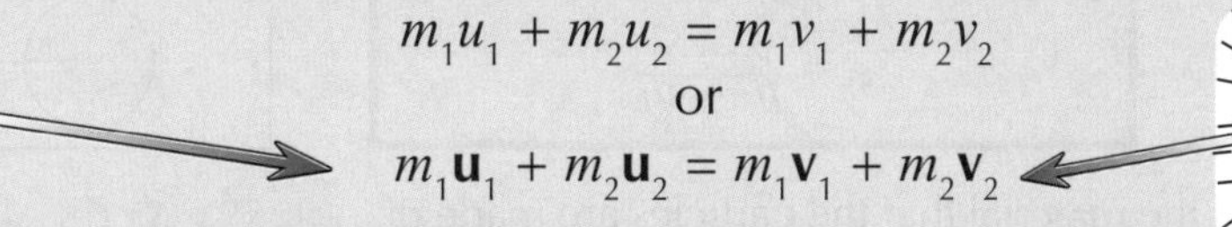

Momentum before collision = momentum after collision

$$m_1u_1 + m_2u_2 = m_1v_1 + m_2v_2$$

or

$$m_1\mathbf{u}_1 + m_2\mathbf{u}_2 = m_1\mathbf{v}_1 + m_2\mathbf{v}_2$$

This is the vector form.

After the collision, the two things might coalesce (stick together) — so this side of the equation would just be $(m_1 + m_2)\mathbf{v}$, as they'd move together with the same velocity.

EXAMPLE a) Two particles A and B, shown below, collide. Following the collision they move separately at different velocities. Find B's velocity after the collision.

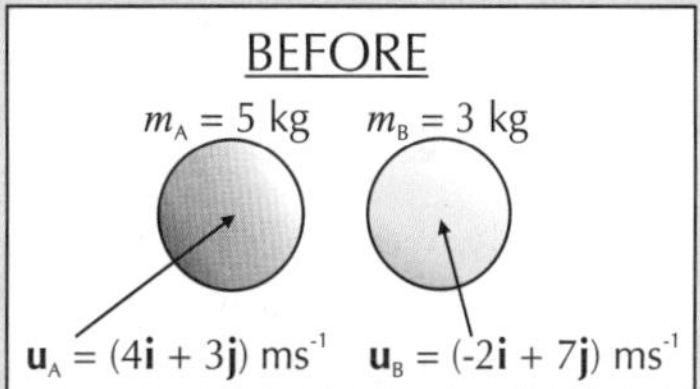

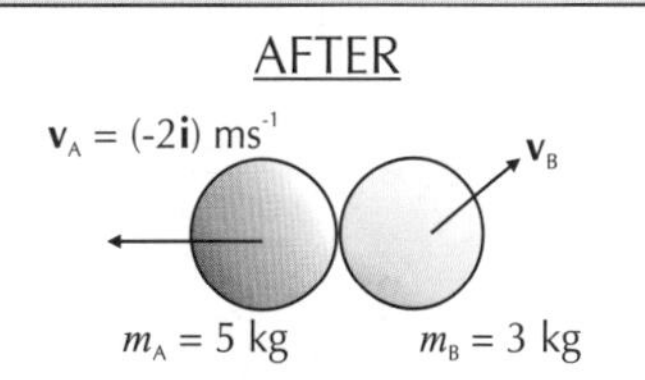

1) Again, it's just a matter of plugging the numbers in:
$$m_A\mathbf{u}_A + m_B\mathbf{u}_B = m_A\mathbf{v}_A + m_B\mathbf{v}_B,$$
where $m_A = 5$, $m_B = 3$, $\mathbf{u}_A = 4\mathbf{i} + 3\mathbf{j}$, $\mathbf{u}_B = -2\mathbf{i} + 7\mathbf{j}$ and $\mathbf{v}_A = -2\mathbf{i}$.

2) $5(4\mathbf{i} + 3\mathbf{j}) + 3(-2\mathbf{i} + 7\mathbf{j}) = 5(-2\mathbf{i}) + 3\mathbf{v}_B$
$\Rightarrow 20\mathbf{i} + 15\mathbf{j} - 6\mathbf{i} + 21\mathbf{j} = -10\mathbf{i} + 3\mathbf{v}_B$
$\Rightarrow 3\mathbf{v}_B = 24\mathbf{i} + 36\mathbf{j}$
$\Rightarrow \mathbf{v}_B = 8\mathbf{i} + 12\mathbf{j}$

So B's new velocity is $(8\mathbf{i} + 12\mathbf{j})$ ms^{-1}.

EXAMPLE b) If the two particles coalesce instead, find their combined speed after the collision, and the direction they travel in.

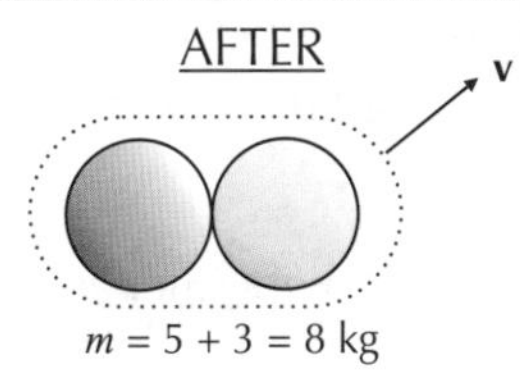

1) Start off as in a), but the 'after' side of the equation is now $(m_A + m_B)\mathbf{v}$ ($\mathbf{v}$ is the velocity of the new combined particle).
$5(4\mathbf{i} + 3\mathbf{j}) + 3(-2\mathbf{i} + 7\mathbf{j}) = (5 + 3)\mathbf{v}$
$\Rightarrow 20\mathbf{i} + 15\mathbf{j} - 6\mathbf{i} + 21\mathbf{j} = 8\mathbf{v}$
$\Rightarrow 8\mathbf{v} = 14\mathbf{i} + 36\mathbf{j} \Rightarrow \mathbf{v} = 1.75\mathbf{i} + 4.5\mathbf{j}$

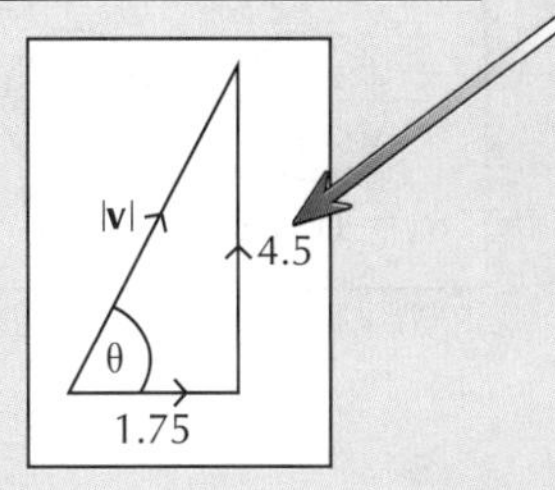

2) Draw a right-angled triangle to represent the velocity vector.

3) Use Pythagoras to find the magnitude:
$|\mathbf{v}| = \sqrt{1.75^2 + 4.5^2} = 4.83$ ms^{-1} to 3 s.f.

4) Use trig to find the angle with the horizontal:
$\theta = \tan^{-1}\left(\frac{4.5}{1.75}\right) = 68.7°$ to 3 s.f.

So the combined particles move away from the collision at 4.83 ms^{-1}, at an angle of 68.7° to the horizontal.

'Connected' particles, joined by a 'light inelastic string' (see M1) can be dealt with in the same way as coalesced particles — when the string between a connected pair is taut, they act as one particle travelling at a common speed.

Mo' mentum mo' problems...

Again, the theory's the same as it was in M1 — you've just got to mind your i's and j's. I find drawing a picture of the situation helps when you're trying to visualise the particles bouncing in all directions. Or, you could draw inspirational doodles and think about that emo type you fancy who sits at the back of class. Less productive though...

Collisions

Oh yes, you've not seen the last of those colliding particles. If you like things loud and dramatic, think demolition balls and high speed crashes. If you're anything like me though you'll be picturing a nice sedate game of snooker.

The **Coefficient of Restitution** is always between **0 and 1**

When two particles collide in a direct impact (i.e. they're moving on the same straight line), the speeds they bounce away at depend on the coefficient of restitution, e. This is known as Newton's Law of Restitution, and looks like this:

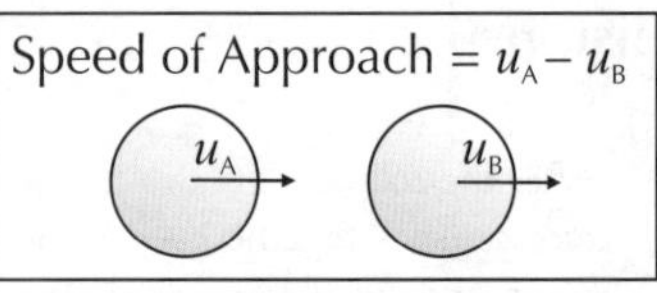

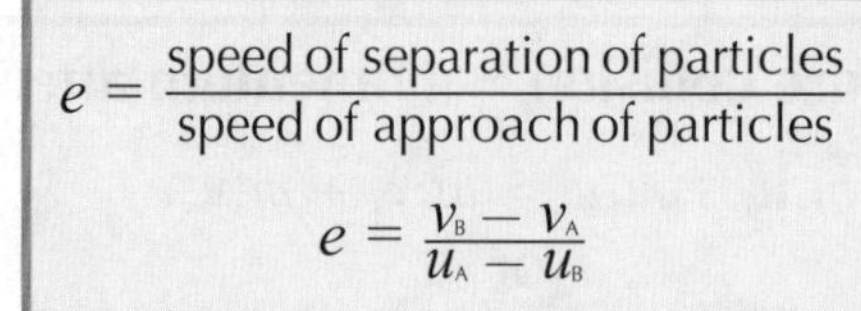

$$e = \frac{\text{speed of separation of particles}}{\text{speed of approach of particles}}$$

$$e = \frac{v_B - v_A}{u_A - u_B}$$

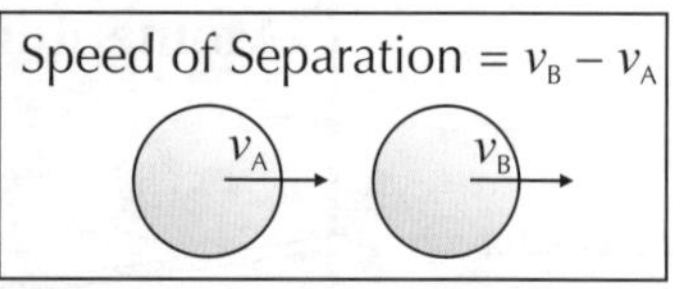

1) The value of e depends on the material that the particles are made of.
2) e always lies between 0 and 1.
3) When $e = 0$ the particles are called 'inelastic', and they'll coalesce.
4) When $e = 1$ the particles are 'perfectly elastic' and they'll bounce apart with no loss of speed.

Balls of modelling clay would be near the $e = 0$ end of the scale, while ping pong balls are nearer to $e = 1$.

EXAMPLE Two particles collide as shown. Find the coefficient of restitution.

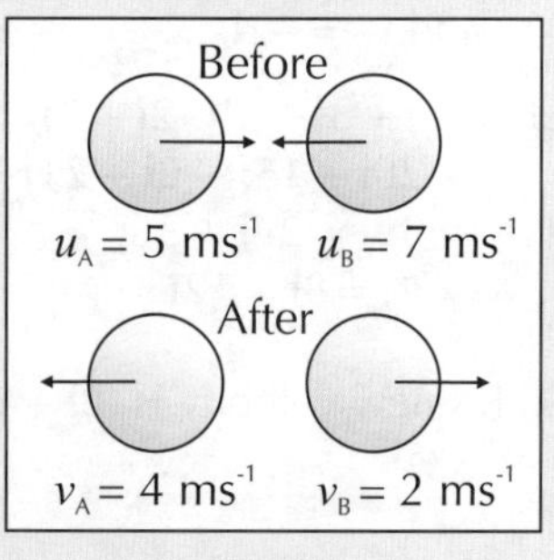

1) Firstly, work out the speeds of approach and separation, taking care with positives and negatives:
Speed of approach = $u_A - u_B = 5 - (-7) = 12$ ms^{-1}.
Speed of separation = $v_B - v_A = 2 - (-4) = 6$ ms^{-1}.

Think of 'left to right' as positive, and so particles travelling 'right to left' will have a negative speed.

2) Use $e = \frac{\text{speed of separation of particles}}{\text{speed of approach of particles}}$:

$e = \frac{6}{12} = 0.5$. So the coefficient of restitution is 0.5.

For **Two Unknown Speeds** — use **Momentum Conservation** too

Often you'll be given the value of e and asked to find the velocities of both particles either before or after impact. As there are two unknowns, you'll need to use the formula for conservation of momentum (on p.181) along with the Law of Restitution to form simultaneous equations.

EXAMPLE Two particles, A and B, are moving in opposite directions in the same straight line, as shown. If $e = \frac{1}{3}$, find the velocities of both particles after impact.

$m_A = 4$ kg $\quad m_B = 12$ kg

$u_A = 10$ ms^{-1} $\quad u_B = 2$ ms^{-1}

1) Use $e = \frac{v_B - v_A}{u_A - u_B}$ to get the first equation:

$\frac{1}{3} = \frac{v_B - v_A}{10 - (-2)} \Rightarrow v_B - v_A = 4$. Call this **equation 1**.

2) Use $m_A u_A + m_B u_B = m_A v_A + m_B v_B$ to get the second equation:
$(4 \times 10) + (12 \times -2) = 4v_A + 12v_B$
$\Rightarrow 16 = 4v_A + 12v_B \Rightarrow v_A + 3v_B = 4$. Call this **equation 2**.

3) **Equation 1** + **equation 2** gives:
$4v_B = 8$, so $v_B = 2$ ms^{-1} (i.e. 2 ms^{-1} going left to right).

4) Substituting in **equation 1** gives:
$2 - v_A = 4$, so $v_A = -2$ ms^{-1} (i.e. 2 ms^{-1} going right to left).

Collisions

There's a saying in Stoke-on-Trent that goes: 'cost kick a bo againt a wo till it bosses?'*
Well, that's kinda what this next bit's about, a.k.a. 'the collision of a particle with a plane surface'.

The **Law of Restitution** also works with a **Smooth Plane Surface**

Particles don't just collide with each other. They can collide with a fixed flat surface — such as when a ball is kicked against a vertical wall, or dropped onto a horizontal floor.

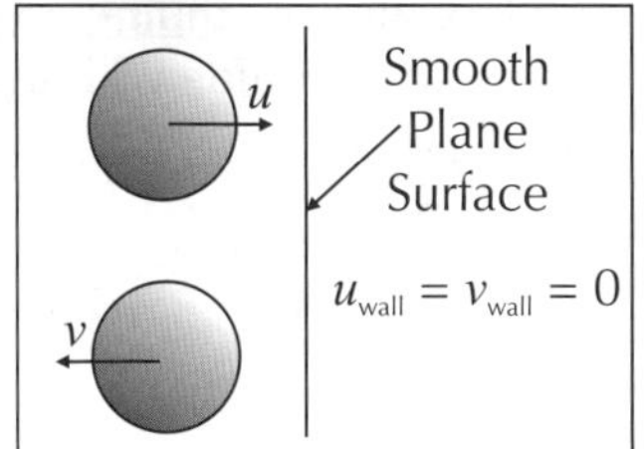

As long as the surface can be modelled as smooth (i.e. no friction) and perpendicular to the motion of the particle, the law can be simplified to:

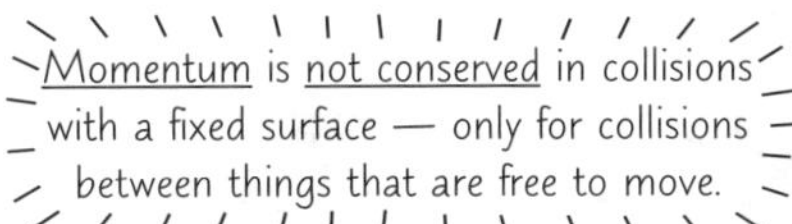

Momentum is not conserved in collisions with a fixed surface — only for collisions between things that are free to move.

$$e = \frac{\text{speed of rebound of particle}}{\text{speed of approach of particle}} = \frac{v}{u}$$

EXAMPLE A ball rolling along a smooth horizontal floor at 6 ms^{-1} hits a smooth vertical wall, with a coefficient of restitution $e = 0.65$. Find the speed of the ball as it rebounds.

BEFORE $u = 6$ ms^{-1} $e = 0.65$

AFTER v

Using $e = \frac{v}{u}$:

$0.65 = \frac{v}{6} \Rightarrow v = 0.65 \times 6 = 3.9$ ms^{-1}.

So the ball rebounds at a speed of 3.9 ms^{-1}. Piece of cake.

Use the **Laws of Motion** for things being **Dropped**

Things get a tiny bit trickier when a particle is dropped onto a horizontal surface because acceleration under gravity comes into play. You should be pretty nifty with equations of motion now though — just remember to use them here.

EXAMPLE A basketball is dropped vertically from rest at a height of 1.4 m onto a horizontal floor. It rebounds to a height of 0.9 m. Find e for the impact with the floor.

1) Assuming the ball is a particle, and the floor is smooth, we can use $e = \frac{v}{u}$.
For the diagram shown, this would be $e = \frac{u_2}{v_1}$, as we need the velocity just before the impact (v_1) and the velocity just after (u_2).

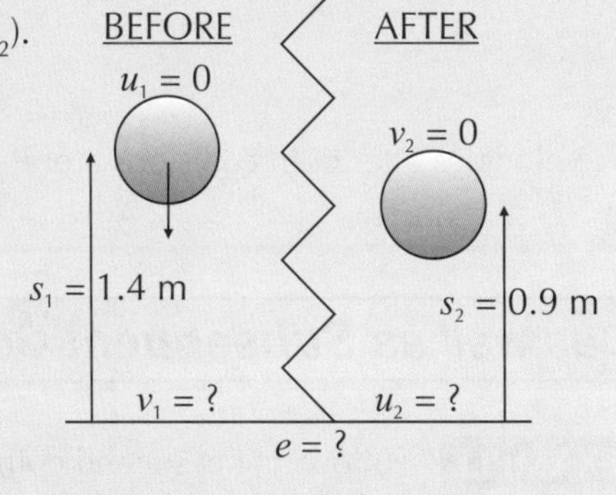

2) Using $v^2 = u^2 + 2as$ before the impact with the floor (where $a = g \approx 9.8$ ms^{-2}):
$v_1^2 = 0 + 2 \times 9.8 \times 1.4 = 27.44$
$\Rightarrow v_1 = 5.238$ ms^{-1} to 4 s.f.

3) Using $v^2 = u^2 + 2as$ after the impact with the floor (where $a = -g$ since the motion is against gravity):
$0 = u_2^2 + 2 \times -9.8 \times 0.9$
$\Rightarrow u_2 = 4.2$ ms^{-1}.

4) Finally, we can find e: $e = \frac{u_2}{v_1} = \frac{4.2}{5.238} = 0.802$ to 3 s.f.

There's loads about using the equations of motion in M1, as well as in Section 1 of M2 (see p 155-157).

Dating Tip #107 — Avoid them if they're on the rebound...

Just when you were thinking this section was a load of balls, along come walls and floors to shake things up a bit. The Law of Restitution is a pretty straightforward formula, but chances are there'll be added complications in the exam questions. Learn how to tackle the four types of question on these two pages and you'll be laughing.

*For those unfamiliar with Potteries dialect, this means 'Can you kick a ball against a wall until it bursts?'

Complex Collisions

You've had an easy ride so far this section, but now it's time to fasten your seatbelt, don your crash helmet, and prepare for some pretty scary collisions. Don't say I didn't warn you...

Solve **Successive** *Collisions* **Step by Step...**

Think of this as a multi-particle pile-up. One particle collides with another, which then shoots off to collide with a third. No extra maths required, but quite a bit of extra thinking.

EXAMPLE Particles P, Q and R are travelling at different speeds along the same smooth straight line, as shown. Particles P and Q collide first ($e = 0.6$), then Q goes on to collide with R ($e = 0.2$). What are the velocities of P, Q and R after the second collision?

0.1 kg, P 20 ms^{-1} → ; 0.4 kg, Q 5 ms^{-1} → ; 2 kg, R ← 1 ms^{-1}

1) Take things step by step. Forget about R for the moment and concentrate on the first collision — the one between P and Q:

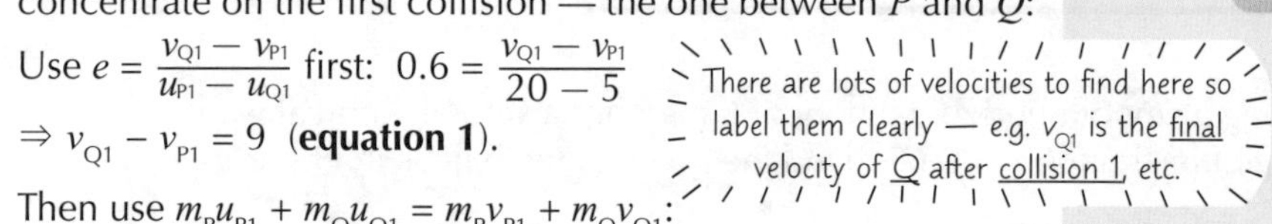

Use $e = \frac{v_{Q1} - v_{P1}}{u_{P1} - u_{Q1}}$ first: $0.6 = \frac{v_{Q1} - v_{P1}}{20 - 5}$

$\Rightarrow v_{Q1} - v_{P1} = 9$ (**equation 1**).

There are lots of velocities to find here so label them clearly — e.g. v_{Q1} is the final velocity of Q after collision 1, etc.

Then use $m_P u_{P1} + m_Q u_{Q1} = m_P v_{P1} + m_Q v_{Q1}$:

$(0.1 \times 20) + (0.4 \times 5) = 0.1v_{P1} + 0.4v_{Q1}$

$\Rightarrow 4 = 0.1v_{P1} + 0.4v_{Q1} \quad \Rightarrow \quad v_{P1} + 4v_{Q1} = 40$ (**equation 2**).

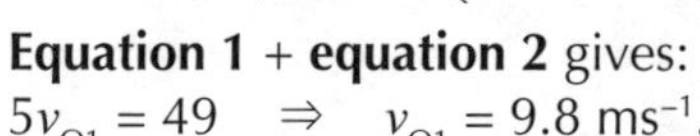

Equation 1 + **equation 2** gives:

$5v_{Q1} = 49 \quad \Rightarrow \quad v_{Q1} = 9.8 \text{ ms}^{-1}$.

Substituting in **equation 1** gives:

$9.8 - v_{P1} = 9 \quad \Rightarrow \quad v_{P1} = 9.8 - 9 = 0.8 \text{ ms}^{-1}$.

Before 1st Collision: 0.1 kg P 20 ms^{-1} → ; 0.4 kg Q 5 ms^{-1} → ; $e = 0.6$

After 1st Collision: P 0.8 ms^{-1} → ; Q 9.8 ms^{-1} →

2) For the second collision, which is between Q and R: $e = \frac{v_{R2} - v_{Q2}}{u_{Q2} - u_{R2}}$.

u_{Q2} is the same as the velocity of Q after the first collision — you found this above (9.8 ms^{-1}), so:

$0.2 = \frac{v_{R2} - v_{Q2}}{9.8 - (-1)} \quad \Rightarrow \quad v_{R2} - v_{Q2} = 2.16$ (**equation 3**).

Then $m_Q u_{Q2} + m_R u_{R2} = m_Q v_{Q2} + m_R v_{R2}$:

$(0.4 \times 9.8) + (2 \times -1) = 0.4v_{Q2} + 2v_{R2}$

$\Rightarrow 1.92 = 0.4v_{Q2} + 2v_{R2} \quad \Rightarrow \quad 0.2v_{Q2} + v_{R2} = 0.96$ (**equation 4**).

Equation 4 – **equation 3** gives:

$1.2v_{Q2} = -1.2 \quad \Rightarrow \quad v_{Q2} = -1 \text{ ms}^{-1}$.

Substituting in **equation 3** gives:

$v_{R2} - (-1) = 2.16 \quad \Rightarrow \quad v_{R2} = 2.16 - 1 = 1.16 \text{ ms}^{-1}$.

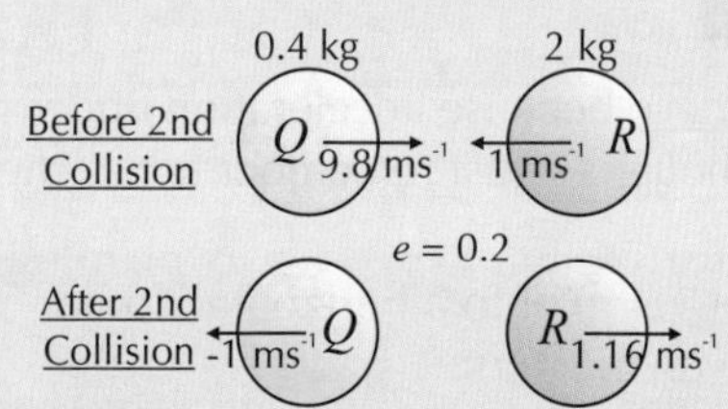

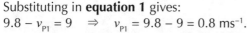

3) Velocities after both collisions are: $P = 0.8 \text{ ms}^{-1}$, $Q = -1 \text{ ms}^{-1}$ and $R = 1.16 \text{ ms}^{-1}$:

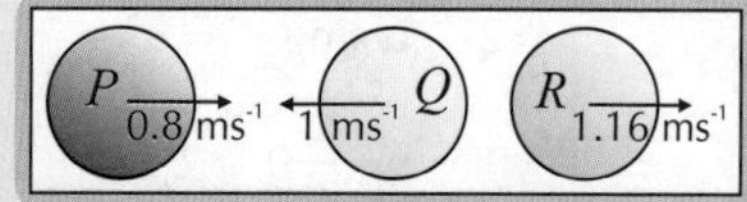

... as well as **Subsequent Collisions** *with a* **Plane Surface**

EXAMPLE Following the second collision, P is removed and R hits a smooth vertical wall at a right angle. How big would e have to be for this impact to allow R to collide again with Q, assuming Q is moving with velocity –1 ms^{-1}?

1) Think things through carefully. Q is currently going at 1 ms^{-1} in the opposite direction. To hit it again, R needs to bounce off the wall with a rebound speed higher than 1 ms^{-1}, so it can 'catch up'. So $v_{R3} > 1$.

2) For the impact with the wall, $e = \frac{v_{R3}}{u_{R3}} \quad \Rightarrow \quad v_{R3} = eu_{R3}$, and so $eu_{R3} > 1$.

3) From the example above, $u_{R3} = v_{R2} = 1.16 \text{ ms}^{-1}$, so $1.16e > 1 \quad \Rightarrow \quad e > \frac{1}{1.16} \quad \Rightarrow \quad e > 0.8620...$

4) So, to 3 s.f., e must be higher than 0.862 for R to collide again with Q.

Complex Collisions

Well they do say 'what goes up must come down'. And up again. And down again. Just look at the economy.

*Particles may have **Successive Rebounds** before coming to **Rest***

EXAMPLE A ball falls from a height of 10 m and rebounds several times from the ground, where $e = 0.8$ for each impact. Find the height the ball reaches after each of the first three bounces, stating any assumptions.

1) Some assumptions — the ball is a particle, air resistance can be ignored, it falls vertically onto a horizontal, smooth, plane surface, under a constant acceleration downwards of $g = 9.8$ ms^{-2}.

2) For each bounce use $v^2 = u^2 + 2as$ to find the approach speed to the ground and the Law of Restitution, $e = \frac{v}{u}$, to find the rebound speed (p. 183). Then use $v^2 = u^2 + 2as$ again to find the height the ball reaches (s) after the bounce.

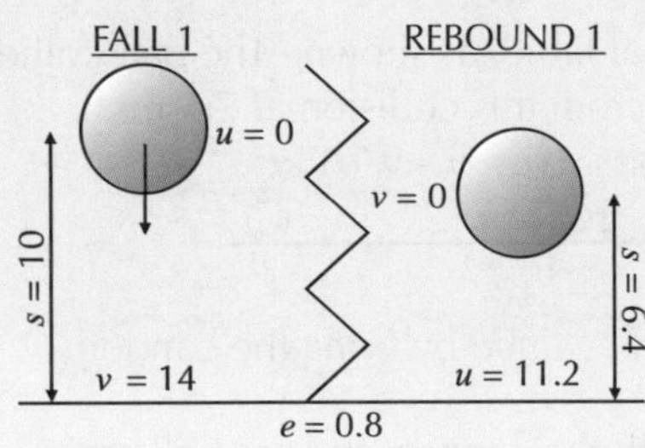

Set v to zero here because we want to know how far it will go upwards (with an acceleration of $-g$) before it stops and falls back down.

BOUNCE 1

Falling: $v^2 = u^2 + 2as$ where $u = 0$, $a = 9.8$ and $s = 10$:
$v^2 = 0 + (2 \times 9.8 \times 10) \Rightarrow v = \sqrt{2 \times 9.8 \times 10} = 14$ ms^{-1}.

Colliding:
$e = \frac{v}{u} \Rightarrow v = eu$, where v is the velocity just after the impact, $e = 0.8$ and u is the velocity just before the impact (i.e. 14 ms^{-1} as found above).
$\Rightarrow v = 0.8 \times 14 = 11.2$ ms^{-1}.

Rebounding:
$v^2 = u^2 + 2as$, where $v = 0$, $a = -9.8$, and u is the velocity just after the impact (i.e. 11.2 ms^{-1} as found above).
$0 = 11.2^2 + (2 \times -9.8)s \Rightarrow$ Height of Rebound 1 $= s = \frac{11.2^2}{2 \times 9.8} = $ 6.4 m.

BOUNCE 2

Falling:
The motion as the ball rises then falls is symmetrical — it covers the same distance under the same acceleration on the 2nd fall as it did on the 1st rebound. So it hits the floor the second time with the same speed it left it at — 11.2 ms^{-1}.

If you're not convinced, put the numbers in the equation of motion again to see for yourself.

Colliding:
Again, $v = eu$, where v is the velocity after the 2nd impact, $e = 0.8$ and $u = 11.2$ ms^{-1} (velocity just before impact). $v = 0.8 \times 11.2 = 8.96$ ms^{-1}.

Rebounding:
$v^2 = u^2 + 2as$, where $v = 0$, $u = 8.96$ (velocity after impact) and $a = -9.8$:
$0 = 8.96^2 + (2 \times -9.8)s \Rightarrow$ Height of Rebound 2 $= s = \frac{8.96^2}{2 \times 9.8} = $ 4.10 m (3 s.f.)

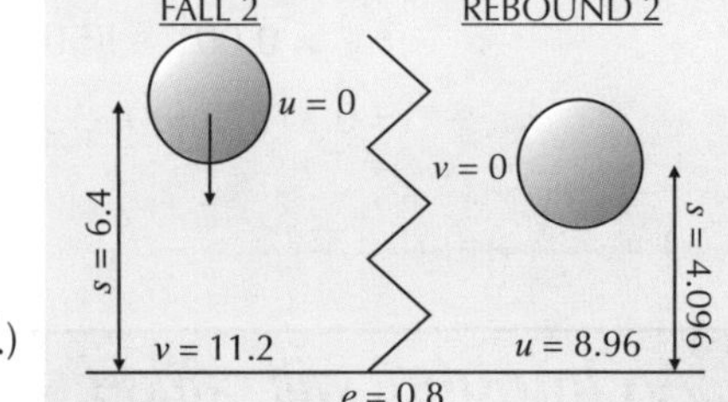

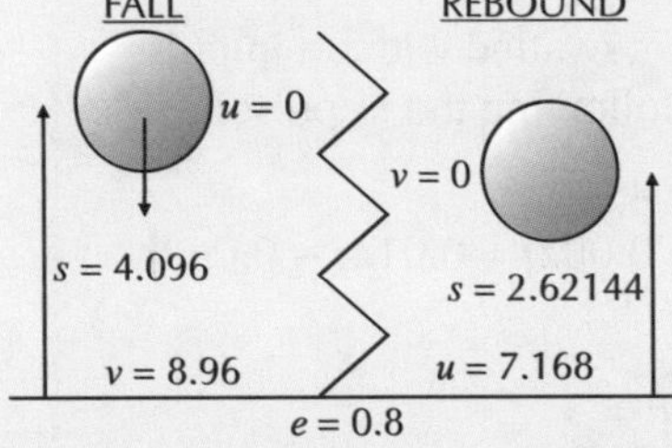

BOUNCE 3

Falling: Using the symmetry of the vertical motion,
velocity just before 3rd impact = velocity after 2nd impact = 8.96 ms^{-1}.

Colliding:
$v = eu$, where v is the velocity after the 3rd impact, $e = 0.8$ and $u = 8.96$ ms^{-1}.
$v = 0.8 \times 8.96 = 7.168$ ms^{-1}.

Rebounding:
$v^2 = u^2 + 2as$, where $v = 0$, $u = 7.168$ and $a = -9.8$:
$0 = 7.168^2 + (2 \times -9.8)s \Rightarrow$ Height of Rebound 3 $= s = \frac{7.168^2}{2 \times 9.8} = $ 2.62 m (3 s.f.)

As the rebound heights form a geometric progression, you could use the sum to infinity formula (see C2) to work out the total distance the bouncing particle will travel before stopping.

Bouncin's what particles do best...

That's as complex as it gets — just break it down into steps, bounce by bounce. It's a bit like those dance mat games, except less sweaty. And I doubt you'll find Madonna doing M2 maths in one of her videos, dressed in a neon pink leotard...

Collisions and Energy

Almost the end of the section, and I guess your energy might be waning. Most things lose kinetic energy when they collide — you need to know how to work out how much. It's enough to make you want a quiet lie down...

Kinetic Energy is only *Conserved* in *Perfectly Elastic* Collisions

For any collision where $e < 1$, some kinetic energy will be lost (it changes into things like heat and sound). The formula for working out how much has been lost is fairly straightforward:

The units of K.E. are Joules, if mass is given in kg and speed in ms^{-1}

$$\text{Loss of K.E. on Impact} = \text{Total K.E. before} - \text{Total K.E. after} = (\tfrac{1}{2}m_1u_1^2 + \tfrac{1}{2}m_2u_2^2) - (\tfrac{1}{2}m_1v_1^2 + \tfrac{1}{2}m_2v_2^2)$$

For velocities given in vector (**i** and **j**) form, find their magnitude (speed) to put into the K.E. formula.

The tricky bit is finding the u's and v's to put in the formula...

EXAMPLE A tiny cannon fires a ball in a straight line across a smooth horizontal table, as shown. The ball collides directly with another, stationary, ball with $e = 0.7$, and moves away from this collision at 7.5 ms^{-1}.

$m_c = 0.05$ kg $m_1 = m_2 = 0.001$ kg

C 1 2

a) Find the loss of K.E. when the balls collide.

1) We first need to find u_1 (the speed of the fired ball before it hits the other) and v_2 (the final speed of the other ball). Use the law of restitution and conservation of momentum (as on p. 181) where $e = 0.7$, $v_1 = 7.5$, and $u_2 = 0$.

2) $e = \frac{v_2 - v_1}{u_1 - u_2} \Rightarrow 0.7 = \frac{v_2 - 7.5}{u_1 - 0} \Rightarrow v_2 - 0.7u_1 = 7.5$ (**eqn 1**).

$m_1u_1 + m_2u_2 = m_1v_1 + m_2v_2$ and since $m_1 = m_2$:

$u_1 + 0 = 7.5 + v_2 \Rightarrow u_1 - v_2 = 7.5$ (**eqn 2**).

Eqn 1 + eqn 2: $0.3u_1 = 15 \Rightarrow u_1 = 50\ ms^{-1}$.

Sub in **eqn 2**: $50 - v_2 = 7.5 \Rightarrow v_2 = 50 - 7.5 = 42.5\ ms^{-1}$.

3) Finally, putting all the values in the K.E. formula:

$$\begin{aligned}\text{Loss of K.E.} &= (\tfrac{1}{2}m_1u_1^2 + \tfrac{1}{2}m_2u_2^2) - (\tfrac{1}{2}m_1v_1^2 + \tfrac{1}{2}m_2v_2^2)\\ &= \tfrac{1}{2}m[(u_1^2 + u_2^2) - (v_1^2 + v_2^2)]\\ &= \tfrac{1}{2} \times 0.001 \times [(50^2 + 0^2) - (7.5^2 + 42.5^2)]\\ &= 0.31875 = 0.319 \text{ J to 3 s.f.}\end{aligned}$$

b) Find the K.E. gained by firing the cannon.

1) Since both the cannon and the ball are stationary before firing, there is no initial K.E. The gain in K.E. is simply $\frac{1}{2}m_cv_c^2 + \frac{1}{2}m_1v_1^2$, where v_1 is the speed of the ball after firing, i.e. 50 ms^{-1}, as calculated in part a). You need to work out the velocity of the cannon (v_c) though.

2) Momentum is conserved so:

$m_cu_c + m_1u_1 = m_cv_c + m_1v_1$

$\Rightarrow 0 + 0 = 0.05v_c + (0.001 \times 50)$

$\Rightarrow v_c = -(0.001 \times 50) \div 0.05 = -1\ ms^{-1}$.

(i.e. the cannon moves backwards at 1 ms^{-1}).

3) Gain in K.E. $= \frac{1}{2}m_cv_c^2 + \frac{1}{2}m_1v_1^2$

$= (\frac{1}{2} \times 0.05 \times (-1)^2) + (\frac{1}{2} \times 0.001 \times 50^2)$

$= 1.275 = 1.28$ J to 3 s.f.

An *Impulse* will cause a *Change in K.E.*

EXAMPLE A fly of mass 0.002 kg is moving at a velocity of $(2\mathbf{i} - \mathbf{j})\ ms^{-1}$ when it is swatted with an impulse of $(0.01\mathbf{i} - 0.06\mathbf{j})$ Ns. How much kinetic energy is gained by the fly following the impulse?

1) Using the impulse formula from p. 180: $I = m\mathbf{v} - m\mathbf{u}$, so

$0.01\mathbf{i} - 0.06\mathbf{j} = 0.002\mathbf{v} - 0.002(2\mathbf{i} - \mathbf{j}) \Rightarrow 0.002\mathbf{v} = 0.01\mathbf{i} - 0.06\mathbf{j} + 0.004\mathbf{i} - 0.002\mathbf{j} = 0.014\mathbf{i} - 0.062\mathbf{j}$

$\Rightarrow \mathbf{v} = (0.014\mathbf{i} - 0.062\mathbf{j}) \div 0.002 = (7\mathbf{i} - 31\mathbf{j})\ ms^{-1}$.

2) The initial speed of the fly $|\mathbf{u}| = \sqrt{2^2 + 1^2} = \sqrt{5}$, so $u^2 = 5$.
After the impulse this becomes $|\mathbf{v}| = \sqrt{7^2 + 31^2} = \sqrt{1010}$, so $v^2 = 1010$.

3) Increase in K.E. $= \frac{1}{2}mv^2 - \frac{1}{2}mu^2 = (\frac{1}{2} \times 0.002 \times 1010) - (\frac{1}{2} \times 0.002 \times 5) = 1.005$ J.

The formula's been tweaked to suit the situation — there's only one 'particle', and there will be an increase rather than a loss in K.E.

I'm not lazy — I'm just conserving my kinetic energy...

There are plenty of different situations where you could be asked to find a change in kinetic energy — but they all use pretty much the same formula, and no doubt require you to calculate some speeds. Just think it through logically to decide whether K.E. will go up or down or whatever. Now make yourself a quick bevvy and a light snack — it's practice time...

M2 Section 4 — Practice Questions

Well that's been a crash course in collisions (ho ho). Don't just sit and hope that you've understood it all — come and have a go. Have a practice lap first...

Warm-up Questions

1) Find the velocity of a particle of mass 0.1 kg, travelling at $(\mathbf{i} + \mathbf{j})$ ms^{-1}, after receiving an impulse of:
a) $2\mathbf{i} + 5\mathbf{j}$ Ns b) $-3\mathbf{i} + \mathbf{j}$ Ns c) $-\mathbf{i} - 6\mathbf{j}$ Ns d) $4\mathbf{i}$ Ns.

2) A 2 kg particle, travelling at $(4\mathbf{i} - \mathbf{j})$ ms^{-1}, receives an impulse, $\mathbf{Q}$, changing its velocity to $(-2\mathbf{i} + \mathbf{j})$ ms^{-1}.
Find:
a) $\mathbf{Q}$ b) $|\mathbf{Q}|$, in Ns to 3 s.f. c) the angle $\mathbf{Q}$ makes with $\mathbf{i}$, in degrees to 3 s.f.

3) Two particles A and B collide, where $m_A = 0.5$ kg and $m_B = 0.4$ kg.
Their initial velocities are $\mathbf{u}_A = (2\mathbf{i} + \mathbf{j})$ ms^{-1} and $\mathbf{u}_B = (-\mathbf{i} - 4\mathbf{j})$ ms^{-1}. Find, to 3 s.f:
a) the speed of B after impact if A moves away from the collision at a velocity of $(-\mathbf{i} - 2\mathbf{j})$ ms^{-1},
b) their combined speed after the impact if they coalesce instead.

4) Two particles travelling directly towards each other at the same speed collide. The impact causes one particle to stop, and the other to go in the opposite direction at half its original speed. Find the value of e.

5) A particle of mass 1 kg travelling at 10 ms^{-1} on a horizontal plane has a collision, where $e = 0.4$.
Find the particle's rebound speed if it collides head-on with:
a) a smooth vertical wall, b) a particle of mass 2 kg travelling at 12 ms^{-1} towards it.

6) Particles A (mass 1 kg), B (4 kg) and C (5 kg) travel in the same line at speeds of $3u$, $2u$ and u, respectively. If A collides with B first ($e = \frac{1}{4}$), then B with C ($e = \frac{1}{3}$), determine whether A and B will collide again.

7) A stationary particle drops vertically from a height of 1 m and rebounds from a smooth horizontal plane surface with $e = 0.5$. Find the height that it reaches after its first, second and third bounce.

8) Find the loss in kinetic energy when a particle of mass 2 kg travelling at 3 ms^{-1} collides with a stationary particle of mass 3 kg on a smooth horizontal plane surface, where $e = 0.3$.

Ready to notch it up a gear? Think you're the Stig of M2?
Well rev her up and let rip — just watch out for those hairpin bends.

Exam Questions

1 A particle of mass 0.4 kg receives an impulse of $(3\mathbf{i} - 8\mathbf{j})$ Ns.
The velocity of the particle just before the impulse is $(-6\mathbf{i} + \mathbf{j})$ ms^{-1}.

a) Find the speed of the particle immediately after the impulse.
Give your answer in ms^{-1} to 3 s.f.
(5 marks)

b) Find the angle between the motion of the particle and the horizontal following the impulse.
Give your answer in degrees to 3 s.f.
(2 marks)

2 A marble of mass 0.02 kg, travelling at 2 ms^{-1}, collides with another, stationary, marble of mass 0.06 kg.
Both can be modelled as smooth spheres on a smooth horizontal plane.
If the collision is perfectly elastic, find the speed of each marble immediately after the collision.
(4 marks)

M2 Section 4 — Practice Questions

Encore encore, more more more...

3 Particles P (of mass $2m$) and Q (of mass m), travelling in a straight line towards each other at the same speed (u) on a smooth horizontal plane surface, collide with a coefficient of restitution of $\frac{3}{4}$.

a) Show that the collision reverses the direction of both particles, with Q having eight times the rebound speed of P. *(6 marks)*

Following the collision, Q goes on to collide with a smooth vertical wall, perpendicular to its path. The coefficient of restitution for the impact with the wall is e_{wall}. Q goes on to collide with P again on the rebound from the wall.

b) Show that $e_{\text{wall}} > \frac{1}{8}$. *(3 marks)*

c) Suppose that $e_{\text{wall}} = \frac{3}{5}$. If after the second collision with P, Q continues to move away from the wall, but with a speed of 0.22 ms^{-1}, find the value of u, the initial speed of both particles, in ms^{-1}. *(7 marks)*

4 A particle of mass $2m$, travelling at a speed of $3u$ on a smooth horizontal plane, collides directly with a particle of mass $3m$ travelling at $2u$ in the same direction. The coefficient of restitution is $\frac{1}{4}$.

a) Find expressions for the speeds of both particles after the collision. Give your answers in terms of u. *(4 marks)*

b) Show that the amount of kinetic energy lost in the collision is $\frac{9mu^2}{16}$. *(4 marks)*

5 Particles A (mass m), B (mass $2m$) and C (mass $4m$) lie on a straight line, as shown:

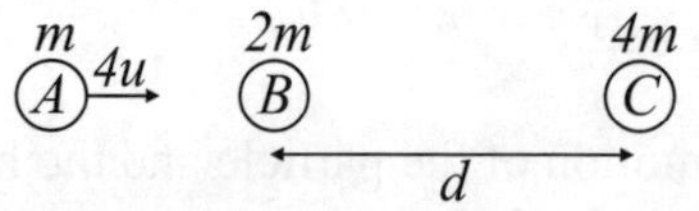

m (A) $\xrightarrow{4u}$ $2m$ (B) $\longleftarrow d \longrightarrow$ $4m$ (C)

B and C are initially stationary when A collides with B at a speed of $4u$ ($u > 0$), causing B to collide with C. The coefficient of restitution between B and C is $2e$, where e is the coefficient of restitution between A and B.

a) Show that the collision between A and B does not reverse the direction of A. *(7 marks)*

By the time B and C collide, A has travelled a distance of $\frac{d}{4}$ since the first collision.

b) Show that $e = \frac{1}{3}$. *(3 marks)*

c) Hence find, in terms of u, the speed of C following its collision with B. *(5 marks)*

Moments

In this lifetime there are moments, moments of... Hang on, I made that gag in M1. In this section there are more moments. A lot more moments (and resolving some forces for good measure). Better get your trig on.

Moment = Force × **Perpendicular** Distance from the force's **Line of Action**

A 'moment' is the turning effect a force has around a point.
The larger the force, and the greater the distance from a point, then the larger the moment.

Often, you'll be given a distance between the point and the force, but this distance won't be perpendicular to the force's 'line of action'. You'll need to resolve to find the perpendicular distance.

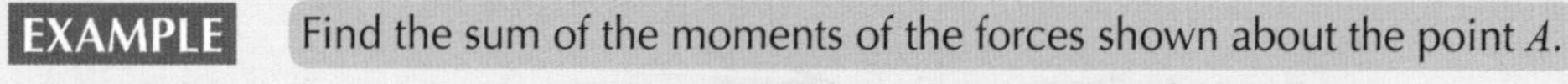

EXAMPLE Find the sum of the moments of the forces shown about the point A.

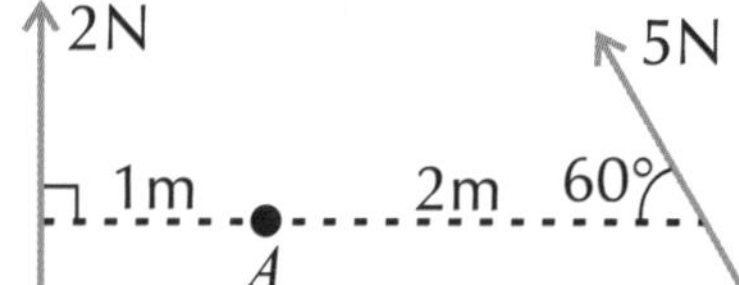

Calculating the clockwise moment is simple as the line of action is perpendicular to A:

$2 \times 1 = 2$ Nm

The units of moments are Nm, unimaginative, but easy to remember.

The anticlockwise moment is trickier as the line of action of the force isn't perpendicular to A. There are two ways to go about finding the moment — by finding the perpendicular distance or finding the perpendicular component of the force.

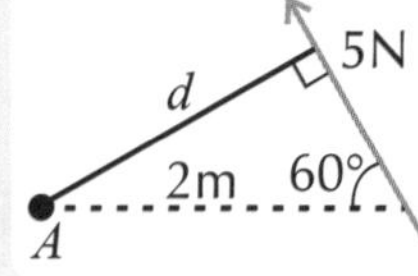

Finding the perpendicular distance:

$d = 2\sin 60°$

So, moment $= 5 \times 2\sin 60° = 10\sin 60° = 5\sqrt{3}$ Nm

Both methods give the same moment. Just choose whichever you find simplest — and be sure to show your workings.

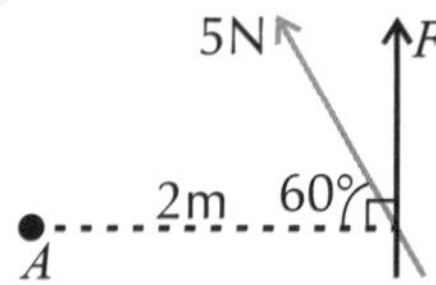

Finding the perpendicular component of the force:

$F = 5\sin 60°$

So, moment $= 5\sin 60° \times 2 = 10\sin 60° = 5\sqrt{3}$ Nm

We can now find the sum of the moments (in this case, taking anticlockwise as negative):

Clockwise + anticlockwise moments $= 2 + (-5\sqrt{3}) = -6.66$ Nm $= 6.66$ Nm anticlockwise

In **Equilibrium** Moments total **Zero** around **Any Point**

If a system is in equilibrium, the moments about any point total zero — so anticlockwise moments = clockwise moments about any point.

EXAMPLE A rod, AB, of length 6 m is held in equilibrium by two strings, as shown. By taking moments, find the mass, m, of the rod. Take $g = 9.8$ ms^{-2}.

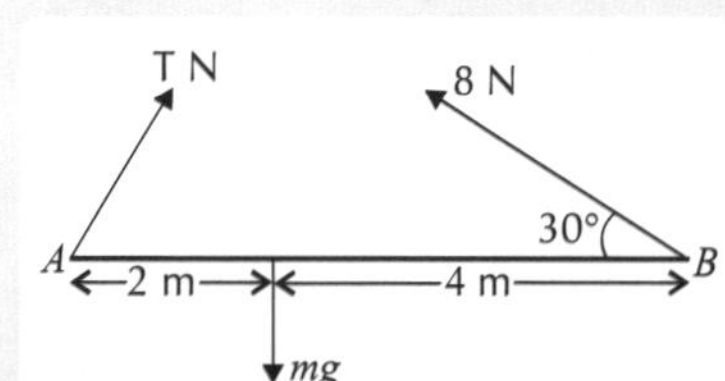

By taking moments about A:
clockwise moments = anticlockwise moments
$2mg = 6\sin 30° \times 8$
$mg = 12 \quad \Rightarrow \quad m = 12 \div 9.8 = 1.22$ kg

Although you *can* take moments about any point (even one not on the rod), it's always easier to take moments about a point that has an unknown force going through it (as in the example above).

Resolve the force, Luke — use the perpendicular distance...

Why do I want to write a musical every time I read a page about moments? Clearly a sci-fi epic would be more appropriate.

Moments

When taking moments, you often need to know where an object's weight acts.
For an object other than a particle, all the weight is considered to act at the centre of mass (see page 164).

The **Weight** acts at the **Centre** of a **Uniform** rod

Mostly, you'll be dealing with rods. A model rod has negligible thickness, so you only need to consider where along its length the centre of mass lies. If the rod is uniform then the weight acts at the centre of the rod.

EXAMPLE A uniform rod, AB, of length l m and mass m kg is suspended in horizontal equilibrium by two inextensible wires, with tensions as shown. Find m.

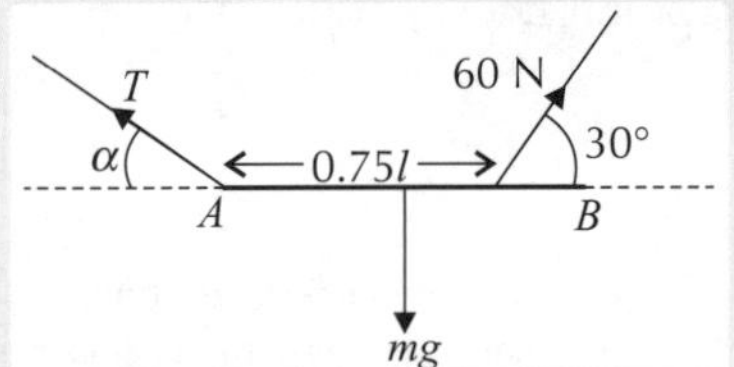

Taking moments about A:

$mg \times 0.5l = 60\sin 30° \times 0.75l$

$mg \times 0.5 = 30 \times 0.75$

$4.9m = 22.5$ so $m = 4.59$ kg (3 s.f.)

You can pick any point to take moments about, but it makes sense to choose A, because that eliminates the unknown force, T.

You can **Calculate** the Centre of Mass for **Non-Uniform** rods

If the weight acts at an unknown point along a rod, the point can be found in the usual way — by taking moments. You might also have to resolve the forces horizontally or vertically to find some missing information.

EXAMPLE A plank of mass 5 kg is supported by a vertical string attached at a point B, as shown. One end of the plank, A, rests upon a pole. The tension in the string is T and the normal reaction at the pole is 70 N. A particle, P, of mass 9 kg rests on the plank 2 m from A, as shown. Find T and the distance, x, between A and the centre of mass of the plank.

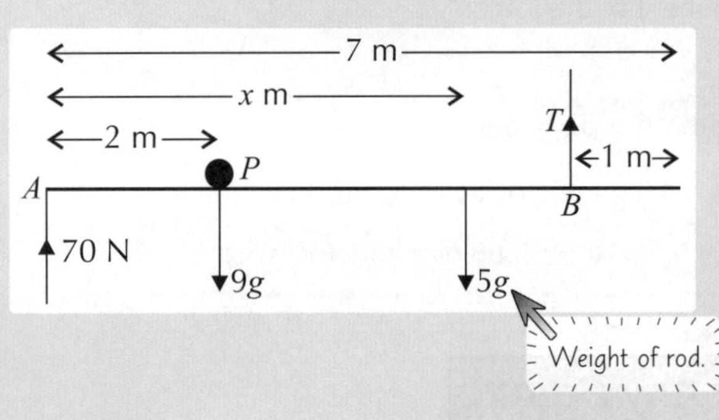

Resolve vertically:
upward forces = downward forces:

$T + 70 = 9g + 5g$

so, $T = 137.2 - 70 = 67.2$ N

Moments about A:
clockwise moments = anticlockwise moments:

$(9g \times 2) + (5g \times x) = 67.2 \times 6$

$49x = 403.2 - 176.4$

so $x = \frac{226.8}{49} = 4.63$ m (3 s.f.)

These statements are only (and always) true at equilibrium.

EXAMPLE A non-uniform rod, AB, of mass 2 kg and length 1 m, is suspended in equilibrium at an angle of θ to the vertical by two vertical strings, as shown. The tensions in the strings are T N and 12 N respectively. Find the distance, x, from A to the rod's centre of mass.

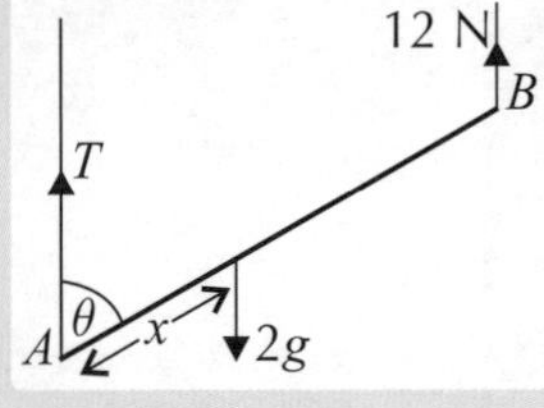

Taking moments about A: clockwise moments = anticlockwise moments

$2g\sin\theta \times x = 12\sin\theta \times 1$

$2\sin\theta$ cancels, so:

$gx = 6$

$x = 0.612$ m (3 s.f.)

There's a diagram I really wanted to put on this page...

...but I couldn't make it fit.
To make it up to you I've put it down here — it's about modelling non-uniform rods. Don't get bogged down worrying that the models used in Mechanics aren't that realistic — it's the ability to do the maths (and pass those exams) that counts. Anyway, you can worry about real life when you're done with school (when there'll be fewer exams).

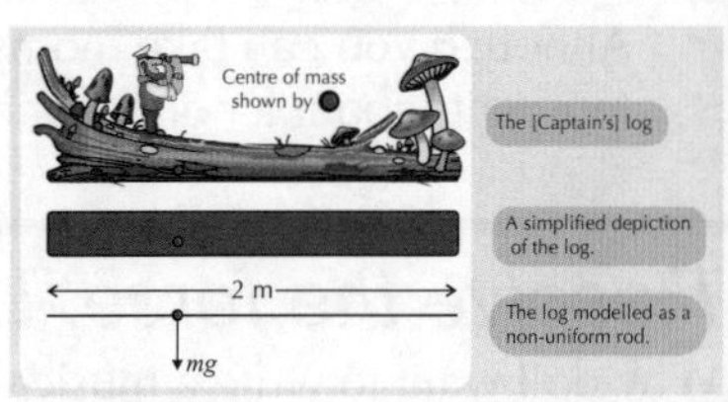

Rigid Bodies

If reactions are at a weird angle, rather than horizontal, vertical or perpendicular to something else, then it's easier to think of them as two components — in two nice, convenient perpendicular directions.

Reactions can have Horizontal and Vertical Components

If a rod is connected to a plane (such as a wall) by a hinge or pivot and the forces holding it in equilibrium aren't parallel, then the reaction at the wall won't be perpendicular to the wall. Don't panic though, components are super-helpful here.

EXAMPLE A uniform rod, AB, is freely hinged on a vertical wall. The rod is held in horizontal equilibrium by a light inextensible string attached at a point C, 0.4 m from the end B at an angle of 45° to the rod, as shown. Given that the rod is 1.2 m long and has mass 2 kg, find the tension in the string and the magnitude of the reaction at the wall.

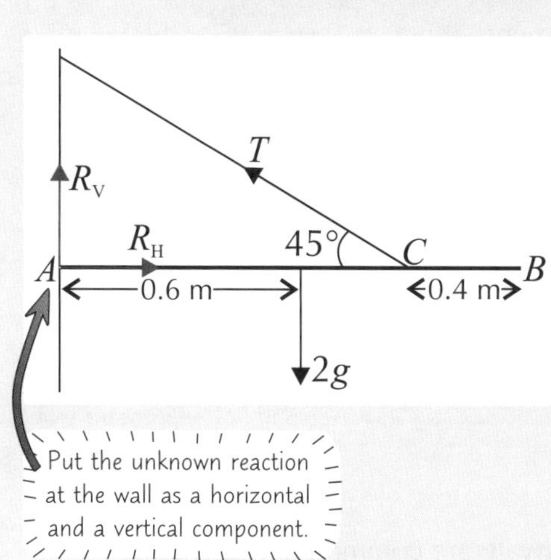

Put the unknown reaction at the wall as a horizontal and a vertical component.

Moments about A:
$T\sin 45° \times (1.2 - 0.4) = 2g \times 0.6$
so, $T\sin 45° = 14.7$
and $T = 20.8$ N

Choose A so that you can ignore the unknown reaction components while finding T.

Resolving horizontally:
$R_H = T\cos 45° = 20.79\cos 45°$
so, $R_H = 14.7$ N

Resolving vertically:
$R_V + T\sin 45° = 2g$
so $R_V = 4.9$ N

The rod is in equilibrium, so the resultant force in any direction is zero.

Magnitude of reaction:
$|R| = \sqrt{R_H^2 + R_V^2} = \sqrt{14.7^2 + 4.9^2}$
so $|R| = 15.5$ N

EXAMPLE A non-uniform rod, AB, of length $6a$ and mass 4 kg is supported by a light strut at an angle of 70° to a vertical wall, as shown. The distance from A to the centre of mass, X, of the rod is xa m. The strut exerts a thrust of 16 N at the centre of the rod. A particle of weight 2 N is placed at B. Find x, and the magnitude and direction of the reaction at A.

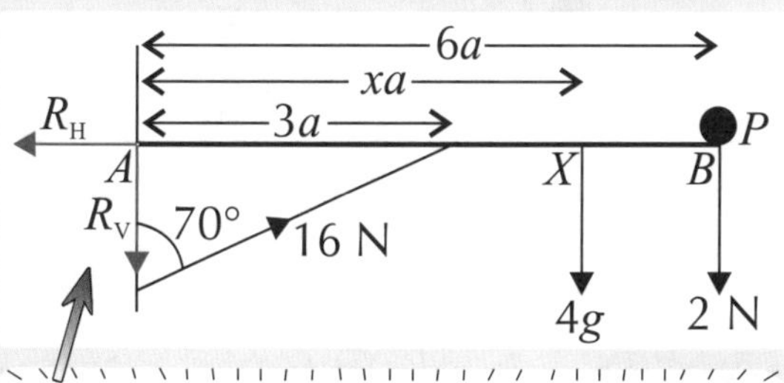

Don't worry if you're not sure which directions the reaction components act in. You'll just get negative numbers if you're wrong (the magnitude will be the same).

Moments about A:
$16\cos 70° \times 3a = (4g \times xa) + (2 \times 6a)$
so $4gxa = 4.417a$
and $x = 0.113$

Resolving horizontally:
$R_H = 16\sin 70°$
$\Rightarrow R_H = 15.04$ N

Resolving vertically:
$R_V + 4g + 2 = 16\cos 70°$
so $R_V = 16\cos 70° - 39.2 - 2 \Rightarrow R_V = -35.73$ N

R_V is negative — so it must go upwards instead of downwards.

Magnitude of reaction:
$|R| = \sqrt{R_H^2 + R_V^2} = \sqrt{15.04^2 + 35.73^2}$
so $|R| = 38.8$ N

Direction of reaction:

$\tan\theta = \dfrac{15.04}{35.73}$

R, 35.7 N, θ, 15.0 N

so $\theta = 22.8°$ to the wall

I'm trying to resist making a pun about rigor mortis...

...so I'll just tell you that it's due to irreversible muscular contraction caused by a shortage of adenosine triphosphate. Nice.

Rigid Bodies and Friction

Where would we be without friction? Well, using a ladder would certainly be trickier. Before getting too distracted by that thought you should really revise this page instead — ladders are featured, I promise.

Friction lets you assume the Reaction is Perpendicular

From the previous page, you know that a rod attached to a wall has a reaction at the wall with a horizontal and vertical component. If the rod is held by friction instead, then the frictional force 'replaces' the vertical component.

EXAMPLE A rod, AB, rests against a rough vertical wall and is held in limiting equilibrium perpendicular to the wall by a light inextensible string attached at B at an angle of θ, as shown, where $\tan\theta = \frac{7}{17}$. The tension in the string is 42 N. The length AB is 5.5 m and the centre of mass is located 3.8 m from B. Find the mass of the rod, m, and the coefficient of friction, μ, between the wall and the rod.

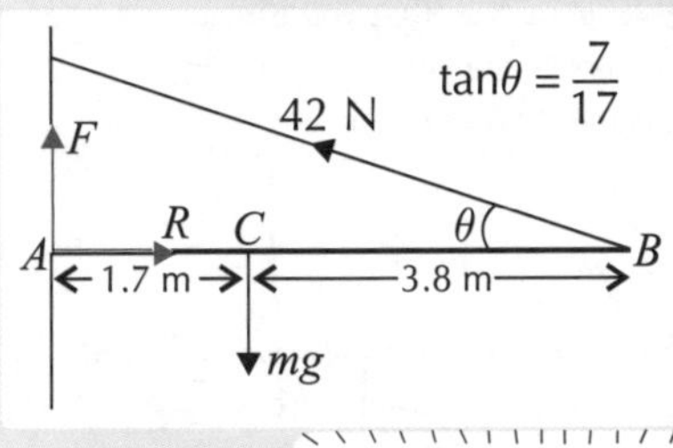

First take moments about A so you can find mg while ignoring the unknowns F and R.

Moments about A: $mg \times 1.7 = 42\sin\theta \times 5.5$
so $mg = 51.7$ N
and $m = 5.3$ kg

Now take moments about a different point to find F. I've taken them about C, but you could have used B.

Moments about C: $1.7 \times F = 3.8 \times 42\sin\theta$
so $F = 35.7$ N

Now you know F, you only need to find R before you can find μ.

Resolving horizontally:
$R = 42\cos\theta$
$R = 38.8$ N

Limiting equilibrium, so $F = \mu R$:
$35.7 = 38.8\mu$
so $\mu = 0.92$

Limiting equilibrium showed up in M1 — it means that the body is on the point of moving.

Multiple Surfaces can exert a Frictional Force

'Ladder' questions, where a rod rests at an angle against the ground and a wall, are common in M2 exams. Often, the ground is modelled as rough and the wall as smooth. Can't take these things for granted though...

The 4 possible combinations of surfaces for 'ladder' questions:

Most common in exams

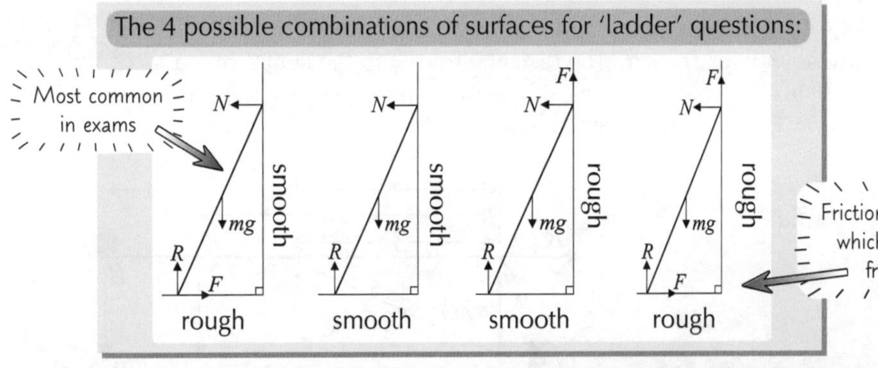

Friction acts to prevent motion — so think about which way the ladder would slip and draw the frictional force in the opposite direction.

EXAMPLE A ladder rests against a smooth wall at an angle of 65° to the rough ground, as shown. The ladder has mass 1.3 kg and length $5x$ m. A cat of mass 4.5 kg sits on the ladder at C, $4x$ m from the base. The ladder is in limiting equilibrium. Model the ladder as a uniform rod and the cat as a particle. Find the coefficient of friction between the ground and the ladder.

R is the normal reaction of the ground and N is the normal reaction of the wall.

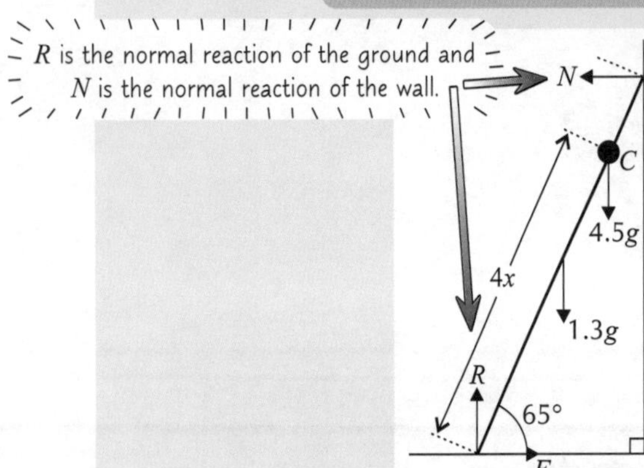

Resolving horizontally: $F = N$

Take moments about the base of the ladder to find N:
$N\sin65° \times 5x = (1.3g\cos65° \times 2.5x) + (4.5g\cos65° \times 4x)$
$4.531xN = 13.46x + 74.55x$

so, $N = \frac{88.01x}{4.531x} = 19.42$ N

Resolve vertically to find R:
$R = 1.3g + 4.5g$
$\Rightarrow R = 56.84$ N

The ladder is in limiting equilibrium, so $F = \mu R$:
Resolving horizontally shows $F = N$, so, $19.42 = 56.84\mu$
and $\mu = 0.342$ (to 3 s.f.)

Rigid Bodies and Friction

A Reaction is always Perpendicular to the Surface

Sometimes a body may be leaning against a surface that isn't vertical. This blows my mind.

EXAMPLE A uniform ladder of length 3 m rests against a smooth wall slanted at 10° to the vertical, as shown. The ladder is at an angle of 60° to the ground. The magnitude of the normal reaction of the wall is 18 N. Find the mass of the ladder.

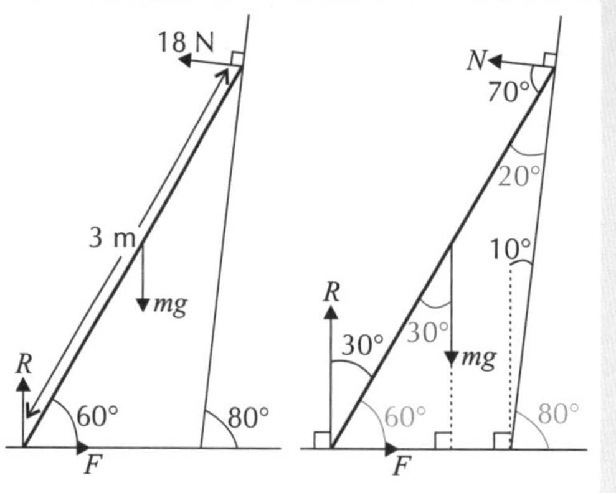

If the wall was vertical then the angles shown in red would be identical as both the weight and the wall would be perpendicular to the ground. Simple. However, the reaction at the wall, N, is perpendicular to the wall, so be careful when resolving forces relative to the ladder.

Moments about the base of the ladder:
$mg\sin 30° \times 1.5 = 18\sin 70° \times 3$
so $m = 6.9$ kg

Bodies can be Supported Along Their Lengths

If a rod is resting on something along its length then the reaction is perpendicular to the rod.

EXAMPLE A uniform rod, AB, rests with end A on rough ground and upon a smooth peg at C, 0.9 m from B. The rod has length 3.3 m and weight 10 N. A particle, P, with weight 25 N is placed at B. Given that the rod is in limiting equilibrium find the magnitude of the normal reaction, N, at the peg and the friction, F, between the rod and the ground.

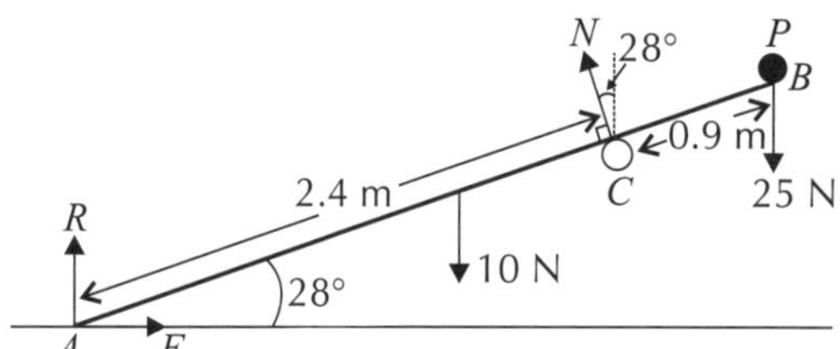

Moments about A:
$2.4N = (10\cos 28° \times 1.65) + (25\cos 28° \times 3.3)$
so $N = 36.4$ N

It's a uniform rod, so its mass acts in the middle.

Resolving horizontally:
$F = N\sin 28° = 36.4\sin 28°$
$\Rightarrow F = 17.1$ N

If equilibrium isn't limiting, $F \leq \mu R$

In limiting equilibrium, friction is at its maximum (i.e. $F = \mu R$). You might be asked to find μ when you don't know if equilibrium is limiting. Just find it in the same way as if equilibrium was limiting, but replace $F = \mu R$ with $F \leq \mu R$.

EXAMPLE A rough peg supports a rod at a point B, 0.2 m from one end of the rod, as shown. The other end of the rod, A, rests on a smooth horizontal plane. The rod is 1.5 m long, with its centre of mass located 1.2 m from A at point C. Given that the rod is in equilibrium at an angle of 15° to the horizontal plane and that the friction at the peg exerts a force of 8 N, show that $\mu \geq 0.3$.

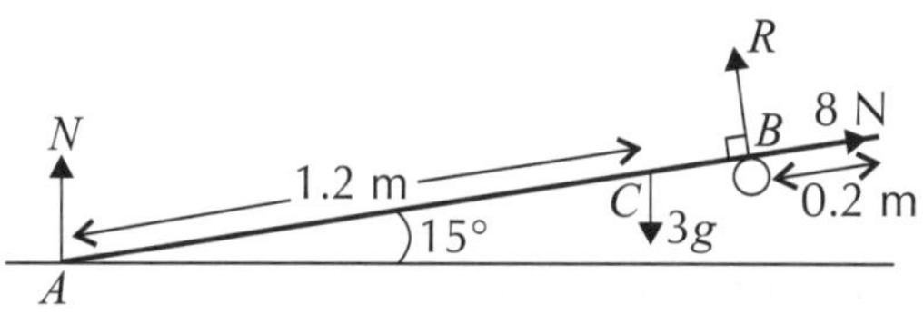

You know F, but to find μ you also need to know R.
Take moments about A to find R:
$R \times (1.5 - 0.2) = 3g\cos 15° \times 1.2$
so $R = 26.2$ N

$F \leq \mu R$
so $\mu \geq 8 \div 26.2$
$\mu \geq 0.3$

...and that's everything you need to know about anything, ever.

If you've been revising M2 sections in order then this is (pretty much) the end — although there's no harm in going back and having another go. Have a nice cup of tea first though — you deserve it. There are also plenty of questions and practice exams coming up that aren't going to answer themselves. Soon you'll be an M2 master (just like you've always wanted).

Section Five — Practice Questions

Time to make like a tree and ~~leaf~~ ~~leave~~ ~~sway gently in the breeze.~~ Darn it, that analogy wasn't really working... Anyway, time to be a dedicated student and practise your statics know-how. Ace.

Warm-up Questions

Take $g = 9.8\ \text{ms}^{-2}$ in each of these questions.

1) What is meant by a 'non-uniform rod'?

2) Calculate the perpendicular distance from a particle, P, to the forces shown in the diagrams below:

a) A, P, 39.6°, 0.8 m

b)

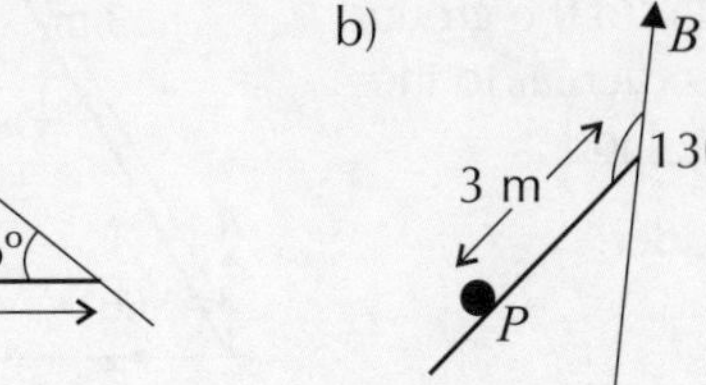

c)

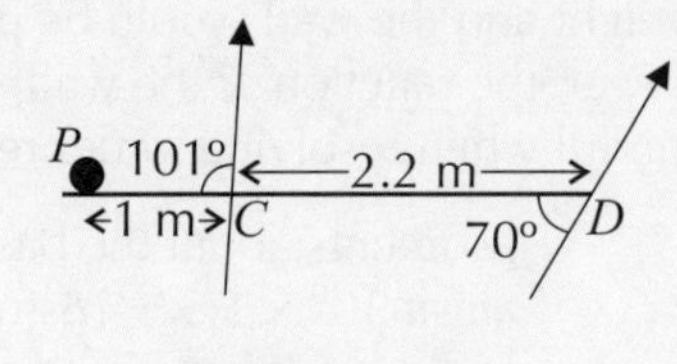

3) a) Calculate the magnitude of T in this diagram.

b) Find the value of x.

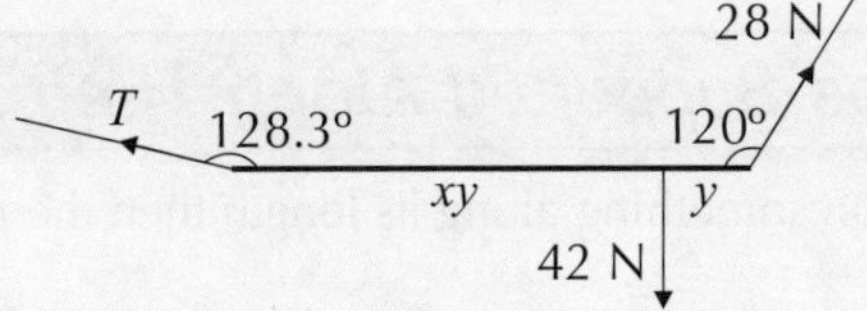

4) A uniform ladder, of length l m, is placed on rough horizontal ground and rests against a smooth vertical wall at an angle of 20° to the wall. Draw a diagram illustrating this system with forces labelled. State what assumptions you would make.

Those practice questions should've been a doddle. Time to step it up a notch with some questions more like those you'll get in the exam. In the words of a fictional dance-squad commander, "don't let me down".

Exam Questions

Whenever a numerical value of g is required in the following questions, take $g = 9.8\ \text{ms}^{-2}$.

1 A uniform ladder, AB, is positioned against a smooth vertical wall and rests upon rough horizontal ground at an angle of θ, as shown. Clive stands on the ladder at point C, two-thirds of the way along the ladder's length from A. The ladder is 4.2 m long and weighs 180 N. The normal reaction at A is 490 N.

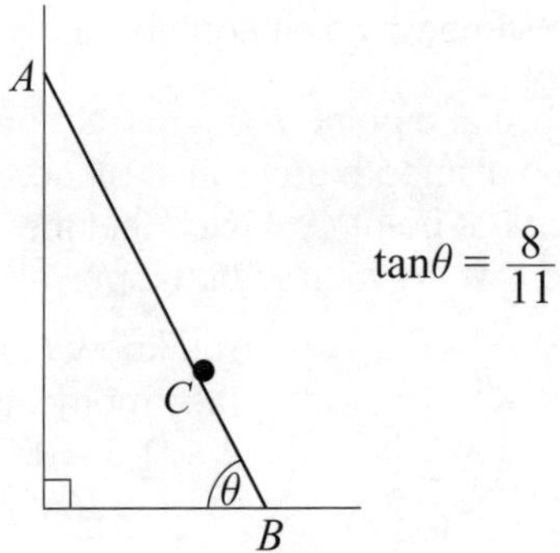

$\tan\theta = \frac{8}{11}$

The ladder rests in limiting equilibrium. Model Clive as a particle and find:

a) the mass of Clive, m, to the nearest kg.

(3 marks)

b) the coefficient of friction, μ, between the ground and the ladder.

(5 marks)

Section Five — Practice Questions

If the previous question was a struggle, then you know what to do — go back a few pages and have another look. These questions will still be here while you're gone. Lurking.

2 A non-uniform rod, AB, is freely hinged at a vertical wall. It is held in horizontal equilibrium by a strut attached to the wall at C at an angle of 55°. The thrust in the strut is 30 N, as shown. The rod has mass 2 kg, centred 0.4 m from A. The total length of the rod is x m.

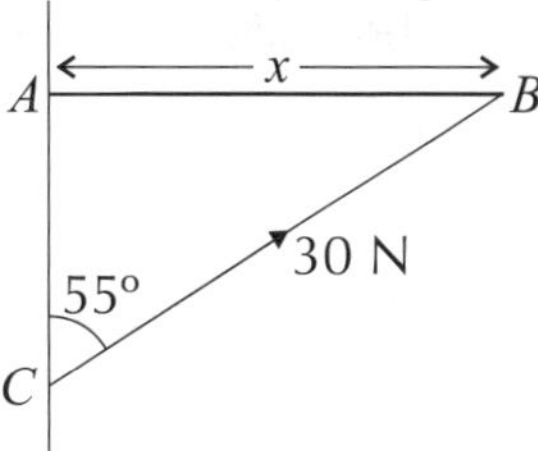

a) Find the length of the rod, x.

(3 marks)

b) Find the magnitude and direction of the reaction at A.

(5 marks)

3 A uniform rod of mass m kg rests in equilibrium against rough horizontal ground at point A and a smooth peg at point B, making an angle of θ with the ground, as shown. The rod is l m long and B is $\frac{3}{4}l$ from A.

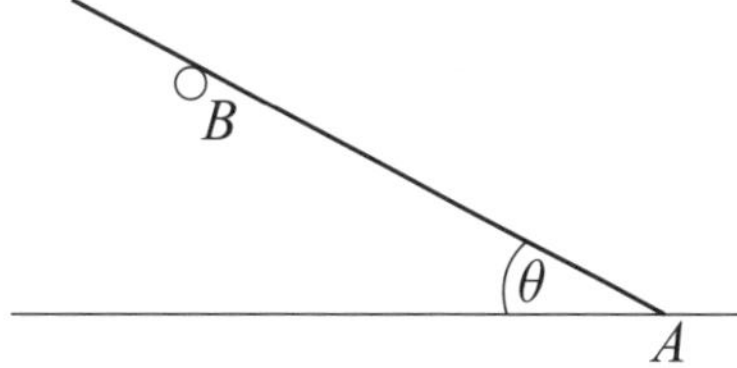

a) Show that the perpendicular reaction at the peg, $P = \frac{2}{3}mg\cos\theta$.

(3 marks)

b) Given that $\sin\theta = \frac{3}{5}$, find the range of values which the coefficient of friction between the rod and the ground could take.

(6 marks)

4 A uniform rod, AB, is held in limiting horizontal equilibrium against a rough wall by an inextensible string connected to the rod at point C and the wall at point D, as shown. A particle of mass m kg rests at point B. The magnitude of the normal reaction of the wall at A is 72.5 N. The mass of the rod is 3 kg.

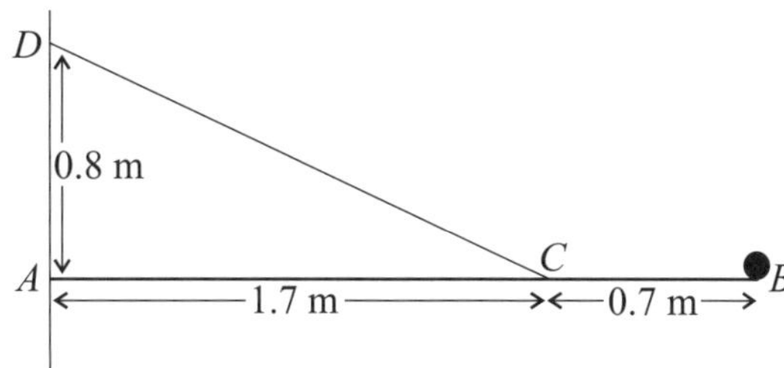

a) Find the tension, T, in the string.

(4 marks)

b) Find m.

(3 marks)

c) Find the magnitude of the frictional force, F, between the wall and the rod.

(3 marks)

General Certificate of Education
Advanced Subsidiary (AS) and Advanced Level

Mechanics M2 — Practice Exam One

Time Allowed: 1 hour 30 min

Calculators may be used for this exam (except those with facilities for symbolic algebra, differentiation or integration).

Whenever a numerical value of g is required, take $g = 9.8 \text{ ms}^{-2}$.

Give any non-exact numerical answers to an appropriate degree of accuracy.

There are 75 marks available for this paper.

1 A freely-hinged beam, AB, attached to a vertical wall is held in equilibrium perpendicular to the wall by a strut attached to the beam at C. The strut is fastened to the wall at point D, making an angle of 60° with the wall, as shown. A particle, P, with a mass of 1.8 kg rests upon the beam at a point 0.2 m from A. The weight of the beam acts at point C. The distance from A to the centre of mass of the beam is 1.1 m.

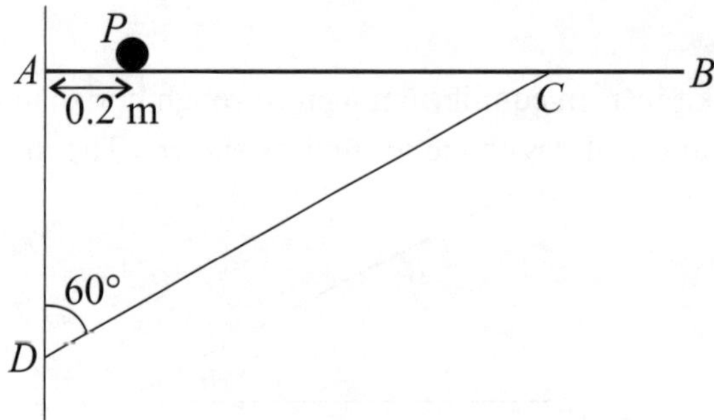

a) Find the magnitude of the vertical component of the reaction at A. *(3 marks)*

Given that the magnitude of the horizontal component of the reaction at A is 35 N find:

b) the magnitude and direction of the reaction at A. *(3 marks)*

c) the tension in the strut. *(3 marks)*

d) the mass of the beam. *(3 marks)*

2 Particle A moves towards a stationary particle B in a straight line on a smooth, horizontal surface, at a speed of $5u$ ms^{-1}. The collision reverses the direction of A's travel, and reduces its speed to u ms^{-1}. Particle A has a mass of 1 kg. The coefficient of restitution for the collision is $\frac{4}{5}$.

a) Find the speed of B after the collision, in terms of u. *(3 marks)*

b) Find the value of M, the mass of particle B. *(3 marks)*

Particle B goes on to collide with a smooth vertical wall, perpendicular to its direction of travel. The coefficient of restitution between B and the wall is e.

c) Find the range of values of e that would allow B to collide again with particle A. *(3 marks)*

3 A car of mass 1300 kg is moving at constant speed up a straight road, which is inclined at an angle of 3° to the horizontal. The car's engine is working at a rate of 20 kW. The magnitude of the resistance to motion from non-gravitational forces is 245 N.

a) Find the speed of the car. *(4 marks)*

When the car is moving at the constant speed found in part a), its engine is switched off. Assuming that the resistance to motion remains constant at 245 N,

b) find the distance the car travels before coming to rest. *(4 marks)*

4 A uniform wire is bent into a frame shaped as a right-angled triangle, as shown below.

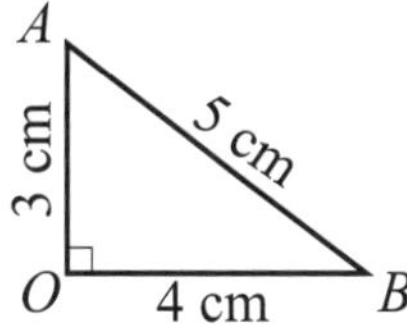

a) Find the distance of the centre of mass of the frame from side OA. *(4 marks)*

b) Show that the centre of mass of the frame is 1 cm away from side OB. *(3 marks)*

The frame is suspended freely from point O, where it hangs in equilibrium.

c) Find the angle that side AB makes with the horizontal.
Give your answer in degrees, to 3 significant figures. *(5 marks)*

5

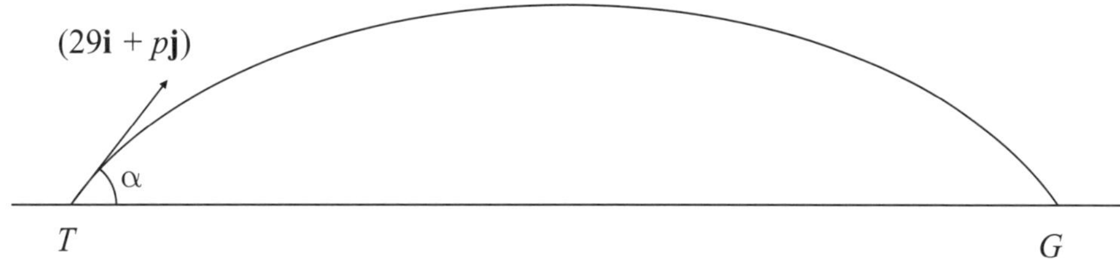

A golf ball is struck from a point T on horizontal ground with velocity $(29\mathbf{i} + p\mathbf{j})$ ms^{-1}, at an angle α to the horizontal. The ball takes 5 seconds to land on the ground at point G.

a) Show that $p = 24.5$ *(3 marks)*

b) Find the initial speed of the ball. *(2 marks)*

c) Find the angle of projection, α. Give your answer to the nearest degree. *(2 marks)*

d) Find the horizontal distance TG. *(2 marks)*

e) Find the maximum height above the ground reached by the golf ball. *(3 marks)*

6

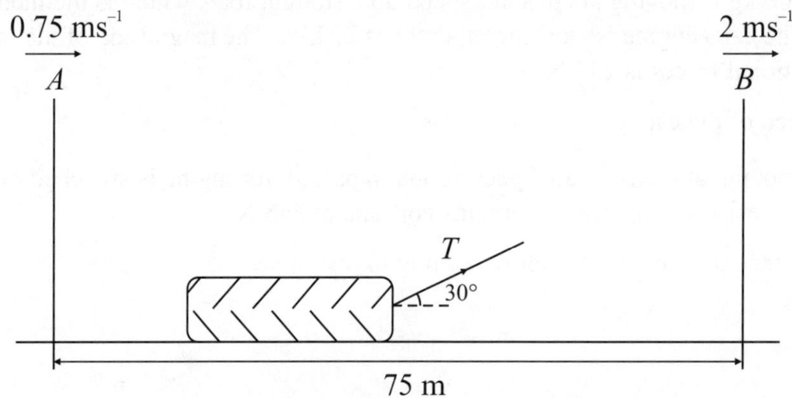

A man is dragging a tractor tyre of mass 160 kg along a straight, horizontal road by means of a rope attached to the tyre at an angle of 30° to the horizontal, as shown in the diagram above.

The man drags the tyre in a straight line between two checkpoints on the road, 75 m apart. The tyre passes through checkpoint *A* with a speed of 0.75 ms^{-1}, and checkpoint *B* with a speed of 2 ms^{-1}. Between the two checkpoints, the tyre experiences a constant resistive force of 270 N.

a) Find the work done by the tension in the rope in moving the tyre from *A* to *B*. *(4 marks)*

b) Find *T*, the constant magnitude of the tension in the rope. *(3 marks)*

7 A particle *P* sets off from the origin at $t = 0$ and starts to move along the *x*-axis in the direction of *x* increasing. After *t* seconds, *P* has velocity *v* ms^{-1}, where:

$$v \begin{cases} 11t - 2t^2 & 0 \leq t \leq 5 \\ 25 - 4t & t > 5 \end{cases}$$

Find:

a) the displacement of *P* from the origin at $t = 5$, *(3 marks)*

b) the time at which *P* changes direction, *(3 marks)*

c) the time taken for *P* to return to the origin, *(5 marks)*

d) the total distance travelled by *P* after 8 seconds. *(4 marks)*

General Certificate of Education
Advanced Subsidiary (AS) and Advanced Level

Mechanics M2 — Practice Exam Two

Time Allowed: 1 hour 30 min

Calculators may be used for this exam (except those with facilities for symbolic algebra, differentiation or integration).

Whenever a numerical value of g is required, take $g = 9.8 \text{ ms}^{-2}$.

Give any non-exact numerical answers to an appropriate degree of accuracy.

There are 75 marks available for this paper.

1 A uniform rod, AB, rests in equilibrium against rough horizontal ground and is held at an angle of θ to the horizontal by a smooth peg, C, where $\cos\theta = 0.91$. AB is 3 m in length and has a mass of 8 kg. The distance $CB = l$ m. The magnitude of the normal reaction at the peg is 54 N.

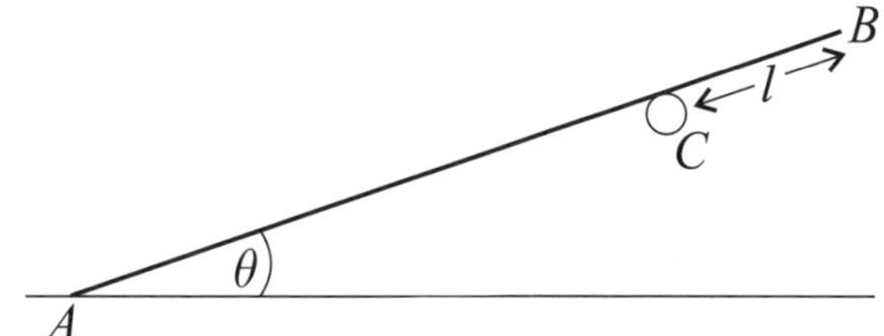

a) Find l. *(3 marks)*

b) Find μ, the coefficient of friction between the ground and the rod. *(6 marks)*

2 A piece of jewellery is made by cutting a triangle from a thin circle of metal, as shown below.

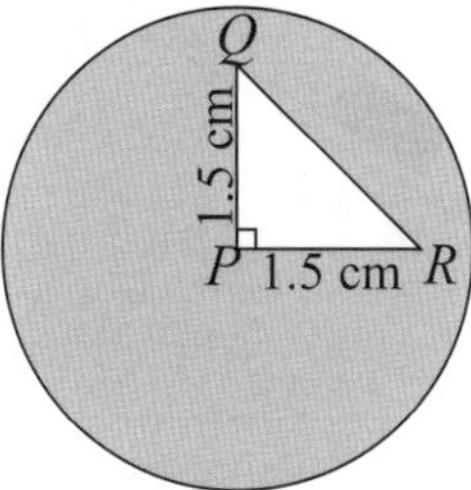

P is the centre of the circle, which has a radius of 2 cm. Triangle PQR is right-angled and isosceles. The shape can be modelled as a uniform lamina.

a) Show that the centre of mass of the shape is 0.070 cm from P, to 3 decimal places. *(5 marks)*

The shape hangs in equilibrium from a pin at point Q, about which it is able to freely rotate. The pin can be modelled as a smooth peg.

b) Find the angle that PQ makes with the vertical.
Give your answer in degrees, to 1 decimal place. *(3 marks)*

3 Three stationary particles, P, Q and R, lie in a line on a smooth horizontal surface. The particles have masses of 0.2 kg, 0.6 kg and 0.7 kg respectively. Particle P is projected towards Q at a speed of 5 ms^{-1}, and collides directly with the particle, with a coefficient of restitution of 0.65.

a) Find the velocities of P and Q immediately after their collision. Give your answer in ms^{-1}, to 3 significant figures. *(4 marks)*

b) Find the size of the impulse P exerts on Q during the collision. Give your answer in Ns, to 3 significant figures. *(2 marks)*

c) Find the total kinetic energy lost in the collision. Give your answer in J, to 3 significant figures. *(3 marks)*

Particle Q then collides directly with R. Q is brought to rest by the collision.

d) Find the size of the coefficient of restitution between Q and R, to 3 significant figures. *(4 marks)*

4 A bus of mass 13 000 kg is travelling along a straight, horizontal road at a constant speed of 14 ms^{-1}. The bus experiences a constant resistance to motion from non-gravitational forces which is modelled as a single force of magnitude 4500 N.

a) Find the rate at which the engine of the bus is working. Give your answer in kW. *(3 marks)*

The bus now moves up a hill inclined at an angle, α, to the horizontal, where $\sin\alpha = \frac{1}{35}$. The engine in the bus now works at a rate of 72 kW.

b) Assuming that the non-gravitational resistance to motion remains constant at 4500 N, find the acceleration of the bus when the speed of the bus is 12 ms^{-1}. *(4 marks)*

5

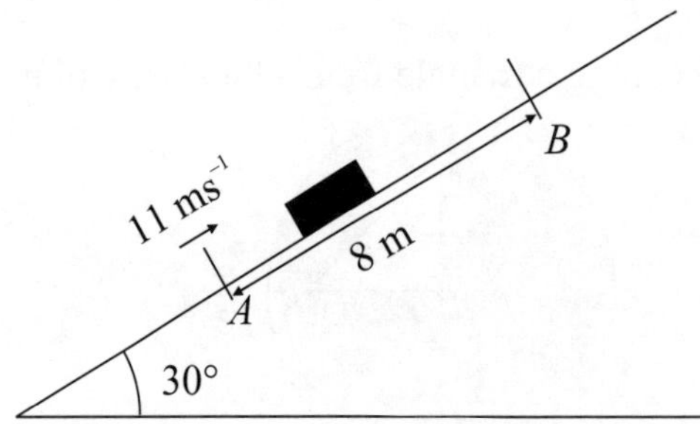

A particle of mass 9 kg is projected from a point A up a rough plane inclined at an angle of 30° to the horizontal. The speed of projection of the particle is 11 ms^{-1}. The particle travels 8 m up the line of greatest slope of the plane, before coming to instantaneous rest at point B. Find:

a) the work done by friction in bringing the particle to rest. *(6 marks)*

b) the coefficient of friction between the particle and the plane. *(4 marks)*

6 A particle P of mass 2.5 kg is moving in a horizontal plane under the action of a single force, **F** newtons. At t seconds, the position vector of P is **r** m, where **r** is given by:

$$\mathbf{r} = (t^3 - 6t^2 + 4t)\mathbf{i} + (7t - 4t^2 + 3)\mathbf{j}$$

Where **i** and **j** are the unit vectors directed due east and due north respectively.

a) Show that when $t = 5$, the velocity of P is $19\mathbf{i} - 33\mathbf{j}$. *(3 marks)*

b) Find the value of t when P is moving due south. *(4 marks)*

c) Find the magnitude of the resultant force acting on P when $t = 3$. *(5 marks)*

When $t = 5$, the particle receives an impulse, which changes its velocity to $5\mathbf{i} - \mathbf{j}$.

d) Find the magnitude of the impulse.
Give your answer in Ns to 3 s.f. *(3 marks)*

e) Find the angle the impulse makes with **i**.
Give your answer in degrees to 3 s.f. *(2 marks)*

7

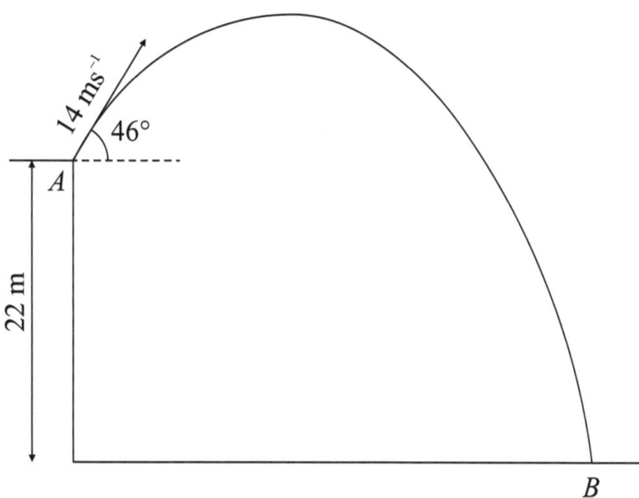

A stone is thrown upwards from point A on a cliff, 22 m above horizontal ground, with speed 14 ms^{-1} at an angle of 46° to the horizontal. After projection, the stone moves freely under gravity and lands at B on the horizontal ground, as shown above. Find:

a) the length of time for which the stone is at least 22 m above the ground. *(4 marks)*

b) the horizontal distance from A to B. *(4 marks)*

c) the speed of the stone as it hits the ground. *(3 marks)*

Answers

C3 Section 1 — Algebra and Functions

Warm-up Questions

1) a) $\frac{4x^2-25}{6x-15} = \frac{(2x+5)(2x-5)}{3(2x-5)} = \frac{2x+5}{3}$

b) $\frac{2x+3}{x-2} \times \frac{4x-8}{2x^2-3x-9}$

$= \frac{2x+3}{x-2} \times \frac{4(x-2)}{(2x+3)(x-3)}$

$= \frac{4}{x-3}$

c) $\frac{x^2-3x}{x+1} \div \frac{x}{2} = \frac{x(x-3)}{x+1} \times \frac{2}{x}$

$= \frac{x-3}{x+1} \times 2 = \frac{2(x-3)}{x+1}$

2) a) $\frac{x}{2x+1} + \frac{3}{x^2} + \frac{1}{x} = \frac{x \cdot x^2}{x^2(2x+1)} + \frac{3(2x+1)}{x^2(2x+1)} + \frac{x(2x+1)}{x^2(2x+1)}$

$= \frac{x^3+6x+3+2x^2+x}{x^2(2x+1)} = \frac{x^3+2x^2+7x+3}{x^2(2x+1)}$

b) $\frac{2}{x^2-1} - \frac{3x}{x-1} + \frac{x}{x+1}$

$= \frac{2}{(x+1)(x-1)} - \frac{3x(x+1)}{(x+1)(x-1)} + \frac{x(x-1)}{(x+1)(x-1)}$

$= \frac{2-3x^2-3x+x^2-x}{(x+1)(x-1)} = \frac{2-2x^2-4x}{(x+1)(x-1)}$

$= \frac{2(1-x^2-2x)}{(x+1)(x-1)}$

3)

$$\begin{array}{r} x^2 - 2x + 7 \text{ r} - 9 \\ x+4 \overline{) x^3 + 2x^2 - x + 19} \\ -\ \underline{x^3 + 4x^2} \\ -2x^2 - x \\ -\ \underline{-2x^2 - 8x} \\ 7x + 19 \\ -\ \underline{7x + 28} \\ -9 \end{array}$$

so $(x^3 + 2x^2 - x + 19) \div (x + 4) = x^2 - 2x + 7$ remainder -9.

4) $2x^3 + 8x^2 + 7x + 8 \equiv (Ax^2 + Bx + C)(x + 3) + D$.
Set $x = -3$: $2(-3)^3 + 8(-3)^2 + 7(-3) + 8 = 0 + D \Rightarrow D = 5$.
Set $x = 0$: $0 + 8 = C(0 + 3) + D \Rightarrow C = 1$.
Equating the coefficients of x^3 gives $2 = A$.
Finally, equating the coefficients of x^2 gives $8 = 3A + B$
$\Rightarrow 8 = (3 \times 2) + B$, so $B = 2$.
So $2x^3 + 8x^2 + 7x + 8 = (2x^2 + 2x + 1)(x + 3) + 5$. The result when $2x^3 + 8x^2 + 7x + 8$ is divided by $(x + 3)$ is $2x^2 + 2x + 1$ remainder 5.

5) a) Range $f(x) \geq -16$. This is a function, and it's one-to-one (the domain is restricted so every x-value is mapped to only one value of $f(x)$).

b) To find the range of this function, you need to find the minimum point of $x^2 - 7x + 10$ — do this by completing the square: $x^2 - 7x + 10 = (x - 3.5)^2 - 12.25 + 10$
$= (x - 3.5)^2 - 2.25$.
As $(x - 3.5)^2 \geq 0$ the minimum value of $x^2 - 7x + 10$ is -2.25, so the range is $f(x) \geq -2.25$.
This is a function, and it's many-to-one (as more than one x-value is mapped to the same value of $f(x)$).

You could also have found the minimum point by differentiating, setting the derivative equal to 0 and solving for x.

c) Range $f(x) \geq 0$. This is not a function as $f(x)$ doesn't exist for $x < 0$.

d) Sketch the graph for this one:

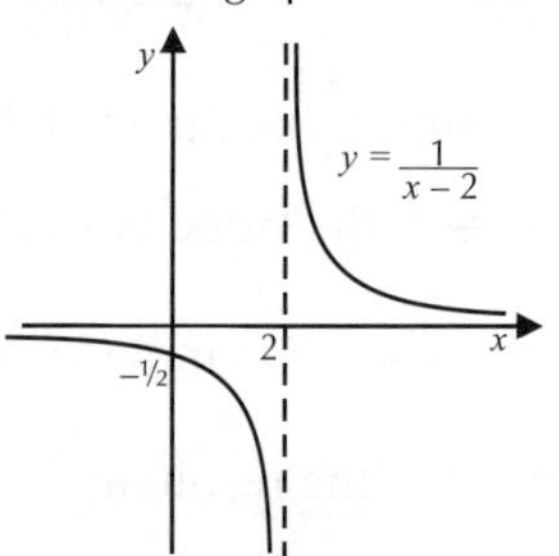

From the graph, the range is $f(x) \in \mathbb{R}$, $f(x) \neq 0$.
This is not a function as it's not defined for $x = 2$.

If you're not sure about any of the domains or ranges for the other parts, draw the graphs and see if that helps you figure it out.

6) a) $fg(2) = f(2(2) + 3) = f(7) = 3/7$.
$gf(1) = g(3/1) = g(3) = 2(3) + 3 = 9$.
$fg(x) = f(2x + 3) = \frac{3}{2x+3}$.

b) $fg(2) = f(2 + 4) = f(6) = 3(6^2) = 3 \times 36 = 108$.
$gf(1) = g(3(1^2)) = g(3) = 3 + 4 = 7$.
$fg(x) = f(x + 4) = 3(x + 4)^2$.

7) f is a one-to-one function so it has an inverse. The domain of the inverse is the range of the function and vice versa, so the domain of $f^{-1}(x)$ is $x \geq 3$ and the range is $f^{-1}(x) \in \mathbb{R}$.

8) Let $y = f(x)$. Then $y = \sqrt{2x-4}$

$y^2 = 2x - 4$

$y^2 + 4 = 2x$

$x = \frac{y^2+4}{2} = \frac{y^2}{2} + 2$

Writing in terms of x and $f^{-1}(x)$ gives the inverse function as $f^{-1}(x) = \frac{x^2}{2} + 2$, which has domain $x \geq 0$ (as the range of f is $x \geq 0$) and range $f^{-1}(x) \geq 2$.

9) a) b)

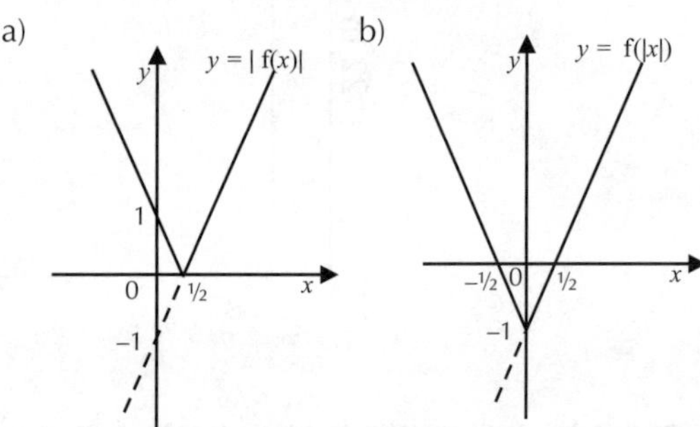

10)

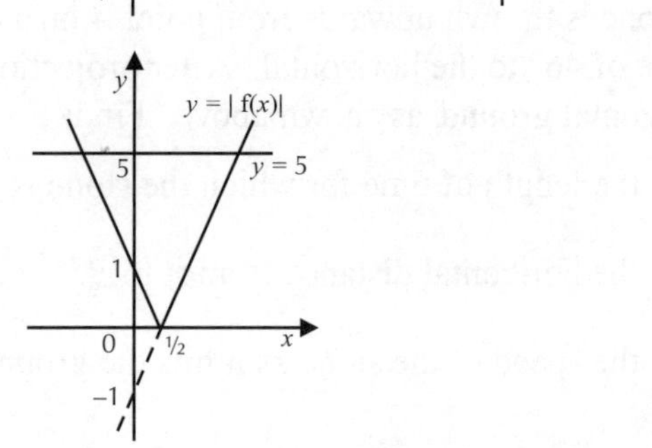

From the graph, $|2x - 1| = 5$ has 2 solutions, one where $2x - 1 = 5$ (so $x = 3$) and one where $-(2x - 1) = 5$ (so $x = -2$).

Answers

11)

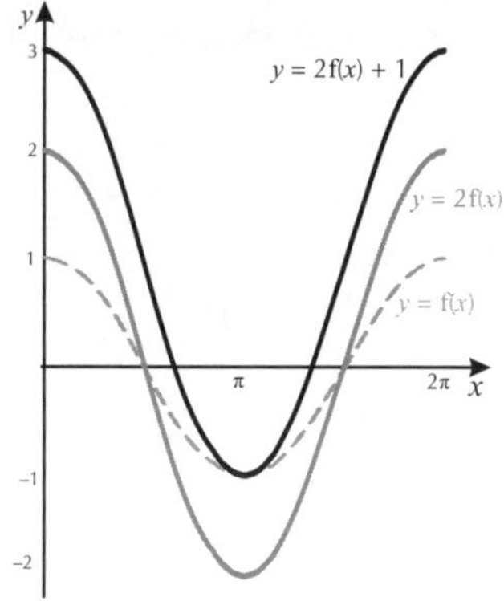

Exam Questions

1 $\frac{2x^2 - 9x - 35}{x^2 - 49} = \frac{(2x+5)(x-7)}{(x+7)(x-7)} = \frac{2x+5}{x+7}$

[3 marks available — 1 mark for factorising the numerator, 1 mark for factorising the denominator and 1 mark for correct answer (after cancelling)]

2 To transform the curve $y = x^3$ into $y = (x - 1)^3$, move it 1 unit ***[1 mark]*** horizontally to the right ***[1 mark]***. To transform this into the curve $y = 2(x - 1)^3$, stretch it vertically ***[1 mark]*** by a scale factor of 2 ***[1 mark]***. Finally, to transform into the curve $y = 2(x - 1)^3 + 4$, the whole curve is moved 4 units ***[1 mark]*** upwards ***[1 mark]***.

3 a) $gf(x) = g(x^2 - 3)$ ***[1 mark]*** $= \frac{1}{x^2 - 3}$ ***[1 mark]***

b) $\frac{1}{x^2 - 3} = \frac{1}{6} \Rightarrow x^2 - 3 = 6 \Rightarrow x^2 = 9 \Rightarrow x = 3, x = -3$

[3 marks available — 1 mark for rearranging to solve equation, 1 mark for each correct solution]

4 First put $x = -6$ into both sides of the identity $x^3 + 15x^2 + 43x - 30 \equiv (Ax^2 + Bx + C)(x + 6) + D$:
$(-6)^3 + 15(-6)^2 + 43(-6) - 30 = D \Rightarrow 36 = D$ ***[1 mark]***.
Now set $x = 0$ to get $-30 = 6C + D$, so $C = -11$ ***[1 mark]***.
Equating the coefficients of x^3 gives $1 = A$. Equating the coefficients of x^2 gives $15 = 6A + B$, so $B = 9$ ***[1 mark]***.
So $x^3 + 15x^2 + 43x - 30 = (x^2 + 9x - 11)(x + 6) + 36$.

You could also do this question by algebraic long division — you just have to use your answer to work out A, B, C and D.

5 a) $fg(6) = f(\sqrt{(3 \times 6) - 2}) = f(\sqrt{16})$ ***[1 mark]***
$= f(4) = 2^4 = 16$ ***[1 mark]***

b) $gf(2) = g(2^2) = g(4)$ ***[1 mark]***
$= \sqrt{(3 \times 4) - 2} = \sqrt{10}$ ***[1 mark]***

c) (i) First, write $y = g(x)$ and rearrange to make x the subject:
$y = \sqrt{3x - 2}$
$\Rightarrow y^2 = 3x - 2$
$\Rightarrow y^2 + 2 = 3x$
$\Rightarrow \frac{y^2 + 2}{3} = x$ ***[1 mark]***
Then replace x with $g^{-1}(x)$ and y with x: $g^{-1}(x) = \frac{x^2 + 2}{3}$ ***[1 mark]***.

(ii) $fg^{-1}(x) = f\left(\frac{x^2 + 2}{3}\right)$ ***[1 mark]***
$= 2^{\frac{x^2 + 2}{3}}$ ***[1 mark]***

6 a) The range of f is $f(x) > 0$ ***[1 mark]***.

b) (i) Let $y = f(x)$. Then $y = \frac{1}{x + 5}$.
Rearrange this to make x the subject:
$y(x + 5) = 1$
$\Rightarrow x + 5 = \frac{1}{y}$ ***[1 mark]***
$\Rightarrow x = \frac{1}{y} - 5$ ***[1 mark]***
Finally, write out in terms of x and $f^{-1}(x)$:
$f^{-1}(x) = \frac{1}{x} - 5$ ***[1 mark]***.

(ii) The domain of the inverse is the same as the range of the function, so $x > 0$ ***[1 mark]***. The range of the inverse is the same as the domain of the function, so $f^{-1}(x) > -5$ ***[1 mark]***.

c)

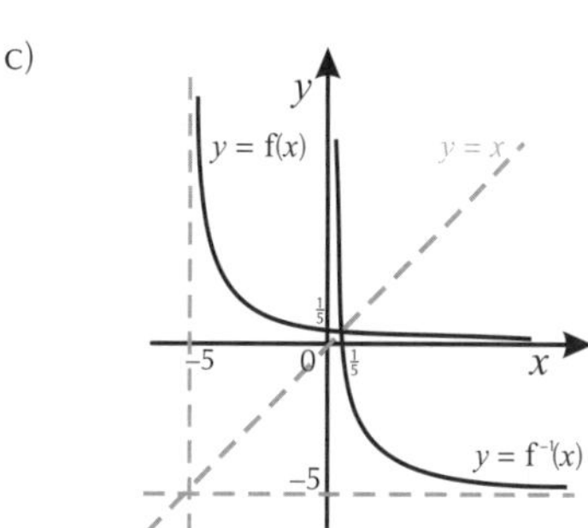

[2 marks available — 1 mark for each correct curve, each with correct intersections and asymptotes as shown]

7 a)

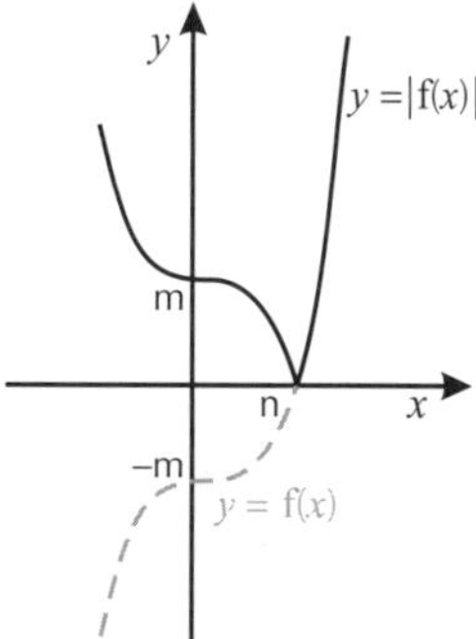

[2 marks available — 1 mark for reflecting in x-axis at x = n, 1 mark for crossing y-axis at y = m]

b)

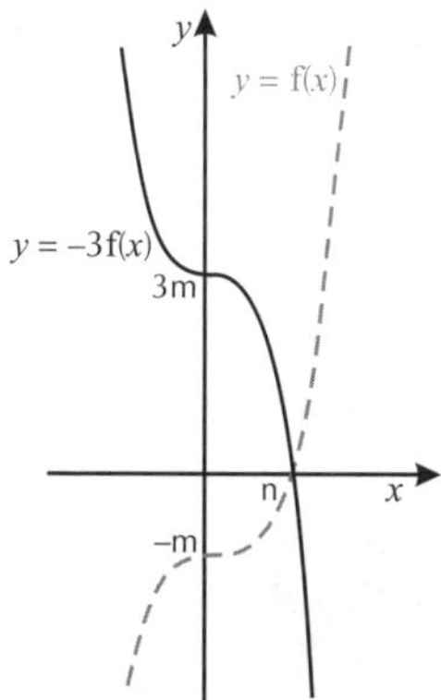

[2 marks available — 1 mark for reflecting in y-axis and 1 mark for crossing y-axis at y = 3m (due to stretch by scale factor 3)]

Answers

c)

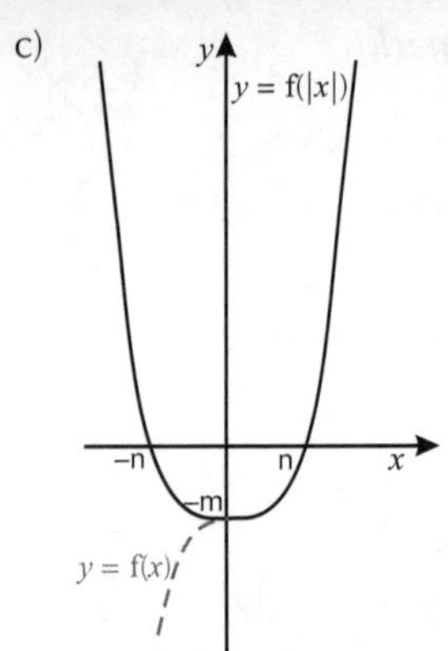

[2 marks available — 1 mark for reflecting in y-axis and 1 mark for crossing the x-axis at –n]

C3 Section 2 — Trigonometry

Warm-up Questions

1) a) $\sin^{-1}\frac{1}{\sqrt{2}} = \frac{\pi}{4}$

b) $\cos^{-1}0 = \frac{\pi}{2}$

c) $\tan^{-1}\sqrt{3} = \frac{\pi}{3}$

2) See p12.

3) a) cosec 30° = 2 (since sin 30° = 0.5)

b) sec 30° = $\frac{2}{\sqrt{3}}$ (since cos 30° = $\frac{\sqrt{3}}{2}$)

c) cot 30° = $\sqrt{3}$ (since tan 30° = $\frac{1}{\sqrt{3}}$)

4) See p13.

5) Divide the whole identity by $\cos^2\theta$ to get:

$\frac{\cos^2\theta}{\cos^2\theta} + \frac{\sin^2\theta}{\cos^2\theta} \equiv \frac{1}{\cos^2\theta}$

$\Rightarrow 1 + \tan^2\theta \equiv \sec^2\theta$

(as sin/cos ≡ tan and 1/cos ≡ sec)

6) Using the identities $\text{cosec}^2\theta \equiv 1 + \cot^2\theta$ and $\sin^2\theta + \cos^2\theta \equiv 1$, the LHS becomes:

$(\text{cosec}^2\theta - 1) + (1 - \cos^2\theta) \equiv \text{cosec}^2\theta - \cos^2\theta$, which is the same as the RHS.

7) $\cos 2\theta \equiv \cos^2\theta - \sin^2\theta$

$\cos 2\theta \equiv 2\cos^2\theta - 1$

$\cos 2\theta \equiv 1 - 2\sin^2\theta$

8) $\sin 2\theta = -\sqrt{3}\sin\theta \Rightarrow \sin 2\theta + \sqrt{3}\sin\theta = 0$

$2\sin\theta\cos\theta + \sqrt{3}\sin\theta = 0$

$\sin\theta(2\cos\theta + \sqrt{3}) = 0$

So either sin θ = 0, so θ = 0°, 180°, 360° or

$2\cos\theta + \sqrt{3} = 0 \Rightarrow \cos\theta = -\frac{\sqrt{3}}{2}$

so θ = 150° or 210°. The set of values for θ is 0°, 150°, 180°, 210°, 360°.

If you don't know where the 180°, 360°, 210° etc. came from, you need to go back over your C2 notes...

9) $\frac{\pi}{12} = \frac{\pi}{3} - \frac{\pi}{4}$, so use the addition formula for cos(*A* – *B*):

$\cos\frac{\pi}{12} = \cos\left(\frac{\pi}{3} - \frac{\pi}{4}\right) = \cos\frac{\pi}{3}\cos\frac{\pi}{4} + \sin\frac{\pi}{3}\sin\frac{\pi}{4}$

As $\cos\frac{\pi}{3} = \frac{1}{2}$, $\cos\frac{\pi}{4} = \frac{1}{\sqrt{2}}$, $\sin\frac{\pi}{3} = \frac{\sqrt{3}}{2}$ and $\sin\frac{\pi}{4} = \frac{1}{\sqrt{2}}$, putting these values into the equation gives:

$\cos\frac{\pi}{3}\cos\frac{\pi}{4} + \sin\frac{\pi}{3}\sin\frac{\pi}{4} = \left(\frac{1}{2}\cdot\frac{1}{\sqrt{2}}\right) + \left(\frac{\sqrt{3}}{2}\cdot\frac{1}{\sqrt{2}}\right)$

$= \frac{1}{2\sqrt{2}} + \frac{\sqrt{3}}{2\sqrt{2}} = \frac{1+\sqrt{3}}{2\sqrt{2}} = \frac{\sqrt{2}(1+\sqrt{3})}{4} = \frac{\sqrt{2}+\sqrt{6}}{4}$

You could also have used $\frac{\pi}{12} = \frac{\pi}{4} - \frac{\pi}{6}$ in your answer.

10) sin(*A* + *B*) ≡ sin *A* cos *B* + cos *A* sin *B*.

As $\sin A = \frac{4}{5}$, $\cos A = \frac{3}{5}$ (from the right-angled triangle with sides of length 3, 4 and 5) and as $\sin B = \frac{7}{25}$, $\cos B = \frac{24}{25}$ (from the right-angled triangle with sides of length 7, 24 and 25). Putting these values into the equation gives:

$\sin A\cos B + \cos A\sin B = \left(\frac{4}{5}\cdot\frac{24}{25}\right) + \left(\frac{3}{5}\cdot\frac{7}{25}\right)$

$= \frac{96}{125} + \frac{21}{125} = \frac{117}{125}$ (= 0.936)

11) $a\cos\theta + b\sin\theta \equiv R\cos(\theta - \alpha)$ or

$b\sin\theta + a\cos\theta \equiv R\sin(\theta + \alpha)$

12) $5\sin\theta - 6\cos\theta \equiv R\sin(\theta - \alpha)$

$\equiv R\sin\theta\cos\alpha - R\cos\theta\sin\alpha$ (using the addition rule for sin).

Equating coefficients of sin θ and cos θ gives:

1. $R\cos\alpha = 5$ and 2. $R\sin\alpha = 6$.

Dividing 2. by 1. to find α: $\frac{R\sin\alpha}{R\cos\alpha} = \tan\alpha$, so $\frac{6}{5} = \tan\alpha$

Solving this gives α = 50.19°.

To find *R*, square equations 1. and 2., then square root:

$R = \sqrt{5^2 + 6^2} = \sqrt{25 + 36} = \sqrt{61}$, so

$5\sin\theta - 6\cos\theta \equiv \sqrt{61}\sin(\theta - 50.19°)$.

13) Use the sin addition formulas:

sin(*x* + *y*) ≡ sin *x* cos *y* + cos *x* sin *y*

sin(*x* – *y*) ≡ sin *x* cos *y* – cos *x* sin *y*

Take the second away from the first:

sin(*x* + *y*) – sin(*x* – *y*) ≡ 2 cos *x* sin *y*.

Let *A* = *x* + *y* and *B* = *x* – *y*, so that *x* = ½(*A* + *B*) and *y* = ½(*A* – *B*). Then

$\sin A - \sin B \equiv 2\cos\left(\frac{A+B}{2}\right)\sin\left(\frac{A-B}{2}\right)$.

Hint: to get the formulas for x and y in terms of A and B, you need to treat A = x + y and B = x – y as a pair of simultaneous equations.

14) Start by putting the LHS over a common denominator:

$\frac{\cos\theta}{\sin\theta} + \frac{\sin\theta}{\cos\theta} \equiv \frac{\cos\theta\cos\theta}{\sin\theta\cos\theta} + \frac{\sin\theta\sin\theta}{\sin\theta\cos\theta}$

$\equiv \frac{\cos^2\theta + \sin^2\theta}{\sin\theta\cos\theta} \equiv \frac{1}{\sin\theta\cos\theta}$

(using the identity $\sin^2\theta + \cos^2\theta \equiv 1$).

Now, $\sin 2\theta \equiv 2\sin\theta\cos\theta$, so $\sin\theta\cos\theta$ = ½ $\sin 2\theta$.

So $\frac{1}{\sin\theta\cos\theta} \equiv \frac{1}{½\sin 2\theta} \equiv 2\,\text{cosec}\,2\theta$, which is the same as the RHS.

Answers

Exam Questions

1 a)

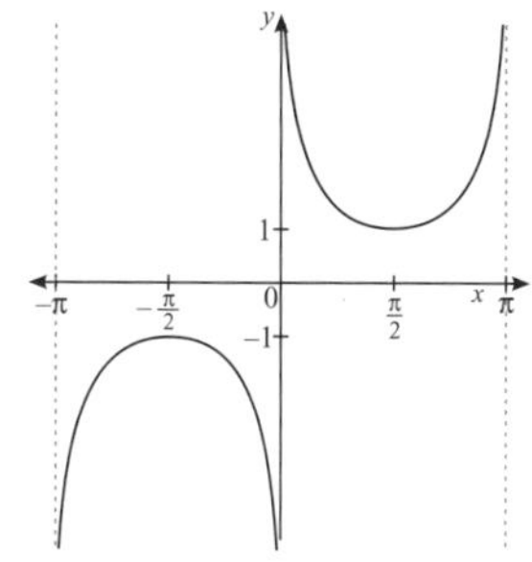

[3 marks available — 1 mark for n-shaped curve in third quadrant and u-shaped curve in first quadrant, 1 mark for asymptotes at 0 and ±π and 1 mark for max/min points of the curves at –1 and 1]

b) If $\operatorname{cosec} x = \frac{5}{4} \Rightarrow \frac{1}{\sin x} = \frac{5}{4} \Rightarrow \sin x = \frac{4}{5}$ ***[1 mark]***.
Solving this for x gives $x = 0.927, 2.21$
[1 mark for each solution, lose a mark if answers aren't given to 3 s.f.].

The second solution can be found by sketching y = sin x:

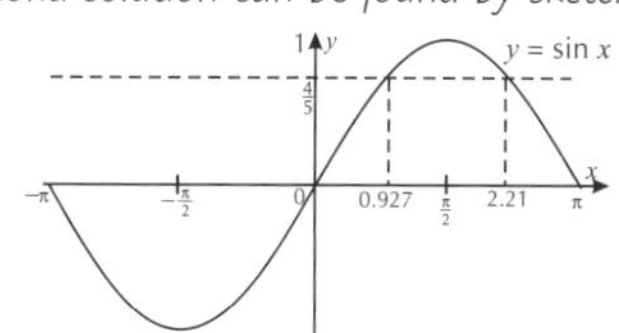

You can see that there are two solutions, one at 0.927, and the other at π – 0.927 = 2.21.

c) $\operatorname{cosec} x = 3\sec x \Rightarrow \frac{1}{\sin x} = \frac{3}{\cos x} \Rightarrow \frac{\cos x}{\sin x} = 3$

$\Rightarrow \frac{1}{\tan x} = 3$ so $\tan x = \frac{1}{3}$

Solving for x gives $x = -2.82, 0.322$, ***[1 mark for appropriate rearranging, 1 mark for each solution.]***.

Again, you need to sketch a graph to find the second solution:

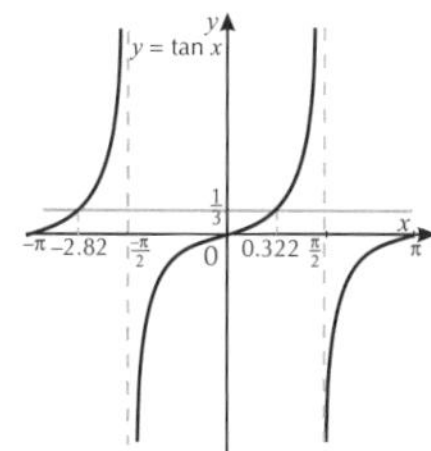

You can see that there are two solutions in the given range, one at 0.322 (this is the one you get from your calculator) and one at –π + 0.322 = –2.82.

2 a) $9\sin\theta + 12\cos\theta \equiv R\sin(\theta + \alpha)$. Using the sin addition formula, $9\sin\theta + 12\cos\theta \equiv R\sin\theta\cos\alpha + R\cos\theta\sin\alpha$.
Equating coefficients of $\sin\theta$ and $\cos\theta$ gives:
$R\cos\alpha = 9$ and $R\sin\alpha = 12$ ***[1 mark]***.

$\frac{R\sin\alpha}{R\cos\alpha} = \tan\alpha$, so $\tan\alpha = \frac{12}{9} = \frac{4}{3}$

Solving this gives $\alpha = 0.927$ ***[1 mark — no other solutions in given range]***.

$R = \sqrt{9^2 + 12^2} = \sqrt{81 + 144} = \sqrt{225} = 15$ ***[1 mark]***,
so $9\sin\theta + 12\cos\theta = 15\sin(\theta + 0.927)$.

b) If $9\sin\theta + 12\cos\theta = 3$, then from part a),
$15\sin(\theta + 0.927) = 3$, so $\sin(\theta + 0.927) = 0.2$. The range for θ is $0 \le \theta \le 2\pi$, which becomes $0.927 \le \theta + 0.927 \le 7.210$.
Solving the equation gives $(\theta + 0.927) = 0.201$ ***[1 mark]***.
As this is outside the range, use a sketch to find values that are in the range:

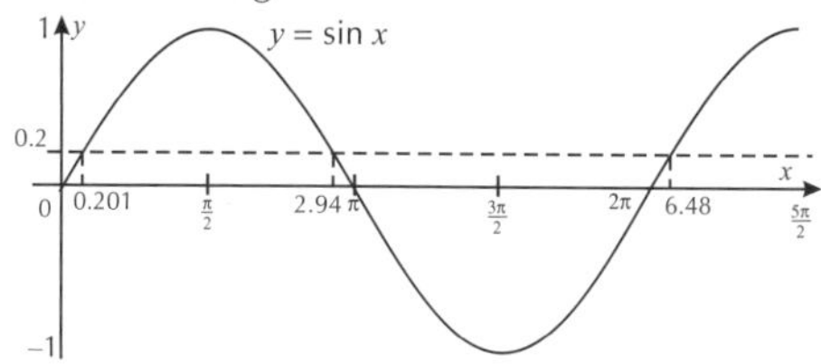

From the graph, it is clear that there are solutions at $\pi - 0.201 = 2.94$ and at $2\pi + 0.201 = 6.48$, so
$(\theta + 0.927) = 2.940, 6.48$ ***[1 mark for each value]***,
so $\theta = 2.01, 5.56$ ***[1 mark for each solution]***.

Be careful with the range — if you hadn't extended the range to 2π + 0.927, you would have missed one of the solutions.

3 $\sin 3x \equiv \sin(2x + x) \equiv \sin 2x\cos x + \cos 2x\sin x$ ***[1 mark]***
$\equiv (2\sin x\cos x)\cos x + (1 - 2\sin^2 x)\sin x$ ***[1 mark]***
$\equiv 2\sin x\cos^2 x + \sin x - 2\sin^3 x$
$\equiv 2\sin x(1 - \sin^2 x) + \sin x - 2\sin^3 x$ ***[1 mark]***
$\equiv 2\sin x - 2\sin^3 x + \sin x - 2\sin^3 x$
$\equiv 3\sin x - 4\sin^3 x$ ***[1 mark]***

4 a) The start and end points of the cos curve (with restricted domain) are (0, 1) and (π, –1), so the coordinates of the start point of arccos (point A) are (–1, π) ***[1 mark]*** and the coordinates of the end point (point B) are (1, 0) ***[1 mark]***.

b) $y = \arccos x$, that is, $y = \cos^{-1}x$, so $x = \cos y$ ***[1 mark]***.

c) $\arccos x = 2$, so $x = \cos 2$ ***[1 mark]*** $\Rightarrow x = -0.416$ ***[1 mark]***.

5 a) $\frac{2\sin x}{1 - \cos x} - \frac{2\cos x}{\sin x} \equiv \frac{2\sin^2 x - 2\cos x + 2\cos^2 x}{\sin x(1 - \cos x)}$ ***[1 mark]***

$\equiv \frac{2 - 2\cos x}{\sin x(1 - \cos x)}$ ***[1 mark]***

$\equiv \frac{2(1 - \cos x)}{\sin x(1 - \cos x)}$ ***[1 mark]***

$\equiv \frac{2}{\sin x} \equiv 2\operatorname{cosec} x$ ***[1 mark]***

b) $2\operatorname{cosec} x = 4$

$\operatorname{cosec} x = 2$ OR $\sin x = \frac{1}{2}$ ***[1 mark]***

$x = \frac{\pi}{6}$ ***[1 mark]***, $x = \frac{5\pi}{6}$ ***[1 mark]***.

6 a) $5\cos\theta + 12\sin\theta \equiv R\cos(\theta - \alpha)$. Using the cos addition formula, $5\cos\theta + 12\sin\theta \equiv R\cos\theta\cos\alpha + R\sin\theta\sin\alpha$.
Equating coefficients gives:
$R\cos\alpha = 5$ and $R\sin\alpha = 12$ ***[1 mark]***.

$\frac{R\sin\alpha}{R\cos\alpha} = \tan\alpha$, so $\tan\alpha = \frac{12}{5}$ ***[1 mark]***.

Solving this gives $\alpha = 67.38°$ ***[1 mark]***.

$R = \sqrt{5^2 + 12^2} = \sqrt{25 + 144} = \sqrt{169} = 13$ ***[1 mark]***,
so $5\cos\theta + 12\sin\theta = 13\cos(\theta - 67.38°)$.

Answers

b) From part (a), if $5\cos\theta + 12\sin\theta = 2$, that means $13\cos(\theta - 67.38^\circ) = 2$, so $\cos(\theta - 67.38^\circ) = \frac{2}{13}$ ***[1 mark]***. The range for θ is $0 \leq \theta \leq 360^\circ$, which becomes $-67.38^\circ \leq \theta - 67.38^\circ \leq 292.62^\circ$ ***[1 mark]***. Solving the equation gives $\theta - 67.38 = 81.15, 278.85$ ***[1 mark]***, so $\theta = 148.53^\circ, 346.23^\circ$ ***[1 mark for each value]***.

Look at the cos graph to get the second solution of $\theta - 67.38^\circ$:

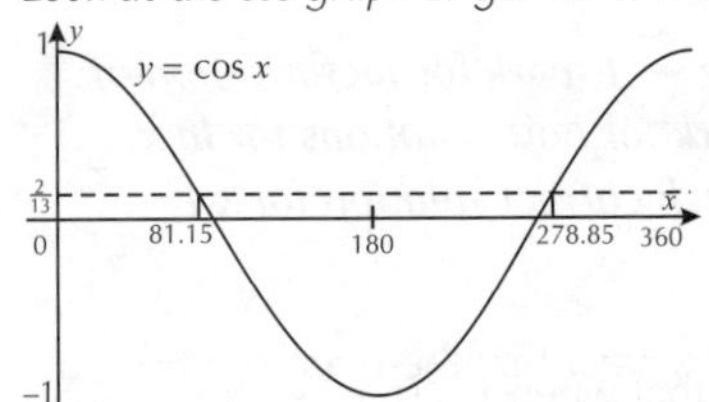

There are two solutions, one at 81.15°, and the other at 360 – 81.15 = 278.85°.

c) The minimum points of the cos curve have a value of –1, so as $5\cos\theta + 12\sin\theta = 13\cos(\theta - 67.38^\circ)$, the minimum value of $5\cos\theta + 12\sin\theta$ is –13 ***[1 mark]***. Hence the minimum value of $(5\cos\theta + 12\sin\theta)^3$ is $(-13)^3 = -2197$ ***[1 mark]***.

7 a) (i) Rearrange the identity $\sec^2\theta \equiv 1 + \tan^2\theta$ to get $\sec^2\theta - 1 \equiv \tan^2\theta$, then replace $\tan^2\theta$ in the equation:

$3\tan^2\theta - 2\sec\theta = 5$

$3(\sec^2\theta - 1) - 2\sec\theta - 5 = 0$ ***[1 mark]***

$3\sec^2\theta - 3 - 2\sec\theta - 5 = 0$

so $3\sec^2\theta - 2\sec\theta - 8 = 0$ ***[1 mark]***

(ii) To factorise this, let $y = \sec\theta$, so the equation becomes $3y^2 - 2y - 8 = 0$, so $(3y + 4)(y - 2) = 0$ ***[1 mark]***. Solving for y gives $y = -\frac{4}{3}$ or $y = 2$. As $y = \sec\theta$, this means that $\sec\theta = -\frac{4}{3}$ or $\sec\theta = 2$ ***[1 mark]***. $\sec\theta = \frac{1}{\cos\theta}$, so $\cos\theta = -\frac{3}{4}$ or $\cos\theta = \frac{1}{2}$ ***[1 mark]***.

b) Let $\theta = 2x$. From above, we know that the solutions to $3\tan^2\theta - 2\sec\theta = 5$ satisfy $\cos\theta = -\frac{3}{4}$ or $\cos\theta = \frac{1}{2}$. The range for x is $0 \leq x \leq 180^\circ$, so as $\theta = 2x$, the range for θ is $0 \leq \theta \leq 360^\circ$ ***[1 mark]***. Solving these equations for θ gives $\theta = 138.59^\circ, 221.41^\circ$ and $\theta = 60^\circ, 300^\circ$ ***[1 mark]***. So, as $\theta = 2x$, $x = \frac{1}{2}\theta$, so $x = 69.30^\circ, 110.70^\circ, 30^\circ, 150^\circ$ ***[1 mark]***.

Once you have the values 60° and 138.59°, you can sketch the graph to find the other values:

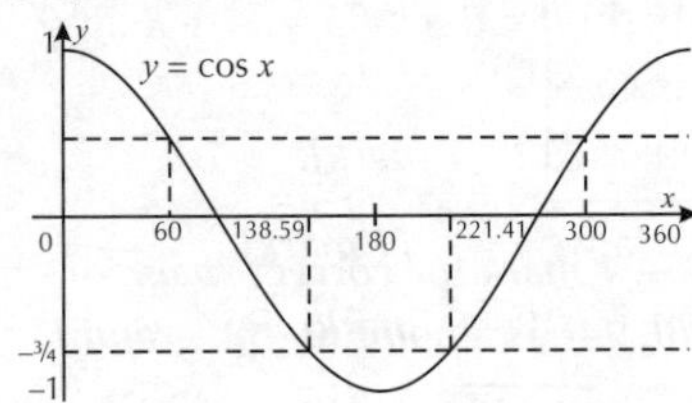

There is a solution at 360 – 60 = 300°, and another at 360 – 138.59 = 221.41°. Don't be fooled by the 2x in this question — you don't need to use the double angle formulas for this one.

C3 Section 3 — Exponentials and Logs

Warm-up Questions

1) a)-d)

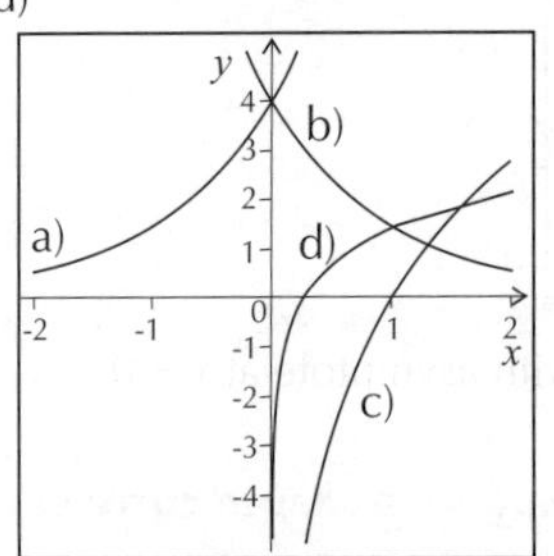

2) a) $e^{2x} = 6 \Rightarrow 2x = \ln 6 \Rightarrow x = \ln 6 \div 2 = 0.8959$ to 4 d.p.

b) $\ln(x + 3) = 0.75 \Rightarrow x + 3 = e^{0.75} \Rightarrow x = e^{0.75} - 3 = -0.8830$ to 4 d.p.

c) $3e^{-4x+1} = 5 \Rightarrow e^{-4x+1} = \frac{5}{3} \Rightarrow e^{4x-1} = \frac{3}{5} \Rightarrow 4x - 1 = \ln\frac{3}{5}$
$\Rightarrow x = (\ln\frac{3}{5} + 1) \div 4 = 0.1223$ to 4 d.p.

d) $\ln x + \ln 5 = \ln 4 \Rightarrow \ln(5x) = \ln 4 \Rightarrow 5x = 4$
$\Rightarrow x = 0.8000$ to 4 d.p.

3) a) $\ln(2x - 7) + \ln 4 = -3 \Rightarrow \ln(4(2x - 7)) = -3$
$\Rightarrow 8x - 28 = e^{-3} \Rightarrow x = \frac{e^{-3} + 28}{8}$ or $\frac{1}{8e^3} + \frac{7}{2}$.

b) $2e^{2x} + e^x = 3$, so if $y = e^x$, $2y^2 + y - 3 = 0$, which will factorise to: $(2y + 3)(y - 1) = 0$, so $e^x = -1.5$ (not possible), and $e^x = 1$, so $x = 0$ is the only solution.

4) a) $y = 2 - e^{x+1}$

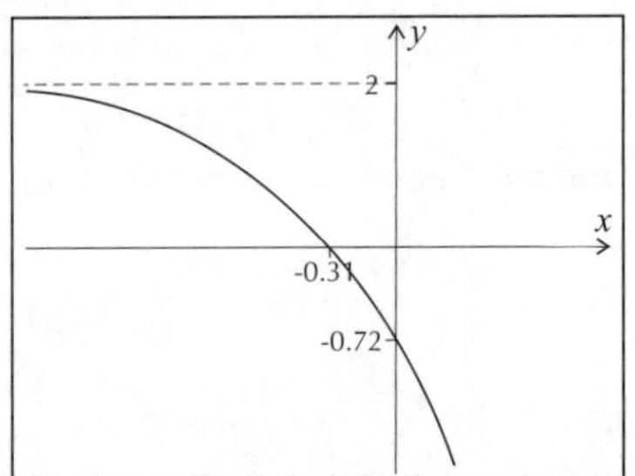

Goes through (0, –0.72) and (–0.31, 0), with asymptote at $y = 2$.

b) $y = 5e^{0.5x} + 5$

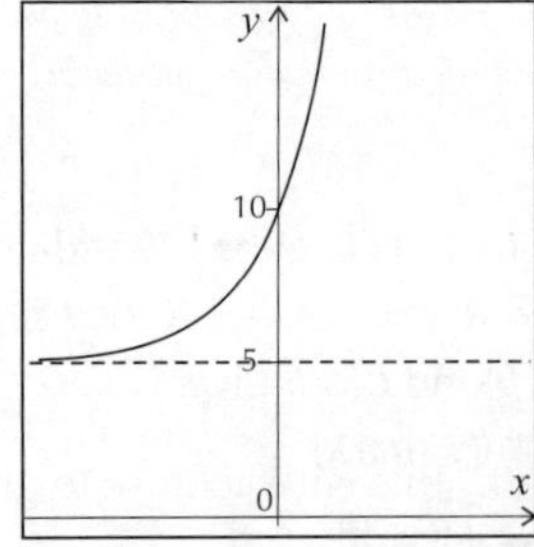

Goes through (0, 10), with asymptote at $y = 5$.

c) $y = \ln(2x) + 1$

Answers

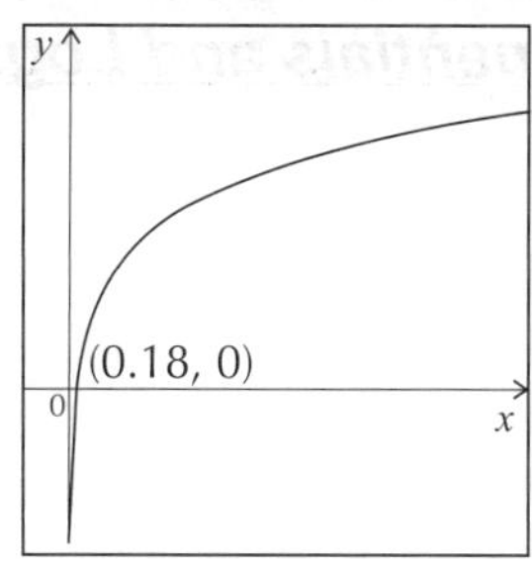

Goes through (0.18, 0), with asymptote at $x = 0$.

d) $y = \ln (x + 5)$

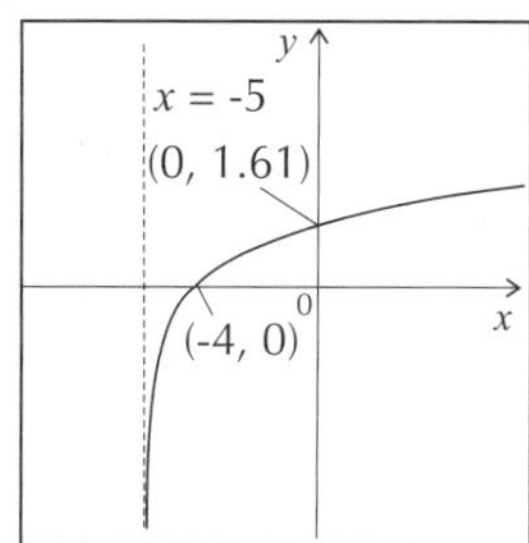

Goes through (0, 1.61) and (−4, 0), with asymptote at $x = -5$.

You can use your 'graph transformation' skills to work out what they'll look like, e.g. d) is just y = ln x shifted 5 to the left.

5) a) $V = 7500e^{-0.2t}$, so when $t = 0$, $V = 7500 \times e^0 = £7500$.

b) $V = 7500 \times e^{(-0.2 \times 10)} = £1015$ to the nearest £.

c) When $V = 500$, $500 = 7500e^{-0.2t}$

$\Rightarrow e^{-0.2t} = \frac{500}{7500} \Rightarrow e^{0.2t} = \frac{7500}{500} \Rightarrow 0.2t = \ln \frac{7500}{500} = 2.7080...$

$\Rightarrow t = 2.7080... \div 0.2 = 13.5$ years.

So it will be 14 years old before the value falls below £500.

d)

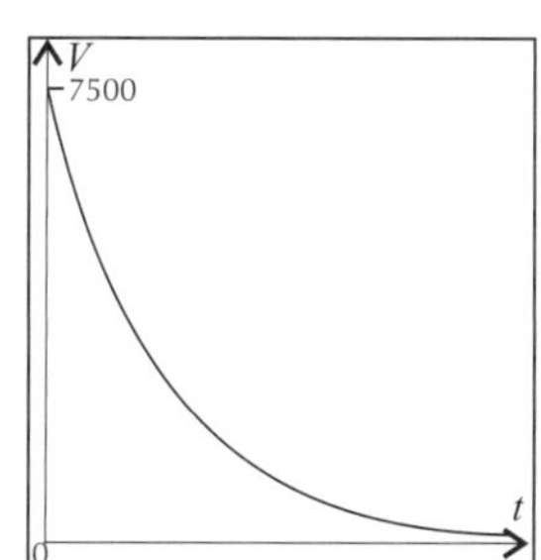

Goes through (0, 7500) with an asymptote at $y = 0$.

Exam Questions

1 a) $6e^x = 3 \Rightarrow e^x = 0.5$ ***[1 mark]*** $\Rightarrow x = \ln 0.5$ ***[1 mark]***.

b) $e^{2x} - 8e^x + 7 = 0$.

(This looks like a quadratic, so use $y = e^x$...)

If $y = e^x$, then $y^2 - 8y + 7 = 0$. This will factorise to give:
$(y - 7)(y - 1) = 0 \Rightarrow y = 7$ and $y = 1$.
So $e^x = 7 \Rightarrow x = \ln 7$, and $e^x = 1 \Rightarrow x = \ln 1 = 0$.

[4 marks available — 1 mark for factorisation of a quadratic, 1 mark for both solutions for e^x, and 1 mark for each correct solution for x.]

c) $4 \ln x = 3 \Rightarrow \ln x = 0.75$ ***[1 mark]*** $\Rightarrow x = e^{0.75}$ ***[1 mark]***.

d) $\ln x + \frac{24}{\ln x} = 10$

(You need to get rid of that fraction, so multiply through by ln x...)

$(\ln x)^2 + 24 = 10 \ln x$
$\Rightarrow (\ln x)^2 - 10 \ln x + 24 = 0$

(...which looks like a quadratic, so use y = ln x...)

$y^2 - 10y + 24 = 0 \Rightarrow (y - 6)(y - 4) = 0$
$\Rightarrow y = 6$ or $y = 4$.
So $\ln x = 6 \Rightarrow x = e^6$, or $\ln x = 4 \Rightarrow x = e^4$.

[4 marks available — 1 mark for factorisation of a quadratic, 1 mark for both solutions for ln x, and 1 mark for each correct solution for x.]

2 $y = e^{ax} + b$

The sketch shows that when $x = 0$, $y = -6$, so:
$-6 = e^0 + b$ ***[1 mark]***
$-6 = 1 + b \Rightarrow b = -7$ ***[1 mark]***.

The sketch also shows that when $y = 0$, $x = \frac{1}{4} \ln 7$, so:
$0 = e^{(\frac{a}{4} \ln 7)} - 7$ ***[1 mark]***
$\Rightarrow e^{(\frac{a}{4} \ln 7)} = 7$
$\Rightarrow \frac{a}{4} \ln 7 = \ln 7 \Rightarrow \frac{a}{4} = 1 \Rightarrow a = 4$ ***[1 mark]***.
The asymptote occurs as $x \to -\infty$, so $e^{4x} \to 0$,
and since $y = e^{4x} - 7$, $y \to -7$.
So the equation of the asymptote is $y = -7$ ***[1 mark]***.

3 a) When $t = 0$ (i.e. when the mink were introduced to the habitat) $M = 74 \times e^0 = 74$, so there were 74 mink originally ***[1 mark]***.

b) After 3 years, $M = 74 \times e^{0.6 \times 3}$ ***[1 mark]*** = 447 mink ***[1 mark]***.

You can't round up here as there are only 447 whole mink.

c) For $M = 10\,000$:
$10\,000 = 74e^{0.6t}$
$\Rightarrow e^{0.6t} = 10\,000 \div 74 = 135.1351$
$\Rightarrow 0.6t = \ln 135.1351 = 4.9063$ ***[1 mark]***
$\Rightarrow t = 4.9063 \div 0.6 = 8.2$ years to reach 10 000, so it would take 9 complete years for the population to exceed 10 000 ***[1 mark]***.

d)

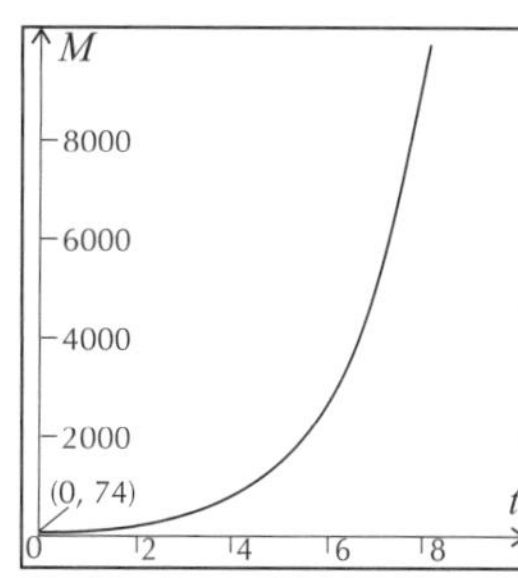

[2 marks available — 1 mark for correct shape of graph, 1 mark for (0, 74) as a point on the graph.]

4 a) $y = \ln (4x - 3)$, and $x = a$ when $y = 1$.
$1 = \ln (4a - 3) \Rightarrow e^1 = 4a - 3$ ***[1 mark]***
$\Rightarrow a = (e^1 + 3) \div 4 = 1.43$ to 2 d.p. ***[1 mark]***.

b) The curve can only exist when $4x - 3 > 0$ ***[1 mark]***
so $x > 3 \div 4$, $x > 0.75$. If $x > b$, then $b = 0.75$ ***[1 mark]***.

Answers

c)

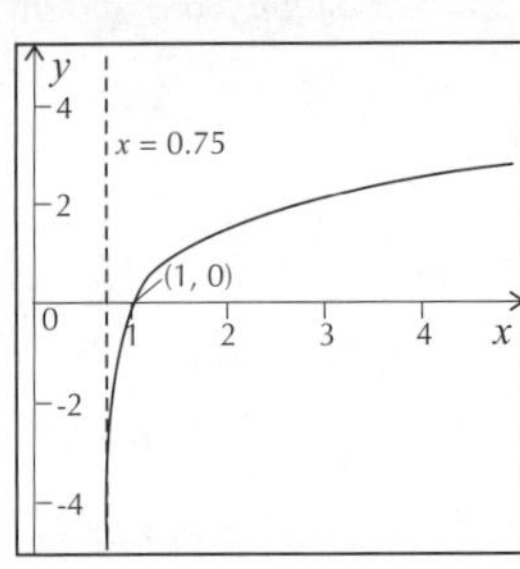

When $y = 0$, $4x - 3 = e^0 = 1$, so $x = 1$.
As $x \to \infty$, $y \to \infty$ gradually.
From (b), there will be an asymptote at $x = 0.75$.

[2 marks available — 1 mark for correct shape including asymptote at x = 0.75, 1 mark for (1, 0) as a point on the graph.]

5 a) $2e^x + 18e^{-x} = 20$

(Multiply through by e^x to remove the e^{-x}, since $e^x \times e^{-x} = 1$)

$2e^{2x} + 18 = 20e^x$

$\Rightarrow 2e^{2x} - 20e^x + 18 = 0 \Rightarrow e^{2x} - 10e^x + 9 = 0$

(This now looks like a quadratic equation, so use $y = e^x$ to simplify...)

$y^2 - 10y + 9 = 0$

$\Rightarrow (y - 1)(y - 9) = 0 \Rightarrow y = 1$ or $y = 9$.

So $e^x = 1 \Rightarrow x = 0$
or $e^x = 9 \Rightarrow x = \ln 9$.

[4 marks available — 1 mark for factorisation of a quadratic, 1 mark for both solutions for e^x, and 1 mark for each correct exact solution for x.]

b) $2 \ln x - \ln 3 = \ln 12$

$\Rightarrow 2 \ln x = \ln 12 + \ln 3$

(Use the log laws to simplify at this point...)

$\Rightarrow \ln x^2 = \ln 36$ ***[1 mark]***

$\Rightarrow x^2 = 36$ ***[1 mark]***

$\Rightarrow x = 6$ ***[1 mark]***

(x must be positive as ln (–6) does not exist.)

6 a) B is the value of A when $t = 0$.
From the table, $B = 50$ ***[1 mark]***.

b) Substitute $t = 5$ and $A = 42$ into $A = 50e^{-kt}$:

$42 = 50e^{-5k} \Rightarrow e^{-5k} = \frac{42}{50} \Rightarrow e^{5k} = \frac{50}{42}$ ***[1 mark]***

$\Rightarrow 5k = \ln\left(\frac{50}{42}\right) = 0.17435$

$\Rightarrow k = 0.17435 \div 5 = 0.0349$ to 3 s.f. ***[1 mark]***.

c) $A = 50e^{-0.0349t}$ (using values from (a) and (b)),
so when $t = 10$, $A = 50 \times e^{-0.0349 \times 10}$ ***[1 mark]***
$= 35$ to the nearest whole ***[1 mark]***.

d) The half-life will be the value of t when A reaches half of the original value of 50, i.e. when $A = 25$.

$25 = 50e^{-0.0349t}$

$\Rightarrow \frac{25}{50} = e^{-0.0349t} \Rightarrow \frac{50}{25} = e^{0.0349t} \Rightarrow e^{0.0349t} = 2$ ***[1 mark]***.

$0.0349t = \ln 2$ ***[1 mark]***

$\Rightarrow t = \ln 2 \div 0.0349 = 20$ days to the nearest day ***[1 mark]***.

C3 Section 4 — Differentiation

Warm-up Questions

1) a) $y = u^{\frac{1}{2}} \Rightarrow \frac{dy}{du} = \frac{1}{2}u^{-\frac{1}{2}} = \frac{1}{2\sqrt{u}} = \frac{1}{2\sqrt{x^3 + 2x^2}}$

$u = x^3 + 2x^2 \Rightarrow \frac{du}{dx} = 3x^2 + 4x$

$\Rightarrow \frac{dy}{dx} = \frac{3x^2 + 4x}{2\sqrt{x^3 + 2x^2}}$.

b) $y = u^{-\frac{1}{2}} \Rightarrow \frac{dy}{du} = -\frac{1}{2}u^{-\frac{3}{2}} = -\frac{1}{2(\sqrt{u})^3} = -\frac{1}{2(\sqrt{x^3 + 2x^2})^3}$

$u = x^3 + 2x^2 \Rightarrow \frac{du}{dx} = 3x^2 + 4x$

$\Rightarrow \frac{dy}{dx} = -\frac{3x^2 + 4x}{2(\sqrt{x^3 + 2x^2})^3}$.

c) $y = e^u \Rightarrow \frac{dy}{du} = e^u = e^{5x^2}$.

$u = 5x^2 \Rightarrow \frac{du}{dx} = 10x$

$\Rightarrow \frac{dy}{dx} = 10xe^{5x^2}$.

d) $y = \ln u \Rightarrow \frac{dy}{du} = \frac{1}{u} = \frac{1}{(6 - x^2)}$

$u = 6 - x^2 \Rightarrow \frac{du}{dx} = -2x$

$\Rightarrow \frac{dy}{dx} = -\frac{2x}{(6 - x^2)}$.

2) a) $x = 2e^y \Rightarrow \frac{dx}{dy} = 2e^y \Rightarrow \frac{dy}{dx} = \frac{1}{2e^y}$.

b) $x = \ln u$ where $u = 2y + 3$

$\frac{dx}{du} = \frac{1}{u} = \frac{1}{2y + 3}$ and $\frac{du}{dy} = 2 \Rightarrow \frac{dx}{dy} = \frac{2}{2y + 3}$

$\Rightarrow \frac{dy}{dx} = \frac{2y + 3}{2} = y + 1.5$.

3) a) For $f(x) = y = \sin^2 (x + 2)$, use the chain rule twice:

$y = u^2$, where $u = \sin (x + 2)$

$\frac{dy}{du} = 2u = 2 \sin (x + 2)$ and $\frac{du}{dx} = \cos (x + 2) \cdot 1$ (by chain rule)

$\Rightarrow \frac{dy}{dx} = f'(x) = 2 \sin (x + 2) \cos (x + 2)$ $[= \sin (2x + 4)]$.

b) $f(x) = y = 2 \cos 3x$:

$y = 2 \cos u$, where $u = 3x$

$\frac{dy}{du} = -2 \sin u = -2 \sin 3x$ and $\frac{du}{dx} = 3$

$\Rightarrow \frac{dy}{dx} = f'(x) = -6 \sin 3x$.

c) $f(x) = y = \sqrt{\tan x} = (\tan x)^{\frac{1}{2}}$:

$y = u^{\frac{1}{2}}$, where $u = \tan x$

$\frac{dy}{du} = \frac{1}{2}u^{-\frac{1}{2}} = \frac{1}{2\sqrt{u}} = \frac{1}{2\sqrt{\tan x}}$ and $\frac{du}{dx} = \sec^2 x$

$\Rightarrow \frac{dy}{dx} = f'(x) = \frac{\sec^2 x}{2\sqrt{\tan x}}$.

4) a) For $y = e^{2x}(x^2 - 3)$, use the product rule:

$u = e^{2x} \Rightarrow \frac{du}{dx} = 2e^{2x}$ (from the chain rule),

$v = x^2 - 3 \Rightarrow \frac{dv}{dx} = 2x$.

$\frac{dy}{dx} = u\frac{dv}{dx} + v\frac{du}{dx} = 2xe^{2x} + 2e^{2x}(x^2 - 3) = 2e^{2x}(x^2 + x - 3)$.

When $x = 0$, $\frac{dy}{dx} = 2e^0(0 + 0 - 3) = 2 \times 1 \times -3 = -6$.

b) For $y = \ln x \sin x$, use the product rule:

$u = \ln x \Rightarrow \frac{du}{dx} = \frac{1}{x}$,

$v = \sin x \Rightarrow \frac{dv}{dx} = \cos x$.

$\frac{dy}{dx} = u\frac{dv}{dx} + v\frac{du}{dx} = \ln x \cos x + \frac{\sin x}{x}$.

When $x = 1$, $\frac{dy}{dx} = \ln 1 \cos 1 + \frac{\sin 1}{1} = 0 + \sin 1$
$= 0.841$ (to 3 s.f.).

Answers

5) For $y = \frac{6x^2+3}{4x^2-1}$, use the quotient rule:

$u = 6x^2 + 3 \Rightarrow \frac{du}{dx} = 12x,$

$v = 4x^2 - 1 \Rightarrow \frac{dv}{dx} = 8x.$

$$\frac{dy}{dx} = \frac{v\frac{du}{dx} - u\frac{dv}{dx}}{v^2} = \frac{12x(4x^2-1) - 8x(6x^2+3)}{(4x^2-1)^2}.$$

At (1, 3), $x = 1$ and so gradient =

$$\frac{dy}{dx} = \frac{12(4-1) - 8(6+3)}{(4-1)^2} = \frac{36-72}{9} = -4.$$

Equation of a straight line is:

$y - y_1 = m(x - x_1)$, where m is the gradient.

So the equation of the tangent at (1, 3) is:

$y - 3 = -4(x - 1) \Rightarrow y = -4x + 7$ (or equivalent).

6) $y = \text{cosec}\,(3x - 2)$, so use chain rule:

$y = \text{cosec}\, u$ where $u = 3x - 2$

$\frac{dy}{du} = -\text{cosec}\, u \cot u = -\text{cosec}\,(3x-2)\cot(3x-2)$

and $\frac{du}{dx} = 3,$

$$\Rightarrow \frac{dy}{dx} = -3\,\text{cosec}\,(3x-2)\cot(3x-2) = \frac{-3}{\sin(3x-2)\tan(3x-2)}.$$

When $x = 0$, $\frac{dy}{dx} = \frac{-3}{\sin(-2)\tan(-2)} = 1.51$ (to 3 s.f.).

7) For $y = \frac{e^x}{\sqrt{x}}$, use the quotient rule:

$u = e^x \Rightarrow \frac{du}{dx} = e^x,$

$v = x^{\frac{1}{2}} \Rightarrow \frac{dv}{dx} = \frac{1}{2}x^{-\frac{1}{2}} = \frac{1}{2\sqrt{x}}.$

$$\frac{dy}{dx} = \frac{v\frac{du}{dx} - u\frac{dv}{dx}}{v^2} = \frac{e^x\sqrt{x} - \frac{e^x}{2\sqrt{x}}}{(\sqrt{x})^2}.$$

Multiplying top and bottom by $2\sqrt{x}$ gives:

$$\frac{dy}{dx} = \frac{2xe^x - e^x}{2x\sqrt{x}} = \frac{e^x(2x-1)}{2x\sqrt{x}}.$$

At the stationary point, $\frac{dy}{dx} = 0,$

$\Rightarrow \frac{e^x(2x-1)}{2x\sqrt{x}} = 0 \Rightarrow e^x(2x - 1) = 0,$

so either $e^x = 0$ or $2x - 1 = 0$. e^x does not exist at 0, so the stationary point must be at $2x - 1 = 0$, $x = \frac{1}{2}$.

To find out the nature of the stationary point, differentiate again: $\frac{dy}{dx} = \frac{e^x(2x-1)}{2x\sqrt{x}}$, so use quotient rule and product rule:

$u = e^x(2x - 1) \Rightarrow$ using product rule $\frac{du}{dx} = 2e^x + e^x(2x - 1)$
$= e^x(2x - 1 + 2) = e^x(2x + 1).$

$v = 2x^{\frac{3}{2}} \Rightarrow \frac{dv}{dx} = 3x^{\frac{1}{2}} = 3\sqrt{x}.$

$$\frac{d^2y}{dx^2} = \frac{v\frac{du}{dx} - u\frac{dv}{dx}}{v^2} = \frac{2x\sqrt{x}e^x(2x+1) - 3\sqrt{x}e^x(2x-1)}{(2x\sqrt{x})^2} = \frac{\sqrt{x}e^x(4x^2-4x+3)}{4x^3}.$$

When $x = \frac{1}{2}$, $\frac{d^2y}{dx^2} > 0$, so it is a minimum point.

Give yourself a big pat on the back if you survived question 7. I told you it was hard...

Exam Questions

1 a) For $y = \ln(3x + 1)\sin(3x + 1)$, use the product rule and the chain rule:

Product rule: $u = \ln(3x + 1)$ and $v = \sin(3x + 1)$.

Using the chain rule for $\frac{du}{dx} = \frac{3}{3x+1}$ ***[1 mark]***.

Using the chain rule for $\frac{dv}{dx} = 3\cos(3x + 1)$ ***[1 mark]***.

So $\frac{dy}{dx} = u\frac{dv}{dx} + v\frac{du}{dx}$

$= [\ln(3x + 1)\cdot 3\cos(3x + 1)] + [\sin(3x + 1)\cdot \frac{3}{3x+1}]$ ***[1 mark]***

$= 3\ln(3x + 1)\cos(3x + 1) + \frac{3\sin(3x+1)}{3x+1}$ ***[1 mark]***.

b) For $y = \frac{\sqrt{x^2+3}}{\cos 3x}$, use the quotient rule and the chain rule:

Quotient rule: $u = \sqrt{x^2+3}$ and $v = \cos 3x$.

Using the chain rule for $\frac{du}{dx} = \frac{2x}{2\sqrt{x^2+3}} = \frac{x}{\sqrt{x^2+3}}$ ***[1 mark]***.

Using the chain rule for $\frac{dv}{dx} = -3\sin 3x$ ***[1 mark]***.

$$\text{So } \frac{dy}{dx} = \frac{v\frac{du}{dx} - u\frac{dv}{dx}}{v^2} = \frac{\left[\cos 3x \cdot \frac{x}{\sqrt{x^2+3}}\right] - \left[\sqrt{x^2+3} \cdot -3\sin 3x\right]}{\cos^2 3x}$$

[1 mark]. Then multiply top and bottom by $\sqrt{x^2+3}$ to get:

$$\frac{dy}{dx} = \frac{x\cos 3x + 3(x^2+3)\sin 3x}{(\sqrt{x^2+3})\cos^2 3x} = \frac{x + 3(x^2+3)\tan 3x}{(\sqrt{x^2+3})\cos 3x}$$

[1 mark].

c) For $y = \sin^3(2x^2)$, use the chain rule twice:

$y = u^3$ where $u = \sin(2x^2)$.

$\frac{dy}{du} = 3u^2 = 3\sin^2(2x^2)$ ***[1 mark]***.

$\frac{du}{dx} = 4x\cos(2x^2)$ (using chain rule again) ***[1 mark]***.

So $\frac{dy}{dx} = 12x\sin^2(2x^2)\cos(2x^2)$ ***[1 mark]***.

d) For $y = 2\text{cosec}\,(3x)$, use the chain rule:

$y = 2\,\text{cosec}\, u$ where $u = 3x$.

$\frac{dy}{du} = -2\text{cosec}\, u \cot u = -2\text{cosec}\, 3x \cot 3x.$

$\frac{du}{dx} = 3$ ***[1 mark for both]***,

so $\frac{dy}{dx} = -6\text{cosec}\, 3x \cot 3x$ ***[1 mark]***.

2 a) For $x = \sqrt{y^2+3y}$, find $\frac{dx}{dy}$ first (using the chain rule):

$x = u^{\frac{1}{2}}$ where $u = y^2 + 3y$.

$\frac{dx}{du} = \frac{1}{2}u^{-\frac{1}{2}} = \frac{1}{2\sqrt{u}} = \frac{1}{2\sqrt{y^2+3y}}$ ***[1 mark]***.

$\frac{du}{dy} = 2y + 3$ ***[1 mark]***.

So $\frac{dx}{dy} = \frac{2y+3}{2\sqrt{y^2+3y}}$ ***[1 mark]***.

(Now, flip the fraction upside down for dy/dx...)

$\frac{dy}{dx} = \frac{2\sqrt{y^2+3y}}{2y+3}$ ***[1 mark]***.

At the point (2, 1), $y = 1$, so:

$\frac{dy}{dx} = \frac{2\sqrt{1^2+3}}{2+3} = \frac{4}{5} = 0.8$ ***[1 mark]***.

b) Equation of a straight line is:

$y - y_1 = m(x - x_1)$, where m is the gradient.

For the tangent at (2, 1), $y_1 = 1$, $x_1 = 2$, and $m = \frac{dy}{dx} = 0.8$.

So the equation is:

$y - 1 = 0.8(x - 2) \Rightarrow y = 0.8x - 0.6$ (or equivalent fractions)

[2 marks available — 1 mark for correct substitution of (2, 1) and gradient from (a), and 1 mark for final answer.]

Answers

3 $f(x) = \sec x = \frac{1}{\cos x}$, so using the quotient rule:

$u = 1 \Rightarrow \frac{du}{dx} = 0$ and $v = \cos x \Rightarrow \frac{dv}{dx} = -\sin x$.

$$\frac{dy}{dx} = \frac{v\frac{du}{dx} - u\frac{dv}{dx}}{v^2} = \frac{(\cos x \cdot 0) - (1 \cdot -\sin x)}{\cos^2 x} = \frac{\sin x}{\cos^2 x}.$$

Since $\tan x = \frac{\sin x}{\cos x}$, and $\sec x = \frac{1}{\cos x}$,

$f'(x) = \frac{dy}{dx} = \frac{\sin x}{\cos x} \times \frac{1}{\cos x} = \sec x \tan x$.

[4 marks available — 1 mark for correct identity for sec x, 1 mark for correct entry into quotient rule, 1 mark for correct answer from quotient rule, and 1 mark for correct rearrangement to sec x tan x.]

4 a) For $y = \sqrt{e^x + e^{2x}}$, use the chain rule:

$y = u^{\frac{1}{2}}$ where $u = e^x + e^{2x}$.

$\frac{dy}{du} = \frac{1}{2}u^{-\frac{1}{2}} = \frac{1}{2\sqrt{u}} = \frac{1}{2\sqrt{e^x + e^{2x}}}$ ***[1 mark]***.

$\frac{du}{dx} = e^x + 2e^{2x}$ ***[1 mark]***.

So $\frac{dy}{dx} = \frac{e^x + 2e^{2x}}{2\sqrt{e^x + e^{2x}}}$ ***[1 mark]***.

b) For $y = 3e^{2x+1} - \ln(1 - x^2) + 2x^3$, use the chain rule for the first 2 parts separately:

For $y = 3e^{2x+1}$, $y = 3e^u$ where $u = 2x + 1$, so $\frac{dy}{du} = 3e^u = 3e^{2x+1}$ and $\frac{du}{dx} = 2$, so $\frac{dy}{dx} = 6e^{2x+1}$ ***[1 mark]***.

For $y = \ln(1 - x^2)$, $y = \ln u$ where $u = 1 - x^2$,

so $\frac{dy}{du} = \frac{1}{u} = \frac{1}{(1 - x^2)}$ and $\frac{du}{dx} = -2x$, so $\frac{dy}{dx} = -\frac{2x}{(1 - x^2)}$ ***[1 mark]***.

So overall: $\frac{dy}{dx} = 6e^{2x+1} + \frac{2x}{(1 - x^2)} + 6x^2$ ***[1 mark]***.

5 a) For $f(x) = 4 \ln 3x$, use the chain rule:

$y = 4 \ln u$ where $u = 3x$, so $\frac{dy}{du} = \frac{4}{u} = \frac{4}{3x}$, and $\frac{du}{dx} = 3$ ***[1 mark for both]***, so $f'(x) = \frac{dy}{dx} = \frac{12}{3x} = \frac{4}{x}$ ***[1 mark]***.

So for $x = 1$, $f'(1) = 4$ ***[1 mark]***.

b) Equation of a straight line is:

$y - y_1 = m(x - x_1)$, where m is the gradient.

For the tangent at $x_1 = 1$, $y_1 = 4\ln 3$, and $m = \frac{dy}{dx} = 4$.

So the equation is:

$y - 4\ln 3 = 4(x - 1) \Rightarrow y = 4(x - 1 + \ln 3)$ (or equivalent).

[3 marks available — 1 mark for finding y = 4ln 3, 1 mark for correct substitution of (1, 4ln3) and gradient from (a), and 1 mark for correct final answer.]

6 For $y = \sin^2 x - 2\cos 2x$, use the chain rule on each part:

For $y = \sin^2 x$, $y = u^2$ where $u = \sin x$, so $\frac{dy}{du} = 2u = 2\sin x$ and $\frac{du}{dx} = \cos x$, so $\frac{dy}{dx} = 2 \sin x \cos x$ ***[1 mark]***.

For $y = 2\cos 2x$, $y = 2\cos u$ where $u = 2x$, so $\frac{dy}{du} = -2\sin u = -2\sin 2x$ and $\frac{du}{dx} = 2$, so $\frac{dy}{dx} = -4\sin 2x$ ***[1 mark]***.

Overall $\frac{dy}{dx} = 2 \sin x \cos x + 4\sin 2x$.

(Think 'double angle formula' for the sin x cos x...)

$\sin 2x \equiv 2 \sin x \cos x$, so:

$\frac{dy}{dx} = \sin 2x + 4\sin 2x = 5\sin 2x$ ***[1 mark]***.

(For gradient of the tangent, put the x value into dy/dx...)

Gradient of the tangent when $x = \frac{\pi}{12}$ is:

$5 \times \sin \frac{\pi}{6} = 2.5$ ***[1 mark]***.

7 For $y = \frac{e^x + x}{e^x - x}$, use the quotient rule:

$u = e^x + x \Rightarrow \frac{du}{dx} = e^x + 1$.

$v = e^x - x \Rightarrow \frac{dv}{dx} = e^x - 1$.

$$\frac{dy}{dx} = \frac{v\frac{du}{dx} - u\frac{dv}{dx}}{v^2} = \frac{(e^x - x)(e^x + 1) - (e^x + x)(e^x - 1)}{(e^x - x)^2}.$$

When $x = 0$, $e^x = 1$, and $\frac{dy}{dx} = \frac{(1 - 0)(1 + 1) - (1 + 0)(1 - 1)}{(1 - 0)^2}$

$= \frac{2 - 0}{1^2} = 2$.

[3 marks available — 1 mark for finding u, v and their derivatives, 1 mark for dy/dx (however rearranged), and 1 mark for dy/dx = 2 when x = 0.]

8 For $x = \sin 4y$, $\frac{dx}{dy} = 4\cos 4y$ ***[1 mark]*** (using chain rule), and so $\frac{dy}{dx} = \frac{1}{4\cos 4y}$ ***[1 mark]***.

At $(0, \frac{\pi}{4})$, $y = \frac{\pi}{4}$ and so $\frac{dy}{dx} = \frac{1}{4\cos \pi} = -\frac{1}{4}$ ***[1 mark]***.

(This is the gradient of the tangent at that point, so to find the gradient of the normal do –1 ÷ gradient of tangent...)

Gradient of normal at $(0, \frac{\pi}{4}) = -1 \div -\frac{1}{4} = 4$ ***[1 mark]***.

Equation of a straight line is:

$y - y_1 = m(x - x_1)$, where m is the gradient.

For the normal at $(0, \frac{\pi}{4})$, $x_1 = 0$, $y_1 = \frac{\pi}{4}$, and m = 4.

So the equation is:

$y - \frac{\pi}{4} = 4(x - 0)$ ***[1 mark]*** $\Rightarrow y = 4x + \frac{\pi}{4}$ (or equivalent) ***[1 mark]***.

9 a) For $y = e^x \sin x$, use the product rule:

$u = e^x \Rightarrow \frac{du}{dx} = e^x$

$v = \sin x \Rightarrow \frac{dv}{dx} = \cos x$

So $\frac{dy}{dx} = u\frac{dv}{dx} + v\frac{du}{dx} = (e^x \cdot \cos x) + (\sin x \cdot e^x)$
$= e^x(\cos x + \sin x)$ ***[1 mark]***.

At the turning points, $\frac{dy}{dx} = 0$, so:

$e^x(\cos x + \sin x) = 0$ ***[1 mark]***

$\Rightarrow$ turning points are when $e^x = 0$ or $\cos x + \sin x = 0$.

e^x cannot be 0, so the turning points are when $\cos x + \sin x = 0$ ***[1 mark]***

$\Rightarrow \sin x = -\cos x \Rightarrow \frac{\sin x}{\cos x} = -1 \Rightarrow \tan x = -1$ ***[1 mark]***.

Look back at C2 for the graph of tan x to help you find all the solutions — it repeats itself every π radians...

There are two solutions for $\tan x = -1$ in the interval $-\pi \le x \le \pi$: $x = -\frac{\pi}{4}$ and $x = \pi - \frac{\pi}{4} = \frac{3\pi}{4}$,

so the values of x at each turning point are $-\frac{\pi}{4}$ ***[1 mark]*** and $\frac{3\pi}{4}$ ***[1 mark]***.

b) To determine the nature of the turning points, find $\frac{d^2y}{dx^2}$ at the points:

Answers

For $\frac{dy}{dx} = e^x(\cos x + \sin x)$, use the product rule:

$u = e^x \Rightarrow \frac{du}{dx} = e^x$

$v = \cos x + \sin x \Rightarrow \frac{dv}{dx} = \cos x - \sin x$, so:

$\frac{d^2y}{dx^2} = u\frac{dv}{dx} + v\frac{du}{dx} = [e^x \cdot (\cos x - \sin x)] + [(\cos x + \sin x) \cdot e^x]$

$= 2e^x \cos x$ ***[1 mark].***

When $x = -\frac{\pi}{4}$, $\frac{d^2y}{dx^2} > 0$ ***[1 mark]***, so this is a minimum point ***[1 mark].***

When $x = \frac{3\pi}{4}$, $\frac{d^2y}{dx^2} < 0$ ***[1 mark]***, so this is a maximum point ***[1 mark].***

C3 Section 5 — Numerical Methods

Warm-up Questions

1) There are 2 roots (graph crosses the x-axis twice in this interval).

2) a) Sin $(2 \times 3) = -0.2794...$ and sin $(2 \times 4) = 0.9893...$
Since $\sin(2x)$ is a continuous function, the change of sign means there is a root between 3 and 4.

b) $\ln(2.1 - 2) + 2 = -0.3025...$
and $\ln(2.2 - 2) + 2 = 0.3905...$
Since the function is continuous for $x > 2$, the change of sign means there is a root between 2.1 and 2.2.

c) Rearrange first to give $x^3 - 4x^2 - 7 = 0$, then:
$4.3^3 - 4 \times (4.3^2) - 7 = -1.453$ and
$4.5^3 - 4 \times (4.5^2) - 7 = 3.125$.
The function is continuous, so the change of sign means there is a root between 4.3 and 4.5.

3) If 1.2 is a root to 1 d.p. then there should be a sign change for f(x) between the upper and lower bounds:
$f(1.15) = 1.15^3 + 1.15 - 3 = -0.3291...$
$f(1.25) = 1.25^3 + 1.25 - 3 = 0.2031...$
There is a change of sign, and the function is continuous, so the root must lie between 1.15 and 1.25, so to 1 d.p. the root is at $x = 1.2$.

4) $x_1 = -\frac{1}{2}\cos(-1) = -0.2701...$
$x_2 = -\frac{1}{2}\cos(-0.2701...) = -0.4818...$
$x_3 = -\frac{1}{2}\cos(-0.4818...) = -0.4430...$
$x_4 = -\frac{1}{2}\cos(-0.4430...) = -0.4517...$
$x_5 = -\frac{1}{2}\cos(-0.4517...) = -0.4498...$
$x_6 = -\frac{1}{2}\cos(-0.4498...) = -0.4502...$
x_4, x_5 and x_6 all round to -0.45, so to 2 d.p. $x = -0.45$.

5) $x_1 = \sqrt{\ln 2 + 4} = 2.1663...$
$x_2 = \sqrt{\ln 2.1663... + 4} = 2.1847...$
$x_3 = \sqrt{\ln 2.1847... + 4} = 2.1866...$
$x_4 = \sqrt{\ln 2.1866... + 4} = 2.1868...$
$x_5 = \sqrt{\ln 2.1868... + 4} = 2.1868...$
x_3, x_4 and x_5 all round to 2.187, so to 3 d.p. $x = 2.187$.

6) a) i) $2x^2 - x^3 + 1 = 0 \Rightarrow 2x^2 - x^3 = -1$
$\Rightarrow x^2(2 - x) = -1 \Rightarrow x^2 = \frac{-1}{2-x} \Rightarrow x = \sqrt{\frac{-1}{2-x}}$.

ii) $2x^2 - x^3 + 1 = 0 \Rightarrow x^3 = 2x^2 + 1$
$\Rightarrow x = \sqrt[3]{2x^2 + 1}$.

iii) $2x^2 - x^3 + 1 = 0 \Rightarrow 2x^2 = x^3 - 1$
$\Rightarrow x^2 = \frac{x^3 - 1}{2} \Rightarrow x = \sqrt{\frac{x^3 - 1}{2}}$.

b) Using $x_{n+1} = \sqrt{\frac{-1}{2 - x_n}}$ with $x_0 = 2.3$ gives:
$x_1 = \sqrt{\frac{-1}{2 - 2.3}} = 1.8257...$
$x_2 = \sqrt{\frac{-1}{2 - 1.8257...}}$ has no real solution
so this formula does not converge to a root.

Using $x_{n+1} = \sqrt[3]{2x_n^2 + 1}$ with $x_0 = 2.3$ gives:
$x_1 = \sqrt[3]{2 \times (2.3)^2 + 1} = 2.2624...$
$x_2 = \sqrt[3]{2 \times (2.2624...)^2 + 1} = 2.2398...$
$x_3 = \sqrt[3]{2 \times (2.2398...)^2 + 1} = 2.2262...$
$x_4 = \sqrt[3]{2 \times (2.2262...)^2 + 1} = 2.2180...$
$x_5 = \sqrt[3]{2 \times (2.2180...)^2 + 1} = 2.2131...$
$x_6 = \sqrt[3]{2 \times (2.2131...)^2 + 1} = 2.2101...$
$x_7 = \sqrt[3]{2 \times (2.2101...)^2 + 1} = 2.2083...$
x_5, x_6 and x_7 all round to 2.21,
so to 2 d.p. $x = 2.21$ is a root.

Using $x_{n+1} = \sqrt{\frac{x_n^3 - 1}{2}}$ with $x_0 = 2.3$ gives:
$x_1 = \sqrt{\frac{2.3^3 - 1}{2}} = 2.3629...$
$x_2 = \sqrt{\frac{2.3629...^3 - 1}{2}} = 2.4691...$
$x_3 = \sqrt{\frac{2.4691...^3 - 1}{2}} = 2.6508...$
$x_4 = \sqrt{\frac{2.6508...^3 - 1}{2}} = 2.9687...$
This sequence is diverging so does not converge to a root.
The only formula that converges to a root is
$x_{n+1} = \sqrt[3]{2x_n^2 + 1}$.

Exam Questions

1 a) There will be a change of sign between f(0.7) and f(0.8) if p lies between 0.7 and 0.8.
$f(0.7) = (2 \times 0.7 \times e^{0.7}) - 3 = -0.1807...$ ***[1 mark]***
$f(0.8) = (2 \times 0.8 \times e^{0.8}) - 3 = 0.5608...$ ***[1 mark]***
f(x) is continuous, and there is a change of sign, so $0.7 < p < 0.8$ ***[1 mark].***

b) If $2xe^x - 3 = 0$, then $2xe^x = 3 \Rightarrow xe^x = \frac{3}{2}$
$\Rightarrow x = \frac{3}{2e^x} \Rightarrow x = \frac{3}{2}e^{-x}$.
[2 marks available — 1 mark for partial rearrangement, 1 mark for correct final answer.]

c) $x_{n+1} = \frac{3}{2}e^{-x_n}$ and $x_0 = 0.7$, so:
$x_1 = \frac{3}{2}e^{-0.7} = 0.74487... = 0.7449$ to 4 d.p.
$x_2 = \frac{3}{2}e^{-0.74487...} = 0.71218... = 0.7122$ to 4 d.p.
$x_3 = \frac{3}{2}e^{-0.71218...} = 0.73585... = 0.7359$ to 4 d.p.
$x_4 = \frac{3}{2}e^{-0.73585...} = 0.71864... = 0.7186$ to 4 d.p.
[3 marks available — 1 mark for x_1 correct, 1 mark for x_2 correct, 1 mark for all 4 correct.]

Answers

d) If the root of f(x) = 0, p, is 0.726 to 3 d.p. then there must be a change of sign in f(x) between the upper and lower bounds of p.
Lower bound = 0.7255.
$f(0.7255) = (2 \times 0.7255 \times e^{0.7255}) - 3 = -0.0025...$
Upper bound = 0.7265.
$f(0.7265) = (2 \times 0.7265 \times e^{0.7265}) - 3 = 0.0045...$
f(x) is continuous, and there's a change of sign, so p = 0.726 to 3 d.p.
[3 marks available — 1 mark for identifying upper and lower bounds, 1 mark for finding value of the function at both bounds, 1 mark for indicating that the change in sign and the fact that it's a continuous function shows the root is correct to the given accuracy.]

2 a) Where $y = \sin 3x + 3x$ and $y = 1$ meet,
$\sin 3x + 3x = 1 \Rightarrow \sin 3x + 3x - 1 = 0$ ***[1 mark]***.
$x = a$ is a root of this equation, so if $x = 0.1$ and $x = 0.2$ produce different signs, then a lies between them. So for the continuous function $f(x) = \sin 3x + 3x - 1$:
$f(0.1) = \sin(3 \times 0.1) + (3 \times 0.1) - 1 = -0.4044...$ ***[1 mark]***
$f(0.2) = \sin(3 \times 0.2) + (3 \times 0.2) - 1 = 0.1646...$ ***[1 mark]***
There is a change of sign, so $0.1 < a < 0.2$ ***[1 mark]***.

b) $\sin 3x + 3x = 1 \Rightarrow 3x = 1 - \sin 3x \Rightarrow x = \frac{1}{3}(1 - \sin 3x)$.
[2 marks available — 1 mark for partial rearrangement, 1 mark for correct final answer.]

c) $x_{n+1} = \frac{1}{3}(1 - \sin 3x_n)$ and $x_0 = 0.2$:
$x_1 = \frac{1}{3}(1 - \sin(3 \times 0.2)) = 0.1451...$ ***[1 mark]***
$x_2 = \frac{1}{3}(1 - \sin(3 \times 0.1451...)) = 0.1927...$
$x_3 = \frac{1}{3}(1 - \sin(3 \times 0.1927...)) = 0.1511...$
$x_4 = \frac{1}{3}(1 - \sin(3 \times 0.1511...)) = 0.1873...$
So $x_4 = 0.187$ to 3 d.p. ***[1 mark]***.

3 a) $x_{n+1} = \sqrt[3]{x_n^2 - 4}$, $x_0 = -1$:
$x_1 = \sqrt[3]{(-1)^2 - 4} = -1.44224... = -1.4422$ to 4 d.p.
$x_2 = \sqrt[3]{(-1.4422...)^2 - 4} = -1.24287... = -1.2429$ to 4 d.p.
$x_3 = \sqrt[3]{(-1.2428...)^2 - 4} = -1.34906... = -1.3491$ to 4 d.p.
$x_4 = \sqrt[3]{(-1.3490...)^2 - 4} = -1.29664... = -1.2966$ to 4 d.p.
[3 marks available — 1 mark for x_1 correct, 1 mark for x_2 correct, 1 mark for all 4 correct.]

b) If b is a root of $x^3 - x^2 + 4 = 0$, then $x^3 - x^2 + 4 = 0$ will rearrange to form $x = \sqrt[3]{x^2 - 4}$, the iteration formula used in (a).
(This is like finding the iteration formula in reverse...)
$x^3 - x^2 + 4 = 0 \Rightarrow x^3 = x^2 - 4 \Rightarrow x = \sqrt[3]{x^2 - 4}$, and so b must be a root of $x^3 - x^2 + 4 = 0$.
[2 marks available — 1 mark for stating that b is a root if one equation can be rearranged into the other, 1 mark for correct demonstration of rearrangement.]

c) If the root of $f(x) = x^3 - x^2 + 4 = 0$, b, is -1.315 to 3 d.p. then there must be a change of sign in f(x) between the upper and lower bounds of b, which are -1.3145 and -1.3155.
$f(-1.3145) = (-1.3145)^3 - (-1.3145)^2 + 4 = 0.00075...$
$f(-1.3155) = (-1.3155)^3 - (-1.3155)^2 + 4 = -0.00706...$
f(x) is continuous, and there's a change of sign, so $b = -1.315$ to 3 d.p.
[3 marks available — 1 mark for identifying upper and lower bounds, 1 mark for finding value of the function at both bounds, 1 mark for indicating that the change in sign and the fact that it's a continuous function shows the root is correct to the given accuracy.]

4 a) For $f(x) = \ln(x + 3) - x + 2$, there will be a change in sign between f(3) and f(4) if the root lies between those values.
$f(3) = \ln(3 + 3) - 3 + 2 = 0.7917...$ ***[1 mark]***
$f(4) = \ln(4 + 3) - 4 + 2 = -0.0540...$ ***[1 mark]***
There is a change of sign, and the function is continuous for $x > -3$, so the root, m, must lie between 3 and 4 ***[1 mark]***.

b) $x_{n+1} = \ln(x_n + 3) + 2$, and $x_0 = 3$, so:
$x_1 = \ln(3 + 3) + 2 = 3.7917...$
$x_2 = \ln(3.7917... + 3) + 2 = 3.9157...$
$x_3 = \ln(3.9157... + 3) + 2 = 3.9337...$
$x_4 = \ln(3.9337... + 3) + 2 = 3.9364...$
$x_5 = \ln(3.9364... + 3) + 2 = 3.9367...$
So $m = 3.94$ to 2 d.p.
[3 marks available — 1 mark for correct substitution of x_0 to find x_1, 1 mark for evidence of correct iterations up to x_5, 1 mark for correct final answer to correct accuracy.]

c) From b), $m = 3.94$ to 2 d.p. If this is correct then there will be a change of sign in f(x) between the upper and lower bounds of m, which are 3.935 and 3.945.
$f(3.935) = \ln(3.935 + 3) - 3.935 + 2 = 0.00158...$
$f(3.945) = \ln(3.945 + 3) - 3.945 + 2 = -0.00697...$
f(x) is continuous for $x > -3$, and there's a change of sign, so $m = 3.94$ is correct to 2 d.p.
[3 marks available — 1 mark for identifying upper and lower bounds, 1 mark for finding value of the function at both bounds, 1 mark for indicating that the change in sign and the fact that it's a continuous function shows the root is correct to the given accuracy.]

Practice Exam One

1 a) For $3\ln x - \ln 3x = 0$, use the log laws to simplify to:
$\ln x^3 - \ln 3x = 0 \Rightarrow \ln \frac{x^3}{3x} = 0 \Rightarrow \ln \frac{x^2}{3} = 0$ ***[1 mark]***.
Taking e to the power of both sides gives:
$\frac{x^2}{3} = e^0 = 1 \Rightarrow x^2 = 3 \Rightarrow x = \sqrt{3}$ (ignore the negative solution as $x > 0$) ***[1 mark]***.

b) Let $y = f(x)$. Now, to find the inverse of $y = 3\ln x - \ln 3x$, make x the subject then swap x and y:
$y = \ln \frac{x^2}{3}$ (from (a)) $\Rightarrow e^y = \frac{x^2}{3} \Rightarrow x^2 = 3e^y$
$\Rightarrow x = \sqrt{3e^y}$ ***[1 mark]***.
So $f^{-1}(x) = \sqrt{3e^x}$ ***[1 mark]***.

c) When $\sqrt{3e^x} = 1$, squaring both sides gives:
$3e^x = 1 \Rightarrow e^x = \frac{1}{3}$ ***[1 mark]***.

Answers

Taking ln of both sides gives:

$x = \ln \frac{1}{3}$ ***[1 mark]***.

d) $f(x) = 3\ln x - \ln 3x$, so differentiating gives:

$f'(x) = \frac{3}{x} - \frac{3}{3x} = \frac{3}{x} - \frac{1}{x} = \frac{2}{x}$ ***[1 mark]***.

So when $x = 1$, $f'(x) = \frac{2}{1} = 2$ ***[1 mark]***.

2 a) (i)

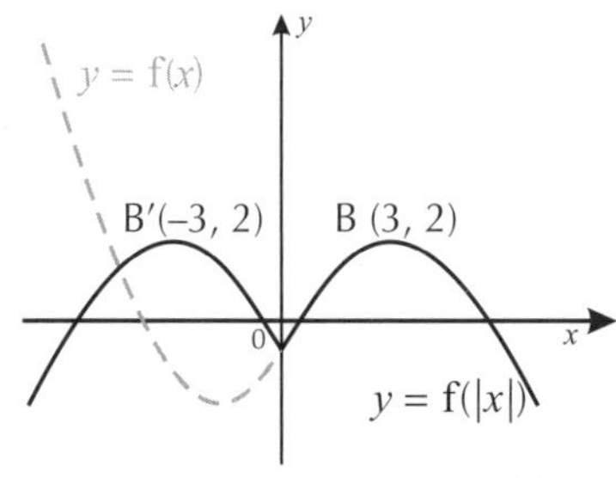

[3 marks available — 1 mark for reflection in the y-axis, 1 mark for each coordinate of B′ after transformation]

(ii)

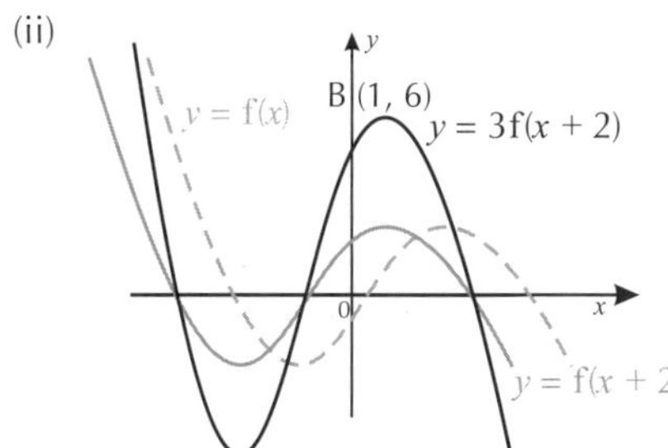

[3 marks available — 1 mark for shape (stretch and translation), 1 mark each for coordinates of A and B after transformation]

The solid grey line shows the graph of y = f(x + 2) — it's easier to do the transformation in two stages, instead of doing it all at once.

b) (i) $gh(4) = g(h(4)) = g\left(\frac{6}{4^2 - 4}\right) = g(0.5)$ ***[1 mark]***

$= \sqrt{(2 \cdot 0.5) + 3} = \sqrt{1 + 3} = \sqrt{4} = 2.$ ***[1 mark]***

(ii) $hg(3) = h(g(3)) = h(\sqrt{(2 \cdot 3) + 3}) = h(3)$ ***[1 mark]***

$= \frac{6}{3^2 - 4} = \frac{6}{9 - 4} = \frac{6}{5} = 1.2$ ***[1 mark]***.

(iii) $hg(x) = h(g(x)) = h(\sqrt{2x + 3})$

$\frac{6}{(\sqrt{2x+3})^2 - 4} = \frac{6}{2x + 3 - 4} = \frac{6}{2x - 1}.$

[3 marks available — 1 mark for functions in the correct order, 1 mark for substituting g(x) into formula for h, 1 mark for simplifying].

3 a) $y = \frac{4x - 1}{\tan x}$, so use quotient rule:

$u = 4x - 1 \Rightarrow \frac{du}{dx} = 4$

$v = \tan x \Rightarrow \frac{dv}{dx} = \sec^2 x$

$\frac{dy}{dx} = \frac{v\frac{du}{dx} - u\frac{dv}{dx}}{v^2} = \frac{4\tan x - (4x - 1)\sec^2 x}{\tan^2 x}$

$= \frac{4}{\tan x} - \frac{(4x - 1)\sec^2 x}{\tan^2 x}.$

Since $\frac{1}{\tan x} = \cot x$, $\sec^2 x = \frac{1}{\cos^2 x}$, and $\tan^2 x = \frac{\sin^2 x}{\cos^2 x}$:

$\frac{dy}{dx} = 4\cot x - \frac{(4x - 1)}{\cos^2 x\left(\frac{\sin^2 x}{\cos^2 x}\right)} = 4\cot x - \frac{(4x - 1)}{\sin^2 x}.$

Since $\frac{1}{\sin^2 x} = \text{cosec}^2\, x$:

$\frac{dy}{dx} = 4\cot x - (4x - 1)\text{cosec}^2\, x.$

[3 marks available — 1 mark for correct expressions for du/dx and dv/dx, 1 mark for correct use of the quotient rule, and 1 mark for reaching the correct expression for dy/dx.]

(You could also use the product rule with y = (4x – 1) cot x.)

b) Maximum point is when $\frac{dy}{dx} = 0$:

$4\cot x - (4x - 1)\text{cosec}^2\, x = 0$ ***[1 mark]***

Dividing through by $\text{cosec}^2\, x$ gives

$\frac{4\cot x}{\text{cosec}^2 x} - (4x - 1) = 0$

$\Rightarrow \frac{4\cot x}{\text{cosec}^2 x} = 4x - 1$ ***[1 mark]***

Now, $\frac{4\cot x}{\text{cosec}^2 x} = \frac{4\cos x \sin^2 x}{\sin x} = 4\cos x \sin x = 2\sin 2x$

(Using the double angle formula sin 2x = 2 sin x cos x...)

So $2\sin 2x = 4x - 1 \Rightarrow 2\sin 2x - 4x + 1 = 0$ ***[1 mark]***.

4 a)

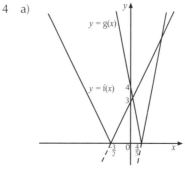

[2 marks available — 1 mark for y = |2x + 3| (with reflection in the x-axis and y-intercept at 3), 1 mark for y = |5x – 4| (with reflection in the x-axis and y-intercept at 4)]

Make sure you draw enough of the graph to show where the lines cross — you'll need it for the next bit of the question.

b) From the graph, it is clear that there are two points where the graphs intersect. One is in the range $-\frac{3}{2} < x < \frac{4}{5}$, where $(2x + 3) > 0$ but $(5x - 4) < 0$. This gives $2x + 3 = -(5x - 4)$ ***[1 mark]***.

The other one is in the range $x > \frac{4}{5}$, where $(2x + 3) > 0$ and $(5x - 4) > 0$, so $2x + 3 = 5x - 4$ ***[1 mark]***. Solving the first equation gives: $2x + 3 = -5x + 4 \Rightarrow 7x = 1$, so $x = \frac{1}{7}$ ***[1 mark]***. Solving the second equation gives:

$2x + 3 = 5x - 4 \Rightarrow 7 = 3x$, so $x = \frac{7}{3}$ ***[1 mark]***.

5 a) $\frac{(x^2 - 9)(3x^2 - 10x - 8)}{(6x + 4)(x^2 - 7x + 12)} = \frac{(x + 3)(x - 3)(3x + 2)(x - 4)}{2(3x + 2)(x - 3)(x - 4)}$

$= \frac{x + 3}{2}$

[2 marks available — 1 mark for correctly factorising numerator <u>or</u> denominator, 1 mark for correct final answer]

Answers

b)
$$\begin{array}{r} 2x+5 \quad r\ x+8 \\ x^2-3x-1\overline{)2x^3-x^2-16x+3} \\ -\underline{2x^3-6x^2-2x} \\ 5x^2-14x+3 \\ -\underline{5x^2-15x-5} \\ x+8 \end{array}$$

so the quotient is $(2x + 5)$ and the remainder is $(x + 8)$.

[4 marks available — up to 2 marks for correct working, 1 mark for quotient and 1 mark for remainder]

If you'd tried to use the remainder theorem formula for this question, you'd have found it a bit tricky as the divisor doesn't factorise easily. Instead, you'd need to equate coefficients of x^3, x^2 and x, as well as putting in $x = 0$.

6 a) $\text{cosec}\,\theta = \frac{5}{3} \Rightarrow \sin\theta = \frac{3}{5}$. Solving for θ gives $\theta = 0.644$, $\pi - 0.644 = 2.50$ (3 s.f.) ***[1 mark for each correct answer]***.

Sketch the graph of $y = \sin x$ to help you find the second solution.

b) (i) The identity $\text{cosec}^2\theta \equiv 1 + \cot^2\theta$ rearranges to give $\text{cosec}^2\theta - 1 \equiv \cot^2\theta$. Putting this into the equation:

$3\,\text{cosec}\,\theta = (\text{cosec}^2\theta - 1) - 17$

$17 + 3\,\text{cosec}\,\theta - (\text{cosec}^2\theta - 1) = 0$

$18 + 3\,\text{cosec}\,\theta - \text{cosec}^2\theta = 0$

as required.

[2 marks available — 1 mark for using correct identity, 1 mark for rearranging into required form]

(ii) To factorise the expression above, let $x = \text{cosec}\,\theta$. Then $18 + 3x - x^2 = 0$, so $(6 - x)(3 + x) = 0$ ***[1 mark]***. The roots of this quadratic occur at $x = 6$ and $x = -3$, so $\text{cosec}\,\theta = 6$ and $\text{cosec}\,\theta = -3$ ***[1 mark]***.

$\text{cosec}\,\theta = 1/\sin\theta$, so $\sin\theta = \frac{1}{6}$ and $\sin\theta = -\frac{1}{3}$.

Solving these equations for θ gives $\theta = 0.167, 2.97$ ***[1 mark]*** and $\theta = 3.48, 5.94$ ***[1 mark]***.

You don't have to use $x = \text{cosec}\,\theta$ — it's just a little easier to factorise without all those pesky cosecs flying around. Have a look back at Section 2 for stuff on cosec etc.

7 a) For $6^x = x + 2$, take ln of both sides:

$\ln 6^x = \ln(x + 2)$ ***[1 mark]***, and using log laws,

$x\ln 6 = \ln(x + 2) \Rightarrow x = \dfrac{\ln(x+2)}{\ln 6}$ ***[1 mark]***.

b) Using $x_{n+1} = \dfrac{\ln(x_n+2)}{\ln 6}$ and $x_0 = 0.5$ gives:

$x_1 = \dfrac{\ln(0.5+2)}{\ln 6} = 0.51139... = 0.5114$ to 4 d.p. ***[1 mark]***

$x_2 = \dfrac{\ln(0.51139...+2)}{\ln 6} = 0.51392... = 0.5139$ to 4 d.p. ***[1 mark]***

$x_3 = \dfrac{\ln(0.51392...+2)}{\ln 6} = 0.51449... = 0.5145$ to 4 d.p. ***[1 mark]***

c) If $x = 0.515$ to 3 d.p., the upper and lower bounds are 0.5155 and 0.5145 ***[1 mark]*** — any value in this range would be rounded to 0.515. $f(x) = 6^x - x - 2$, and at point P, $f(x) = 0$. $f(0.5145) = -0.000537$ and $f(0.5155) = 0.00297$ ***[1 mark for both f(0.5145) negative and f(0.5155) positive]***. There is a change of sign, and since $f(x)$ is continuous there must be a root in this interval ***[1 mark]***.

8 $\sin 2\theta \equiv 2\sin\theta\cos\theta$, so $3\sin 2\theta\tan\theta \equiv 6\sin\theta\cos\theta\tan\theta$ ***[1 mark]***. As $\tan\theta \equiv \dfrac{\sin\theta}{\cos\theta}$,

$6\sin\theta\cos\theta\tan\theta \equiv 6\sin\theta\cos\theta\dfrac{\sin\theta}{\cos\theta} \equiv 6\sin^2\theta$ ***[1 mark]***,

so $3\sin 2\theta\tan\theta = 5 \Rightarrow 6\sin^2\theta = 5$ ***[1 mark]***.

Then $\sin^2\theta = \frac{5}{6} \Rightarrow \sin\theta = \pm\sqrt{\frac{5}{6}} = \pm 0.9129$ ***[1 mark]***.

Solving this for θ gives $\theta = 1.15, 1.99, 4.29, 5.13$ ***[2 marks for all 4 correct answers, 1 mark for 2 correct answers]***.

Don't forget the solutions for the negative square root as well — they're easy to miss. Drawing a sketch here is really useful — you can see that there are 4 solutions you need to find:

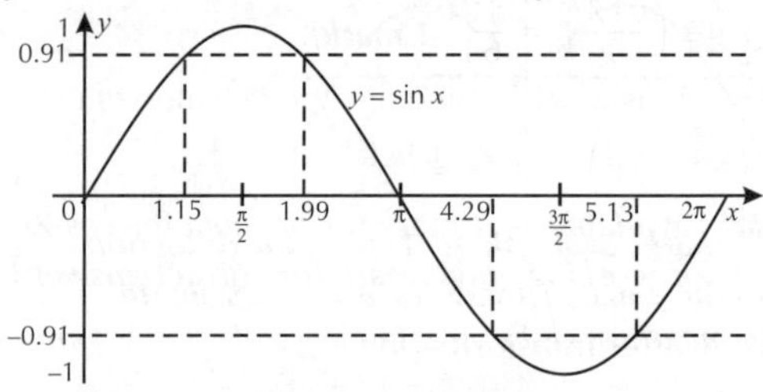

9 a) For $x = \dfrac{e^y + 2y}{e^y - 2y}$, use the quotient rule to find $\dfrac{dx}{dy}$:

$u = e^y + 2y \Rightarrow \dfrac{du}{dy} = e^y + 2$

$v = e^y - 2y \Rightarrow \dfrac{dv}{dy} = e^y - 2$

$$\frac{dx}{dy} = \frac{v\frac{du}{dy} - u\frac{dv}{dy}}{v^2} = \frac{(e^y - 2y)(e^y + 2) - (e^y + 2y)(e^y - 2)}{(e^y - 2y)^2}$$

$$= \frac{(e^{2y} + 2e^y - 2ye^y - 4y) - (e^{2y} - 2e^y + 2ye^y - 4y)}{(e^y - 2y)^2}$$

$$= \frac{4e^y - 4ye^y}{(e^y - 2y)^2} = \frac{4e^y(1-y)}{(e^y - 2y)^2}.$$

$$\frac{dy}{dx} = \frac{1}{\frac{dx}{dy}} = \frac{(e^y - 2y)^2}{4e^y(1-y)}.$$

[3 marks available — 1 mark for correct expressions for du/dy and dv/dy, 1 mark for finding expression for dx/dy using the quotient rule, and 1 mark for correct (or equivalent) expression for dy/dx]

b) At the point (1, 0), $y = 0$ and so $e^y = e^0 = 1$. So the gradient at that point is:

$\dfrac{dy}{dx} = \dfrac{(1-0)^2}{4(1-0)} = \dfrac{1}{4}$.

The gradient of the normal at that point is $-1 \div \frac{1}{4} = -4$.

Equation of a straight line is $y - y_1 = m(x - x_1)$, so at (1, 0) with $m = -4$, the equation of the normal is:

$y - 0 = -4(x - 1) \Rightarrow y = -4x + 4$.

[3 marks available — 1 mark for finding gradient of the normal, 1 mark for correct substitution of –4 and (1, 0) into equation, and 1 mark for rearrangement into the correct form.]

10 a) $\sec x = \dfrac{1}{\cos x}$, so as $\cos x = \frac{8}{9}$, $\sec x = \frac{9}{8}$ ***[1 mark]***.

b) The right-angled triangle with angle x, hypotenuse of length 9 and the adjacent side of length 8 (which gives the $\cos x$ value as stated) has the opposite side of length

Answers

$\sqrt{9^2 - 8^2} = \sqrt{81 - 64} = \sqrt{17}$ ***[1 mark]***. It looks like this:

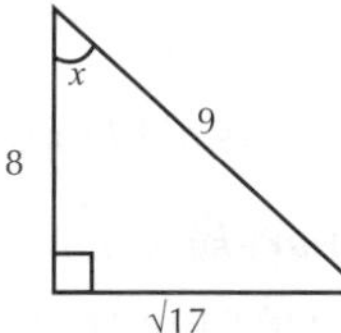

So the value of $\sin x = \frac{\sqrt{17}}{9}$ (opposite / hypotenuse).

$\text{cosec} x = \frac{1}{\sin x}$, so $\text{cosec } x = \frac{9}{\sqrt{17}}$ ***[1 mark]***.

c) For the triangle described in part (b), the value of $\tan x$ is given by opposite / adjacent $= \frac{\sqrt{17}}{8}$ ***[1 mark]***.

So $\tan^2 x = \left(\frac{\sqrt{17}}{8}\right)^2 = \frac{17}{64}$ ***[1 mark]***.

d) $\cos 2x = 2\cos^2 x - 1$. Using the known value of $\cos x$,
$\cos 2x = 2 \cdot \left(\frac{8}{9}\right)^2 - 1 = 2 \cdot \frac{64}{81} - 1 = \frac{47}{81}$.
[3 marks available — 1 mark for formula for cos 2x, 1 mark for working and 1 mark for correct answer.]

You could have used the other versions of the cos 2x formula here ($\cos^2 x - \sin^2 x$ or $1 - 2\sin^2 x$) — just use the values you found for sin x in part b).

Practice Exam Two

1 a) $\sqrt{2}\cos\theta - 3\sin\theta \equiv R\cos(\theta + \alpha)$. Using the cos addition rule, $R\cos(\theta + \alpha) \equiv R\cos\theta\cos\alpha - R\sin\theta\sin\alpha$,
so $R\cos\alpha = \sqrt{2}$ and $R\sin\alpha = 3$ ***[1 mark]***.

$\frac{R\sin\alpha}{R\cos\alpha} = \tan\alpha$, so $\tan\alpha = \frac{3}{\sqrt{2}}$

Solving this gives $\alpha = 1.13$ (3 s.f.) ***[1 mark]***.

$R = \sqrt{(\sqrt{2})^2 + 3^2} = \sqrt{2 + 9} = \sqrt{11}$ ***[1 mark]***,
$\sqrt{2}\cos\theta - 3\sin\theta = \sqrt{11}\cos(\theta + 1.13)$.

b) If $\sqrt{2}\cos\theta - 3\sin\theta = 3$, then $\sqrt{11}\cos(\theta + 1.13) = 3$.
So $\cos(\theta + 1.13) = \frac{3}{\sqrt{11}}$. Solving this gives $\theta + 1.13 = 0.441$ (3 s.f.) ***[1 mark]***. The range of solutions becomes $1.13 \le \theta + 1.13 \le 7.41$ $(2\pi + 1.13)$. To find the other values of θ within the new range, $2\pi - 0.441 = 5.84$, $2\pi + 0.441 = 6.72$ ***[1 mark]***. Subtracting 1.13 gives $\theta = 4.71, 5.59$ ***[1 mark for each correct value]***.

You can sketch the graph to help you find all the values of θ.

c) $(\sqrt{2}\cos\theta - 3\sin\theta)^4 = (\sqrt{11}\cos(\theta + 1.13))^4$. The maximum values occur when $\cos(\theta + 1.13) = \pm 1$. This value is $(\pm\sqrt{11})^4 = 121$ ***[1 mark]***. Solving $\cos(\theta + 1.13) = 1$ gives the location of one maximum as $2\pi - 1.13 = 5.15$. Solving $\cos(\theta + 1.13) = -1$ gives the location of the other maximum as $\pi - 1.13 = 2.01$. So the maximum values occur at $\theta = 2.01$ and $\theta = 5.15$ ***[1 mark]***.
Since $(\sqrt{11}\cos(\theta + 1.13))^4 \ge 0$, the minimum value is 0 ***[1 mark]*** and it occurs when $\cos(\theta + 1.13) = 0$. Solving this gives the locations of the minimums at $\frac{\pi}{2} - 1.13 = 0.44$ and $\frac{3\pi}{2} - 1.13 = 3.58$ ***[1 mark]***.

This one was a bit nasty — if you didn't realise that $(\sqrt{11}\cos(\theta + 1.13))^4$ is never negative, you'd have got the minimum values wrong.

2 a) g has range $g(x) \ge -9$ ***[1 mark]***, as the minimum value of g is -9.

b) Neither f nor g are one-to-one functions, so they don't have inverses ***[1 mark]***.

f and g are many-to-one not one-to-one, as more than one value of x is mapped to the same f(x) or g(x) value, e.g. x = 1 and x = −1 are both mapped to f(x) = 1 and g(x)= −8.

c) (i) $fg(4) = f(4^2 - 9) = f(7)$ ***[1 mark]*** $= \frac{1}{7^2} = \frac{1}{49}$ ***[1 mark]***.

(ii) $gf(1) = g(1/1^2) = g(1)$ ***[1 mark]*** $= 1^2 - 9 = -8$ ***[1 mark]***.

d) (i) $fg(x) = f(x^2 - 9)$ ***[1 mark]*** $= \frac{1}{(x^2 - 9)^2}$ ***[1 mark]***.
The domain of fg is $x \in \mathbb{R}$, $x \neq \pm 3$ ***[1 mark]***, as the denominator of the function can't be 0.

(ii) From part (i), you know that $fg(x) = \frac{1}{(x^2 - 9)^2}$, so

$$\frac{1}{(x^2 - 9)^2} = \frac{1}{256} \Rightarrow (x^2 - 9)^2 = 256 \quad \textbf{[1 mark]}$$
$$x^2 - 9 = \pm\sqrt{256} = \pm 16 \quad \textbf{[1 mark]}$$
$$x^2 = 9 \pm 16 = 25, -7 \quad \textbf{[1 mark]}$$
$$x = \sqrt{25} = \pm 5 \quad \textbf{[1 mark]}$$

You can ignore $x^2 = -7$, as this has no solutions in $x \in \mathbb{R}$.

3 a) $\frac{x^2 + 5x - 14}{2x^2 - 4x} = \frac{(x + 7)(x - 2)}{2x(x - 2)} = \frac{x + 7}{2x}$
[3 marks available — 1 mark for factorising the numerator, 1 mark for factorising the denominator and 1 mark for cancelling to obtain correct answer]

b) $\frac{x^2 + 5x - 14}{2x^2 - 4x} + \frac{14}{x(x - 4)} = \frac{x + 7}{2x} + \frac{14}{x(x - 4)}$
$= \frac{(x + 7)(x - 4)}{2x(x - 4)} + \frac{2 \cdot 14}{2x(x - 4)}$
$= \frac{x^2 + 3x - 28 + 28}{2x(x - 4)} = \frac{x^2 + 3x}{2x(x - 4)}$
$= \frac{x(x + 3)}{2x(x - 4)} = \frac{x + 3}{2(x - 4)}$
[3 marks available — 1 mark for putting fractions over a common denominator, 1 mark for multiplying out and simplifying the numerator and 1 mark for cancelling to obtain correct answer]

4 a) $f(x) = (\sqrt{x + 2})\ln(x + 2)$,
so $f(7) = (\sqrt{7 + 2})\ln(7 + 2) = (\sqrt{9})\ln 9 = 3\ln 9$ ***[1 mark]***.
Using the log laws:
$f(7) = 3\ln(3^2) = 2 \times 3\ln 3 = 6\ln 3$ ***[1 mark]***.

b) For $y = (\sqrt{x + 2})\ln(x + 2)$, use the product rule:
$u = \sqrt{x + 2} = (x + 2)^{\frac{1}{2}} \Rightarrow \frac{du}{dx} = \frac{1}{2}(x + 2)^{-\frac{1}{2}} = \frac{1}{2\sqrt{x + 2}}$
$v = \ln(x + 2) \Rightarrow \frac{dv}{dx} = \frac{1}{x + 2}$.
$f'(x) = \frac{dy}{dx} = u\frac{dv}{dx} + v\frac{du}{dx} = \frac{\sqrt{x + 2}}{x + 2} + \frac{\ln(x + 2)}{2\sqrt{x + 2}}$.
So $f'(7) = \frac{\sqrt{7 + 2}}{7 + 2} + \frac{\ln(7 + 2)}{2\sqrt{7 + 2}} = \frac{3}{9} + \frac{\ln 9}{2 \times 3}$.
Since, using log laws, $\ln 9 = \ln 3^2 = 2\ln 3$,
$f'(7) = \frac{1}{3} + \frac{2\ln 3}{2 \times 3} = \frac{1}{3} + \frac{\ln 3}{3} = \frac{1}{3}(1 + \ln 3)$.
[4 marks available — 1 mark for correct expressions for du/dx and dv/dx, 1 mark for correct use of product rule formula, 1 mark for correct substitution of x = 7, and 1 mark for correct rearrangement using the log laws]

Answers

c) Equation of a straight line is $y - y_1 = m(x - x_1)$. For the tangent at $x = 7$, $y = 6\ln 3$ (from (a)) and $m = \frac{1}{3}(1 + \ln 3)$ (from (b)), so the equation of the tangent is:

$y - 6\ln 3 = \frac{1}{3}(1 + \ln 3)(x - 7)$

$\Rightarrow y = \frac{1}{3}(1 + \ln 3)(x - 7) + 6\ln 3$

$\Rightarrow 3y = (1 + \ln 3)(x - 7) + 18\ln 3$

$\Rightarrow 3y = x + x\ln 3 - 7 - 7\ln 3 + 18\ln 3$

$\Rightarrow 3y = x + x\ln 3 + 11\ln 3 - 7$.

[2 marks available — 1 mark for correct substitution of m, y_1 and x_1 into equation, 1 mark for correct rearrangement to give final answer]

5 a) $\frac{1 + \cos x}{2} = \frac{1}{2}\left(1 + \cos 2\left(\frac{x}{2}\right)\right)$ ***[1 mark]***

$= \frac{1}{2}\left(1 + \left(2\cos^2\frac{x}{2} - 1\right)\right)$ ***[1 mark]***

$= \frac{1}{2}\left(2\cos^2\frac{x}{2}\right) = \cos^2\frac{x}{2}$ ***[1 mark]***

b) As $\cos^2\frac{x}{2} = 0.75$, then $\frac{1 + \cos x}{2} = 0.75$.

So $1 + \cos x = 1.5$

$\cos x = 0.5 \Rightarrow x = \frac{\pi}{3}, \frac{5\pi}{3}$.

[4 marks available — 2 marks for rearranging equation to get in terms of cos x, 1 mark for each correct answer]

You should know the solutions to cos x = 0.5 from the trig triangles from Section 2.

6 a) $y = e^{2x} - 5e^x + 3x$, so, using chain rule:

$\frac{dy}{dx} = 2e^{2x} - 5e^x + 3$.

[2 marks available — 1 mark for $2e^{2x}$, 1 mark for rest of answer.]

b) Differentiating again gives: $\frac{d^2y}{dx^2} = 4e^{2x} - 5e^x$.

[2 marks available — 1 mark for $4e^{2x}$, 1 mark for $-5e^x$]

c) Stationary points occur when $\frac{dy}{dx} = 0$, so:

$2e^{2x} - 5e^x + 3 = 0$ ***[1 mark]***.

(This looks like a quadratic, so substitute y = eˣ and factorise...)

$2y^2 - 5y + 3 = 0 \Rightarrow (2y - 3)(y - 1) = 0$ ***[1 mark]***.

So the solutions are:

$2y - 3 = 0 \Rightarrow y = \frac{3}{2} \Rightarrow e^x = \frac{3}{2} \Rightarrow x = \ln\frac{3}{2}$ ***[1 mark]***, and

$y - 1 = 0 \Rightarrow y = 1 \Rightarrow e^x = 1 \Rightarrow x = \ln 1 = 0$ ***[1 mark]***.

d) To determine the nature of the stationary points, find $\frac{d^2y}{dx^2}$ at $x = 0$ and $x = \ln\frac{3}{2}$:

$\frac{d^2y}{dx^2} = 4e^{2x} - 5e^x$ (from (b)), so when $x = 0$:

$\frac{d^2y}{dx^2} = 4e^0 - 5e^0 = 4 - 5 = -1$ ***[1 mark]***,

so $\frac{d^2y}{dx^2} < 0$, which means the point is a maximum ***[1 mark]***.

When $x = \ln\frac{3}{2}$:

$\frac{d^2y}{dx^2} = 4e^{2\ln\frac{3}{2}} - 5e^{\ln\frac{3}{2}} = 4\left(\frac{3}{2}\right)^2 - 5\left(\frac{3}{2}\right) = \frac{3}{2}$ ***[1 mark]***,

so $\frac{d^2y}{dx^2} > 0$, which means the point is a minimum ***[1 mark]***.

7 a) $P = 5700e^{-0.15t}$, so when $t = 0$, $P = 5700e^0 = 5700$ ***[1 mark]***.

b) At the start of 2020, $t = 10$,

so $P = 5700e^{-0.15 \times 10} = 1271.8419...$

$= 1271$

[2 marks available — 1 mark for correct substitution of t = 10, 1 mark for correct final answer]

Remember — round down as there are only 1271 whole birds.

c) When $P = 1000$: $1000 = 5700e^{-0.15t} \Rightarrow 1000 = \frac{5700}{e^{0.15t}}$

$\Rightarrow e^{0.15t} = \frac{5700}{1000} = 5.7$ ***[1 mark]***. Take ln of both sides:

$0.15t = \ln 5.7 \Rightarrow t = \frac{\ln 5.7}{0.15} = 11.6031...$ years.

So the population will drop below 1000 in the year 2021 ***[1 mark]***.

d)

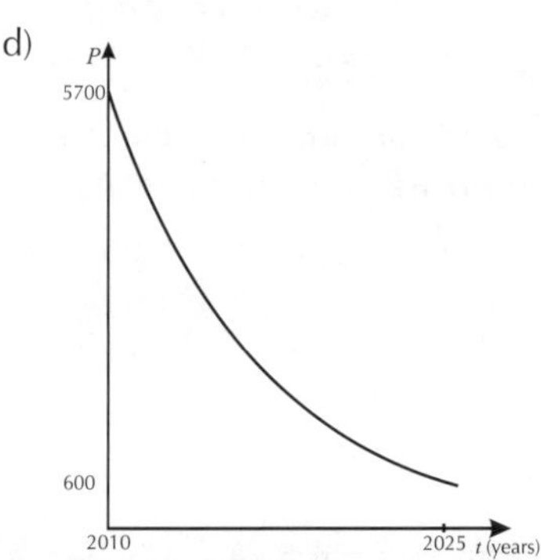

[3 marks available — 1 mark for correct shape of graph, 1 mark for (0, 5700) labelled, 1 mark for calculating P when t = 15 (the population ≈ 600 in 2025)]

8 a) To find the inverse, let $y = f(x)$, so $y = 4(x^2 - 1)$. Now make x the subject: $y = 4(x^2 - 1) \Rightarrow \frac{y}{4} = x^2 - 1 \Rightarrow \frac{y}{4} + 1 = x^2$

so $x = \sqrt{\frac{y}{4} + 1}$ ***[1 mark]*** (you can ignore the negative square root, as the domain of f(x) is $x \geq 0$). Finally, replace y with x and x with $f^{-1}(x)$: $f^{-1}(x) = \sqrt{\frac{x}{4} + 1}$ ***[1 mark]***.

$f^{-1}(x)$ is a reflection of f(x) in the line $y = x$ ***[1 mark]***, so the point at which the lines f(x) and $f^{-1}(x)$ meet is also the point where $f^{-1}(x)$ meets the line $y = x$. At this point, $x = \sqrt{\frac{x}{4} + 1}$ ***[1 mark]***.

b) Let $g(x) = \sqrt{\frac{x}{4} + 1} - x$ ***[1 mark]***.

If there is a root in the interval $1 < x < 2$ then there will be a change of sign for g(x) between 1 and 2:

$g(1) = \sqrt{\frac{1}{4} + 1} - 1 = 0.1180...$

$g(2) = \sqrt{\frac{2}{4} + 1} - 2 = -0.7752...$ ***[1 mark for both]***

There is a change of sign, so there is a root in the interval $1 < x < 2$ ***[1 mark]***.

c) $x_{n+1} = \sqrt{\frac{x_n}{4} + 1}$, and $x_0 = 1$, so:

$x_1 = \sqrt{\frac{1}{4} + 1} = 1.1180...$ ***[1 mark]***

$x_2 = \sqrt{\frac{1.1180...}{4} + 1} = 1.1311...$

$x_3 = \sqrt{\frac{1.1311...}{4} + 1} = 1.1326...$ ***[1 mark]***

So $x = 1.13$ to 3 s.f. ***[1 mark]***.

Answers

C4 Section 1 — Algebra and Functions

Warm-up Questions

For these questions, you can use the substitution method or the equating coefficients method. I've just shown one method for each.

1) a) $\frac{4x+5}{(x+4)(2x-3)} \equiv \frac{A}{(x+4)} + \frac{B}{(2x-3)}$

$4x + 5 \equiv A(2x - 3) + B(x + 4)$

Using substitution method:

substitute $x = -4$: $-11 = -11A \Rightarrow A = 1$

substitute $x = 1.5$: $11 = 5.5B \Rightarrow B = 2$

$\frac{4x+5}{(x+4)(2x-3)} \equiv \frac{1}{(x+4)} + \frac{2}{(2x-3)}$

b) $\frac{-7x-7}{(3x+1)(x-2)} \equiv \frac{A}{(3x+1)} + \frac{B}{(x-2)}$

$-7x - 7 \equiv A(x - 2) + B(3x + 1)$

Using equating coefficients method:

coefficients of x: $-7 = A + 3B$

constants: $-7 = -2A + B$

Solving simultaneously: $A = 2$, $B = -3$

$\frac{-7x-7}{(3x+1)(x-2)} \equiv \frac{2}{(3x+1)} - \frac{3}{(x-2)}$

c) $\frac{x-18}{(x+4)(3x-4)} \equiv \frac{A}{(x+4)} + \frac{B}{(3x-4)}$

$x - 18 \equiv A(3x - 4) + B(x + 4)$

Using substitution method:

substitute $x = -4$: $-22 = -16A \Rightarrow A = \frac{11}{8}$.

And using equating coefficients method:

coefficients of x: $1 = 3A + B$

Substituting $A = \frac{11}{8}$: $1 = 3A + B \Rightarrow B = 1 - \frac{33}{8} = -\frac{25}{8}$.

$\frac{x-18}{(x+4)(3x-4)} \equiv \frac{11}{8(x+4)} - \frac{25}{8(3x-4)}$

Don't worry if you get fractions for your coefficients — just put the numerator on the top and the denominator on the bottom.

d) Factorise the denominator:

$\frac{5x}{x^2+x-6} \equiv \frac{5x}{(x+3)(x-2)} \equiv \frac{A}{(x+3)} + \frac{B}{(x-2)}$

$5x \equiv A(x - 2) + B(x + 3)$

Using substitution method:

substitute $x = -3$: $-15 = -5A \Rightarrow A = 3$

substitute $x = 2$: $10 = 5B \Rightarrow B = 2$

$\frac{5x}{x^2+x-6} \equiv \frac{3}{(x+3)} + \frac{2}{(x-2)}$

e) Factorise the denominator:

$\frac{6+4y}{9-y^2} \equiv \frac{6+4y}{(3-y)(3+y)} \equiv \frac{A}{(3-y)} + \frac{B}{(3+y)}$

$6 + 4y \equiv A(3 + y) + B(3 - y)$

Using substitution method:

substitute $y = 3$: $18 = 6A \Rightarrow A = 3$

substitute $y = -3$: $-6 = 6B \Rightarrow B = -1$

$\frac{6+4y}{9-y^2} \equiv \frac{3}{(3-y)} - \frac{1}{(3+y)}$

f) $\frac{10x^2+32x+16}{(x+3)(2x+4)(x-2)} \equiv \frac{A}{(x+3)} + \frac{B}{(2x+4)} + \frac{C}{(x-2)}$

$10x^2 + 32x + 16$

$\equiv A(2x + 4)(x - 2) + B(x + 3)(x - 2) + C(x + 3)(2x + 4)$

Using substitution method:

substitute $x = 2$: $120 = 40C \Rightarrow C = 3$

substitute $x = -3$: $10 = 10A \Rightarrow A = 1$

substitute $x = -2$: $-8 = -4B \Rightarrow B = 2$

$\frac{10x^2+32x+16}{(x+3)(2x+4)(x-2)} \equiv \frac{1}{(x+3)} + \frac{2}{(2x+4)} + \frac{3}{(x-2)}$

g) Factorise the denominator:

$\frac{4x^2+12x+6}{x^3+3x^2+2x} \equiv \frac{4x^2+12x+6}{x(x^2+3x+2)} \equiv \frac{4x^2+12x+6}{x(x+1)(x+2)}$

$\equiv \frac{A}{x} + \frac{B}{(x+1)} + \frac{C}{(x+2)}$

$4x^2 + 12x + 6 \equiv A(x + 1)(x + 2) + Bx(x + 2) + Cx(x + 1)$

Using substitution method:

substitute $x = -1$: $-2 = -B \Rightarrow B = 2$

substitute $x = 0$: $6 = 2A \Rightarrow A = 3$

substitute $x = -2$: $-2 = 2C \Rightarrow C = -1$

$\frac{4x^2+12x+6}{x^3+3x^2+2x} \equiv \frac{3}{x} + \frac{2}{(x+1)} - \frac{1}{(x+2)}$

h) $\frac{-11x^2+6x+11}{(2x+1)(3-x)(x+2)} \equiv \frac{A}{(2x+1)} + \frac{B}{(3-x)} + \frac{C}{(x+2)}$

$-11x^2 + 6x + 11$

$\equiv A(3 - x)(x + 2) + B(2x + 1)(x + 2) + C(2x + 1)(3 - x)$

Using substitution method:

substitute $x = 3$: $-70 = 35B \Rightarrow B = -2$

substitute $x = -2$: $-45 = -15C \Rightarrow C = 3$

substitute $x = -0.5$: $5.25 = 5.25A \Rightarrow A = 1$

$\frac{-11x^2+6x+11}{(2x+1)(3-x)(x+2)} \equiv \frac{1}{(2x+1)} - \frac{2}{(3-x)} + \frac{3}{(x+2)}$

2) a) $\frac{2x+2}{(x+3)^2} \equiv \frac{A}{(x+3)} + \frac{B}{(x+3)^2}$

$2x + 2 \equiv A(x + 3) + B$

Using substitution method:

substitute $x = -3$: $-4 = B$

substitute $x = 0$: $2 = 3A - 4 \Rightarrow A = 2$

$\frac{2x+2}{(x+3)^2} \equiv \frac{2}{(x+3)} - \frac{4}{(x+3)^2}$

b) $\frac{6x^2+17x+5}{x(x+2)^2} \equiv \frac{A}{x} + \frac{B}{(x+2)} + \frac{C}{(x+2)^2}$

$6x^2 + 17x + 5 \equiv A(x + 2)^2 + Bx(x + 2) + Cx$

substitute $x = -2$: $-5 = -2C \Rightarrow C = \frac{5}{2}$

substitute $x = 0$: $5 = 4A \Rightarrow A = \frac{5}{4}$

coefficients of x^2: $6 = A + B$

substitute $A = \frac{5}{4}$: $6 = \frac{5}{4} + B \Rightarrow B = \frac{19}{4}$

$\frac{6x^2+19x+8}{x(x+2)^2} \equiv \frac{5}{4x} + \frac{19}{4(x+2)} + \frac{5}{2(x+2)^2}$

Answers

c) $\frac{-18x+14}{(2x-1)^2(x+2)} \equiv \frac{A}{(2x-1)} + \frac{B}{(2x-1)^2} + \frac{C}{(x+2)}$

$-18x + 14 \equiv A(2x-1)(x+2) + B(x+2) + C(2x-1)^2$

substitute $x = -2$: $50 = 25C \Rightarrow C = 2$

substitute $x = 0.5$: $5 = 2.5B \Rightarrow B = 2$

coefficients of x^2: $0 = 2A + 4C$

substitute $C = 2$: $0 = 2A + 8 \Rightarrow A = -4$

$\frac{-18x+14}{(2x-1)^2(x+2)} \equiv \frac{-4}{(2x-1)} + \frac{2}{(2x-1)^2} + \frac{2}{(x+2)}$

d) Factorise the denominator:

$\frac{8x^2-x-5}{x^3-x^2} \equiv \frac{8x^2-x-5}{x^2(x-1)} \equiv \frac{A}{x} + \frac{B}{x^2} + \frac{C}{(x-1)}$

$8x^2 - x - 5 \equiv Ax(x-1) + B(x-1) + Cx^2$

coefficients of x^2: $8 = A + C$ (eq. 1)

coefficients of x: $-1 = -A + B$ (eq. 2)

constants: $-5 = -B \Rightarrow B = 5$

substitute $B = 5$ in eq. 2: $-1 = -A + 5 \Rightarrow A = 6$

substitute $A = 6$ in eq. 1: $8 = 6 + C \Rightarrow C = 2$

$\frac{8x^2-x-5}{x^3-x^2} \equiv \frac{6}{x} + \frac{5}{x^2} + \frac{2}{(x-1)}$

3) a) Expand the denominator:

$\frac{2x^2+18x+26}{(x+2)(x+4)} \equiv \frac{2x^2+18x+26}{x^2+6x+8}$

Divide the fraction:

$$\begin{array}{r} 2 \\ x^2+6x+8\overline{)2x^2+18x+26} \\ \underline{2x^2+12x+16} \\ 6x+10 \end{array}$$

$\frac{2x^2+18x+26}{(x+2)(x+4)} \equiv 2 + \frac{6x+10}{(x+2)(x+4)}$

Now express $\frac{6x+10}{(x+2)(x+4)}$ as partial fractions:

$\frac{6x+10}{(x+2)(x+4)} \equiv \frac{A}{(x+2)} + \frac{B}{(x+4)}$

$6x + 10 \equiv A(x+4) + B(x+2)$

substitute $x = -4$: $-14 = -2B \Rightarrow B = 7$

substitute $x = -2$: $-2 = 2A \Rightarrow A = -1$

So overall $\frac{2x^2+18x+26}{(x+2)(x+4)} \equiv 2 - \frac{1}{(x+2)} + \frac{7}{(x+4)}$

b) Expand the denominator:

$\frac{3x^2+9x+2}{x(x+1)} \equiv \frac{3x^2+9x+2}{x^2+x}$

Divide the fraction:

$$\begin{array}{r} 3 \\ x^2+x\overline{)3x^2+9x+2} \\ \underline{3x^2+3x} \\ 6x+2 \end{array}$$

$\frac{3x^2+9x+2}{x(x+1)} \equiv 3 + \frac{6x+2}{x(x+1)}$

Now express $\frac{6x+2}{x(x+1)}$ as partial fractions:

$\frac{6x+2}{x(x+1)} \equiv \frac{A}{x} + \frac{B}{(x+1)}$

$6x + 2 \equiv A(x+1) + Bx$

substitute $x = -1$: $-4 = -B \Rightarrow B = 4$

substitute $x = 0$: $2 = A$

So overall $\frac{3x^2+9x+2}{x(x+1)} \equiv 3 + \frac{2}{x} + \frac{4}{(x+1)}$

c) Expand the denominator:

$\frac{24x^2-70x+53}{(2x-3)^2} \equiv \frac{24x^2-70x+53}{4x^2-12x+9}$

Divide the fraction:

$$\begin{array}{r} 6 \\ 4x^2-12x+9\overline{)24x^2-70x+53} \\ \underline{24x^2-72x+54} \\ 2x-1 \end{array}$$

$\frac{24x^2-70x+53}{(2x-3)^2} \equiv 6 + \frac{2x-1}{(2x-3)^2}$

Now express $\frac{2x-1}{(2x-3)^2}$ as partial fractions:

$\frac{2x-1}{(2x-3)^2} \equiv \frac{A}{(2x-3)} + \frac{B}{(2x-3)^2}$

$2x - 1 \equiv A(2x-3) + B$

substitute $x = 1.5$: $2 = B$

substitute $x = 0$, and $B = 2$: $-1 = -3A + 2 \Rightarrow A = 1$

So overall $\frac{24x^2-70x+53}{(2x-3)^2} \equiv 6 + \frac{1}{(2x-3)} + \frac{2}{(2x-3)^2}$

d) Expand the denominator:

$\frac{3x^3-2x^2-2x-3}{(x+1)(x-2)} \equiv \frac{3x^3-2x^2-2x-3}{x^2-x-2}$

Divide the fraction using $f(x) = q(x)d(x) + r(x)$:

$3x^3 - 2x^2 - 2x - 3 = (Ax + B)(x^2 - x - 2) + Cx + D$

coefficients of x^3: $3 = A$

coefficients of x^2: $-2 = -A + B$

substitute $A = 3$: $-2 = -3 + B \Rightarrow B = 1$

coefficients of x: $-2 = -2A - B + C$

substitute $A = 3$ and $B = 1$: $-2 = -6 - 1 + C \Rightarrow C = 5$

constants: $-3 = -2B + D$

substitute $B = 1$: $-3 = -2 + D \Rightarrow D = -1$

$\frac{3x^3-2x^2-2x-3}{(x+1)(x-2)} \equiv 3x + 1 + \frac{5x-1}{(x+1)(x-2)}$

Now express $\frac{5x-1}{(x+1)(x-2)}$ as partial fractions:

$\frac{5x-1}{(x+1)(x-2)} \equiv \frac{M}{(x+1)} + \frac{N}{(x-2)}$

$5x - 1 \equiv M(x-2) + N(x+1)$

substitute $x = 2$: $9 = 3N \Rightarrow N = 3$

substitute $x = -1$: $-6 = -3M \Rightarrow M = 2$

So overall $\frac{3x^3-2x^2-2x-3}{(x+1)(x-2)} \equiv 3x + 1 + \frac{2}{(x+1)} + \frac{3}{(x-2)}$

I used the remainder theorem to divide this fraction, because it's a bit trickier than the rest have been. You could have used the remainder theorem in 3)a)-c) too, but I reckon they were easier to do with long division.

Answers

Exam Questions

1 Add the partial fractions and equate the numerators:
$5 + 9x \equiv A + B(1 + 3x)$ ***[1 mark]***
Using substitution method:
substitute $x = -\frac{1}{3}$: $2 = A \Rightarrow A = 2$ ***[1 mark]***
substitute $x = 0$: $5 = 2 + B \Rightarrow B = 3$ ***[1 mark]***

2 Expand the denominator:
$$\frac{18x^2 - 15x - 62}{(3x+4)(x-2)} \equiv \frac{18x^2 - 15x - 62}{3x^2 - 2x - 8}$$
Divide the fraction:
$$\begin{array}{r} 6 \\ 3x^2 - 2x - 8 \overline{) 18x^2 - 15x - 62} \\ \underline{18x^2 - 12x - 48} \\ -3x - 14 \end{array}$$
Watch out for the negative signs here. You're subtracting the bottom line from the top, so be sure to get it right.

You could use alternative methods — e.g. the remainder theorem for the division. You'll still get the marks, so use the one you're happiest with unless they tell you otherwise.
$$\frac{18x^2 - 15x - 62}{(3x+4)(x-2)} \equiv 6 + \frac{-3x - 14}{(3x+4)(x-2)}$$
$A = 6$ ***[1 mark]***
$$\frac{-3x - 14}{(3x+4)(x-2)} \equiv \frac{B}{(3x+4)} + \frac{C}{(x-2)}$$
$-3x - 14 \equiv B(x - 2) + C(3x + 4)$ ***[1 mark]***
substitute $x = 2$: $-20 = 10C \Rightarrow C = -2$ ***[1 mark]***
coefficients of x: $-3 = B + 3C$
$-3 = B - 6 \Rightarrow B = 3$ ***[1 mark]***

I used the equating coefficients method for the last bit, because I realised that I'd need to substitute $-\frac{4}{3}$ in for x, and I really couldn't be bothered.

3 $5x^2 + 3x + 6 \equiv A(2x - 1)^2 + B(3 + x) + C(2x - 1)(3 - x)$
[1 mark]
Using substitution method:
substitute $x = 3$: $60 = 25A \Rightarrow A = \frac{12}{5}$ ***[1 mark]***
substitute $x = \frac{1}{2}$: $\frac{35}{4} = \frac{5}{2}B \Rightarrow B = \frac{7}{2}$ ***[1 mark]***
coefficients of x^2: $5 = 4A - 2C$
substitute $A = \frac{12}{5}$: $5 = \frac{48}{5} - 2C$
$-\frac{23}{5} = -2C \Rightarrow C = \frac{23}{10}$ ***[1 mark]***

4 Expand the denominator:
$$\frac{-80x^2 + 49x - 9}{(5x-1)(2-4x)} \equiv \frac{-80x^2 + 49x - 9}{-20x^2 + 14x - 2}$$
Divide the fraction:
$$\begin{array}{r} 4 \\ -20x^2 + 14x - 2 \overline{) -80x^2 + 49x - 9} \\ \underline{-80x^2 + 56x - 8} \\ -7x - 1 \end{array}$$
$$\frac{-80x^2 + 49x - 9}{(5x-1)(2-4x)} \equiv 4 + \frac{-7x - 1}{(5x-1)(2-4x)}$$ ***[1 mark]***
$$\frac{-7x - 1}{(5x-1)(2-4x)} \equiv \frac{A}{(5x-1)} + \frac{B}{(2-4x)}$$
$-7x - 1 \equiv A(2 - 4x) + B(5x - 1)$ ***[1 mark]***
substitute $x = 0.5$: $-4.5 = 1.5B \Rightarrow B = -3$ ***[1 mark]***
coefficients of x: $-7 = -4A + 5B$
substitute $B = -3$: $-7 = -4A - 15$
$8 = -4A \Rightarrow A = -2$ ***[1 mark]***

5 a) Expand the denominator:
$$\frac{3x^2 + 12x - 11}{(x+3)(x-1)} \equiv \frac{3x^2 + 12x - 11}{x^2 + 2x - 3}$$
Divide the fraction:
$$\begin{array}{r} 3 \\ x^2 + 2x - 3 \overline{) 3x^2 + 12x - 11} \\ \underline{3x^2 + 6x - 9} \\ 6x - 2 \end{array} \Rightarrow -2 + 6x$$ ***[1 mark]***
$$\frac{3x^2 + 12x - 11}{(x+3)(x-1)} \equiv 3 + \frac{-2 + 6x}{(x+3)(x-1)}$$
$A = 3$ ***[1 mark]***, $B = -2$ ***[1 mark]***, $C = 6$ ***[1 mark]***

b) $$\frac{3x^2 + 12x - 11}{(x+3)(x-1)} \equiv 3 + \frac{-2 + 6x}{(x+3)(x-1)} \equiv 3 + \frac{M}{(x+3)} + \frac{N}{(x-1)}$$
$-2 + 6x \equiv M(x - 1) + N(x + 3)$
substitute $x = 1$: $4 = 4N \Rightarrow N = 1$ ***[1 mark]***
substitute $x = -3$: $-20 = -4M \Rightarrow M = 5$ ***[1 mark]***
So overall $\frac{3x^2 + 12x - 11}{(x+3)(x-1)} \equiv 3 + \frac{5}{(x+3)} + \frac{1}{(x-1)}$ ***[1 mark]***

C4 Section 2 — Coordinate Geometry in the (x, y) Plane

Warm-up Questions

1) a) Substitute the values of t into the parametric equations to find the corresponding values of x and y:
$t = 0 \Rightarrow x = \frac{6-0}{2} = 3$, $y = 2(0)^2 + 0 + 4 = 4$
$t = 1 \Rightarrow x = \frac{6-1}{2} = 2.5$, $y = 2(1)^2 + 1 + 4 = 7$
$t = 2 \Rightarrow x = \frac{6-2}{2} = 2$, $y = 2(2)^2 + 2 + 4 = 14$
$t = 3 \Rightarrow x = \frac{6-3}{2} = 1.5$, $y = 2(3)^2 + 3 + 4 = 25$

b) Use the given values in the parametric equations and solve for t:
(i) $\frac{6-t}{2} = -7 \Rightarrow t = 20$
(ii) $2t^2 + t + 4 = 19$
$\Rightarrow 2t^2 + t - 15 = 0$
$\Rightarrow (2t - 5)(t + 3) = 0$
$\Rightarrow t = 2.5, t = -3$

c) Rearrange the parametric equation for x to make t the subject:
$x = \frac{6-t}{2} \Rightarrow 2x = 6 - t \Rightarrow t = 6 - 2x$
Now substitute this into the parametric equation for y:
$y = 2t^2 + t + 4$
$= 2(6 - 2x)^2 + (6 - 2x) + 4$
$= 2(36 - 24x + 4x^2) + 10 - 2x$
$y = 8x^2 - 50x + 82.$

Answers

2) a) Substitute the values of θ into the parametric equations to find the corresponding values of x and y:

(i) $x = 2\sin\frac{\pi}{4} = \frac{2}{\sqrt{2}} = \sqrt{2}$

$y = \cos^2\frac{\pi}{4} + 4 = \left(\cos\frac{\pi}{4}\right)^2 + 4 = \left(\frac{1}{\sqrt{2}}\right)^2 + 4 = \frac{1}{2} + 4 = \frac{9}{2}$

So the coordinates are $\left(\sqrt{2}, \frac{9}{2}\right)$.

(ii) $x = 2\sin\frac{\pi}{6} = 2 \times \frac{1}{2} = 1$

$y = \cos^2\frac{\pi}{6} + 4 = \left(\cos\frac{\pi}{6}\right)^2 + 4 = \left(\frac{\sqrt{3}}{2}\right)^2 + 4 = \frac{3}{4} + 4 = \frac{19}{4}$

So the coordinates are $\left(1, \frac{19}{4}\right)$.

b) Use the identity $\cos^2\theta = 1 - \sin^2\theta$ in the equation for y so both equations are in terms of $\sin\theta$:

$y = \cos^2\theta + 4$
$= 1 - \sin^2\theta + 4$
$= 5 - \sin^2\theta$

Rearrange the equation for x to get $\sin^2\theta$ in terms of x:

$x = 2\sin\theta \Rightarrow \frac{x}{2} = \sin\theta \Rightarrow \sin^2\theta = \frac{x^2}{4}$

So $y = 5 - \sin^2\theta \Rightarrow y = 5 - \frac{x^2}{4}$

c) $x = 2\sin\theta$, and $-1 \leq \sin\theta \leq 1$ so $-2 \leq x \leq 2$.

I know what you're thinking — this answer section would be brightened up immensely by a cheery song-and-dance number. Sorry, no such luck I'm afraid. Here's the next answer instead...

3) Use the identity $\cos 2\theta = 1 - 2\sin^2\theta$ in the equation for y:

$y = 3 + 2\cos 2\theta$
$= 3 + 2(1 - 2\sin^2\theta)$
$= 5 - 4\sin^2\theta$

Rearrange the equation for x to get $\sin^2\theta$ in terms of x:

$x = \frac{\sin\theta}{3} \Rightarrow 3x = \sin\theta \Rightarrow \sin^2\theta = 9x^2$

So $y = 5 - 4\sin^2\theta$
$\Rightarrow y = 5 - 4(9x^2)$
$\Rightarrow y = 5 - 36x^2$

4) a) (i) On the y-axis:

$x = 0 \Rightarrow t^2 - 1 = 0 \Rightarrow t = \pm 1$

If $t = 1$, $y = 4 + \frac{3}{1} = 7$

If $t = -1$, $y = 4 + \frac{3}{-1} = 1$

So the curve crosses the y-axis at (0, 1) and (0, 7).

(ii) Substitute the parametric equations into the equation of the line:

$x + 2y = 14$
$\Rightarrow (t^2 - 1) + 2(4 + \frac{3}{t}) = 14$
$\Rightarrow t^2 - 1 + 8 + \frac{6}{t} = 14$
$\Rightarrow t^2 - 7 + \frac{6}{t} = 0$
$\Rightarrow t^3 - 7t + 6 = 0$
$\Rightarrow (t - 1)(t^2 + t - 6) = 0$
$\Rightarrow (t - 1)(t - 2)(t + 3) = 0$
$\Rightarrow t = 1, t = 2, t = -3$

When $t = 1$, $x = 0$, $y = 7$ (from part (i))

When $t = 2$, $x = 2^2 - 1 = 3$, $y = 4 + \frac{3}{2} = 5.5$

When $t = -3$, $x = (-3)^2 - 1 = 8$, $y = 4 + \frac{3}{-3} = 3$

So the curve crosses the line $x + 2y = 14$ at (0, 7), (3, 5.5) and (8, 3).

b) Use $\int y\,dx = \int y\frac{dx}{dt}\,dt$

$\frac{dx}{dt} = 2t$, so $\int y\,dx = \int \left(4 + \frac{3}{t}\right)2t\,dt = \int 8t + 6\,dt$

Exam Questions

1 a) Substitute the given value of θ into the parametric equations:

$\theta = \frac{\pi}{3} \Rightarrow x = 1 - \tan\frac{\pi}{3} = 1 - \sqrt{3}$

$y = \frac{1}{2}\sin\left(\frac{2\pi}{3}\right) = \frac{1}{2}\left(\frac{\sqrt{3}}{2}\right) = \frac{\sqrt{3}}{4}$

So $P = \left(1 - \sqrt{3}, \frac{\sqrt{3}}{4}\right)$

[2 marks available — 1 mark for substituting $\theta = \frac{\pi}{3}$ into the parametric equations, 1 mark for both coordinates of P correct.]

b) Use $y = -\frac{1}{2}$ to find the value of θ:

$-\frac{1}{2} = \frac{1}{2}\sin 2\theta \Rightarrow \sin 2\theta = -1$
$\Rightarrow 2\theta = -\frac{\pi}{2}$
$\Rightarrow \theta = -\frac{\pi}{4}$

You can also find θ using the parametric equation for x, with x = 2.

[2 marks available — 1 mark for substituting given x- or y-value into the correct parametric equation, 1 mark for finding the correct value of θ.]

c) $x = 1 - \tan\theta \Rightarrow \tan\theta = 1 - x$

$y = \frac{1}{2}\sin 2\theta$
$= \frac{1}{2}\left(\frac{2\tan\theta}{1 + \tan^2\theta}\right)$
$= \frac{\tan\theta}{1 + \tan^2\theta}$
$= \frac{(1 - x)}{1 + (1 - x)^2}$
$= \frac{1 - x}{1 + 1 - 2x + x^2}$
$= \frac{1 - x}{x^2 - 2x + 2}$

[3 marks available — 1 mark for using the given identity to rearrange one of the parametric equations, 1 mark for eliminating θ from the parametric equation for y, 1 mark for correctly expanding to give the Cartesian equation given in the question.]

Just think, if you lived in the Bahamas, you could be doing this revision on the beach. (Please ignore that comment if you actually do live in the Bahamas. Or anywhere else where you can revise on the beach.)

2 a) Substitute $y = 1$ into the parametric equation for y:

$t^2 - 2t + 2 = 1$
$\Rightarrow t^2 - 2t + 1 = 0$
$\Rightarrow (t - 1)^2 = 0$
$\Rightarrow t = 1$ ***[1 mark]***

So a is the value of x when $t = 1$.

$a = t^3 + t = 1^3 + 1 = 2$ ***[1 mark]***

Answers

b) Substitute the parametric equations for x and y into the equation of the line:

$8y = x + 6$

$\Rightarrow \; 8(t^2 - 2t + 2) = (t^3 + t) + 6$ ***[1 mark]***

$\Rightarrow \; 8t^2 - 16t + 16 = t^3 + t + 6$

$\Rightarrow \; t^3 - 8t^2 + 17t - 10 = 0$

We know that this line passes through K, and from a) we know that $t = 1$ at K, so $t = 1$ is a solution of this equation, and $(t - 1)$ is a factor:

$\Rightarrow \; (t - 1)(t^2 - 7t + 10) = 0$ ***[1 mark]***

$\Rightarrow \; (t - 1)(t - 2)(t - 5) = 0$

So $t = 2$ at L and $t = 5$ at M. ***[1 mark]***

If you got stuck on this bit, go back and look up 'factorising cubics' in your AS notes.

Substitute $t = 2$ and $t = 5$ back into the parametric equations: ***[1 mark]***

If $t = 2$, then $x = 2^3 + 2 = 10$
and $y = 2^2 - 2(2) + 2 = 2$

If $t = 5$, then $x = 5^3 + 5 = 130$
and $y = 5^2 - 2(5) + 2 = 17$

So $L = (10, 2)$ ***[1 mark]***
and $M = (130, 17)$ ***[1 mark]***

3 a) The area $R = \int_4^{18} y\,dx$ ***[1 mark]***

$\frac{dx}{dt} = 2t + 3$ ***[1 mark]***

Change the limits of the integral:

$x = 18 \Rightarrow t^2 + 3t - 18 = 0 \Rightarrow (t - 3)(t + 6) = 0 \Rightarrow t = 3, t = -6$

$x = 4 \Rightarrow t^2 + 3t - 4 = 0 \Rightarrow (t - 1)(t + 4) = 0 \Rightarrow t = 1, t = -4$

$t > 0$, so we can ignore the negative values of t, so the limits are $t = 3$ and $t = 1$. ***[1 mark]***

$$\text{So } R = \int_4^{18} y\,dx = \int_1^3 y\frac{dx}{dt}\,dt$$
$$= \int_1^3 \left(t^2 + \frac{1}{t^3}\right)(2t + 3)\,dt$$
$$= \int_1^3 \left(\frac{t^5 + 1}{t^3}\right)(2t + 3)\,dt$$
$$= \int_1^3 \frac{(t^5 + 1)(2t + 3)}{t^3}\,dt \quad \textbf{\textit{[1 mark]}}$$

b)
$$R = \int_1^3 \frac{(t^5 + 1)(2t + 3)}{t^3}\,dt$$
$$= \int_1^3 \frac{2t^6 + 3t^5 + 2t + 3}{t^3}\,dt$$
$$= \int_1^3 \frac{2t^6}{t^3} + \frac{3t^5}{t^3} + \frac{2t}{t^3} + \frac{3}{t^3}\,dt$$
$$= \int_1^3 2t^3 + 3t^2 + 2t^{-2} + 3t^{-3}\,dt \quad \textbf{\textit{[1 mark]}}$$
$$= \left[\frac{t^4}{2} + t^3 - 2t^{-1} - \frac{3}{2}t^{-2}\right]_1^3 \quad \textbf{\textit{[1 mark]}}$$
$$= \left(\frac{81}{2} + 27 - \frac{2}{3} - \frac{1}{6}\right) - \left(\frac{1}{2} + 1 - 2 - \frac{3}{2}\right) \quad \textbf{\textit{[1 mark]}}$$
$$= \frac{200}{3} - (-2)$$
$$= \frac{206}{3} \quad \textbf{\textit{[1 mark]}}$$

4 a) Use the x- or y-coordinate of H in the relevant parametric equation to find θ:

At H, $3 + 4\sin\theta = 5$

$\Rightarrow 4\sin\theta = 2$

$\Rightarrow \sin\theta = \frac{1}{2}$

$\Rightarrow \theta = \frac{\pi}{6}$

OR

At H, $\frac{1 + \cos 2\theta}{3} = \frac{1}{2}$

$\Rightarrow 1 + \cos 2\theta = \frac{3}{2}$

$\Rightarrow \cos 2\theta = \frac{1}{2}$

$\Rightarrow 2\theta = \frac{\pi}{3}$

$\Rightarrow \theta = \frac{\pi}{6}$

[2 marks available — 1 mark for substituting one coordinate of H into the correct parametric equation, 1 mark finding the correct value of θ.]

b) $R = \int_{-1}^{5} y\,dx$

To get the integral with respect to θ, we need to use

$\int y\,dx = \int y\frac{dx}{d\theta}\,d\theta$ ***[1 mark]***

$\frac{dx}{d\theta} = 4\cos\theta$ ***[1 mark]***

Change the limits of the integral:

$x = 5 \Rightarrow \theta = \frac{\pi}{6}$, from part a)

$x = -1 \Rightarrow 3 + 4\sin\theta = -1$

$\Rightarrow 4\sin\theta = -4$

$\Rightarrow \sin\theta = -1$

$\Rightarrow \theta = -\frac{\pi}{2}$ ***[1 mark]***

$$\text{So } R = \int_{-1}^{5} y\,dx = \int_{-\frac{\pi}{2}}^{\frac{\pi}{6}} y\frac{dx}{d\theta}\,d\theta$$
$$= \int_{-\frac{\pi}{2}}^{\frac{\pi}{6}} \left(\frac{1 + \cos 2\theta}{3}\right)(4\cos\theta)\,d\theta \quad \textbf{\textit{[1 mark]}}$$
$$= \int_{-\frac{\pi}{2}}^{\frac{\pi}{6}} \frac{4}{3}(1 + \cos 2\theta)(\cos\theta)\,d\theta$$
$$= \int_{-\frac{\pi}{2}}^{\frac{\pi}{6}} \frac{4}{3}(2\cos^2\theta)(\cos\theta)\,d\theta$$

(Using $\cos 2\theta \equiv 2\cos^2\theta - 1$) ***[1 mark]***

$$= \frac{8}{3}\int_{-\frac{\pi}{2}}^{\frac{\pi}{6}} \cos^3\theta\,d\theta$$

c) Rearrange the parametric equation for x to make $\sin\theta$ the subject:

$x = 3 + 4\sin\theta \;\Rightarrow\; \sin\theta = \frac{x - 3}{4}$ ***[1 mark]***

Use the identity $\cos 2\theta = 1 - 2\sin^2\theta$ to rewrite the parametric equation for y in terms of $\sin\theta$:

$$y = \frac{1 + \cos 2\theta}{3}$$
$$= \frac{1 + (1 - 2\sin^2\theta)}{3} \quad \textbf{\textit{[1 mark]}}$$
$$= \frac{2 - 2\sin^2\theta}{3}$$
$$= \frac{2}{3}(1 - \sin^2\theta)$$
$$= \frac{2}{3}\left(1 - \left(\frac{x - 3}{4}\right)^2\right) \quad \textbf{\textit{[1 mark]}}$$
$$= \frac{2}{3}\left(1 - \frac{(x - 3)^2}{16}\right)$$
$$= \frac{2}{3}\left(\frac{16 - (x^2 - 6x + 9)}{16}\right)$$
$$= \frac{2}{3}\left(\frac{-x^2 + 6x + 7}{16}\right)$$
$$= \frac{-x^2 + 6x + 7}{24} \quad \textbf{\textit{[1 mark]}}$$

d) $-\frac{\pi}{2} \le \theta \le \frac{\pi}{2} \Rightarrow -1 \le \sin\theta \le 1$

$\Rightarrow -4 \le 4\sin\theta \le 4$

$\Rightarrow -1 \le 3 + 4\sin\theta \le 7$

$\Rightarrow -1 \le x \le 7$ ***[1 mark]***

As Shakespeare himself might have put it "That section was a ruddy pain in the backside, but at least it's finished."*
**Arnold Shakespeare (1948–)*

C4 Section 3 — Sequences and Series
Warm-up Questions

1) a) $(1+2x)^3 = 1 + 3(2x) + \frac{3\times 2}{1\times 2}(2x)^2 + \frac{3\times 2\times 1}{1\times 2\times 3}(2x)^3$

$= 1 + 6x + 12x^2 + 8x^3$

You could have used Pascal's Triangle to get the coefficients here. I've done it the long way because I like to show off.

b) $(1-x)^4 = 1 + 4(-x) + \frac{4\times 3}{1\times 2}(-x)^2 + \frac{4\times 3\times 2}{1\times 2\times 3}(-x)^3 + \frac{4\times 3\times 2\times 1}{1\times 2\times 3\times 4}(-x)^4$

$= 1 - 4x + 6x^2 - 4x^3 + x^4$

c) $(1-4x)^4 = 1 + 4(-4x) + \frac{4\times 3}{1\times 2}(-4x)^2 + \frac{4\times 3\times 2}{1\times 2\times 3}(-4x)^3 + \frac{4\times 3\times 2\times 1}{1\times 2\times 3\times 4}(-4x)^4$

$= 1 - 16x + 96x^2 - 256x^3 + 256x^4$

Be extra careful with terms like $(-4x)^2$... remember to square <u>everything</u> in the brackets — the x, the 4 <u>and</u> the minus.

2) Positive integer values (and zero).

3) a) $(1+x)^{-4}$

$\approx 1 + (-4)x + \frac{-4\times -5}{1\times 2}x^2 + \frac{-4\times -5\times -6}{1\times 2\times 3}x^3$

$= 1 - 4x + 10x^2 - 20x^3$

b) $(1-3x)^{-3} \approx 1 + (-3)(-3x) + \frac{-3\times -4}{1\times 2}(-3x)^2 + \frac{-3\times -4\times -5}{1\times 2\times 3}(-3x)^3$

$= 1 + 9x + 54x^2 + 270x^3$

c) $(1-5x)^{\frac{1}{2}}$

$\approx 1 + \frac{1}{2}(-5x) + \frac{\frac{1}{2}\times -\frac{1}{2}}{1\times 2}(-5x)^2 + \frac{\frac{1}{2}\times -\frac{1}{2}\times -\frac{3}{2}}{1\times 2\times 3}(-5x)^3$

$= 1 - \frac{5}{2}x - \frac{25}{8}x^2 - \frac{125}{16}x^3$

4) a) $\left|\frac{dx}{c}\right| < 1$ (or $|x| < |\frac{c}{d}|$)

b) 3) a): expansion valid for $|x| < 1$

3) b): expansion valid for $|-3x| < 1 \Rightarrow |-3||x| < 1 \Rightarrow |x| < \frac{1}{3}$

3) c): expansion valid for $|-5x| < 1 \Rightarrow |-5||x| < 1 \Rightarrow |x| < \frac{1}{5}$

5) a) $(3+2x)^{-2} = \left(3\left(1+\frac{2}{3}x\right)\right)^{-2} = \frac{1}{9}\left(1+\frac{2}{3}x\right)^{-2}$

$\approx \frac{1}{9}\left(1 + (-2)\left(\frac{2}{3}x\right) + \frac{-2\times -3}{1\times 2}\left(\frac{2}{3}x\right)^2\right)$

$= \frac{1}{9}\left(1 - \frac{4}{3}x + \frac{4}{3}x^2\right)$

$= \frac{1}{9} - \frac{4}{27}x + \frac{4}{27}x^2$

This expansion is valid for $\left|\frac{2x}{3}\right| < 1 \Rightarrow \frac{2}{3}|x| < 1 \Rightarrow |x| < \frac{3}{2}$.

b) $(8-x)^{\frac{1}{3}} = \left(8\left(1-\frac{1}{8}x\right)\right)^{\frac{1}{3}} = 2\left(1-\frac{1}{8}x\right)^{\frac{1}{3}}$

$\approx 2\left(1 + \frac{1}{3}\left(-\frac{1}{8}x\right) + \frac{\frac{1}{3}\times -\frac{2}{3}}{1\times 2}\left(-\frac{1}{8}x\right)^2\right)$

$= 2\left(1 - \frac{1}{24}x - \frac{1}{576}x^2\right)$

$= 2 - \frac{1}{12}x - \frac{1}{288}x^2$

This expansion is valid for $\left|\frac{-x}{8}\right| < 1 \Rightarrow \frac{|-1||x|}{8} < 1$
$\Rightarrow |x| < 8$.

Exam Questions

1 a) $f(x) = (9-4x)^{-\frac{1}{2}} = (9)^{-\frac{1}{2}}\left(1-\frac{4}{9}x\right)^{-\frac{1}{2}} = \frac{1}{3}\left(1-\frac{4}{9}x\right)^{-\frac{1}{2}}$

$= \frac{1}{3}\left[1 + \left(-\frac{1}{2}\right)\left(-\frac{4}{9}x\right) + \frac{\left(-\frac{1}{2}\right)\times\left(-\frac{3}{2}\right)}{1\times 2}\left(-\frac{4}{9}x\right)^2 + \frac{\left(-\frac{1}{2}\right)\times\left(-\frac{3}{2}\right)\times\left(-\frac{5}{2}\right)}{1\times 2\times 3}\left(-\frac{4}{9}x\right)^3 + \ldots\right]$

$= \frac{1}{3}\left(1 + \left(-\frac{1}{2}\right)\left(-\frac{4}{9}x\right) + \frac{\left(\frac{3}{4}\right)}{2}\left(-\frac{4}{9}x\right)^2 + \frac{\left(-\frac{15}{8}\right)}{6}\left(-\frac{4}{9}x\right)^3 + \ldots\right)$

$= \frac{1}{3}\left(1 + \left(-\frac{1}{2}\right)\left(-\frac{4}{9}x\right) + \frac{3}{8}\left(-\frac{4}{9}x\right)^2 + \left(-\frac{5}{16}\right)\left(-\frac{4}{9}x\right)^3 + \ldots\right)$

$= \frac{1}{3}\left(1 + \frac{2}{9}x + \frac{2}{27}x^2 + \frac{20}{729}x^3 + \ldots\right)$

$= \frac{1}{3} + \frac{2}{27}x + \frac{2}{81}x^2 + \frac{20}{2187}x^3 + \ldots$

[5 marks available in total:
- ***1 mark for factorising out $(9)^{-\frac{1}{2}}$ or $\frac{1}{3}$***
- ***1 mark for expansion of an expression of the form $(1+ax)^{-\frac{1}{2}}$***
- ***2 marks for the penultimate line of working — 1 for the first two terms in brackets correct, 1 for the 3rd and 4th terms in brackets correct.***
- ***1 mark for the final answer correct]***

Multiplying out those coefficients can be pretty tricky. Don't try to do things all in one go — you won't be penalised for writing an extra line of working, but you probably will lose marks if your final answer's wrong.

b) $(2-x)\left(\frac{1}{3} + \frac{2}{27}x + \frac{2}{81}x^2 + \frac{20}{2187}x^3 + \ldots\right)$

You only need the first three terms of the expansion, so just write the terms up to x^2 when you multiply out the brackets:

$= \frac{2}{3} + \frac{4}{27}x + \frac{4}{81}x^2 + \ldots$

$\quad - \frac{1}{3}x - \frac{2}{27}x^2 + \ldots$

$= \frac{2}{3} - \frac{5}{27}x - \frac{2}{81}x^2 + \ldots$

[4 marks available in total:
- ***1 mark for multiplying your answer to part (a) by (2 – x)***
- ***1 mark for multiplying out brackets to find constant term, two x-terms and two x^2-terms.***
- ***1 mark for correct constant and x-terms in final answer***
- ***1 mark for correct x^2-term in final answer]***

2 a) $36x^2 + 3x - 10 \equiv A(1-3x)^2 + B(4+3x)(1-3x) + C(4+3x)$
[1 mark]

Answers

Let $x = \frac{1}{3}$, then $4 + 1 - 10 = 5C \Rightarrow -5 = 5C \Rightarrow C = -1$
[1 mark]

Let $x = -\frac{4}{3}$, then $64 - 4 - 10 = 25A \Rightarrow 50 = 25A \Rightarrow A = 2$
[1 mark]

Equate the terms in x^2:
$36 = 9A - 9B = 18 - 9B \Rightarrow -18 = 9B \Rightarrow B = -2$ ***[1 mark]***

b) $f(x) = \frac{2}{(4+3x)} - \frac{2}{(1-3x)} - \frac{1}{(1-3x)^2}$

Expand each term separately:

$2(4 + 3x)^{-1} = 2\left(4\left(1 + \frac{3}{4}x\right)\right)^{-1} = \frac{1}{2}\left(1 + \frac{3}{4}x\right)^{-1}$

$= \frac{1}{2}\left(1 + (-1)\left(\frac{3}{4}x\right) + \frac{(-1)\times(-2)}{1\times 2}\left(\frac{3}{4}x\right)^2 + \ldots\right)$

$= \frac{1}{2}\left(1 - \frac{3}{4}x + \frac{9}{16}x^2 + \ldots\right) = \frac{1}{2} - \frac{3}{8}x + \frac{9}{32}x^2 + \ldots$

Now the second term: $-2(1 - 3x)^{-1} =$

$-2\left(1 + (-1)(-3x) + \frac{(-1)\times(-2)}{1\times 2}(-3x)^2 + \ldots\right)$

$= -2(1 + 3x + 9x^2 + \ldots) = -2 - 6x - 18x^2 + \ldots$

And the final term: $-(1 - 3x)^{-2} =$

$-\left(1 + (-2)(-3x) + \frac{(-2)\times(-3)}{1\times 2}(-3x)^2 + \ldots\right)$

$= -(1 + 6x + 27x^2 + \ldots) = -1 - 6x - 27x^2 + \ldots$

Putting it all together gives

$\frac{1}{2} - \frac{3}{8}x + \frac{9}{32}x^2 - 2 - 6x - 18x^2 - 1 - 6x - 27x^2$

$= -\frac{5}{2} - \frac{99}{8}x - \frac{1431}{32}x^2 + \ldots$

[6 marks available in total:
- ***1 mark for rewriting f(x) in the form*** ***$A(4 + 3x)^{-1} + B(1 - 3x)^{-1} + C(1 - 3x)^{-2}$***
- ***1 mark for correct binomial expansion of $(4 + 3x)^{-1}$***
- ***1 mark for correct binomial expansion of $(1 - 3x)^{-1}$***
- ***1 mark for correct binomial expansion of $(1 - 3x)^{-2}$***
- ***1 mark for correct constant and x-terms in final answer***
- ***1 mark for correct x^2-term in final answer]***

You know what, I can't think of anything else remotely useful, witty or interesting to say about binomials... Seriously, I'm going to have to resort to slightly weird jokes in a minute... You've been warned...

c) Expansion of $(4 + 3x)^{-1}$ is valid for $\left|\frac{3x}{4}\right| < 1 \Rightarrow \frac{3|x|}{4} < 1$
$\Rightarrow |x| < \frac{4}{3}$

Expansions of $(1 - 3x)^{-1}$ and $(1 - 3x)^{-2}$ are valid for
$\left|\frac{-3x}{1}\right| < 1 \Rightarrow \frac{|-3||x|}{1} < 1 \Rightarrow |x| < \frac{1}{3}$

The combined expansion is valid for the narrower of these two ranges. So the expansion of f(x) is valid for $|x| < \frac{1}{3}$.

[2 marks available in total:
- ***1 mark for identifying the valid range of the expansion of f(x) as being the narrower of the two valid ranges shown***
- ***1 mark for correct answer]***

3 a) $(16 + 3x)^{\frac{1}{4}} = 16^{\frac{1}{4}}\left(1 + \frac{3}{16}x\right)^{\frac{1}{4}} = 2\left(1 + \frac{3}{16}x\right)^{\frac{1}{4}}$

$\approx 2\left(1 + \left(\frac{1}{4}\right)\left(\frac{3}{16}x\right) + \frac{\frac{1}{4}\times -\frac{3}{4}}{1\times 2}\left(\frac{3}{16}x\right)^2\right)$

$= 2\left(1 + \left(\frac{1}{4}\right)\left(\frac{3}{16}x\right) + \left(-\frac{3}{32}\right)\left(\frac{9}{256}x^2\right)\right)$

$= 2\left(1 + \frac{3}{64}x - \frac{27}{8192}x^2\right)$

$= 2 + \frac{3}{32}x - \frac{27}{4096}x^2$

[5 marks available in total:
- ***1 mark for factorising out $16^{\frac{1}{4}}$ or 2***
- ***1 mark for expansion of an expression of the form $(1 + ax)^{\frac{1}{4}}$***
- ***2 marks for the penultimate line of working — 1 for the first two terms in brackets correct, 1 for the 3rd term in brackets correct.***
- ***1 mark for the final answer correct]***

b) (i) $16 + 3x = 12.4 \Rightarrow x = -1.2$

So $(12.4)^{\frac{1}{4}} \approx 2 + \frac{3}{32}(-1.2) - \frac{27}{4096}(-1.2)^2$

$= 2 - 0.1125 - 0.0094921875$

$= 1.878008$ (to 6 d.p.)

[2 marks available in total:
- ***1 mark for substituting $x = -1.2$ into the expansion from part (a)***
- ***1 mark for correct answer]***

(ii) Percentage error

$= \left|\frac{\text{real value} - \text{estimate}}{\text{real value}}\right| \times 100$ ***[1 mark]***

$= \left|\frac{\sqrt[4]{12.4} - 1.878008}{\sqrt[4]{12.4}}\right| \times 100$

$= \frac{|1.876529\ldots - 1.878008|}{1.876529\ldots} \times 100$

$= 0.0788\%$ (to 3 s.f.) ***[1 mark]***

Why did the binomial expansion cross the road?
Don't be silly, binomial expansions can't move independently...
...can they?

4 a) $\left(1 - \frac{4}{3}x\right)^{-\frac{1}{2}}$

$\approx 1 + \left(-\frac{1}{2}\right)\left(-\frac{4}{3}x\right) + \frac{(-\frac{1}{2})\times(-\frac{3}{2})}{1\times 2}\left(-\frac{4}{3}x\right)^2$
$+ \frac{(-\frac{1}{2})\times(-\frac{3}{2})\times(-\frac{5}{2})}{1\times 2\times 3}\left(-\frac{4}{3}x\right)^3$

$= 1 + \left(-\frac{1}{2}\right)\left(-\frac{4}{3}x\right) + \frac{\left(\frac{3}{4}\right)}{2}\left(-\frac{4}{3}x\right)^2 + \frac{\left(-\frac{15}{8}\right)}{6}\left(-\frac{4}{3}x\right)^3$

$= 1 + \left(-\frac{1}{2}\right)\left(-\frac{4}{3}x\right) + \frac{3}{8}\left(\frac{16}{9}x^2\right) + \left(-\frac{15}{48}\right)\left(-\frac{64}{27}x^3\right)$

$= 1 + \frac{2}{3}x + \frac{2}{3}x^2 + \frac{20}{27}x^3$

[4 marks available in total:
- ***1 mark for writing out binomial expansion formula with $n = -\frac{1}{2}$***
- ***1 mark for writing out binomial expansion formula substituting $-\frac{4}{3}x$ for x***
- ***1 mark for correct constant and x-terms in final answer***
- ***1 mark for correct x^2- and x^3-terms in final answer]***

b) $\sqrt{\frac{27}{(3-4x)}} = \sqrt{\frac{27}{3\left(1-\frac{4}{3}x\right)}} = \sqrt{\frac{9}{\left(1-\frac{4}{3}x\right)}} = \frac{3}{\sqrt{\left(1-\frac{4}{3}x\right)}}$

$= 3\left(1 - \frac{4}{3}x\right)^{-\frac{1}{2}}$

$\approx 3\left(1 + \frac{2}{3}x + \frac{2}{3}x^2\right)$

$= 3 + 2x + 2x^2$

So $a = 3$, $b = 2$, $c = 2$.

Answers

Expansion is valid for $\left|-\frac{4}{3}x\right| < 1 \Rightarrow \left|-\frac{4}{3}\right||x| < 1 \Rightarrow |x| < \frac{3}{4}$

[3 marks available in total:
• 1 mark for showing expression is equal to $3\left(1-\frac{4}{3}x\right)^{-\frac{1}{2}}$
• 1 mark for using expansion from part a) to find the correct values of a, b and c.
• 1 mark for correct valid range]

Doctor, doctor, I keep thinking I'm a binomial expansion...
I'm sorry, I don't think I can help you, I'm a cardiologist.

5 a) (i) $\sqrt{\frac{1+2x}{1-3x}} = \frac{\sqrt{1+2x}}{\sqrt{1-3x}} = (1+2x)^{\frac{1}{2}}(1-3x)^{-\frac{1}{2}}$ ***[1 mark]***

$(1+2x)^{\frac{1}{2}} \approx 1 + \frac{1}{2}(2x) + \frac{(\frac{1}{2})\times(-\frac{1}{2})}{1\times 2}(2x)^2$

$= 1 + x - \frac{1}{2}x^2$ ***[1 mark]***

$(1-3x)^{-\frac{1}{2}} \approx 1 + \left(-\frac{1}{2}\right)(-3x) + \frac{(-\frac{1}{2})\times(-\frac{3}{2})}{1\times 2}(-3x)^2$

$= 1 + \frac{3}{2}x + \frac{27}{8}x^2$ ***[1 mark]***

$\sqrt{\frac{1+2x}{1-3x}} \approx \left(1 + x - \frac{1}{2}x^2\right)\left(1 + \frac{3}{2}x + \frac{27}{8}x^2\right)$ ***[1 mark]***

$\approx 1 + \frac{3}{2}x + \frac{27}{8}x^2 + x + \frac{3}{2}x^2 - \frac{1}{2}x^2$
(ignoring any terms in x^3 or above)

$= 1 + \frac{5}{2}x + \frac{35}{8}x^2$ ***[1 mark]***

(ii) Expansion of $(1+2x)^{\frac{1}{2}}$ is valid for $|2x| < 1 \Rightarrow |x| < \frac{1}{2}$

Expansion of $(1-3x)^{-\frac{1}{2}}$ is valid for $|-3x| < 1$

$\Rightarrow |-3||x| < 1 \Rightarrow |x| < \frac{1}{3}$

The combined expansion is valid for the narrower of these two ranges.

So the expansion of $\sqrt{\frac{1+2x}{1-3x}}$ is valid for $|x| < \frac{1}{3}$.

[2 marks available in total:
• 1 mark for identifying the valid range of the expansion as being the narrower of the two valid ranges shown
• 1 mark for correct answer]

b) $x = \frac{2}{15} \Rightarrow \sqrt{\frac{1+2x}{1-3x}} = \sqrt{\frac{1+\frac{4}{15}}{1-\frac{6}{15}}} = \sqrt{\frac{\frac{19}{15}}{\frac{9}{15}}} = \sqrt{\frac{19}{9}} = \frac{1}{3}\sqrt{19}$

[1 mark]

$\Rightarrow \sqrt{19} \approx 3\left(1 + \frac{5}{2}\left(\frac{2}{15}\right) + \frac{35}{8}\left(\frac{2}{15}\right)^2\right)$

$= 3\left(1 + \frac{1}{3} + \frac{7}{90}\right)$

$= 3\left(\frac{127}{90}\right)$

$= \frac{127}{30}$ ***[1 mark]***

The binomial expansion walks into a bar and asks for a pint. The barman says, "I'm sorry, I can't serve alcohol in a joke that may be read by under-18s."

6 a) $13x - 17 \equiv A(2x-1) + B(5-3x)$ ***[1 mark]***

Let $x = \frac{1}{2}$, then $\frac{13}{2} - 17 = B(5 - \frac{3}{2}) \Rightarrow -\frac{21}{2} = \frac{7}{2}B \Rightarrow B = -3$

[1 mark]

Let $x = \frac{5}{3}$, then $\frac{65}{3} - 17 = A(\frac{10}{3} - 1) \Rightarrow \frac{14}{3} = \frac{7}{3}A \Rightarrow A = 2$

[1 mark]

b) (i) $(2x-1)^{-1} = -(1-2x)^{-1}$ ***[1 mark]***

$\approx -\left(1 + (-1)(-2x) + \frac{(-1)\times(-2)}{1\times 2}(-2x)^2\right)$

$= -(1 + 2x + 4x^2)$

$= -1 - 2x - 4x^2$ ***[1 mark]***

(ii) $(5-3x)^{-1} = 5^{-1}\left(1 - \frac{3}{5}x\right)^{-1} = \frac{1}{5}\left(1 - \frac{3}{5}x\right)^{-1}$

$\approx \frac{1}{5}\left(1 + (-1)\left(-\frac{3}{5}x\right) + \frac{(-1)\times(-2)}{1\times 2}\left(-\frac{3}{5}x\right)^2\right)$

$= \frac{1}{5}\left(1 + \frac{3}{5}x + \frac{9}{25}x^2\right)$

$= \frac{1}{5} + \frac{3}{25}x + \frac{9}{125}x^2$

[5 marks available in total:
• 1 mark for factorising out 5^{-1} or $\frac{1}{5}$
• 1 mark for expansion of an expression of the form $(1 + ax)^{-1}$
• 2 marks for the penultimate line of working — 1 mark for the first two terms in brackets correct, 1 mark for the 3rd term in brackets correct.
• 1 mark for the final answer correct]

c) $\frac{13x-17}{(5-3x)(2x-1)} = \frac{2}{(5-3x)} - \frac{3}{(2x-1)}$

$= 2(5-3x)^{-1} - 3(2x-1)^{-1}$ ***[1 mark]***

$\approx 2\left(\frac{1}{5} + \frac{3}{25}x + \frac{9}{125}x^2\right) - 3(-1 - 2x - 4x^2)$

$= \frac{2}{5} + \frac{6}{25}x + \frac{18}{125}x^2 + 3 + 6x + 12x^2$

$= \frac{17}{5} + \frac{156}{25}x + \frac{1518}{125}x^2$

[1 mark]

C4 Section 4 — Differentiation
Warm-up Questions

1) a) $\frac{dx}{dt} = 2t$, $\frac{dy}{dt} = 9t^2 - 4$, so $\frac{dy}{dx} = \frac{dy}{dt} \div \frac{dx}{dt} = \frac{9t^2-4}{2t}$

b) The stationary points are when $\frac{9t^2-4}{2t} = 0$

$\Rightarrow 9t^2 = 4 \Rightarrow t = \pm\frac{2}{3}$

$t = \frac{2}{3} \Rightarrow x = \left(\frac{2}{3}\right)^2 = \frac{4}{9}$, $y = 3\left(\frac{2}{3}\right)^3 - 4\left(\frac{2}{3}\right) = \frac{8}{9} - \frac{8}{3} = -\frac{16}{9}$

$t = -\frac{2}{3} \Rightarrow x = \left(-\frac{2}{3}\right)^2 = \frac{4}{9}$,

$y = 3\left(-\frac{2}{3}\right)^3 - 4\left(-\frac{2}{3}\right) = -\frac{8}{9} + \frac{8}{3} = \frac{16}{9}$

So the stationary points are $\left(\frac{4}{9}, -\frac{16}{9}\right)$ and $\left(\frac{4}{9}, \frac{16}{9}\right)$.

2) a) Differentiate each term separately with respect to x:

$\frac{d}{dx}4x^2 - \frac{d}{dx}2y^2 = \frac{d}{dx}7x^2y$

Differentiate $4x^2$ first:

$\Rightarrow 8x - \frac{d}{dx}2y^2 = \frac{d}{dx}7x^2y$

Differentiate $2y^2$ using chain rule:

$\Rightarrow 8x - \frac{d}{dy}2y^2\frac{dy}{dx} = \frac{d}{dx}7x^2y$

$\Rightarrow 8x - 4y\frac{dy}{dx} = \frac{d}{dx}7x^2y$

Answers

Differentiate $7x^2y$ using product rule:

$\Rightarrow 8x - 4y\frac{dy}{dx} = 7x^2\frac{d}{dx}y + y\frac{d}{dx}7x^2$

$\Rightarrow 8x - 4y\frac{dy}{dx} = 7x^2\frac{dy}{dx} + 14xy$

Rearrange to make $\frac{dy}{dx}$ the subject:

$\Rightarrow (4y + 7x^2)\frac{dy}{dx} = 8x - 14xy$

$\Rightarrow \frac{dy}{dx} = \frac{8x - 14xy}{4y + 7x^2}$

For implicit differentiation questions, you need to know what you're doing with the chain rule and product rule. If you're struggling to keep up with what's going on here, go back to C3 and refresh your memory.

b) Differentiate each term separately with respect to x:

$\frac{d}{dx}3x^4 - \frac{d}{dx}2xy^2 = \frac{d}{dx}y$

Differentiate $3x^4$ first:

$\Rightarrow 12x^3 - \frac{d}{dx}2xy^2 = \frac{dy}{dx}$

Differentiate $2xy^2$ using product rule:

$\Rightarrow 12x^3 - \left(y^2\frac{d}{dx}2x + 2x\frac{d}{dy}y^2\frac{dy}{dx}\right) = \frac{dy}{dx}$

$\Rightarrow 12x^3 - 2y^2 - 4xy\frac{dy}{dx} = \frac{dy}{dx}$

Rearrange to make $\frac{dy}{dx}$ the subject:

$\Rightarrow (1 + 4xy)\frac{dy}{dx} = 12x^3 - 2y^2$

$\Rightarrow \frac{dy}{dx} = \frac{12x^3 - 2y^2}{1 + 4xy}$

c) Use the product rule to differentiate each term separately with respect to x:

$\frac{d}{dx}\cos x \sin y = \frac{d}{dx}xy$

$\Rightarrow \cos x\frac{d}{dx}(\sin y) + \sin y\frac{d}{dx}(\cos x) = x\frac{d}{dx}y + y\frac{d}{dx}x$

Use the chain rule on $\frac{d}{dx}(\sin y)$:

$\Rightarrow \cos x\frac{d}{dy}(\sin y)\frac{dy}{dx} + \sin y\frac{d}{dx}(\cos x) = x\frac{d}{dx}y + y\frac{d}{dx}x$

$\Rightarrow (\cos x \cos y)\frac{dy}{dx} - \sin y \sin x = x\frac{dy}{dx} + y$

Rearrange to make $\frac{dy}{dx}$ the subject:

$\Rightarrow (\cos x \cos y - x)\frac{dy}{dx} = y + \sin x \sin y$

$\Rightarrow \frac{dy}{dx} = \frac{\sin x \sin y + y}{\cos x \cos y - x}$

Make sure you learn how to differentiate trig functions. Chances are they'll come up in your C4 exam. And even if they don't, that sort of skill will make you a hit at parties. Trust me.

3) a) At (1, –4), $\frac{dy}{dx} = \frac{8x - 14xy}{4y + 7x^2}$

$= \frac{8(1) - 14(1)(-4)}{4(-4) + 7(1)^2} = \frac{8 + 56}{-16 + 7} = -\frac{64}{9}$

b) At (1, 1), $\frac{dy}{dx} = \frac{12x^3 - 2y^2}{1 + 4xy}$

$= \frac{12(1)^3 - 2(1)^2}{1 + 4(1)^2(1)} = \frac{12 - 2}{1 + 4} = \frac{10}{5} = 2$

So the gradient of the normal is $-\frac{1}{2}$.

4) Take the log of both sides of the equation:

$y = a^x \Rightarrow \ln y = \ln a^x$

$\Rightarrow \ln y = x \ln a$ (using log laws)

Now use implicit differentiation to find $\frac{dy}{dx}$:

$\ln y = x \ln a \Rightarrow \frac{d}{dx}(\ln y) = \frac{d}{dx}(x \ln a)$

$\Rightarrow \frac{d}{dy}(\ln y)\frac{dy}{dx} = \ln a$

$\Rightarrow \frac{1}{y}\frac{dy}{dx} = \ln a$

$\Rightarrow \frac{dy}{dx} = y \ln a$

So as $y = a^x$, $\frac{dy}{dx} = a^x \ln a$

5) $A = 2(x)(2x) + 2(x)(3x) + 2(2x)(3x)$

$= 4x^2 + 6x^2 + 12x^2$

$= 22x^2$

So $\frac{dA}{dx} = 44x$

$V = (x)(2x)(3x) = 6x^3$

So $\frac{dV}{dx} = 18x^2$

By the chain rule:

$\frac{dA}{dt} = \frac{dA}{dx} \times \frac{dx}{dt} = 44x \times \frac{dx}{dt}$

To find $\frac{dx}{dt}$, use the chain rule again:

$\frac{dx}{dt} = \frac{dx}{dV} \times \frac{dV}{dt} = \frac{1}{\left(\frac{dV}{dx}\right)} \times \frac{dV}{dt} = \frac{1}{18x^2} \times 3 = \frac{1}{6x^2}$

So $\frac{dA}{dt} = 44x \times \frac{1}{6x^2} = \frac{22}{3x}$

Exam Questions

1 a) Start by differentiating x and y with respect to θ:

$\frac{dy}{d\theta} = 2\cos\theta$ ***[1 mark]***

$\frac{dx}{d\theta} = 3 + 3\sin 3\theta$ ***[1 mark]***

$\frac{dy}{dx} = \frac{dy}{d\theta} \div \frac{dx}{d\theta} = \frac{2\cos\theta}{3 + 3\sin 3\theta}$ ***[1 mark]***

b) (i) We need the value of θ at $(\pi + 1, \sqrt{3})$:

$y = 2\sin\theta = \sqrt{3}$, for $-\pi \leq \theta \leq \pi \Rightarrow \theta = \frac{\pi}{3}$ or $\frac{2\pi}{3}$ ***[1 mark]***

If $\theta = \frac{\pi}{3}$, then $x = 3\theta - \cos 3\theta = \pi - \cos\pi = \pi + 1$.

If $\theta = \frac{2\pi}{3}$, then $x = 3\theta - \cos 3\theta = 2\pi - \cos 2\pi = 2\pi - 1$.

So at $(\pi + 1, \sqrt{3})$, $\theta = \frac{\pi}{3}$ ***[1 mark]***

$\theta = \frac{\pi}{3} \Rightarrow \frac{dy}{dx} = \frac{2\cos\frac{\pi}{3}}{3 + 3\sin\pi} = \frac{2\left(\frac{1}{2}\right)}{3 + 0} = \frac{1}{3}$ ***[1 mark]***

(ii) $\theta = \frac{\pi}{6} \Rightarrow x = \frac{\pi}{2} - \cos\frac{\pi}{2} = \frac{\pi}{2} - 0 = \frac{\pi}{2}$

$\theta = \frac{\pi}{6} \Rightarrow y = 2\sin\frac{\pi}{6} = 2 \times \frac{1}{2} = 1$

So $\theta = \frac{\pi}{6}$ at the point $(\frac{\pi}{2}, 1)$ ***[1 mark]***

$\theta = \frac{\pi}{6} \Rightarrow \frac{dy}{dx} = \frac{2\cos\frac{\pi}{6}}{3 + 3\sin\frac{\pi}{2}} = \frac{2\left(\frac{\sqrt{3}}{2}\right)}{3 + 3(1)} = \frac{\sqrt{3}}{6}$ ***[1 mark]***

Answers

Gradient of normal = $-\frac{1}{\left(\frac{dy}{dx}\right)} = -\frac{6}{\sqrt{3}} = -\frac{6\sqrt{3}}{3}$
$= -2\sqrt{3}$ **[1 mark]**
So the normal is $y = -2\sqrt{3}x + c$ for some c.
$\Rightarrow 1 = -2\sqrt{3} \times \frac{\pi}{2} + c = -\pi\sqrt{3} + c$
$\Rightarrow c = 1 + \pi\sqrt{3}$
The equation of the normal is $y = -2\sqrt{3}x + 1 + \pi\sqrt{3}$
[1 mark]

2 a) c is the value of y when $x = 2$. If $x = 2$, then
$6x^2y - 7 = 5x - 4y^2 - x^2 \Rightarrow 6(2)^2y - 7 = 5(2) - 4y^2 - (2)^2$
$\Rightarrow 24y - 7 = 6 - 4y^2$
$\Rightarrow 4y^2 + 24y - 13 = 0$
$\Rightarrow (2y + 13)(2y - 1) = 0$
$\Rightarrow y = -6.5$ or $y = 0.5$ **[1 mark]**
$c > 0$, so $c = 0.5$ **[1 mark]**

b) (i) Q is another point on C where $y = 0.5$.
If $y = 0.5$, then $6x^2y - 7 = 5x - 4y^2 - x^2$
$\Rightarrow 6x^2(0.5) - 7 = 5x - 4(0.5)^2 - x^2$ **[1 mark]**
$\Rightarrow 3x^2 - 7 = 5x - 1 - x^2$
$\Rightarrow 4x^2 - 5x - 6 = 0$
$\Rightarrow (x - 2)(4x + 3)$
$\Rightarrow x = 2$ or $x = -0.75$
$x \neq 2$, as $x = 2$ at the other point where T crosses C.
So the coordinates of Q are $(-0.75, 0.5)$. **[1 mark]**

(ii) To find the gradient of C, use implicit differentiation.
Differentiate each term separately with respect to x:
$\frac{d}{dx}6x^2y - \frac{d}{dx}7 = \frac{d}{dx}5x - \frac{d}{dx}4y^2 - \frac{d}{dx}x^2$ **[1 mark]**
Differentiate x-terms and constant terms:
$\Rightarrow \frac{d}{dx}6x^2y - 0 = 5 - \frac{d}{dx}4y^2 - 2x$ **[1 mark]**
Differentiate y-terms using chain rule:
$\Rightarrow \frac{d}{dx}6x^2y = 5 - \frac{d}{dy}4y^2\frac{dy}{dx} - 2x$
$\Rightarrow \frac{d}{dx}6x^2y = 5 - 8y\frac{dy}{dx} - 2x$ **[1 mark]**
Differentiate xy-terms using product rule:
$\Rightarrow 6x^2\frac{dy}{dx} + y\frac{d}{dx}6x^2 = 5 - 8y\frac{dy}{dx} - 2x$
$\Rightarrow 6x^2\frac{dy}{dx} + 12xy = 5 - 8y\frac{dy}{dx} - 2x$ **[1 mark]**
Rearrange to make $\frac{dy}{dx}$ the subject:
$\Rightarrow 6x^2\frac{dy}{dx} + 8y\frac{dy}{dx} = 5 - 2x - 12xy$
$\Rightarrow \frac{dy}{dx} = \frac{5 - 2x - 12xy}{6x^2 + 8y}$ **[1 mark]**
So at $Q = (-0.75, 0.5)$,
$$\frac{dy}{dx} = \frac{5 - 2\left(-\frac{3}{4}\right) - 12\left(-\frac{3}{4}\right)\left(\frac{1}{2}\right)}{6\left(-\frac{3}{4}\right)^2 + 8\left(\frac{1}{2}\right)} = \frac{5 + \frac{3}{2} + \frac{9}{2}}{\frac{27}{8} + 4}$$
$$= \frac{11}{\left(\frac{59}{8}\right)} = 11 \times \frac{8}{59} = \frac{88}{59}$$ **[1 mark]**

3 a) $y = 4^x \Rightarrow \frac{dy}{dx} = 4^x \ln 4$ **[1 mark]**
So $\frac{dy}{dx} = \ln 4 \Rightarrow 4^x = 1 \Rightarrow x = 0 \Rightarrow y = 4^0 = 1$
$\frac{dy}{dx} = \ln 4$ at coordinates $(0, 1)$ **[1 mark]**

b) Use the chain rule to find $\frac{dy}{dx}$:
Let $u = (x - 4)^3$.
Then $\frac{dy}{dx} = \frac{dy}{du} \times \frac{du}{dx} = \frac{d}{du}(4^u) \times \frac{d}{dx}(x - 4)^3$ **[1 mark]**
$= (4^u \ln 4)(3(x - 4)^2 \times 1)$
(using chain rule again to find $\frac{du}{dx}$)
$= 4^{(x-4)^3}\, 3(x - 4)^2 \ln 4$ **[1 mark]**
So when $x = 3$, $\frac{dy}{dx} = 4^{(3-4)^3}\, 3(3 - 4)^2 \ln 4$ **[1 mark]**
$\frac{dy}{dx} = 4^{-1}\, 3 \ln 4 = \frac{3}{4} \ln 4 = 1.040$ (to 3 d.p.) **[1 mark]**

4 a) (i) Using implicit differentiation:
$3e^x + 6y = 2x^2y \Rightarrow \frac{d}{dx}3e^x + \frac{d}{dx}6y = \frac{d}{dx}2x^2y$ **[1 mark]**
$\Rightarrow 3e^x + 6\frac{dy}{dx} = 2x^2\frac{dy}{dx} + y\frac{d}{dx}2x^2$
$\Rightarrow 3e^x + 6\frac{dy}{dx} = 2x^2\frac{dy}{dx} + 4xy$ **[1 mark]**
$\Rightarrow 2x^2\frac{dy}{dx} - 6\frac{dy}{dx} = 3e^x - 4xy$
$\Rightarrow \frac{dy}{dx} = \frac{3e^x - 4xy}{2x^2 - 6}$ **[1 mark]**

(ii) At the stationary points of C, $\frac{dy}{dx} = 0$
$\Rightarrow \frac{3e^x - 4xy}{2x^2 - 6} = 0$ **[1 mark]**
$\Rightarrow 3e^x - 4xy = 0$
$\Rightarrow y = \frac{3e^x}{4x}$ **[1 mark]**

b) Substitute $y = \frac{3e^x}{4x}$ into the original equation of curve C:
$3e^x + 6y = 2x^2y \Rightarrow 3e^x + 6\frac{3e^x}{4x} = 2x^2\frac{3e^x}{4x}$ **[1 mark]**
$\Rightarrow 3e^x(1 + \frac{3}{2x} - \frac{x}{2}) = 0$
$3e^x = 0$ has no solutions, so $(1 + \frac{3}{2x} - \frac{x}{2}) = 0$ **[1 mark]**
$\Rightarrow x^2 - 2x - 3 = 0$
$\Rightarrow (x + 1)(x - 3) = 0$
$\Rightarrow x = -1$ or $x = 3$
$x = -1 \Rightarrow y = \frac{3e^{-1}}{4(-1)} = -\frac{3}{4e}$
$x = 3 \Rightarrow y = \frac{3e^3}{4(3)} = \frac{1}{4}e^3$
So the stationary points of C are $(-1, -\frac{3}{4e})$ and $(3, \frac{1}{4}e^3)$
[2 marks — 1 mark for each correct pair of coordinates]
Don't forget — if the question asks you for an exact answer, that usually means leaving it in terms of something like π or ln or, in this case, e.

5 a) First find the value of t when $y = -6$:
$y = 2 - t^3 = -6 \Rightarrow t^3 = 8 \Rightarrow t = 2$ **[1 mark]**
$\Rightarrow x = 2^2 + 2(2) - 3 = 5$
Now find the gradient of the curve:
$\frac{dy}{dt} = -3t^2$, $\frac{dx}{dt} = 2t + 2$
So $\frac{dy}{dx} = \frac{dy}{dt} \div \frac{dx}{dt} = \frac{-3t^2}{2t + 2}$ **[1 mark]**
So when $t = 2$, $\frac{dy}{dx} = \frac{-3(2)^2}{2(2) + 2} = \frac{-12}{6} = -2$ **[1 mark]**
So the tangent at $y = -6$ is
$y = -2x + c \Rightarrow -6 = -2(5) + c \Rightarrow c = 4$
The equation of L is $y = -2x + 4$ **[1 mark]**

Answers

b) (i) Sub $y = 2 - t^3$ and $x = t^2 + 2t - 3$ into the equation of L:
$y = -2x + 4$
$\Rightarrow 2 - t^3 = -2(t^2 + 2t - 3) + 4$ ***[1 mark]***
$\Rightarrow 2 - t^3 = -2t^2 - 4t + 10$
$\Rightarrow t^3 - 2t^2 - 4t + 8 = 0$
We know from part (a) that $t = 2$ is a root, so take out $(t - 2)$ as a factor:
$\Rightarrow (t - 2)(t^2 - 4) = 0$ ***[1 mark]***
$\Rightarrow (t - 2)(t + 2)(t - 2) = 0$
$\Rightarrow t = 2$ or $t = -2$ ***[1 mark]***
So t must be -2 at P.
$t = -2 \Rightarrow x = (-2)^2 + 2(-2) - 3 = -3$, $y = 2 - (-2)^3 = 10$.
The coordinates of P are $(-3, 10)$. ***[1 mark]***

(ii) At P, $t = -2$, so $\frac{dy}{dx} = \frac{-3(-2)^2}{2(-2)+2} = \frac{-12}{-2} = 6$.
[1 mark]
So the gradient of the normal at P is
$-\frac{1}{\left(\frac{dy}{dx}\right)} = -\frac{1}{6}$ ***[1 mark]***
The equation of the normal at P is
$y = -\frac{1}{6}x + c \Rightarrow 10 = -\frac{(-3)}{6} + c \Rightarrow c = \frac{19}{2}$
So the normal to the curve at point P is
$y = -\frac{1}{6}x + \frac{19}{2}$ ***[1 mark]***

6 a) Start by finding the missing side length of the triangular faces. Call the missing length s:

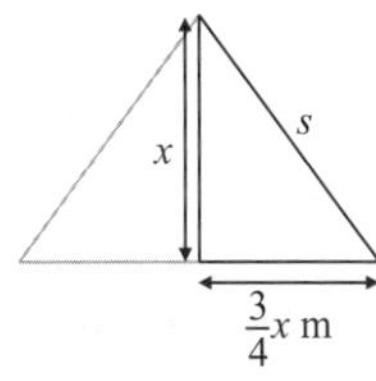

$s = \sqrt{x^2 + \left(\frac{3}{4}x\right)^2}$
$= \sqrt{x^2 + \frac{9}{16}x^2}$
$= \sqrt{\frac{25}{16}x^2}$
$= \frac{5}{4}x$ ***[1 mark]***
Now find A by adding up the area of each of the faces:
$A = 2(\frac{1}{2} \times \frac{3}{2}x \times x) + (\frac{3}{2}x \times 4x) + 2(\frac{5}{4}x \times 4x)$ ***[1 mark]***
$= \frac{3}{2}x^2 + 6x^2 + 10x^2$
$= \frac{35}{2}x^2$ ***[1 mark]***

b) $\frac{dA}{dt} = 0.07$
$A = \frac{35}{2}x^2 \Rightarrow \frac{dA}{dx} = 35x$ ***[1 mark]***
Using chain rule, $\frac{dx}{dt} = \frac{dx}{dA} \times \frac{dA}{dt}$ ***[1 mark]***
$= \frac{1}{\left(\frac{dA}{dx}\right)} \times \frac{dA}{dt} = \frac{1}{35x} \times 0.07$
$= \frac{0.07}{35 \times 0.5} = 0.004$ m s^{-1} ***[1 mark]***

(c) First you need to figure out what the question is asking for. 'Find the rate of change of V' means we're looking for $\frac{dV}{dt}$.
Start by finding an expression for V:
$V = (\frac{1}{2} \times \frac{3}{2}x \times x) \times 4x = 3x^3$ ***[1 mark]***
So $\frac{dV}{dx} = 9x^2$ ***[1 mark]***
Using chain rule, $\frac{dV}{dt} = \frac{dV}{dx} \times \frac{dx}{dt}$ ***[1 mark]***
$= 9x^2 \times \frac{0.07}{35x} = \frac{9(1.2)^2 \times 0.07}{35 \times 1.2} = 0.0216$ m s^{-1} ***[1 mark]***

C4 Section 5 — Integration 1

Warm-up Questions

1) $2e^{2x} + C$

2) $\frac{1}{3}e^{3x-5} + C$

3) $\frac{2}{3}\ln|x| + C$

4) $\ln|2x + 1| + C$

5) a) Just integrate each term separately: $\int \cos 4x \, dx = \frac{1}{4}\sin 4x$, $\int \sec^2 7x = \frac{1}{7}\tan 7x \, dx$. Putting these bits together gives: $\frac{1}{4}\sin 4x - \frac{1}{7}\tan 7x + C$.

b) Again, just integrate each term separately: $\int 6\sec 3x \tan 3x \, dx = 2\sec 3x$, $\int -\mathrm{cosec}^2 \frac{x}{5} \, dx = 5\cot\frac{x}{5}$. Putting these bits together gives: $2\sec 3x + 5\cot\frac{x}{5} + C$.

6) $\ln|\sin x| + C$

7) $e^{x^3} + C$

8) $4\ln|x^5 + x^3 - 3x| + C$

9) Use the double angle formula for tan $2x$ to write $\frac{2\tan 3x}{1 - \tan^2 3x}$ as tan $6x$. The integral becomes
$\int \tan 6x \, dx = \int \frac{\sin 6x}{\cos 6x} dx = -\frac{1}{6}\ln|\cos 6x| + C$.
Don't forget to double the coefficient of x when you use the double angle formula.

10) From the identity $\sec^2 x \equiv 1 + \tan^2 x$, write $2\tan^2 3x$ as $2\sec^2 3x - 2$. The integral becomes:
$\int 2\sec^2 3x - 2 + 2 \, dx$
$= \int 2\sec^2 3x \, dx = \frac{2}{3}\tan 3x + C$.

Exam Questions

1 a) $-\frac{1}{2}e^{(5-6x)} + C$
[1 mark for answer in the form $ke^{(5-6x)}$, 1 mark for the correct value of k]

b) $-\ln|\cot x + 2x| + C$
[1 mark for answer in the form $k\ln|f(x)|$, 1 mark for correct value of k and 1 mark for correct function f(x). Lose 1 mark if C is missed off both answers a) and b)]

2 Use the identity $\mathrm{cosec}^2 x \equiv 1 + \cot^2 x$ to write $2\cot^2 x$ as $2\mathrm{cosec}^2 x - 2$ ***[1 mark]***. The integral becomes:
$\int 2\mathrm{cosec}^2 x - 2 \, dx = -2\cot x - 2x + C$
[1 mark for $-2\cot x$, 1 mark for $-2x + C$].

Answers

C4 Section 6 — Integration 2

Warm-up Questions

1) If $u = e^x - 1$, then $\frac{du}{dx} = e^x$ (so $\frac{du}{e^x} = dx$) and $e^x + 1 = u + 2$. Substituting this into the integral gives:

$$\int e^x(u+2)u^2\frac{du}{e^x} = \int (u+2)u^2du$$
$$= \int u^3 + 2u^2du = \frac{1}{4}u^4 + \frac{2}{3}u^3 + C$$
$$= \frac{1}{4}(e^x - 1)^4 + \frac{2}{3}(e^x - 1)^3 + C$$

Make sure you put $u = e^x - 1$ back into your final answer.

2) If $u = \sec x$, then $\frac{du}{dx} = \sec x \tan x$ (so $\frac{du}{\sec x \tan x} = dx$). Change the limits: when $x = \frac{\pi}{4}$, $u = \sec\frac{\pi}{4} = \sqrt{2}$ and when $x = \frac{\pi}{3}$, $u = \sec\frac{\pi}{3} = 2$. Substituting into the integral gives:

$$\int_{\sqrt{2}}^{2} \sec x \tan x\, u^3 \frac{du}{\sec x \tan x} = \int_{\sqrt{2}}^{2} u^3\,du = [\tfrac{1}{4}u^4]_{\sqrt{2}}^{2}$$
$$= [\tfrac{1}{4}(2)^4] - [\tfrac{1}{4}(\sqrt{2})^4]$$
$$= \tfrac{1}{4}(16) - \tfrac{1}{4}(4) = 4 - 1 = 3.$$

3) Let $u = \ln x$ and let $\frac{dv}{dx} = 3x^2$. So $\frac{du}{dx} = \frac{1}{x}$ and $v = x^3$. Putting these into the formula gives:

$$\int 3x^2 \ln x\,dx = x^3\ln x - \int \frac{x^3}{x}dx = [x^3\ln x] - \int x^2 dx$$
$$= x^3\ln x - \tfrac{1}{3}x^3 + C = x^3(\ln x - \tfrac{1}{3}) + C$$

4) Let $u = 4x$, and let $\frac{dv}{dx} = \cos 4x$. So $\frac{du}{dx} = 4$ and $v = \frac{1}{4}\sin 4x$. Putting these into the formula gives:

$$\int 4x\cos 4x\,dx = 4x(\tfrac{1}{4}\sin 4x) - \int 4(\tfrac{1}{4}\sin 4x)dx$$
$$= x\sin 4x + \tfrac{1}{4}\cos 4x + C$$

5) First, find the partial fractions: If

$$\frac{3x+10}{(2x+3)(x-4)} \equiv \frac{A}{2x+3} + \frac{B}{x-4},$$

then $3x + 10 \equiv A(x-4) + B(2x+3)$.
From this, you get the simultaneous equations $3 = A + 2B$ and $10 = -4A + 3B$. Solving these gives $A = -1$ and $B = 2$:

$$\frac{3x+10}{(2x+3)(x-4)} = \frac{-1}{2x+3} + \frac{2}{x-4}.$$

Now putting this into the integral gives:

$$\int \frac{-1}{2x+3} + \frac{2}{x-4}\,dx = -\frac{1}{2}\ln|2x+3| + 2\ln|x-4| + C$$

6) If $y = \frac{1}{x}$ then $y^2 = \frac{1}{x^2}$. Putting this into the integral gives:

$$V = \pi\int_2^4 \frac{1}{x^2}dx = \pi\left[-\frac{1}{x}\right]_2^4 = \pi\left[\left(-\tfrac{1}{4}\right) - \left(-\tfrac{1}{2}\right)\right] = \frac{\pi}{4}.$$

7) a) If $x = t^2$, then $\frac{dx}{dt} = 2t$. Find the limits in terms of t: $4 = t^2 \Rightarrow t = 2$ (as $t > 0$) and $9 = t^2 \Rightarrow t = 3$ (as $t > 0$).

Now integrate using the formula:

$$\int_{x=4}^{x=9} y\,dx = \int_{t=2}^{t=3} y\frac{dx}{dt}dt = \int_2^3 \frac{2t}{t}dt = \int_2^3 2\,dt$$
$$= [2t]_2^3 = 6 - 4 = 2$$

b) $y = \frac{1}{t}$, so $y^2 = \frac{1}{t^2}$. Using $\frac{dx}{dt}$ and the limits from part a):

$$\pi\int_{t=2}^{t=3} y^2\frac{dx}{dt}dt = \pi\int_2^3 \frac{2t}{t^2}dt = \pi\int_2^3 \frac{2}{t}dt$$
$$= \pi[2\ln|t|]_2^3 = \pi(2\ln 3 - 2\ln 2)$$
$$= \pi(\ln 9 - \ln 4) = \pi\ln\frac{9}{4}$$

It's really easy to forget to change the limits from x to t — ignore this warning at your own risk.

8) $\frac{dy}{dx} = \frac{1}{y}\cos x \Rightarrow y\,dy = \cos x\,dx$

so $\int y\,dy = \int \cos x\,dx \Rightarrow \frac{y^2}{2} = \sin x + C_0$

$\Rightarrow y^2 = 2\sin x + C_1$ (where $C_1 = 2C_0$)

9) a) $\frac{dS}{dt} = kS$

b) Solving the differential equation above gives:

$\frac{dS}{dt} = kS \Rightarrow \int \frac{1}{S}dS = \int k\,dt$

$\ln|S| = kt + C$

$S = Ae^{kt}$ where $A = e^C$

For the initial population, $t = 0$. Put $S = 30$ and $t = 0$ into the equation to find the value of A: $30 = Ae^0 \Rightarrow A = 30$. Now, use $S = 150$, $k = 0.2$ and $A = 30$ to find t:

$150 = 30e^{0.2t} \Rightarrow 5 = e^{0.2t} \Rightarrow \ln 5 = 0.2t$, so $t = 8.047$.

It will take the squirrels 8 weeks before they can take over the forest.

Go squirrels go!

10) For the Trapezium Rule using 4 strips, $h = 1.5$ and you need to work out the values of y at $x = 0, 1.5, 3, 4.5, 6$:

$x_0 = 0$, $y_0 = -108$, $x_1 = 1.5$, $y_1 = -1.6875$, $x_2 = 3$, $y_2 = 0$, $x_3 = 4.5$, $y_3 = 413.4375$, $x_4 = 6$, $y_4 = 5400$.

Putting these values into the formula gives:

$A \approx 0.75[-108 + 2(-1.6875 + 0 + 413.4375) + 5400]$
$= 4586.625$.

Using 6 strips, $h = 1$ and you need the y-values for $x = 0, 1, 2, 3, 4, 5, 6$. You already know the values for $x = 0, 3, 6$.
($x_0 = 0$, $y_0 = -108$), $x_1 = 1$, $y_1 = 0$, $x_2 = 2$, $y_2 = 0$, ($x_3 = 3$, $y_3 = 0$), $x_4 = 4$, $y_4 = 108$, $x_5 = 5$, $y_5 = 1152$, ($x_6 = 6$, $y_6 = 5400$).

Putting these values into the formula gives:

$A \approx \frac{1}{2}[-108 + 2(0 + 0 + 0 + 108 + 1152) + 5400] = 3906$.

To calculate the percentage error, you must first work out the exact value of the integral:

$$\int_0^6 (6x - 12)(x^2 - 4x + 3)^2dx = [(x^2 - 4x + 3)^3]_0^6$$
$$= (6^2 - 4(6) + 3)^3 - (0 - 0 + 3)^3$$
$$= 3375 - 27 = 3348.$$

This uses the formula $\int (n+1)f'(x)[f(x)]^n dx = [f(x)]^{n+1} + C$.

Now work out the error for 4 strips:

$$\frac{4586.625 - 3348}{3348} \times 100 = 37.00\% \text{ (4 s.f.)}$$

and for 6 strips: $\frac{3906 - 3348}{3348} \times 100 = 16.67\%$ (4 s.f.).

Neither of these estimates was particularly accurate — but the one with more strips had a lower % error (as you would expect).

Exam Questions

1 $$V = \pi\int_{\frac{\pi}{4}}^{\frac{\pi}{3}} y^2\,dx = \pi\int_{\frac{\pi}{4}}^{\frac{\pi}{3}} \operatorname{cosec}^2 x\,dx = \pi[-\cot x]_{\frac{\pi}{4}}^{\frac{\pi}{3}}$$
$$= \pi[(-\cot\tfrac{\pi}{3}) - (-\cot\tfrac{\pi}{4})]$$
$$= \pi[-\tfrac{1}{\sqrt{3}} + 1] = 1.328 \text{ (3 d.p.)}.$$

[3 marks available — 1 mark for correct function for y^2, 1 mark for integrating, 1 mark for substituting in values of x to obtain correct answer]

Don't forget π here.

Answers

2 a) When $x = \frac{\pi}{2}$, $y = \frac{\pi}{2}\sin\frac{\pi}{2} = \frac{\pi}{2} = 1.5708$ ***[1 mark]***,
and when $x = \frac{3\pi}{4}$, $y = \frac{3\pi}{4}\sin\frac{3\pi}{4} = 1.6661$ ***[1 mark]***

b) The width of each strip (h) is $\frac{\pi}{4}$, so the Trapezium Rule is:

$$A = \frac{1}{2}\frac{\pi}{4}[0 + 2(0.5554 + 1.5708 + 1.6661) + 0]$$
$$= \frac{\pi}{8}[2(3.7923)] = 2.978 \text{ (3 d.p.)}.$$

[4 marks available — 1 mark for correct value of h, 2 marks for correct use of formula, 1 mark for correct answer]

You're given the Trapezium Rule on the formula sheet (it's hidden away in the C2 section), but it's a good idea to learn it anyway.

c) Let $u = x$, so $\frac{du}{dx} = 1$. Let $\frac{dv}{dx} = \sin x$, so $v = -\cos x$ ***[1 mark for both parts correct]***. Using integration by parts,

$$\int_0^{\pi} x\sin x\,dx = [-x\cos x]_0^{\pi} - \int_0^{\pi} -\cos x\,dx \quad \textbf{[1 mark]}$$
$$= [-x\cos x]_0^{\pi} + [\sin x]_0^{\pi} \quad \textbf{[1 mark]}$$
$$= (\pi - 0) + (0) = \pi \quad \textbf{[1 mark]}$$

If you'd tried to use u = sin x, you'd have ended up with a more complicated function to integrate ($x^2\cos x$).

d) To find the percentage error, divide the difference between the approximate answer and the exact answer by the exact answer and multiply by 100:

$$\frac{\pi - 2.978}{\pi} \times 100 = 5.2\% \text{ (2 s.f.)}.$$

[2 marks available — 1 mark for appropriate method and 1 mark for correct answer]

3 a) $\frac{dy}{dx} = \frac{\cos x\cos^2 y}{\sin x} \Rightarrow \frac{1}{\cos^2 y}dy = \frac{\cos x}{\sin x}dx$

$\Rightarrow \int \sec^2 y\,dy = \int \frac{\cos x}{\sin x}dx$

$\Rightarrow \tan y = \ln|\sin x| + C$

[4 marks available — 1 mark for separating the variables into functions of x and y, 1 mark for correct integration of RHS, 1 mark for correct integration of LHS, 1 mark for general solution]

b) If $y = \pi$ when $x = \frac{\pi}{6}$, that means that

$\tan\pi = \ln|\sin\frac{\pi}{6}| + C$

$0 = \ln|\frac{1}{2}| + C$ ***[1 mark]***

As $\ln \frac{1}{2} = \ln 1 - \ln 2 = -\ln 2$ (as $\ln 1 = 0$), it follows that $C = \ln 2$.

So $\tan y = \ln|\sin x| + \ln 2$ or $\tan y = \ln|2\sin x|$ ***[1 mark]***.

This is the particular solution — you found the general solution in part a).

4 If $u = \ln x$, then $\frac{du}{dx} = \frac{1}{x}$, so $x\,du = dx$. Changing the limits: when $x = 1$, $u = \ln 1 = 0$. When $x = 2$, $u = \ln 2$. Substituting all this into the integral gives:

$$\int_1^2 \frac{8}{x}(\ln x + 2)^3\,dx = \int_0^{\ln 2}\frac{8}{x}(u+2)^3 x\,du = \int_0^{\ln 2} 8(u+2)^3\,du$$
$$= [2(u+2)^4]_0^{\ln 2}$$
$$= [2(\ln 2 + 2)^4] - [2(0+2)^4]$$
$$= 105.21 - 32 = 73.21 \text{ (4 s.f.)}.$$

[6 marks available — 1 mark for finding substitution for dx, 1 mark for finding correct limits, 1 mark for correct integral in terms of u, 2 marks for correct integration (1 for an answer in the form k(u + 2)ⁿ, 1 mark for correct values of k and n), 1 mark for final answer (to 4 s.f.)]

5 a) $\frac{dm}{dt} = k\sqrt{m}$, $k > 0$ ***[1 mark for RHS, 1 mark for LHS]***

b) First solve the differential equation to find m:

$\frac{dm}{dt} = k\sqrt{m} \Rightarrow \frac{1}{\sqrt{m}}dm = k\,dt$

$\Rightarrow \int m^{-\frac{1}{2}}dm = \int k\,dt$ ***[1 mark]***

$\Rightarrow 2m^{\frac{1}{2}} = kt + C$

$\Rightarrow m = \left(\frac{1}{2}(kt + C)\right)^2 = \frac{1}{4}(kt + C)^2$ ***[1 mark]***

At the start of the campaign, $t = 0$. Putting $t = 0$ and $m = 900$ into the equation gives: $900 = \frac{1}{4}(0 + C)^2 \Rightarrow 3600 = C^2 \Rightarrow C = 60$ (C must be positive, otherwise the sales would be decreasing). ***[1 mark]***. This gives the equation $m = \frac{1}{4}(kt + 60)^2$ ***[1 mark]***.

c) Substituting $t = 5$ and $k = 2$ into the equation gives:
$m = \frac{1}{4}((2 \times 5) + 60)^2 = 1225$ tubs sold.

[3 marks available — 2 marks for substituting correct values of t and k, 1 mark for answer]

C4 Section 7 — Vectors

Warm-up Questions

1) Any multiples of the vectors will do:

a) e.g. **a** and 4**a**

b) e.g. 6**i** + 8**j** – 4**k** and 9**i** + 12**j** – 6**k**

c) e.g. $\begin{pmatrix}2\\4\\-2\end{pmatrix}$ and $\begin{pmatrix}4\\8\\-4\end{pmatrix}$

2) a) **b** – **a** b) **a** – **b** c) **b** – **c** d) **c** – **a**

3) 2**i** – 4**j** + 5**k**

4) a) $\sqrt{3^2 + 4^2 + (-2)^2} = \sqrt{29}$

b) $\sqrt{1^2 + 2^2 + (-1)^2} = \sqrt{6}$

5) a) $\sqrt{(3-1)^2 + (-1-2)^2 + (-2-3)^2} = \sqrt{38}$

b) $\sqrt{1^2 + 2^2 + 3^2} = \sqrt{14}$

c) $\sqrt{3^2 + (-1)^2 + (-2)^2} = \sqrt{14}$

6) a) **r** = (4**i** + **j** + 2**k**) + t(3**i** + **j** – **k**) or **r** = $\begin{pmatrix}4\\1\\2\end{pmatrix} + t\begin{pmatrix}3\\1\\-1\end{pmatrix}$

b) **r** = (2**i** – **j** + **k**) + t((2**j** + 3**k**) – (2**i** – **j** + **k**))
⇒ **r** = (2**i** – **j** + **k**) + t(–2**i** + 3**j** + 2**k**)

or **r** = $\begin{pmatrix}2\\-1\\1\end{pmatrix} + t\begin{pmatrix}-2\\3\\2\end{pmatrix}$

7) E.g. If $t = 1$, ((3 + 1(–1)), (2 + 1(3)), (4 + 1(0))) = (2, 5, 4)
If $t = 2$, ((3 + 2(–1)), (2 + 2(3)), (4 + 2(0))) = (1, 8, 4)
If $t = -1$, ((3 + –1(–1)), (2 + –1(3)), (4 + –1(0))) = (4, –1, 4)

Answers

8) a) $(3\mathbf{i} + 4\mathbf{j}).(\mathbf{i} - 2\mathbf{j} + 3\mathbf{k}) = 3 - 8 + 0 = -5$

b) $\begin{pmatrix}4\\2\\1\end{pmatrix} \cdot \begin{pmatrix}3\\-4\\-3\end{pmatrix} = (4 \times 3) + (2 \times -4) + (1 \times -3) = 1$

9) a) $\begin{pmatrix}2\\-1\\2\end{pmatrix} + t\begin{pmatrix}-4\\6\\-2\end{pmatrix} = \begin{pmatrix}3\\2\\4\end{pmatrix} + u\begin{pmatrix}-1\\3\\0\end{pmatrix}$

Where the lines intersect, these 3 equations are true:

$2 - 4t = 3 - u$

$-1 + 6t = 2 + 3u$

$2 - 2t = 4$

Solve the third equation to give $t = -1$.

Substituting $t = -1$ in either of the other equations gives $u = -3$.

Substituting $t = -1$ and $u = -3$ in the remaining equation gives a true result, so the lines intersect.

Substituting $t = -1$ in the first vector equation gives the position vector of the intersection point:

$\begin{pmatrix}6\\-7\\4\end{pmatrix}$

You'll often have to solve a pair of equations simultaneously (both variables will usually be in all three equations).

b) To find the angle between the lines, only consider the direction components of the vector equations:

$\begin{pmatrix}-4\\6\\-2\end{pmatrix} \cdot \begin{pmatrix}-1\\3\\0\end{pmatrix} = 4 + 18 + 0 = 22$

magnitude of 1st vector: $\sqrt{(-4)^2 + 6^2 + (-2)^2} = \sqrt{56}$

magnitude of 2nd vector: $\sqrt{(-1)^2 + 3^2 + (0)^2} = \sqrt{10}$

$\cos\theta = \frac{22}{\sqrt{56}\sqrt{10}} = \Rightarrow \theta = 21.6°$

10) Find values for a, b and c that give a scalar product of 0 when the two vectors are multiplied together.

$(3\mathbf{i} + 4\mathbf{j} - 2\mathbf{k}).(a\mathbf{i} + b\mathbf{j} + c\mathbf{k}) = 3a + 4b - 2c = 0$

E.g. $a = 2$, $b = 1$, $c = 5$

Perpendicular vector = $(2\mathbf{i} + \mathbf{j} + 5\mathbf{k})$

Just pick values for a and b, then see what value of c is needed to make the scalar product zero.

Exam Questions

1 a) $\overrightarrow{AB} = \mathbf{b} - \mathbf{a} = \begin{pmatrix}3\\2\\1\end{pmatrix} - \begin{pmatrix}1\\5\\9\end{pmatrix} = \begin{pmatrix}2\\-3\\-8\end{pmatrix}$

[2 marks available — 1 mark for attempting to subtract position vector a from position vector b, 1 mark for correct answer.]

b) l_1: $\mathbf{r} = \mathbf{c} + \mu(\mathbf{d} - \mathbf{c}) = \begin{pmatrix}-2\\4\\3\end{pmatrix} + \mu\left(\begin{pmatrix}5\\-1\\-7\end{pmatrix} - \begin{pmatrix}-2\\4\\3\end{pmatrix}\right)$ ***[1 mark]***

$\mathbf{r} = \begin{pmatrix}-2\\4\\3\end{pmatrix} + \mu\begin{pmatrix}7\\-5\\-10\end{pmatrix}$ ***[1 mark]***

c) Equation of line through AB:

$\overrightarrow{AB}$: $\mathbf{r} = \mathbf{a} + t(\mathbf{b} - \mathbf{a}) = \begin{pmatrix}1\\5\\9\end{pmatrix} + t\begin{pmatrix}2\\-3\\-8\end{pmatrix}$ ***[1 mark]***

At intersection of lines:

$\begin{pmatrix}1\\5\\9\end{pmatrix} + t\begin{pmatrix}2\\-3\\-8\end{pmatrix} = \begin{pmatrix}-2\\4\\3\end{pmatrix} + \mu\begin{pmatrix}7\\-5\\-10\end{pmatrix}$ ***[1 mark]***

Any two of: $1 + 2t = -2 + 7\mu$

$5 - 3t = 4 - 5\mu$

$9 - 8t = 3 - 10\mu$ ***[1 mark]***

Solving any two equations simultaneously gives $t = 2$ or $\mu = 1$ ***[1 mark]***

Substituting $t = 2$ in the equation of the line through AB (or $\mu = 1$ in the equation for l_1) gives: (5, –1, –7) ***[1 mark]***

d) i) Vectors needed are $\begin{pmatrix}2\\-3\\-8\end{pmatrix}$ and $\begin{pmatrix}7\\-5\\-10\end{pmatrix}$ (direction vector of l_1).

$\begin{pmatrix}2\\-3\\-8\end{pmatrix} \cdot \begin{pmatrix}7\\-5\\-10\end{pmatrix} = 14 + 15 + 80 = 109$ ***[1 mark]***

magnitude of 1st vector: $\sqrt{2^2 + (-3)^2 + (-8)^2} = \sqrt{77}$

magnitude of 2nd vector: $\sqrt{7^2 + (-5)^2 + (-10)^2} = \sqrt{174}$ ***[1 mark]***

$\cos\theta = \frac{109}{\sqrt{77}\sqrt{174}}$ ***[1 mark]***

$\Rightarrow \theta = 19.7°$ ***[1 mark]***

ii) Draw a diagram:

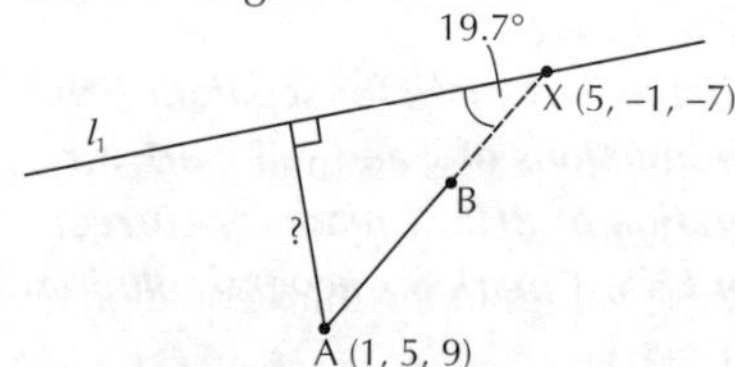

[1 mark for showing that the shortest distance is perpendicular to l_1]

X is the intersection point found in part c) — (5, –1, –7)

Distance from A to X =

$\sqrt{(5-1)^2 + (-1-5)^2 + (-7-9)^2} = \sqrt{308}$

[1 mark]

Now you've got a right-angled triangle, so just use trig to find the side you want:

Shortest distance from A to l_1

$= \sqrt{308} \times \sin 19.7°$ ***[1 mark]*** = 5.9 units ***[1 mark]***

The tricky thing here is figuring out how to go about it. Drawing a diagram definitely helps you see what you know and what you need to work out. Often, you'll be meant to use something you worked out in a previous part of the question.

2 a) $-3(\mathbf{i} - 4\mathbf{j} + 2\mathbf{k}) = -3\mathbf{i} + 12\mathbf{j} - 6\mathbf{k}$ ***[1 mark]***

b) **i** component: $3 + (\mu \times 1) = 2$ gives $\mu = -1$ ***[1 mark]***

So $\mathbf{r} = (3\mathbf{i} - 3\mathbf{j} - 2\mathbf{k}) - 1(\mathbf{i} - 4\mathbf{j} + 2\mathbf{k}) = 2\mathbf{i} + \mathbf{j} - 4\mathbf{k}$ ***[1 mark]***

This is the position vector of the point A(2, 1, –4)

Answers

c) B lies on l_2 so it has position vector
$\mathbf{b} = (10\mathbf{i} - 21\mathbf{j} + 11\mathbf{k}) + \lambda(-3\mathbf{i} + 12\mathbf{j} - 6\mathbf{k})$ ***[1 mark]***

So $\overrightarrow{AB} = \mathbf{b} - \mathbf{a}$
$= ((10\mathbf{i} - 21\mathbf{j} + 11\mathbf{k}) + \lambda(-3\mathbf{i} + 12\mathbf{j} - 6\mathbf{k})) - (2\mathbf{i} + \mathbf{j} - 4\mathbf{k})$
$= (8 - 3\lambda)\mathbf{i} + (-22 + 12\lambda)\mathbf{j} + (15 - 6\lambda)\mathbf{k}$ ***[1 mark]***

You know the scalar product of the direction vector of l_1 and $\overrightarrow{AB}$ must equal zero as they're perpendicular:
$(\mathbf{i} - 4\mathbf{j} + 2\mathbf{k}).((8 - 3\lambda)\mathbf{i} + (-22 + 12\lambda)\mathbf{j} + (15 - 6\lambda)\mathbf{k})$ ***[1 mark]***
$= (8 - 3\lambda) + (88 - 48\lambda) + (30 - 12\lambda)$
$= 126 - 63\lambda = 0$
$\Rightarrow \lambda = 2$ ***[1 mark]***

Substitute in $\lambda = 2$ to find the position vector $\mathbf{b}$:

$\mathbf{b} = (10\mathbf{i} - 21\mathbf{j} + 11\mathbf{k}) + 2(-3\mathbf{i} + 12\mathbf{j} - 6\mathbf{k})$ ***[1 mark]***
$= 4\mathbf{i} + 3\mathbf{j} - \mathbf{k}$

Position vector of B = $4\mathbf{i} + 3\mathbf{j} - \mathbf{k}$ ***[1 mark]***

You could have multiplied $\overrightarrow{AB}$ by the direction bit of the l_2 vector equation, as $\overrightarrow{AB}$ is perpendicular to both l_1 and l_2. But the numbers for the l_1 vector are smaller, making your calculations easier.

d) $\overrightarrow{AB} = \mathbf{b} - \mathbf{a}$
$= (4\mathbf{i} + 3\mathbf{j} - \mathbf{k}) - (2\mathbf{i} + \mathbf{j} - 4\mathbf{k}) = 2\mathbf{i} + 2\mathbf{j} + 3\mathbf{k}$ ***[1 mark]***
$|\overrightarrow{AB}| = \sqrt{2^2 + 2^2 + 3^2} = \sqrt{17} = 4.1$ ***[1 mark]***

3 a) At an intersection point: $\begin{pmatrix}3\\0\\-2\end{pmatrix} + \lambda\begin{pmatrix}1\\3\\-2\end{pmatrix} = \begin{pmatrix}0\\2\\1\end{pmatrix} + \mu\begin{pmatrix}2\\-5\\-3\end{pmatrix}$

[1 mark]

This gives equations: $3 + \lambda = 2\mu$
$3\lambda = 2 - 5\mu$
$-2 - 2\lambda = 1 - 3\mu$ ***[1 mark]***

Solving the first two equations simultaneously gives:
$\lambda = -1$, $\mu = 1$ ***[1 mark]***
Substituting these values in the third equation gives:
$-2 - 2(-1) = 1 - 3(1) \Rightarrow 0 \neq -2$ ***[1 mark]***

So the lines don't intersect.

You could have solved any two of the equations simultaneously, then substituted the results in the remaining equation to show that they don't work and there's no intersection point.

b) (i) At the intersection point of PQ and l_1:

$$\begin{pmatrix}3\\0\\-2\end{pmatrix} + \lambda\begin{pmatrix}1\\3\\-2\end{pmatrix} = \begin{pmatrix}5\\4\\-9\end{pmatrix} + t\begin{pmatrix}0\\2\\3\end{pmatrix}$$ ***[1 mark]***

This gives equations: $3 + \lambda = 5$
$3\lambda = 4 + 2t$
$-2 - 2\lambda = -9 + 3t$

[1 mark for any two equations]

Solving two of these equations gives: $\lambda = 2$, $t = 1$
[1 mark]

Intersection point $= \begin{pmatrix}5\\4\\-9\end{pmatrix} + 1\begin{pmatrix}0\\2\\3\end{pmatrix} = \begin{pmatrix}5\\6\\-6\end{pmatrix} = (5, 6, -6)$
[1 mark]

(ii) If perpendicular, the scalar product of direction vectors of lines will equal 0:

$$\begin{pmatrix}0\\2\\3\end{pmatrix} \cdot \begin{pmatrix}1\\3\\-2\end{pmatrix}$$ ***[1 mark]***

$= (0 \times 1) + (2 \times 3) + (3 \times -2) = 0$ ***[1 mark]***

(iii) Call intersection point X.

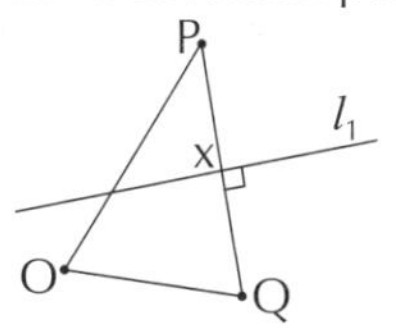

$\overrightarrow{PX} = \mathbf{x} - \mathbf{p}$

$$= \begin{pmatrix}5\\6\\-6\end{pmatrix} - \begin{pmatrix}5\\8\\-3\end{pmatrix} = \begin{pmatrix}0\\-2\\-3\end{pmatrix}$$ ***[1 mark]***

$$\overrightarrow{OQ} = \overrightarrow{OP} + 2\overrightarrow{PX} = \begin{pmatrix}5\\8\\-3\end{pmatrix} + 2\begin{pmatrix}0\\-2\\-3\end{pmatrix}$$ ***[1 mark]***

$$= \begin{pmatrix}5\\4\\-9\end{pmatrix}$$ ***[1 mark]***

The trick with this one is to realise that point Q lies the same distance from the intersection point as P does — drawing a quick sketch will definitely help.

4 a) $(\overrightarrow{OA}).(\overrightarrow{OB})$ ***[1 mark]***
$= (3\mathbf{i} + 2\mathbf{j} + \mathbf{k}).(3\mathbf{i} - 4\mathbf{j} - \mathbf{k}) = 9 - 8 - 1 = 0$ ***[1 mark]***
Therefore, side OA is perpendicular to side OB, and the triangle has a right angle. ***[1 mark]***

You could also have found the lengths $|OA|$, $|OB|$ and $|AB|$ and shown by Pythagoras that AOB is a right-angled triangle ($|AB|^2 = |OA|^2 + |OB|^2$).

b) $\overrightarrow{BA} = \mathbf{a} - \mathbf{b} = (3\mathbf{i} + 2\mathbf{j} + \mathbf{k}) - (3\mathbf{i} - 4\mathbf{j} - \mathbf{k}) = (6\mathbf{j} + 2\mathbf{k})$ ***[1 mark]***
$\overrightarrow{BO} = -3\mathbf{i} + 4\mathbf{j} + \mathbf{k}$
$\overrightarrow{BA}.\overrightarrow{BO} = 24 + 2 = 26$ ***[1 mark]***
$|\overrightarrow{BA}| = \sqrt{6^2 + 2^2} = \sqrt{40}$
$|\overrightarrow{BO}| = \sqrt{(-3)^2 + 4^2 + 1^2} = \sqrt{26}$ ***[1 mark]***
$\cos\angle ABO = \dfrac{\overrightarrow{BA} \cdot \overrightarrow{BO}}{|\overrightarrow{BA}| \cdot |\overrightarrow{BO}|} = \dfrac{26}{\sqrt{40}\sqrt{26}}$ ***[1 mark]***

$\angle ABO = 36.3°$ ***[1 mark]***

c) (i) $\overrightarrow{AC} = \mathbf{c} - \mathbf{a} = (3\mathbf{i} - \mathbf{j}) - (3\mathbf{i} + 2\mathbf{j} + \mathbf{k}) = (-3\mathbf{j} - \mathbf{k})$ ***[1 mark]***
$|\overrightarrow{AC}| = \sqrt{(-3)^2 + (-1)^2} = \sqrt{10}$
$|\overrightarrow{OC}| = \sqrt{3^2 + (-1)^2} = \sqrt{10}$ ***[1 mark]***
Sides AC and OC are the same length, so the triangle is isosceles. ***[1 mark]***

(ii) You know side lengths AC and OC from part c)(i). Calculate length of OA:
$|\overrightarrow{OA}| = \sqrt{3^2 + 2^2 + 1^2} = \sqrt{14}$ ***[1 mark]***

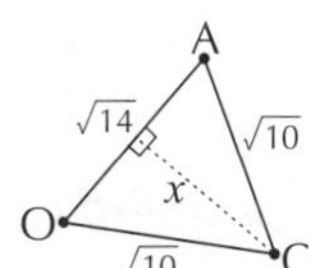

Answers

Now find the height of the triangle, x, using Pythagoras:

$$x = \sqrt{(\sqrt{10})^2 - \left(\frac{\sqrt{14}}{2}\right)^2} = \sqrt{6.5} \quad \textbf{[1 mark]}$$

Area = ½(base × height)
= ½($\sqrt{14} \times \sqrt{6.5}$) ***[1 mark]***
= 4.77 square units ***[1 mark]***

d) (i) $\mathbf{r} = \mathbf{a} + t(\mathbf{b} - \mathbf{a})$
$\mathbf{r} = (3\mathbf{i} + 2\mathbf{j} + \mathbf{k}) + t((3\mathbf{i} - 4\mathbf{j} - \mathbf{k}) - (3\mathbf{i} + 2\mathbf{j} + \mathbf{k}))$ ***[1 mark]***
$\mathbf{r} = (3\mathbf{i} + 2\mathbf{j} + \mathbf{k}) + t(-6\mathbf{j} - 2\mathbf{k})$ ***[1 mark]***

(ii) **k** component: $1 - 2t = 1,\ t = 0$ ***[1 mark]***
$\mathbf{r} = (3\mathbf{i} + 2\mathbf{j} + \mathbf{k}) + 0(6\mathbf{j} + 2\mathbf{k}) = 3\mathbf{i} + 2\mathbf{j} + \mathbf{k}$
$a = 3$ ***[1 mark]***, $b = 2$ ***[1 mark]***

Practice Exam One

1 As $y = \sqrt{\sin x}$, $y^2 = \sin x$. Putting this into the formula:

$$V = \pi\int_0^\pi \sin x\,dx = \pi[-\cos x]_0^\pi = -\pi[(-1) - 1] = 2\pi.$$

[4 marks available — 1 mark for correct expression for y^2, 1 mark for formula for volume of revolution, 1 mark for correct integration of sin x, 1 mark for correct answer]

2 a) When $x = 1.5$, $y = \frac{3\ln 1.5}{(1.5)^2} = 0.54062$ ***[1 mark]***, and when $x = 3$, $y = \frac{3\ln 3}{3^2} = 0.36620$ ***[1 mark]***.

b) $h = 0.5$. Putting h and the values from the table into the Trapezium Rule formula:

$$A \approx \frac{0.5}{2}[0 + 2(0.54062 + 0.51986 + 0.43982) + 0.36620]$$
$$= \frac{1}{4}[2(1.5003) + 0.36620] = 0.8417$$

[3 marks available — 1 mark for putting the correct numbers into the trapezium rule formula, 1 mark for some correct working and 1 mark for correct answer]

c) Let $u = \ln x$, so $\frac{du}{dx} = \frac{1}{x}$. Let $\frac{dv}{dx} = \frac{3}{x^2}$, so $v = -\frac{3}{x}$.
Putting this into the formula for integration by parts gives:

$$3\int_1^3 \frac{\ln x}{x^2}\,dx = 3\left[-\frac{\ln x}{x}\right]_1^3 - 3\int_1^3 -\frac{1}{x}\frac{1}{x}\,dx$$
$$= 3\left[-\frac{\ln x}{x}\right]_1^3 + 3\int_1^3 \frac{1}{x^2}\,dx = 3\left[-\frac{\ln x}{x}\right]_1^3 + 3\left[-\frac{1}{x}\right]_1^3$$
$$= \frac{-3\ln 3}{3} + \frac{3\ln 1}{1} - \frac{3}{3} + \frac{3}{1}$$
$$= -\ln 3 - 1 + 3 = 2 - \ln 3 = 0.90139$$

[5 marks available — 1 mark for correct expression for du/dx, 1 mark for correct expression for v, 1 mark for correct formula for integration by parts, 1 mark for correct working and 1 mark for correct answer]

If the question asked for the exact value, you'd leave your answer as 2 – ln 3.

3 If $x = \sin\theta$, then $\frac{dx}{d\theta} = \cos\theta$, so $dx = d\theta\cos\theta$ ***[1 mark]***.
Change the limits: as $x = \sin\theta$, $\theta = \sin^{-1}x$,
so when $x = 0$, $\theta = 0$ and when $x = 0.5$, $\theta = \frac{\pi}{6}$ ***[1 mark]***.
Putting all this into the integral gives:

$$\int_0^{\frac{1}{2}} \frac{x}{1 - x^2}\,dx = \int_0^{\frac{\pi}{6}} \frac{\sin\theta}{1 - \sin^2\theta}\cos\theta\,d\theta \quad \textbf{[1 mark]}$$

Using the identity $\sin^2\theta + \cos^2\theta = 1$, replace $1 - \sin^2\theta$:

$$\int_0^{\frac{\pi}{6}} \frac{\sin\theta\cos\theta}{\cos^2\theta}\,d\theta = \int_0^{\frac{\pi}{6}} \frac{\sin\theta}{\cos\theta}\,d\theta = \int_0^{\frac{\pi}{6}} \tan\theta\,d\theta \quad \textbf{[1 mark]}$$
$$= [-\ln|\cos\theta|]_0^{\frac{\pi}{6}} \quad \textbf{[1 mark]}$$
$$= -\ln\left|\cos\frac{\pi}{6}\right| + \ln|\cos 0| = -\ln\frac{\sqrt{3}}{2} + \ln 1$$
$$= -\ln\sqrt{3} + \ln 2$$
$$= \ln 2 - \ln\sqrt{3}\left(= \ln\frac{2}{\sqrt{3}}\right) \quad \textbf{[1 mark]}$$

Be careful when the substitution is of the form $x = f(\theta)$ rather than $\theta = f(x)$ — when you change the limits, you need to find the inverse of $f(\theta)$ then put in the given values of x.

4 a) (i) $\frac{dx}{d\theta} = \frac{\cos\theta}{2}$, $\frac{dy}{d\theta} = 2\sin 2\theta$ ***[1 mark]***

So $\frac{dy}{dx} = \frac{dy}{d\theta} \times \frac{d\theta}{dx} = \frac{dy}{d\theta} \div \frac{dx}{d\theta}$ ***[1 mark]***

$= 2\sin 2\theta \div \frac{\cos\theta}{2} = \frac{4\sin 2\theta}{\cos\theta}$ ***[1 mark]***

(ii) $\theta = \frac{\pi}{6} \Rightarrow \frac{dy}{dx} = \frac{4\sin(\frac{\pi}{3})}{\cos(\frac{\pi}{6})} = \frac{4\left(\frac{\sqrt{3}}{2}\right)}{\left(\frac{\sqrt{3}}{2}\right)} = 4$ ***[1 mark]***

$x = \frac{1}{2}\sin\frac{\pi}{6} - 3 = \frac{1}{2} \times \frac{1}{2} - 3 = \frac{1}{4} - 3 = -\frac{11}{4}$

$y = 5 - \cos\frac{\pi}{3} = 5 - \frac{1}{2} = \frac{9}{2}$

[1 mark for x and y values both correct]

So $y = mx + c$

$\rightarrow \frac{9}{2} = 4 \times -\frac{11}{4} + c = -11 + c$

$\Rightarrow c = 11 + \frac{9}{2} = \frac{31}{2}$

The equation of the tangent when $\theta = \frac{\pi}{6}$ is $y = 4x + \frac{31}{2}$
[1 mark]

b) Rewrite the equation for y using the identity
$\cos 2\theta \equiv 1 - 2\sin^2\theta$:
$y = 5 - \cos 2\theta = 5 - (1 - 2\sin^2\theta) = 4 + 2\sin^2\theta$ ***[1 mark]***
Now rearrange the equation for x to make $\sin\theta$ the subject:
$x = \frac{\sin\theta}{2} - 3 \Rightarrow 2x + 6 = \sin\theta$ ***[1 mark]***
Sub this into the equation for y:
$y = 4 + 2\sin^2\theta = 4 + 2(2x + 6)^2$
$\Rightarrow y = 4 + 2(4x^2 + 24x + 36)$
$\Rightarrow y = 8x^2 + 48x + 76$ ***[1 mark]***

5 a) $5x + 4 \equiv A(1 + 3x) + B(2 - x)$ ***[1 mark]***
let $x = 2$: $14 = 7A$ ***[1 mark]*** $\Rightarrow A = 2$ ***[1 mark]***.
Equating coefficients of x: $5 = 3A - B$ ***[1 mark]*** $\Rightarrow B = 1$ ***[1 mark]***.

b) As $\frac{5x + 4}{(2 - x)(1 + 3x)} \equiv \frac{2}{(2 - x)} + \frac{1}{(1 + 3x)}$, you want the binomial expansion of $\frac{2}{(2 - x)} + \frac{1}{(1 + 3x)}$. This can be written as $2(2 - x)^{-1} + (1 + 3x)^{-1}$. Taking each term in turn,

$$2(2 - x)^{-1} = 2\left(2\left(1 - \tfrac{1}{2}x\right)\right)^{-1} = 2\left(\tfrac{1}{2}\left(1 - \tfrac{1}{2}x\right)^{-1}\right) = \left(1 - \tfrac{1}{2}x\right)^{-1}$$
$$= 1 + (-1)\left(-\tfrac{1}{2}x\right) + \frac{(-1)(-2)}{1 \times 2}\left(-\tfrac{1}{2}x\right)^2 + \frac{(-1)(-2)(-3)}{1 \times 2 \times 3}\left(-\tfrac{1}{2}x\right)^3$$
$$= 1 + \tfrac{1}{2}x + \tfrac{1}{4}x^2 + \tfrac{1}{8}x^3$$

Answers

and $(1 + 3x)^{-1} =$

$1 + (-1)(3x) + \frac{(-1)(-2)}{1 \times 2}(3x)^2 + \frac{(-1)(-2)(-3)}{1 \times 2 \times 3}(3x)^3$

$= 1 - 3x + 9x^2 - 27x^3$

So $2(2 - x)^{-1} + (1 + 3x)^{-1} = 1 + \frac{1}{2}x + \frac{1}{4}x^2 + \frac{1}{8}x^3 + 1 - 3x +$

$9x^2 - 27x^3 = 2 - \frac{5}{2}x + \frac{37}{4}x^2 - \frac{215}{8}x^3$.

[6 marks available in total:
- ***1 mark for rewriting f(x) in partial fractions***
- ***1 mark for correct binomial expansion of $(2 - x)^{-1}$***
- ***1 mark for correct binomial expansion of $(1 + 3x)^{-1}$***
- ***1 mark for correct constant and x-terms in final answer***
- ***1 mark for correct x^2-term in final answer***
- ***1 mark for correct x^3-term in final answer]***

c) Expansion of $(1 + 3x)^{-1}$ is valid for $\left|\frac{3x}{1}\right| < 1 \Rightarrow \frac{3|x|}{1} < 1$

$\Rightarrow |x| < \frac{1}{3}$

Expansion of $(2 - x)^{-1}$ is valid for $\left|\frac{-x}{2}\right| < 1 \Rightarrow \frac{|-1||x|}{2} < 1$

$\Rightarrow |x| < 2$

The combined expansion is valid for the narrower of these two ranges. So the expansion in part b) is valid for $|x| < \frac{1}{3}$.

[2 marks available in total:
- ***1 mark for identifying the valid range of one of the expansions.***
- ***1 mark for correct answer]***

6 a) Differentiate each term with respect to x:

$x^3 + x^2y = y^2 - 1$

$\Rightarrow \frac{d}{dx}x^3 + \frac{d}{dx}x^2y = \frac{d}{dx}y^2 - \frac{d}{dx}1$

Differentiate x^3 and 1 first:

$\Rightarrow 3x^2 + \frac{d}{dx}x^2y = \frac{d}{dx}y^2 - 0$ ***[1 mark]***

Differentiate y^2 using the chain rule:

$\Rightarrow 3x^2 + \frac{d}{dx}x^2y = \frac{d}{dy}y^2\frac{dy}{dx}$ ***[1 mark]***

$\Rightarrow 3x^2 + \frac{d}{dx}x^2y = 2y\frac{dy}{dx}$

Differentiate x^2y using the product rule:

$\Rightarrow 3x^2 + x^2\frac{d}{dx}y + y\frac{d}{dx}x^2 = 2y\frac{dy}{dx}$

$\Rightarrow 3x^2 + x^2\frac{dy}{dx} + 2xy = 2y\frac{dy}{dx}$ ***[1 mark]***

Rearrange to make $\frac{dy}{dx}$ the subject:

$\Rightarrow (2y - x^2)\frac{dy}{dx} = 3x^2 + 2xy$

$\Rightarrow \frac{dy}{dx} = \frac{3x^2 + 2xy}{2y - x^2}$ ***[1 mark]***

b) (i) Substitute $x = 1$ into the original equation:

$x = 1 \Rightarrow (1)^3 + (1)^2y = y^2 - 1$ ***[1 mark]***

$\Rightarrow y^2 - y - 2 = 0$

$\Rightarrow (y - 2)(y + 1) = 0$

$\Rightarrow y = 2$ or $y = -1$

$a > b$, so $a = 2$, $b = -1$ ***[1 mark]***

(ii) At $Q = (1, -1)$,

$\frac{dy}{dx} = \frac{3(1)^2 + 2(1)(-1)}{2(-1) - (1)^2} = \frac{3-2}{-2-1} = -\frac{1}{3}$ ***[1 mark]***

So the gradient of the normal at $Q = 3$. ***[1 mark]***

$(y - y_1) = m(x - x_1)$

$\Rightarrow (y + 1) = 3(x - 1)$

$\Rightarrow y = 3x - 4$ ***[1 mark]***

7 a) Vector equation of line through P and Q:

$\mathbf{r} = \begin{pmatrix}-2\\-2\\-1\end{pmatrix} + \mu\left(\begin{pmatrix}-5\\-4\\1\end{pmatrix} - \begin{pmatrix}-2\\-2\\-1\end{pmatrix}\right)$

$\mathbf{r} = \begin{pmatrix}-2\\-2\\-1\end{pmatrix} + \mu\begin{pmatrix}-3\\-2\\2\end{pmatrix}$ ***[1 mark]***

Where lines intersect:

$-1 + 2\lambda = -2 - 3\mu$

$2\lambda = -2 - 2\mu$

$3 + \lambda = -1 + 2\mu$ ***[1 mark]***

Solving any pair of equations simultaneously gives $\lambda = -2$ and $\mu = 1$. ***[1 mark]***

Substitute these values into the remaining equation to show that the lines intersect. E.g. $3 + \lambda = -1 + 2\mu$

$\Rightarrow 3 + -2 = -1 + 2(1) \Rightarrow 1 = 1$ ***[1 mark]***

Intersection point:

$\mathbf{r} = \begin{pmatrix}-2\\-2\\-1\end{pmatrix} + \mu\begin{pmatrix}-3\\-2\\2\end{pmatrix} \Rightarrow \mathbf{r} = \begin{pmatrix}-2\\-2\\-1\end{pmatrix} + 1\begin{pmatrix}-3\\-2\\2\end{pmatrix} = \begin{pmatrix}-5\\-4\\1\end{pmatrix}$

$\Rightarrow (-5, -4, 1)$ ***[1 mark]***

b) $\overrightarrow{OT} = 3\begin{pmatrix}-2\\-2\\-1\end{pmatrix} = \begin{pmatrix}-6\\-6\\-3\end{pmatrix}$ ***[1 mark]***

$\overrightarrow{QT} = \begin{pmatrix}-6\\-6\\-3\end{pmatrix} - \begin{pmatrix}-5\\-4\\1\end{pmatrix} = \begin{pmatrix}-1\\-2\\-4\end{pmatrix}$ ***[1 mark]***

$|\overrightarrow{QT}| = \sqrt{(-1)^2 + (-2)^2 + (-4)^2} = \sqrt{21}$ ***[1 mark]***

c) $\overrightarrow{PV} = \begin{pmatrix}0\\f\\g\end{pmatrix} - \begin{pmatrix}-2\\-2\\-1\end{pmatrix} = \begin{pmatrix}2\\f+2\\g+1\end{pmatrix}$ ***[1 mark]***

The scalar product of $\overrightarrow{PV}$ and the direction vector of L_1 must be zero as they're perpendicular.

$(2 \times 2) + (2 \times (f + 2)) + (1 \times (g + 1)) = 0$ ***[1 mark]***

$4 + 2f + 4 + g + 1 = 0 \Rightarrow 2f + g = -9$ ***[1 mark]***

d) $\cos\alpha = \frac{(2 \times 1) + (2 \times 1) + (1 \times 1)}{(\sqrt{2^2 + 2^2 + 1^2}) \times (\sqrt{1^2 + 1^2 + 1^2})}$ ***[1 mark]***

$\cos\alpha = \frac{5}{(\sqrt{9}) \times (\sqrt{3})} = 0.962$ ***[1 mark]***

$\alpha = 15.8°$ (3 s.f.) ***[1 mark]***

8 a) $\frac{dN}{dt} = k\sqrt{N}$, $k > 0$ ***[1 mark for LHS, 1 mark for RHS]***

When $N = 36$, $\frac{dN}{dt} = 0.36$. Putting these values into the equation gives $0.36 = k\sqrt{36} = 6k \Rightarrow k = 0.06$ ***[1 mark]*** (the population is increasing so ignore the negative square root).

So the differential equation is $\frac{dN}{dt} = 0.06\sqrt{N}$ ***[1 mark]***.

b) (i) $\frac{dN}{dt} = \frac{kN}{\sqrt{t}} \Rightarrow \int \frac{1}{N}\,dN = \int \frac{k}{\sqrt{t}}\,dt$

$\ln|N| = 2k\sqrt{t} + C$ ***[1 mark]***

$\Rightarrow N = e^{2k\sqrt{t} + C} = Ae^{2k\sqrt{t}}$, where $A = e^C$ ***[1 mark]***

Answers

For the initial population, $t = 0$, so $N = 25$ when $t = 0$. Putting these values into the equation:
$25 = Ae^0 \Rightarrow 25 = A$, so the equation for N is:
$N = 25e^{2k\sqrt{t}}$ ***[1 mark].***

(ii) When initial population has doubled, $N = 50$ ***[1 mark].*** Put this value and the value for k into the equation and solve for t:
$50 = 25e^{2(0.05)\sqrt{t}} \Rightarrow 2 = e^{0.1\sqrt{t}} \Rightarrow \ln 2 = 0.1\sqrt{t}$ ***[1 mark]***
$10\ln 2 = \sqrt{t} \Rightarrow (10\ln 2)^2 = t \Rightarrow t = 48.045$
So it will take 48 weeks ***[1 mark]*** (to the nearest week) for the population to double.

Practice Exam Two

1 a) $5x^2 + 10x - 13 \equiv A(2-x)(1+4x) + B(1+4x) + C(2-x)^2$
[1 mark]
Substitute values of x to make the brackets on the RHS equal to zero: ***[1 mark]***
Let $x = 2$, then $5(2)^2 + 10(2) - 13 = B(1 + 4(2))$
$\Rightarrow 27 = 9B \Rightarrow B = 3$ ***[1 mark]***
Let $x = -\frac{1}{4}$, then $5\left(-\frac{1}{4}\right)^2 + 10\left(-\frac{1}{4}\right) - 13 = C\left(2 - \left(-\frac{1}{4}\right)\right)^2$
$\Rightarrow \frac{5}{16} - \frac{5}{2} - 13 = C\frac{81}{16} \Rightarrow -\frac{243}{16} = \frac{81}{16}C \Rightarrow C = -3$ ***[1 mark]***
Equate the terms in x^2:
$5 = -4A + C = -4A - 3 \Rightarrow 8 = -4A \Rightarrow A = -2$ ***[1 mark]***
so $\frac{5x^2+10x-13}{(2-x)^2(1+4x)} = \frac{-2}{2-x} + \frac{3}{(2-x)^2} - \frac{3}{1+4x}$.

b) $\int \frac{5x^2+10x-13}{(2-x)^2(1+4x)}\,dx \equiv \int \frac{-2}{2-x} + \frac{3}{(2-x)^2} - \frac{3}{1+4x}\,dx$

$= 2\ln|2-x| + \frac{3}{2-x} - \frac{3}{4}\ln|1+4x| + C$

[4 marks available — 1 mark for using partial fractions from part a), 1 mark for each correct term of the answer (not including C)]

2 a) $(1-x)^{-\frac{1}{2}} \approx 1 + \left(-\frac{1}{2}\right)(-x) + \frac{\left(-\frac{1}{2}\right)\times\left(-\frac{3}{2}\right)}{1\times 2}(-x)^2 + \frac{\left(-\frac{1}{2}\right)\times\left(-\frac{3}{2}\right)\times\left(-\frac{5}{2}\right)}{1\times 2\times 3}(-x)^3$ ***[1 mark]***

$= 1 + \frac{x}{2} + \frac{3}{8}x^2 + \frac{5}{16}x^3$ ***[1 mark]***

b) (i) $(25-4x)^{-\frac{1}{2}}$

$= (25)^{-\frac{1}{2}}\left(1 - \frac{4}{25}x\right)^{-\frac{1}{2}} = \frac{1}{5}\left(1 - \frac{4}{25}x\right)^{-\frac{1}{2}}$ ***[1 mark]***

$= \frac{1}{5}\left(1 + \frac{1}{2}\left(\frac{4}{25}x\right) + \frac{3}{8}\left(\frac{4}{25}x\right)^2 + \frac{5}{16}\left(\frac{4}{25}x\right)^3\right)$ ***[1 mark]***

$= \frac{1}{5}\left(1 + \frac{1}{2}\left(\frac{4}{25}x\right) + \frac{3}{8}\left(\frac{16}{625}x^2\right) + \frac{5}{16}\left(\frac{64}{15625}x^3\right)\right)$

$= \frac{1}{5}\left(1 + \frac{2}{25}x + \frac{6}{625}x^2 + \frac{4}{3125}x^3\right)$

$= \frac{1}{5} + \frac{2}{125}x$ ***[1 mark]*** $+ \frac{6}{3125}x^2 + \frac{4}{15625}x^3$ ***[1 mark]***

(ii) The expansion is valid for $\left|\frac{-4x}{25}\right| < 1 \Rightarrow \frac{|-4||x|}{25} < 1$
$\Rightarrow |x| < \frac{25}{4}$ ***[1 mark]***

c) $25 - 4x = 20 \Rightarrow x = \frac{5}{4}$ ***[1 mark]***
So $\frac{1}{\sqrt{20}} = \left(25 - 4\left(\frac{5}{4}\right)\right)^{-\frac{1}{2}}$
$\approx \frac{1}{5} + \frac{2}{125}\left(\frac{5}{4}\right) + \frac{6}{3125}\left(\frac{5}{4}\right)^2 + \frac{4}{15625}\left(\frac{5}{4}\right)^3$ ***[1 mark]***
$= \frac{1}{5} + \frac{2}{125}\left(\frac{5}{4}\right) + \frac{6}{3125}\left(\frac{25}{16}\right) + \frac{4}{15625}\left(\frac{125}{64}\right)$
$= \frac{1}{5} + \frac{1}{50} + \frac{3}{1000} + \frac{1}{2000}$
$= \frac{447}{2000}$ ***[1 mark]***

3 a) Let $u = 4x$, so $\frac{du}{dx} = 4$. Let $\frac{dv}{dx} = e^{-2x}$, so $v = -\frac{1}{2}e^{-2x}$.

Putting this into the integral gives:
$\int 4xe^{-2x}dx = [4x(-\frac{1}{2}e^{-2x})] - \int 4(-\frac{1}{2}e^{-2x})\,dx$
$= -2xe^{-2x} + \int 2e^{-2x}dx$
$= -2xe^{-2x} - e^{-2x} + C \; (= -e^{-2x}(2x+1) + C)$

[4 marks available — 1 mark for correct choice of u and dv/dx, 1 mark for correct differentiation and integration to obtain du/dx and v, 1 mark for correct integration by parts method, 1 mark for answer]

b) As $u = \ln x$, $\frac{du}{dx} = \frac{1}{x}$, so $x\,du = dx$ ***[1 mark]***. The limits $x = 1$ and $x = 2$ become $u = \ln 1 = 0$ and $u = \ln 2$ ***[1 mark]***.
$\left(\frac{\ln x}{\sqrt{x}}\right)^2 = \frac{(\ln x)^2}{x}$ ***[1 mark]***. So the integral is:
$\int_0^{\ln 2} \frac{u^2}{x}x\,du = \int_0^{\ln 2} u^2\,du$ ***[1 mark]***
$= \left[\frac{u^3}{3}\right]_0^{\ln 2} = \frac{(\ln 2)^3}{3} = 0.111$ (3 s.f.) ***[1 mark]***.

4 a) As $x = \tan\theta$, $\frac{dx}{d\theta} = \sec^2\theta$. When $x = \frac{1}{\sqrt{3}}$, $\tan\theta = \frac{1}{\sqrt{3}}$, so $\theta = \frac{\pi}{6}$. When $x = 1$, $\tan\theta = 1$, so $\theta = \frac{\pi}{4}$. $y = \sin\theta$, so $y^2 = \sin^2\theta$. Putting all this into the formula to find a volume of revolution:

$V = \pi\int_a^b y^2\frac{dx}{d\theta}\,d\theta = \pi\int_{\frac{\pi}{6}}^{\frac{\pi}{4}} \sin^2\theta\sec^2\theta\,d\theta$

$= \pi\int_{\frac{\pi}{6}}^{\frac{\pi}{4}} \sin^2\theta\frac{1}{\cos^2\theta}\,d\theta = \pi\int_{\frac{\pi}{6}}^{\frac{\pi}{4}} \tan^2\theta\,d\theta = \pi\int_{\frac{\pi}{6}}^{\frac{\pi}{4}} \sec^2\theta - 1\,d\theta$.

[5 marks available — 1 mark for correct expression for dx/dθ, 1 mark for new limits, 1 mark for using for πy² in integral, 1 mark for using dx/dθ dθ in integral, 1 mark for simplifying to obtain final integral]

This uses the identity $\sec^2\theta \equiv 1 + \tan^2\theta$ to write $\tan^2\theta$ as $\sec^2\theta - 1$.

b)
$\pi\int_{\frac{\pi}{6}}^{\frac{\pi}{4}} \sec^2\theta - 1\,d\theta = \pi[\tan\theta - \theta]_{\frac{\pi}{6}}^{\frac{\pi}{4}}$
$= \pi\left[\left(\tan\frac{\pi}{4} - \frac{\pi}{4}\right) - \left(\tan\frac{\pi}{6} - \frac{\pi}{6}\right)\right]$
$= \pi\left[\left(1 - \frac{\pi}{4}\right) - \left(\frac{1}{\sqrt{3}} - \frac{\pi}{6}\right)\right] = 0.505$ (3 s.f.).

[3 marks available — 1 mark for integrating sec²θ – 1, 1 mark for substituting in values of θ, 1 mark for correct answer]

5 a) (i) Replace h with x in the height formula:
$x = \sqrt{\frac{2}{3}}a \Rightarrow a = \sqrt{\frac{3}{2}}x$ ***[1 mark]***

(ii) Sub $a = \sqrt{\frac{3}{2}}x$ into the expression for volume:
$V = \frac{\sqrt{2}}{12}\left(\sqrt{\frac{3}{2}}x\right)^3 = \frac{\sqrt{2}}{12} \times \frac{3\sqrt{3}}{2\sqrt{2}}x^3 = \frac{\sqrt{3}}{8}x^3$ ***[1 mark]***

Answers

b) From the question, $\frac{dV}{dt} = 240$ ***[1 mark]***
and differentiating the answer to part a) gives $\frac{dV}{dx} = \frac{3\sqrt{3}}{8}x^2$ ***[1 mark]***

Using chain rule, $\frac{dx}{dt} = \frac{dx}{dV} \times \frac{dV}{dt}$ ***[1 mark]***

$= \frac{1}{\left(\frac{dV}{dx}\right)} \times \frac{dV}{dt} = \frac{8}{3\sqrt{3}x^2} \times 240 = \frac{640}{\sqrt{3}x^2}$ ***[1 mark]***

So when $x = 8$, $\frac{dx}{dt} = \frac{640}{64\sqrt{3}} = \frac{10}{\sqrt{3}}$ cm min^{-1}.
[1 mark — allow decimal equivalent]

c) (i) $\frac{dV}{dt} = \frac{dV}{dx} \times \frac{dx}{dt}$ ***[1 mark]***

$= \frac{3\sqrt{3}x^2}{8} \times \frac{32}{9\sqrt{3}} = \frac{4x^2}{3}$ ***[1 mark]***

So when $x = 12$, $\frac{dV}{dt} = \frac{4 \times 144}{3} = 192$ cm^3 min^{-1}
[1 mark]

(ii) $\frac{dV}{dt}$ is the overall rate of change of the volume of water in the container, i.e. the difference between the rate at which the water is being poured in (240) and the rate at which it's leaking out (r).

So $240 - r = \frac{dV}{dt} = 192 \Rightarrow r = 48$ cm^3 min^{-1}
[1 mark]

6 a) First, rearrange the equation into the form $\frac{dy}{dx} = f(x)g(y)$:
$\frac{dy}{dx} = 2y\frac{e^{2x}+x}{e^{2x}+x^2}$.
Then separate out the variables and integrate:
$\frac{1}{y}dy = \frac{2(e^{2x}+x)}{e^{2x}+x^2}dx \Rightarrow \int \frac{1}{y}dy = \int \frac{2(e^{2x}+x)}{e^{2x}+x^2}dx$
$\Rightarrow \ln|y| = \ln|e^{2x}+x^2| + C$
$\Rightarrow y = A(e^{2x}+x^2)$.
[7 marks available — 1 mark for separating variables, 1 mark for integrating LHS correctly, 1 mark for spotting that RHS is of the form f′(x)/f(x), 1 mark for integrating this correctly, 1 mark for adding C, 1 mark for simplifying to remove ln, 1 mark for rearranging to get in terms of y]

For this one, you need to spot that $2(e^{2x} + x)$ is the derivative of $e^{2x} + x^2$. A is just a constant (= e^C). You don't need the modulus signs around y as you're told that $y \geq 0$.

b) (i) Substitute $y = 3$ and $x = 0$ ***[1 mark]*** into the equation above to find the value of A:
$3 = A(e^0 + 0^2) \Rightarrow 3 = A \cdot 1 \Rightarrow A = 3$.
So the particular solution is $y = 3(e^{2x} + x^2)$. ***[1 mark]***

(ii) When $x = 3$, $y = 3(e^{2 \cdot 3} + 3^2) = 3e^6 + 27$. ***[1 mark]***
So $y = 3e^6 + 27$ ***[1 mark]***.

You have to leave the e^6 in your answer because you're asked for the exact value.

7 a) Differentiate each term with respect to x:
$\sin \pi x - \cos \frac{\pi y}{2} = 0.5$
$\Rightarrow \frac{d}{dx}(\sin \pi x) - \frac{d}{dx}\left(\cos\frac{\pi y}{2}\right) = \frac{d}{dx}(0.5)$
Differentiate $\sin \pi x$ and 0.5 first:
$\Rightarrow \pi \cos \pi x - \frac{d}{dx}\left(\cos\frac{\pi y}{2}\right) = 0$

Differentiate $\cos \frac{\pi y}{2}$ using the chain rule:
$\Rightarrow \pi \cos \pi x - \frac{d}{dy}\left(\cos\frac{\pi y}{2}\right)\frac{dy}{dx} = 0$ ***[1 mark]***

$\Rightarrow \pi \cos \pi x + \left(\frac{\pi}{2}\sin\frac{\pi y}{2}\right)\frac{dy}{dx} = 0$

Rearrange to make $\frac{dy}{dx}$ the subject:
$\Rightarrow \frac{dy}{dx} = -\frac{\pi \cos \pi x}{\frac{\pi}{2}\sin\frac{\pi y}{2}} = -\frac{2\cos \pi x}{\sin\frac{\pi y}{2}}$ ***[1 mark]***

b) (i) The stationary point is where the gradient is zero.
$\frac{dy}{dx} = 0 \Rightarrow -\frac{2\cos \pi x}{\sin\frac{\pi y}{2}} = 0 \Rightarrow \cos \pi x = 0$ ***[1 mark]***
$\Rightarrow x = \frac{1}{2}$ or $x = \frac{3}{2}$ ***[1 mark]***
$x = \frac{3}{2} \Rightarrow \sin\frac{3\pi}{2} - \cos\frac{\pi y}{2} = 0.5$
$\Rightarrow -1 - \cos\frac{\pi y}{2} = 0.5$
$\Rightarrow \cos\frac{\pi y}{2} = -1.5$
So y has no solutions when $x = \frac{3}{2}$ ***[1 mark]***
$x = \frac{1}{2} \Rightarrow \sin\frac{\pi}{2} - \cos\frac{\pi y}{2} = 0.5$
$\Rightarrow 1 - \cos\frac{\pi y}{2} = 0.5$
$\Rightarrow \cos\frac{\pi y}{2} = 0.5$
$\Rightarrow \frac{\pi y}{2} = \frac{\pi}{3}$
$\Rightarrow y = \frac{2}{3}$
So the only stationary point of the graph of $\sin \pi x - \cos\frac{\pi y}{2} = 0.5$ for the given ranges of x and y is at $\left(\frac{1}{2}, \frac{2}{3}\right)$. ***[1 mark]***

(ii) $x = \frac{1}{6} \Rightarrow \sin\frac{\pi}{6} - \cos\frac{\pi y}{2} = 0.5$ ***[1 mark]***
$\Rightarrow 0.5 - \cos\frac{\pi y}{2} = 0.5$
$\Rightarrow \cos\frac{\pi y}{2} = 0$
$\Rightarrow \frac{\pi y}{2} = \frac{\pi}{2}$
$\Rightarrow y = 1$ ***[1 mark]***
At $\left(\frac{1}{6}, 1\right)$, $\frac{dy}{dx} = -\frac{2\cos\frac{\pi}{6}}{\sin\frac{\pi}{2}} = \frac{-2\left(\frac{\sqrt{3}}{2}\right)}{1} = -\sqrt{3}$ ***[1 mark]***

8 a) (i) The scalar product of perpendicular lines is 0.
So $\mathbf{x.y} = 15p - 12 + 3q = 0$
So $\mathbf{x.z} = \frac{3}{2}p - \frac{6}{5} + 4q = 0$ ***[1 mark]***
Solving simultaneously gives $p = \frac{4}{5}$ ***[1 mark]***, $q = 0$ ***[1 mark]***

(ii) $|\mathbf{y}| = \sqrt{15^2 + (-20)^2 + 3^2} = \sqrt{634}$ ***[1 mark]***
Unit vector in the direction of $\mathbf{y}$
$= \frac{1}{\sqrt{634}}(15\mathbf{i} - 20\mathbf{j} + 3\mathbf{k})$ ***[1 mark]***

Unit vectors have a magnitude of 1 — that's all there is to it.

b) $\cos\alpha = \frac{\mathbf{y.z}}{|\mathbf{y}||\mathbf{z}|} = \frac{74.5}{(\sqrt{634}) \times \left(\sqrt{\left(\frac{3}{2}\right)^2 + (-2)^2 + 4^2}\right)}$ ***[1 mark]***

$= \frac{74.5}{118.77} = 0.627$ ***[1 mark]*** $\Rightarrow \alpha = 51°$ ***[1 mark]***

Answers

S2 Section 1 — The Binomial Distribution

Warm-up Questions

1) a) There are 21 objects altogether, so if all the balls were different colours, there would be 21! ways to arrange them. But since 15 of the objects are identical, you need to divide this figure by 15!. So there are 21! ÷ 15! = 39 070 080 possible arrangements.

b) There are $\frac{16!}{4!4!4!4!} = 63\,063\,000$ possible arrangements.

You'd be a while counting all these on your fingers.

2) a) $P(5\text{ heads}) = 0.5^5 \times 0.5^5 \times \binom{10}{5}$

$= 0.5^{10} \times \frac{10!}{5!5!} = 0.246$ (to 3 sig.fig.).

b) $P(9\text{ heads}) = 0.5^9 \times 0.5 \times \binom{10}{9}$

$= 0.5^{10} \times \frac{10!}{9!1!} = 0.00977$ (to 3 sig.fig.).

3) a) Binomial — there are a fixed number of independent trials (30) with two possible results ('prime' / 'not prime'), a constant probability of success, and the random variable is the total number of successes.

b) Binomial — there are a fixed number of independent trials (however many students are in the class) with two possible results ('heads' / 'tails'), a constant probability of success, and the random variable is the total number of successes.

c) Not binomial — the probability of being dealt an ace changes each time, since the total number of cards decreases as each card is dealt.

d) Not binomial — the number of trials is not fixed.

It's weird to have to write actual sentences in a maths exam, but be ready for it.

4) a) Use tables with $n = 10$ and $p = 0.5$.
If X represents the number of heads, then:
$P(X \geq 5) = 1 - P(X < 5) = 1 - P(X \leq 4)$
$= 1 - 0.3770 = 0.6230$

b) $P(X \geq 9) = 1 - P(X < 9) = 1 - P(X \leq 8)$
$= 1 - 0.9893 = 0.0107$

You do have to be prepared to monkey around with the numbers the tables give you.

5) a) You can't use tables here (because they don't include $p = 0.27$ or $n = 14$), so you have to use the probability function.

$$P(X = 4) = \binom{14}{4} \times 0.27^4 \times (1 - 0.27)^{10}$$
$$= 0.229 \text{ (to 3 sig.fig.)}$$

b) $P(X < 2) = P(X = 0) + P(X = 1)$

$$= \binom{14}{0} \times 0.27^0 \times (1 - 0.27)^{14} + \binom{14}{1} \times 0.27^1 \times (1 - 0.27)^{13}$$
$$= 0.012204... + 0.063195...$$
$$= 0.0754 \text{ (to 3 sig.fig.)}$$

c) $P(5 < X \leq 8) = P(X = 6) + P(X = 7) + P(X = 8)$

$$= \binom{14}{6} \times 0.27^6 \times (1 - 0.27)^8 + \binom{14}{7} \times 0.27^7 \times (1 - 0.27)^7 + \binom{14}{8} \times 0.27^8 \times (1 - 0.27)^6$$
$$= 0.093825... + 0.039660... + 0.012835...$$
$$= 0.146 \text{ (to 3 sig.fig.)}$$

6) For parts a)-c), use tables with $n = 25$ and $p = 0.15$.

a) $P(X \leq 3) = 0.4711$

b) $P(X \leq 7) = 0.9745$

c) $P(X \leq 15) = 1.0000$

For parts d)-f), define a new random variable $T \sim B(15, 0.35)$. Then use tables with $n = 15$ and $p = 0.35$.

d) $P(Y \leq 3) = P(T \geq 12) = 1 - P(T < 12)$
$= 1 - P(T \leq 11) = 1 - 0.9995 = 0.0005$

e) $P(Y \leq 7) = P(T \geq 8) = 1 - P(T < 8)$
$= 1 - P(T \leq 7) = 1 - 0.8868 = 0.1132$

f) $P(Y \leq 15) = 1$ (since 15 is the maximum possible value).

These last few parts (where you can't use the tables without a bit of messing around first) are quite awkward, so make sure you get lots of practice.

7) From tables:

a) $P(X \leq 15) = 0.9997$

b) $P(X < 4) = P(X \leq 3) = 0.1302$

c) $P(X > 7) = 1 - P(X \leq 7) = 1 - 0.0639 = 0.9361$

For parts d)-f) where $X \sim B(n, p)$ with $p > 0.5$, define a new random variable $Y \sim B(n, q)$, where $q = 1 - p$. Then use tables.

d) Define $Y \sim B(50, 0.2)$. Then $P(X \geq 40) = P(Y \leq 10) = 0.5836$

e) Define $Y \sim B(30, 0.3)$. Then $P(X = 20) = P(Y = 10)$
$= P(Y \leq 10) - P(Y \leq 9) = 0.7304 - 0.5888 = 0.1416$

f) Define $Y \sim B(10, 0.25)$. Then $P(X = 7) = P(Y = 3)$
$= P(Y \leq 3) - P(Y \leq 2) = 0.7759 - 0.5256 = 0.2503$

8) a) mean = 20 × 0.4 = 8; variance = 20 × 0.4 × 0.6 = 4.8

b) mean = 40 × 0.15 = 6; variance = 40 × 0.15 × 0.85 = 5.1

c) mean = 25 × 0.45 = 11.25;
variance = 25 × 0.45 × 0.55 = 6.1875

d) mean = 50 × 0.8 = 40; variance = 50 × 0.8 × 0.2 = 8

e) mean = 30 × 0.7 = 21; variance = 30 × 0.7 × 0.3 = 6.3

f) mean = 45 × 0.012 = 0.54;
variance = 45 × 0.012 × 0.988 = 0.53352

Answers

Exam Questions

1 a) (i) Define a new random variable $Y \sim B(12, 0.4)$.
Then $P(X < 8) = P(Y > 4) = 1 - P(Y \le 4)$
$= 1 - 0.4382$ ***[1 mark]*** $= 0.5618$ ***[1 mark]***

(ii) $P(X = 5) = P(Y = 7) = P(Y \le 7) - P(Y \le 6)$ ***[1 mark]***
$= 0.9427 - 0.8418 = 0.1009$ ***[1 mark]***

Or you could use the probability function for part (ii):

$P(X = 5) = \binom{12}{5} \times 0.6^5 \times 0.4^7 = 0.1009$

(iii) $P(3 < X \le 7) = P(X$ is greater than 3 and less than or equal to 7$) = P(Y$ is less than 9 and greater than or equal to 5$) = P(5 \le Y < 9) = P(5 \le Y \le 8)$ ***[1 mark]***
$= P(Y \le 8) - P(Y \le 4)$ ***[1 mark]*** $= 0.9847 - 0.4382$
$= 0.5465$ ***[1 mark]***

b) (i) $P(Y = 4) = 0.8^4 \times 0.2^7 \times \frac{11!}{4!7!}$ ***[1 mark]***
$= 0.00173$ (to 3 sig. fig.) ***[1 mark]***

(ii) $E(Y) = 11 \times 0.8 = 8.8$ ***[1 mark]***

(ii) $Var(Y) = 11 \times 0.8 \times 0.2 = 1.76$ ***[1 mark]***

2 a) (i) Let X represent the number of apples that contain a maggot. Then $X \sim B(40, 0.15)$ ***[1 mark]***.
$P(X < 6) = P(X \le 5) = 0.4325$ ***[1 mark]***

(ii) $P(X > 2) = 1 - P(X \le 2)$ ***[1 mark]***
$= 1 - 0.0486 = 0.9514$ ***[1 mark]***

(iii) $P(X = 12) = P(X \le 12) - P(X \le 11)$ ***[1 mark]***
$= 0.9957 - 0.9880 = 0.0077$ ***[1 mark]***

Or you could use the probability function for part (iii):

$P(X = 12) = \binom{40}{12} \times 0.15^{12} \times 0.85^{28} = 0.0077$

b) The probability that a crate contains more than 2 apples with maggots is 0.9514 (from part a) (ii)).
So define a random variable Y, where Y is the number of crates that contain more than 2 apples with maggots.
Then $Y \sim B(3, 0.9514)$ ***[1 mark]***.
You need to find $P(Y = 2) + P(Y = 3)$. This is:

$0.9514^2 \times (1 - 0.9514) \times \binom{3}{2}$

$+ 0.9514^3 \times (1 - 0.9514)^0 \times \binom{3}{3}$ ***[1 mark]***

$= 0.1320 + 0.8612 = 0.993$ (to 3 d.p.) ***[1 mark]***

3 a) (i) The probability of Simon being able to solve each crossword needs to remain the same ***[1 mark]***, and all the outcomes need to be independent (i.e. Simon solving or not solving a puzzle one day should not affect whether he will be able to solve it on another day) ***[1 mark]***.

(ii) The total number of puzzles he solves (or the number he fails to solve) ***[1 mark]***.

b) $P(X = 4) = p^4 \times (1 - p)^{14} \times \frac{18!}{4!14!}$ ***[1 mark]***

$P(X = 5) = p^5 \times (1 - p)^{13} \times \frac{18!}{5!13!}$ ***[1 mark]***

So $p^4 \times (1 - p)^{14} \times \frac{18!}{4!14!} = p^5 \times (1 - p)^{13} \times \frac{18!}{5!13!}$ ***[1 mark]***

Dividing by things that occur on both sides gives:

$\frac{1 - p}{14} = \frac{p}{5}$ ***[1 mark]***, or $5 = 19p$.

This means $p = \frac{5}{19}$ ***[1 mark]***.

S2 Section 2 — The Poisson Distribution
Warm-up Questions

1) a) $P(X = 2) = \frac{e^{-3.1} \times 3.1^2}{2!} = 0.2165$ (to 4 d.p.).

b) $P(X = 1) = \frac{e^{-3.1} \times 3.1}{1!} = 0.1397$ (to 4 d.p.).

c) $P(X = 0) = \frac{e^{-3.1} \times 3.1^0}{0!} = 0.0450$ (to 4 d.p.).

d) $P(X < 3) = P(X = 0) + P(X = 1) + P(X = 2)$
$= 0.0450 + 0.1397 + 0.2165 = 0.4012$

e) $P(X \ge 3) = 1 - P(X < 3)$
$= 1 - 0.4012 = 0.5988$ (to 4 d.p.).

2) a) $P(X = 2) = \frac{e^{-8.7} \times 8.7^2}{2!} = 0.0063$ (to 4 d.p.).

b) $P(X = 1) = \frac{e^{-8.7} \times 8.7}{1!} = 0.0014$ (to 4 d.p.).

c) $P(X = 0) = \frac{e^{-8.7} \times 8.7^0}{0!} = 0.0002$ (to 4 d.p.).

d) $P(X < 3) = P(X = 0) + P(X = 1) + P(X = 2)$
$= 0.0002 + 0.0014 + 0.0063 = 0.0079$

e) $P(X \ge 3) = 1 - P(X < 3)$
$= 1 - 0.0079 = 0.9921$ (to 4 d.p.).

3) a) $E(X) = Var(X) = 8$
standard deviation $= \sigma = \sqrt{8} = 2.828$ (to 3 d.p.).

b) $E(X) = Var(X) = 12.11$
standard deviation $= \sigma = \sqrt{12.11} = 3.480$ (to 3 d.p.).

c) $E(X) = Var(X) = 84.2227$
standard deviation $= \sigma = \sqrt{84.2227} = 9.177$ (to 3 d.p.).

4) Using tables:

a) $P(X \le \mu) = P(X \le 9) = 0.5874$
$P(X \le \mu - \sigma) = P(X \le 6) = 0.2068$

b) $P(X \le \mu) = P(X \le 4) = 0.6288$
$P(X \le \mu - \sigma) = P(X \le 2) = 0.2381$

5) a) The defective products occur randomly, singly and (on average) at a constant rate, and the random variable represents the number of 'events' (i.e. defective products) within a fixed period, so this would follow a Poisson distribution.

b) There is a fixed number of trials in this situation, and so this situation would be modelled by a binomial distribution. (Or you could say it won't follow a Poisson distribution, as the events don't occur at a constant rate over the 25 trials.)

Answers

c) If the random variable represents the number of people joining the queue within a fixed period, and assuming that the people join the queue randomly, singly and (on average) at a constant rate, then this would follow a Poisson distribution.

You do need to make a couple of assumptions here — the Poisson model wouldn't work if you had, say, big groups of factory workers all coming in together a couple of minutes after the lunchtime hooter sounds.

d) The mistakes occur randomly, singly and (on average) at a constant rate, and the random variable represents the number of mistakes within a fixed 'period' (i.e. the number of pages in the document), so this would follow a Poisson distribution.

6) a) The number of atoms decaying in an hour would follow the Poisson distribution Po(2000). So the number decaying in a minute would follow Po(2000 ÷ 60) = Po(33.3).

b) The number of atoms decaying in a day would follow Po(2000 × 24) = Po(48 000).

7) a) If X represents the number of atoms from the first sample decaying per minute, then $X \sim$ Po(60). And if Y represents the number of atoms from the second sample decaying per minute, then $Y \sim$ Po(90). So $X + Y$ (the total number of atoms decaying per minute) ~ Po(60 + 90) = Po(150).

b) The total number of atoms decaying per hour would be distributed as Po(150 × 60) = Po(9000).

8) a) $P(X \leq 2) = 0.0138$

b) $P(X \leq 7) = 0.4530$

c) $P(X \leq 5) = 0.1912$

d) $P(X < 9) = P(X \leq 8) = 0.5925$

e) $P(X \geq 8) = 1 - P(X < 8) = 1 - P(X \leq 7)$
$= 1 - 0.4530 = 0.5470$

f) $P(X > 1) = 1 - P(X \leq 1) = 1 - 0.0030 = 0.9970$

g) $P(X > 7) = 1 - P(X \leq 7) = 1 - 0.4530 = 0.5470$

h) $P(X = 6) = P(X \leq 6) - P(X \leq 5) = 0.3134 - 0.1912 = 0.1222$

i) $P(X = 4) = P(X \leq 4) - P(X \leq 3) = 0.0996 - 0.0424 = 0.0572$

j) $P(X = 3) = P(X \leq 3) - P(X \leq 2) = 0.0424 - 0.0138 = 0.0286$

9) a) No — n is not very large, and p is not very small.

b) Yes — n is large, and p is small, so approximate with Po(7).

c) Not really — n is large, but p isn't as small as you'd like.

d) Not really — n is quite small (and so you don't really need to approximate it anyway).

e) This is perfect for a Poisson approximation — n is enormous and p is tiny. It should follow Po(0.1) very closely.

f) If Y represents the number of 'successes' in 80 trials, then define a new random variable X representing the number of 'failures' in those 80 trials. Then $X \sim$ B(80, 0.1). Since n is quite large, and p is quite small, you could approximate X with Po(80 × 0.1) = Po(8). Then $Y = 80 - X$.

10) If X represents the number of geese in a random square metre of field, then $X \sim$ Po(1) — since the 'rate' at which geese occur is constant, they're randomly scattered, and geese only occur singly.

a) $P(X = 0) = \frac{e^{-1} \times 1^0}{0!} = 0.3679$

b) $P(X = 1) = \frac{e^{-1} \times 1^1}{1!} = 0.3679$

c) $P(X = 2) = \frac{e^{-1} \times 1^2}{2!} = 0.1839$

d) $P(X > 2) = 1 - P(X \leq 2) = 1 - (0.3679 + 0.3679 + 0.1839)$
$= 1 - 0.9197 = 0.0803$

This is one of those questions where you could use either your Poisson tables or the probability function.

Exam Questions

1 a) Events need to happen at a constant average rate ***[1 mark]*** and singly ("one at a time") ***[1 mark]***.

You could also have had "events occur randomly" or "independently".

b) (i) If X represents the number of chaffinches visiting the observation spot, then $X \sim$ Po(7) ***[1 mark]***.
Using tables, $P(X < 4) = P(X \leq 3) = 0.0818$ ***[1 mark]***.

(ii) $P(X \geq 7) = 1 - P(X < 7) = 1 - P(X \leq 6)$ ***[1 mark]***
$= 1 - 0.4497 = 0.5503$ ***[1 mark]***

(iii) $P(X = 9) = P(X \leq 9) - P(X \leq 8)$ ***[1 mark]***
$= 0.8305 - 0.7291 = 0.1014$ ***[1 mark]***

Or you could work this last one out using the formula:
$P(X = 9) = \frac{e^{-7}7^9}{9!} = 0.1014$
— you get the same answer either way, obviously.

c) The number of birds of any species visiting per hour would follow the distribution Po(22 + 7) = Po(29) ***[1 mark]***. So the total number of birds visiting in a random 15-minute period will follow Po(29 ÷ 4) = Po(7.25) ***[1 mark]***.

$$P(X = 3) = \frac{e^{-7.25} \times 7.25^3}{3!} \textbf{\textit{ [1 mark]}}$$
$$= 0.045 \text{ (to 3 d.p.)} \textbf{\textit{ [1 mark]}}.$$

2 a) (i) If the mean is 20, then the number of calls per hour follows Po(20). So the number of calls in a random 30-minute period follows Po(20 ÷ 2) = Po(10) ***[1 mark]***.
Using tables for $\lambda = 10$:
$P(X = 8) = P(X \leq 8) - P(X \leq 7)$ ***[1 mark]***
$= 0.3328 - 0.2202 = 0.1126$ ***[1 mark]***

Or you could work this out using the formula:
$P(X = 8) = \frac{e^{-10}10^8}{8!} = 0.1126.$

(ii) $P(X > 8) = 1 - P(X \leq 8)$ ***[1 mark]***
$= 1 - 0.3328 = 0.6672$ ***[1 mark]***

b) In this context, independently means that receiving a phone call at one particular instant does not affect whether or not a call will be received at a different instant. ***[1 mark]***.

Answers

3 a) The number of trials here is fixed (= 400) and the probability of the engineer being unable to fix a fault is constant (= 0.02). This means X (the total number of unsuccessful call-outs) will follow a binomial distribution ***[1 mark]***. In fact, $X \sim B(400, 0.02)$ ***[1 mark]***.

b) (i) To approximate a binomial distribution $B(n, p)$ with a Poisson distribution, n should be large ***[1 mark]*** and p should be small ***[1 mark]***.

(ii) $Po(400 \times 0.02) = Po(8)$ ***[1 mark]***.

(iii) Mean = 8 and variance = 8 ***[1 mark]***.

(iv) P(engineer unable to fix fewer than 10 faults) $= P(X < 10) = P(X \leq 9)$ ***[1 mark]***.
Using Poisson tables for $\lambda = 8$:
$P(X \leq 9) = 0.7166$ ***[1 mark]***.

S2 Section 3 — Continuous Random Variables

Warm-up Questions

1) a) Sketch the p.d.f.:

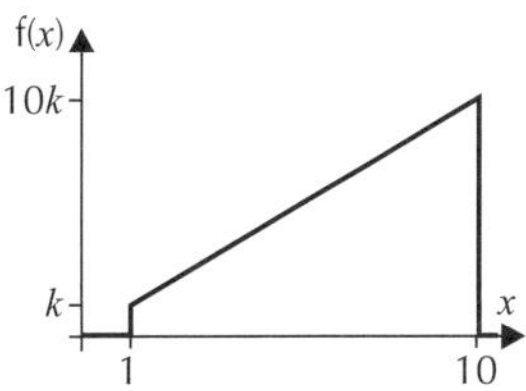

Area under p.d.f. $= \frac{10k + k}{2} \times (10 - 1) = \frac{99k}{2} = 1$.

So $k = \frac{2}{99}$.

b) Sketch the p.d.f.:

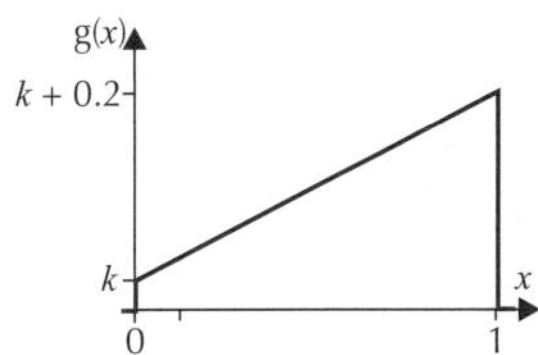

Area under p.d.f. $= \frac{2k + 0.2}{2} \times 1 = k + 0.1 = 1$.

So $k = 0.9$.

2 a) Sketch the p.d.f.:

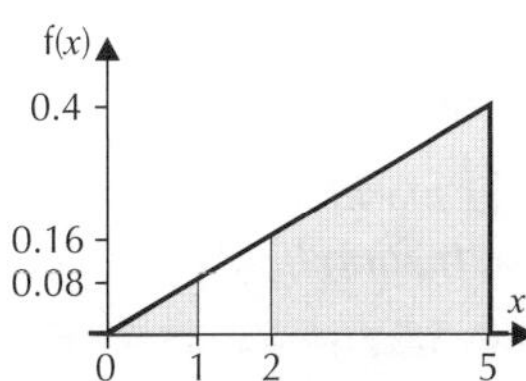

(i) Area under p.d.f. between $x = 0$ and $x = 1$ is:
$1 \times 0.08 \div 2 = 0.04$, so $P(X < 1) = 0.04$.

(ii) Area under p.d.f. between $x = 2$ and $x = 5$ is:
$\frac{0.16 + 0.4}{2} \times 3 = 0.84$, so $P(2 \leq X \leq 5) = 0.84$.

(iii) Area under p.d.f. at the point $x = 4$ is 0.
So $P(X = 4) = 0$.

b) Sketch the p.d.f.:

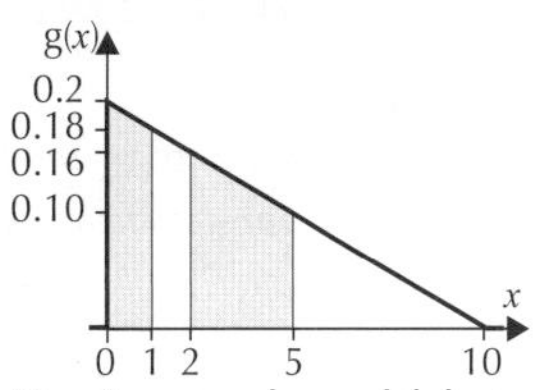

(i) Area under p.d.f. between $x = 0$ and $x = 1$ is:
$\frac{0.2 + 0.18}{2} \times 1 = 0.19$, so $P(X < 1) = 0.19$.

(ii) Area under p.d.f. between $x = 2$ and $x = 5$ is:
$\frac{0.16 + 0.1}{2} \times 3 = 0.39$, so $P(2 \leq X \leq 5) = 0.39$.

(iii) Area under p.d.f. at the point $x = 4$ is 0.
So $P(X = 4) = 0$.

3 a) $\int_{-\infty}^{\infty} f(x)dx = k\int_0^5 x^2 dx = k\left[\frac{x^3}{3}\right]_0^5 = \frac{125k}{3} = 1$, so $k = \frac{3}{125}$.

$P(X < 1) = \int_0^1 \frac{3}{125}x^2 dx = \frac{3}{125}\left[\frac{x^3}{3}\right]_0^1 = \frac{1}{125}$.

b) $\int_{-\infty}^{\infty} g(x)dx = \int_0^2 (0.1x^2 + kx)dx$

$= \left[\frac{0.1x^3}{3} + \frac{kx^2}{2}\right]_0^2 = \frac{0.8}{3} + 2k = 1$.

So $k = \frac{1}{2} - \frac{0.4}{3} = \frac{15 - 4}{30} = \frac{11}{30}$

$P(X < 1) = \int_0^1 \left(0.1x^2 + \frac{11}{30}x\right)dx = \left[\frac{0.1x^3}{3} + \frac{11x^2}{60}\right]_0^1$

$= \frac{0.1}{3} + \frac{11}{60} = \frac{13}{60}$

4 a) $\int_{-\infty}^{\infty} f(x)dx = \int_0^2 (0.1x^2 + 0.2)dx$

$= \left[\frac{0.1x^3}{3} + 0.2x\right]_0^2 = \frac{0.8}{3} + 0.4 \neq 1$

So f(x) is not a p.d.f.

b) $g(x) < 0$ for $-1 \leq x < 0$, so g(x) is not a p.d.f.

5 a) Integrate the pieces of the p.d.f., and then make sure the 'joins' are smooth using a suitable constant of integration (k).

$$F(x) = \begin{cases} 0 \text{ for } x < 0 \\ 0.04x^2 + k \text{ for } 0 \leq x \leq 5 \\ 1 \text{ for } x > 5 \end{cases}$$

Since F(0) = 0 and F(5) = 1, the pieces of this function join smoothly with $\underline{k = 0}$.

b) Integrate the pieces of the p.d.f., and then make sure the 'joins' are smooth using a suitable constant of integration (k).

$$G(x) = \begin{cases} 0 \text{ for } x < 0 \\ 0.2x - 0.01x^2 + k \text{ for } 0 \leq x \leq 10 \\ 1 \text{ for } x > 10 \end{cases}$$

Since G(0) = 0 and G(10) = 1, the pieces of this function join smoothly with $\underline{k = 0}$.

Answers

c) Integrate the pieces of the p.d.f., and then make sure the 'joins' are smooth using suitable constants of integration (k_1-k_3).

$$H(x) = \begin{cases} 0 \text{ for } x < 0 \\ x^2 + k_1 \text{ for } 0 \leq x \leq 0.5 \\ x + k_2 \text{ for } 0.5 \leq x \leq 1 \\ 3x - x^2 + k_3 \text{ for } 1 \leq x \leq 1.5 \\ 1 \text{ for } x > 1.5 \end{cases}$$

H(0) = 0 means that $k_1 = 0$, which then gives H(0.5) = 0.25.
H(0.5) = 0.25 means that $k_2 = -0.25$, giving H(1) = 0.75.
H(1) = 0.75 means that $k_3 = -1.25$, giving H(1.5) = 1.
This means all the joins are now 'smooth'.

d) Integrate the pieces of the p.d.f., and then make sure the 'joins' are smooth using suitable constants of integration (k_1 and k_2).

$$M(x) = \begin{cases} 0 \text{ for } x < 2 \\ 0.5x - 0.05x^2 + k_1 \text{ for } 2 \leq x \leq 4 \\ 0.1x + k_2 \text{ for } 4 \leq x \leq 10 \\ 1 \text{ for } x > 10 \end{cases}$$

M(2) = 0 means that $k_1 = -0.8$, which gives M(4) = 0.4.
M(4) = 0.4 means that $k_2 = 0$, which gives M(10) = 1.
This means all the joins are now 'smooth'.

6 a) Differentiate the different parts of the c.d.f.:

$$f(x) = \begin{cases} 4x^3 \text{ for } 0 \leq x \leq 1 \\ 0 \text{ otherwise} \end{cases}$$

b)

$$g(x) = \begin{cases} \frac{1}{50}(x-1) \text{ for } 1 \leq x < 6 \\ \frac{3}{8} \text{ for } 6 \leq x \leq 8 \\ 0 \text{ otherwise} \end{cases}$$

7 a) $E(X) = \int_{-\infty}^{\infty} xf(x)dx = \int_0^5 0.08x^2dx = 0.08\left[\frac{x^3}{3}\right]_0^5$

$= \frac{125 \times 0.08}{3} = \frac{10}{3}$

$\text{Var}(X) = \int_{-\infty}^{\infty} x^2f(x)dx - \mu^2 = \int_0^5 0.08x^3dx - \left(\frac{10}{3}\right)^2$

$= 0.08\left[\frac{x^4}{4}\right]_0^5 - \left(\frac{10}{3}\right)^2 = \frac{625 \times 0.08}{4} - \left(\frac{10}{3}\right)^2$

$= \frac{25}{2} - \left(\frac{10}{3}\right)^2 = \frac{25}{18} = 1.39$ (to 2 d.p.).

$E(Y) = \int_{-\infty}^{\infty} yg(y)dy = \int_0^{10} 0.02y(10-y)dy$

$= 0.02\left[5y^2 - \frac{y^3}{3}\right]_0^{10}$

$= 0.02\left(500 - \frac{1000}{3}\right) = 10 - \frac{20}{3} = \frac{10}{3}$

$\text{Var}(Y) = \int_{-\infty}^{\infty} y^2g(y)dy - \mu^2$

$= \int_0^{10} 0.02y^2(10-y)dy - \left(\frac{10}{3}\right)^2$

$= 0.02\left[\frac{10y^3}{3} - \frac{y^4}{4}\right]_0^{10} - \left(\frac{10}{3}\right)^2$

$= 0.02 \times \left(\frac{10\,000}{3} - \frac{10\,000}{4}\right) - \left(\frac{10}{3}\right)^2$

$= \frac{50}{3} - \left(\frac{10}{3}\right)^2 = \frac{50}{9} = 5.56$ (to 2 d.p.).

b) $E(4X + 2) = 4E(X) + 2 = 4 \times \frac{10}{3} + 2 = \frac{46}{3}$

$E(3Y - 4) = 3E(Y) - 4 = 3 \times \frac{10}{3} - 4 = 6$

$\text{Var}(4X + 2) = 16 \times \text{Var}(X)$

$= 16 \times \frac{25}{18} = \frac{200}{9} = 22.22$ (to 2 d.p.).

$\text{Var}(3Y - 4) = 9 \times \text{Var}(Y) = 9 \times \frac{50}{9} = 50$

c) Sketch the p.d.f.:

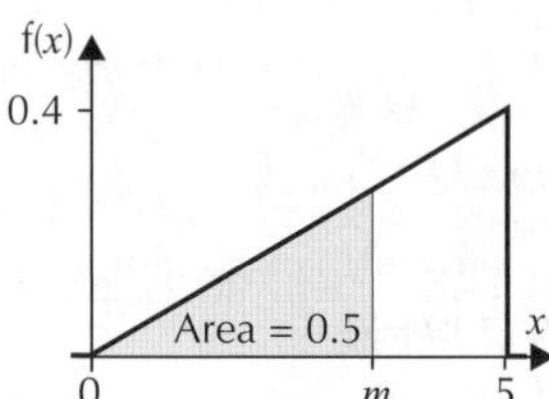

The mode is the value of x where the p.d.f. reaches its maximum, so mode = 5.
The median is m, where:

$\int_0^m 0.08xdx = 0.08\left[\frac{x^2}{2}\right]_0^m = 0.04m^2 = 0.5$

So the median = $\sqrt{12.5}$ = 3.54 (to 2 d.p.).

Or you could work out the median by finding F(x), and then solving F(m) = 0.5.

d) The lower quartile is Q_1, where:

$\int_0^{Q_1} 0.08xdx = 0.08\left[\frac{x^2}{2}\right]_0^{Q_1} = 0.04Q_1^2 = 0.25$

So $Q_1 = \sqrt{6.25} = 2.5$.

The upper quartile is Q_3, where:

$\int_0^{Q_3} 0.08xdx = 0.08\left[\frac{x^2}{2}\right]_0^{Q_3} = 0.04Q_3^2 = 0.75$

So $Q_3 = \sqrt{18.75}$.

This means the interquartile range is:
$\sqrt{18.75} - 2.5 = 1.83$ (to 2 d.p.).

Exam Questions

1 a) $\int_{-\infty}^{\infty} f(x)dx = \frac{1}{k}\int_0^2 (x+4)dx = \frac{1}{k}\left[\frac{x^2}{2} + 4x\right]_0^2 = \frac{10}{k}$ ***[1 mark]***

This must be equal to 1 ***[1 mark]***.

So $k = 10$ ***[1 mark]***.

There aren't many certainties in life, but "Your S2 exam will test if you know that the total area under a p.d.f. = 1" is one of them.

b) Integrate the pieces of the p.d.f., and then make sure the 'joins' are smooth using a constant of integration (k). ***[1 mark]***.

$$F(x) = \begin{cases} 0 \text{ for } x < 0 \\ 0.05x^2 + 0.4x + k \text{ for } 0 \leq x \leq 2 \\ 1 \text{ for } x > 2 \end{cases}$$

[1 mark for each part correctly found]

Answers

All the joins are 'smooth' if $k = 0$, so the c.d.f. is:

$$F(x) = \begin{cases} 0 & \text{for } x < 0 \\ 0.05x^2 + 0.4x & \text{for } 0 \leq x \leq 2 \\ 1 & \text{for } x > 2 \end{cases}$$

[1 mark for final answer]

You must define a c.d.f. for all values of x. Don't just do the tricky bits in the middle and assume you're finished.

c) $E(X) = \int_{-\infty}^{\infty} xf(x)dx = \int_0^2 0.1(x^2 + 4x)dx$ ***[1 mark]***

$= 0.1\left[\frac{x^3}{3} + 2x^2\right]_0^2$ ***[1 mark]***

$= 0.1\left(\frac{8}{3} + 8\right) = \frac{32}{30} = \frac{16}{15} = 1.07$ (to 2 d.p.) ***[1 mark]***

d) (i) $\text{Var}(X) = \int_{-\infty}^{\infty} x^2 f(x)dx - \mu^2$

$= 0.1\int_0^2 (x^3 + 4x^2)dx - \left(\frac{16}{15}\right)^2$ ***[1 mark]***

$= 0.1\left[\frac{x^4}{4} + \frac{4x^3}{3}\right]_0^2 - \left(\frac{16}{15}\right)^2$ ***[1 mark]***

$= 0.1\left(4 + \frac{32}{3}\right) - \left(\frac{16}{15}\right)^2$

$= \frac{44}{30} - \left(\frac{16}{15}\right)^2 = \frac{74}{225}$

$= 0.329$ (to 3 d.p.). ***[1 mark]***

If you worked out the integral but forgot to subtract the square of the mean, then you've just thrown a few marks away — at least, you would have done if that had been a real exam.

(ii) $\text{Var}(4X - 2) = 16 \times \text{Var}(X)$ ***[1 mark]***

$= 16 \times \frac{74}{225} = \frac{1184}{225} = 5.262$ (to 3 d.p.). ***[1 mark]***

e) Use the c.d.f. from part b) to find the median.
The median is m, where $0.05m^2 + 0.4m = 0.5$ ***[1 mark]***.
This simplifies to: $m^2 + 8m - 10 = 0$ ***[1 mark]***.
Using the quadratic formula (and choosing the positive answer ***[1 mark]***) gives

$m = \frac{-8 + \sqrt{104}}{2} = 1.099$ (to 3 d.p.) ***[1 mark]***.

f) The mode is at the highest point of the p.d.f. within the range of possible values. Since f(x) has a positive gradient, this must be at the greatest possible value of x, so the mode of X is 2 ***[1 mark]***.

The mode is the easiest of the three 'averages' to work out, but you get fewest marks for doing it. Such is life, I suppose. That's the beauty of S2 really — it's less about statistics and more about the cruelty of life generally.

g) mean < median < mode, so the skew is negative ***[1 mark]***.

2 a) Using the third part of the c.d.f., F(3) = 0.5 ***[1 mark]***.
So F(3) must also equal 0.5 using the second part of the c.d.f., which means that $2k = 0.5$, or $k = 0.25$ ***[1 mark]***.

Make sure the bits of a cumulative distribution function join together smoothly.

b) Q_1 is given by $F(Q_1) = 0.25$ ***[1 mark]***. Since F(3) = 0.5, the lower quartile must lie in the region described by the second part of the c.d.f., so solve $0.25(Q_1 - 1) = 0.25$, or $Q_1 = 2$ ***[1 mark]***.

Q_3 is given by $F(Q_3) = 0.75$ ***[1 mark]***. Since F(3) = 0.5, the upper quartile must lie in the region described by the third part of the c.d.f., so solve $0.5(Q_3 - 2) = 0.75$, or $Q_3 = 3.5$ ***[1 mark]***.

So the interquartile range is 3.5 – 2 = 1.5 ***[1 mark]***.

c) (i) Differentiate to find the p.d.f.:

$$f(x) = \begin{cases} 0.25 & \text{for } 1 \leq x < 3 \text{ [1 mark]} \\ 0.5 & \text{for } 3 \leq x \leq 4 \text{ [1 mark]} \\ 0 & \text{otherwise [1 mark]} \end{cases}$$

(ii)

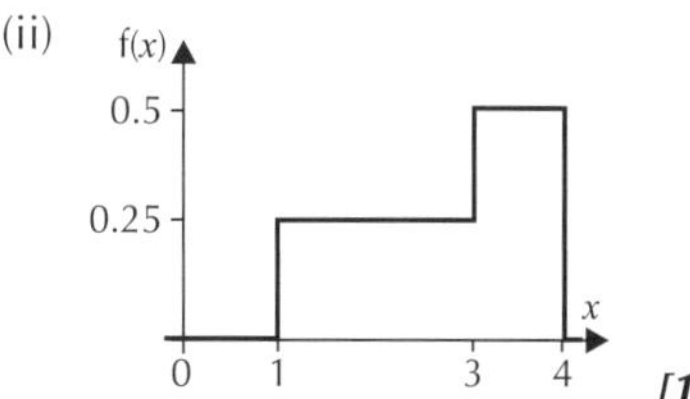

[1 mark]

I always draw a graph of the p.d.f. whether the question asks me to or not. You should too. It not only makes questions easier, but you'll often get marks for doing something that you were going to do anyway. It's like free marks.

d) (i) $\mu = \int_{-\infty}^{\infty} xf(x)dx$

$= \int_1^3 0.25x dx + \int_3^4 0.5x dx$ ***[1 mark]***

$= [0.125x^2]_1^3 + [0.25x^2]_3^4$ ***[1 mark]***

$= 1 + \frac{7}{4} = \frac{11}{4} = 2.75$ ***[1 mark]***

(ii) $\text{Var}(X) = \sigma^2 = \int_{-\infty}^{\infty} x^2 f(x)dx - \mu^2$

$= \int_1^3 0.25x^2 dx + \int_3^4 0.5x^2 dx - 2.75^2$ ***[1 mark]***

$= \left[\frac{0.25x^3}{3}\right]_1^3 + \left[\frac{0.5x^3}{3}\right]_3^4 - 2.75^2$ ***[1 mark]***

$= \frac{13}{6} + \frac{37}{6} - \left(\frac{11}{4}\right)^2 = \frac{25}{3} - \frac{121}{16}$

$= \frac{37}{48} = 0.771$ (to 3 d.p.) ***[1 mark]***.

I hope you remembered to subtract the square of the mean.

(iii) $P(X < \mu - \sigma) = P(X < 2.75 - \sqrt{0.771}) = P(X < 1.87)$ ***[1 mark]***. Using the above sketch, the area under the p.d.f. between $x = 1$ and $x = 1.87$ is:
$(1.87 - 1) \times 0.25 = 0.218$ (to 3 d.p.) ***[1 mark]***.

And that, as they say, is that.

S2 Section 4 — Continuous Distributions Warm-up Questions

1) a)

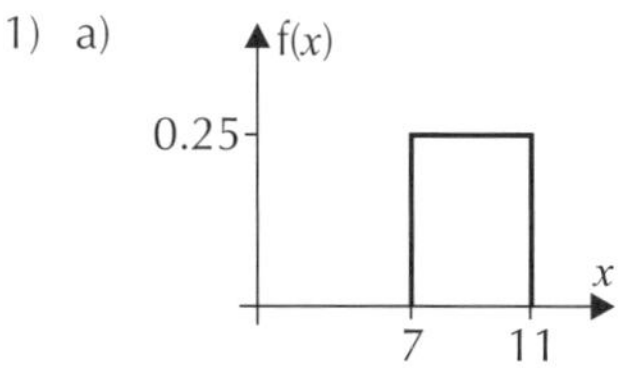

b)

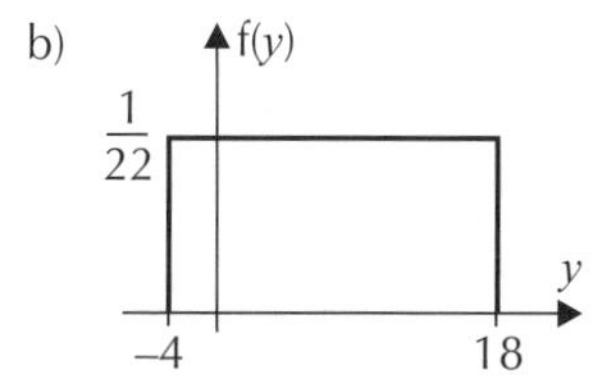

Answers

2) a) First sketch the p.d.f.:

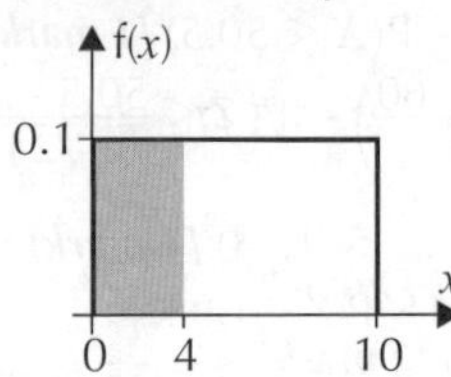

The shaded area represents P(X < 4).
This is 4 × 0.1 = 0.4.

b) Similarly, P(X ≥ 8) = 2 × 0.1 = 0.2.

c) P(X = 5) = 0 [P(X = k) = 0 for any k and any continuous random variable X.]

d) P(3 < X ≤ 7) = 4 × 0.1 = 0.4.

3) Y ~ U[5 × 1 + 2, 5 × 4 + 2] = U[7, 22].
So the p.d.f. looks like this:

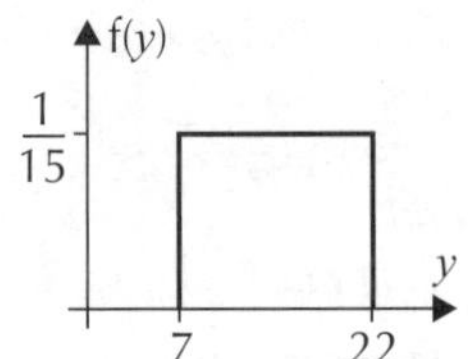

4) $\mathrm{E}(X) = \frac{a+b}{2}$, $\mathrm{Var}(X) = \frac{(b-a)^2}{12}$,

$$\mathrm{F}(x) = \begin{cases} 0 \text{ for } x < a \\ \frac{x-a}{b-a} \text{ for } a \le x \le b \\ 1 \text{ for } x > b \end{cases}$$

$$\int_{-\infty}^{\infty} x \cdot \mathrm{f}(x)\mathrm{d}x = \int_{-\infty}^{\infty} x \cdot \frac{1}{b-a}\mathrm{d}x = \frac{1}{b-a}\int_a^b x\,\mathrm{d}x$$

$$= \frac{1}{b-a}\left[\frac{x^2}{2}\right]_a^b = \frac{1}{b-a}\left[\frac{b^2}{2} - \frac{a^2}{2}\right]$$

$$= \frac{b^2-a^2}{2(b-a)} = \frac{(b-a)(b+a)}{2(b-a)} = \frac{b+a}{2}$$

Which is the same as E(X) = $\frac{a+b}{2}$.

5) a) $\mathrm{E}(X) = \frac{a+b}{2} = \frac{4+19}{2} = \frac{23}{2}$

$$\mathrm{Var}(X) = \frac{(b-a)^2}{12} = \frac{(19-4)^2}{12} = \frac{225}{12} = \frac{75}{4}$$

$$\mathrm{F}(x) = \begin{cases} 0 \text{ for } x < 4 \\ \frac{x-4}{15} \text{ for } 4 \le x \le 19 \\ 1 \text{ for } x > 19 \end{cases}$$

b) E(Y) = E(6X – 3) = 6E(X) – 3 = $6 \times \frac{23}{2} - 3 = 66$

Var(Y) = Var(6X – 3) = 6^2Var(X) = $36 \times \frac{75}{4} = 675$

Since Y ~ U[6 × 4 – 3, 6 × 19 – 3] = U[21, 111], its c.d.f. is

$$\mathrm{G}(x) = \begin{cases} 0 \text{ for } x < 21 \\ \frac{x-21}{90} \text{ for } 21 \le x \le 111 \\ 1 \text{ for } x > 111 \end{cases}$$

6) The error could be anything from –0.5 to 0.5 with equal probability. So X ~ U[–0.5, 0.5].

7) a) The p.d.f. of X is a rectangle of height 1 ÷ 4 = 0.25, while the p.d.f. of Y is a rectangle of height 1 ÷ 20 = 0.05.
P(X < 6) = (6 – 4) × 0.25 = 0.5.
P(Y > 0) = (12 – 0) × 0.05 = 0.6.
So P(X < 6 and Y > 0) = 0.5 × 0.6 = 0.3.

b) P(X < 6 or Y > 0) = P(X < 6) + P(Y > 0) – P(X < 6 and Y > 0)
= 0.5 + 0.6 – 0.3 = 0.8

8) Let X be the number of minutes the train is delayed. Then X ~ U[0, 12], and its p.d.f. would be a rectangle of height $\frac{1}{12}$.

a) P(late for work) = P(X > 8) = $4 \times \frac{1}{12} = \frac{1}{3}$

b) P(on time for work) = P(X ≤ 8) = $1 - \frac{1}{3} = \frac{2}{3}$
Since the delays are random, the individual delays are independent and the probabilities can be multiplied.
So P(on time every day) = $\left(\frac{2}{3}\right)^5 = \frac{32}{243}$.

c) P(late more than once) = 1 – P(never late) – P(late once).
So P(late more than once)

$$= 1 - \left(\frac{2}{3}\right)^5 - 5\left(\frac{2}{3}\right)^4 \times \frac{1}{3} = \frac{243-32-80}{243} = \frac{131}{243}$$

9) Use the normal approximation X ~ N(45, 24.75).

a) $\mathrm{P}(X > 50) \approx \mathrm{P}(X > 50.5) = \mathrm{P}\left(Z > \frac{50.5-45}{\sqrt{24.75}}\right)$
$= \mathrm{P}(Z > 1.11)$
$= 1 - \mathrm{P}(Z \le 1.11)$
$= 1 - 0.8665 = 0.1335$

b) $\mathrm{P}(X \le 45) \approx \mathrm{P}(X < 45.5) = \mathrm{P}\left(Z < \frac{45.5-45}{\sqrt{24.75}}\right)$
$= \mathrm{P}(Z < 0.10)$
$= 0.5398$

c) $\mathrm{P}(40 < X \le 47) \approx \mathrm{P}(X \le 47.5) - \mathrm{P}(X \le 40.5)$
$= \mathrm{P}\left(Z \le \frac{47.5-45}{\sqrt{24.75}}\right) - \mathrm{P}\left(Z \le \frac{40.5-45}{\sqrt{24.75}}\right)$
$= \mathrm{P}(Z \le 0.50) - \mathrm{P}(Z \le -0.90)$
$= \mathrm{P}(Z \le 0.50) - (1 - \mathrm{P}(Z \le 0.90))$
$= 0.6915 - 1 + 0.8159 = 0.5074$

10) Use the normal approximation X ~ N(25, 25).

a) $\mathrm{P}(X \le 20) \approx \mathrm{P}(X \le 20.5) = \mathrm{P}\left(Z \le \frac{20.5-25}{5}\right)$
$= \mathrm{P}(Z \le -0.9)$
$= 1 - \mathrm{P}(Z \le 0.9)$
$= 1 - 0.8159 = 0.1841$

b) $\mathrm{P}(X > 15) \approx \mathrm{P}(X > 15.5) = \mathrm{P}\left(Z > \frac{15.5-25}{5}\right)$
$= \mathrm{P}(Z > -1.90)$
$= \mathrm{P}(Z < 1.90) = 0.9713$

c) $\mathrm{P}(20 \le X < 30) \approx \mathrm{P}(X \le 29.5) - \mathrm{P}(X \le 19.5)$
$= \mathrm{P}\left(Z \le \frac{29.5-25}{5}\right) - \mathrm{P}\left(Z \le \frac{19.5-25}{5}\right)$
$= \mathrm{P}(Z \le 0.90) - \mathrm{P}(Z \le -1.10)$
$= \mathrm{P}(Z \le 0.90) - (1 - \mathrm{P}(Z \le 1.10))$
$= 0.8159 - 1 + 0.8643 = 0.6802$

Answers

11) Here $X \sim \text{Po}(50)$, you need to find $P(X > 55)$. λ is large, so use the normal approximation $X \sim N(50, 50)$.

$$P(X > 55) \approx P(X > 55.5) = P\left(Z > \frac{55.5 - 50}{\sqrt{50}}\right)$$
$$= P(Z > 0.78)$$
$$= 1 - P(Z \leq 0.78)$$
$$= 1 - 0.7823 = 0.2177$$

12) People join the queue (on average) at a constant rate. Assuming they join the queue randomly and singly, the total number of people joining the queue in a 15-minute period follows a Poisson distribution, Po(7).

a) If X represents the number of people joining the queue in a 7-hour day, then $X \sim \text{Po}(7 \times 28) = \text{Po}(196)$. λ is large, so use the normal approximation $X \sim N(196, 196)$.

$$P(X > 200) \approx P(X > 200.5) = P\left(Z > \frac{200.5 - 196}{14}\right)$$
$$= P(Z > 0.32)$$
$$= 1 - P(Z < 0.32)$$
$$= 1 - 0.6255 = 0.3745$$

b) Let C represent the number of people out of the 200 customers who are seen within 1 minute.
Then $C \sim B(200, 0.7)$.
n is large, and $np = 200 \times 0.7 = 140$ and $nq = 200 \times 0.3 = 60$ are both large, so use the normal approximation, i.e. $C \sim N(140, 42)$.
You need to find $P(C < 70\% \text{ of } 200)$, i.e. $P(C < 140)$.

$$P(C < 140) \approx P(C \leq 139.5) = P\left(Z \leq \frac{139.5 - 140}{\sqrt{42}}\right)$$
$$= P(Z \leq -0.08)$$
$$= 1 - P(Z \leq 0.08)$$
$$= 1 - 0.5319 = 0.4681$$

Exam Questions

1 a) (i) Need n to be large ("as large as possible") ***[1 mark]*** and p to be close to 0.5 ***[1 mark]***.

Engrave upon your heart all the conditions required for the various approximations to work. Well... actually, that might be considered to be cheating, so don't do that. But make sure you know them.

(ii) A binomial distribution is discrete ***[1 mark]***, whereas a normal distribution is continuous. The continuity correction means probabilities can be calculated for the continuous normal distribution that correspond approximately to the discrete binomial probabilities ***[1 mark]***.

b) (i) n is large and p is fairly close to 0.5, so use the normal approximation N(60, 24) ***[1 mark]***.

$$P(X \geq 65) \approx P(X > 64.5)$$
$$= P\left(Z > \frac{64.5 - 60}{\sqrt{24}}\right) \textbf{ [1 mark]}$$
$$= P(Z > 0.92)$$
$$= 1 - P(Z \leq 0.92) \textbf{ [1 mark]}$$
$$= 1 - 0.8212 = 0.1788 \textbf{ [1 mark]}$$

(ii) $P(50 < X < 62)$

$$\approx P(X < 61.5) - P(X < 50.5) \textbf{ [1 mark]}$$
$$= P\left(Z < \frac{61.5 - 60}{\sqrt{24}}\right) - P\left(Z < \frac{50.5 - 60}{\sqrt{24}}\right)$$
$$= P(Z < 0.31) - P(Z < -1.94) \textbf{ [1 mark]}$$
$$= P(Z < 0.31) - (1 - P(Z < 1.94))$$
$$= 0.6217 - (1 - 0.9738) = 0.5955 \textbf{ [1 mark]}$$

All the usual tricks involved there... normal approximation, continuity correction, subtracting values of $\Phi(z)$ (the function in your big 'normal distribution table'). They'll all be there on exam day too.

2 a) X is equally likely to take any value between 0 and 20, so $X \sim U[0, 20]$ ***[1 mark for using a continuous uniform distribution, 1 mark for the correct limits]***

b)

f(x)
0.05
x
0
20

[1 mark]

You probably haven't earned many marks for drawing rectangles since you were about 6 years old and in primary school. So it's nice that the skill you learnt way back then is now helping you pass S2.

c) $E(X) = \frac{0 + 20}{2} = 10$ ***[1 mark]***

$\text{Var}(X) = \frac{(20 - 0)^2}{12}$ ***[1 mark]***

$= \frac{400}{12} = 33.3$ (to 3 sig. fig.) ***[1 mark]***.

d) (i) $P(X > 5) = (20 - 5) \times 0.05 = 0.75$ ***[1 mark]***

(ii) $P(X = 2) = 0$ ***[1 mark]***

3 a) The normal approximation is: $Y \sim N(\mu, \sigma^2)$.

$P(X \leq 151) \approx P(Y \leq 151.5)$ ***[1 mark]***

$= P\left(Z \leq \frac{151.5 - \mu}{\sigma}\right) = 0.8944$ ***[1 mark]***.

From tables, $\frac{151.5 - \mu}{\sigma} = 1.25$.

So $\underline{\mu + 1.25\sigma = 151.5}$ ***[1 mark]***.

$P(X > 127) \approx P(Y > 127.5)$ ***[1 mark]***

$= P\left(Z > \frac{127.5 - \mu}{\sigma}\right) = 0.9970$ ***[1 mark]***.

This means $P\left(Z \leq \frac{127.5 - \mu}{\sigma}\right) = 0.0030$.

But this probability is less than 0.5, so $\frac{127.5 - \mu}{\sigma} < 0$.

So find $1 - 0.0030 = 0.9970$.

$P(Z \leq z) = 0.9970$ means $z = 2.75$.

This tells you that $\frac{127.5 - \mu}{\sigma} = -2.75$,

or $\underline{\mu - 2.75\sigma = 127.5}$ ***[1 mark]***.

Answers

Now you can subtract the underlined equations to give $4\sigma = 24$, or $\sigma = 6$ ***[1 mark]***.
This then gives $\mu = 144$ ***[1 mark]***.

I call this question "The Beast" — there's loads to do here. But as always in maths, when something looks hard, the best thing to do is take a deep breath, look at the information you have (here, some probabilities from a normal approximation), and write down some formulas containing that information. Then you can start piecing things together, and try to find out things you don't yet know. The worst thing you can do is panic and start thinking it's too hard. That's what Luke Skywalker did in that film before Yoda told him to chill out a bit. Something like that anyway.

b) You know $\mu = \underline{np = 144}$ ***[1 mark]***
and $\sigma^2 = \underline{np(1-p) = 36}$ ***[1 mark]***.
Divide the second underlined equation by the first to give $1 - p = 36 \div 144 = 0.25$, or $p = 0.75$ ***[1 mark]***.
Then $n = 144 \div 0.75 = 192$ ***[1 mark]***.

Phew... made it.

4 a) Let X represent the number of items that the new customer could order per week. Then X follows a Poisson distribution with an average of 40, and so $X \sim \text{Po}(40)$ ***[1 mark]***.

b) Here, λ is quite large, and so X will approximately follow the normal distribution N(40, 40) ***[1 mark]***.

$$P(X > 50) \approx P(X > 50.5) = P\left(Z > \frac{50.5 - 40}{\sqrt{40}}\right) \text{ [1 mark]}$$
$$= P(Z > 1.66)$$
$$= 1 - P(Z \le 1.66)$$
$$= 1 - 0.9515 = 0.0485 \text{ [1 mark]}$$

c) The probability that the factory will not be able to meet the new customer's order in two consecutive weeks will be $0.0485^2 = 0.00235...$, which is less than 0.01.
So the manager should sign the contract ***[1 mark for 'yes', with a clear explanation]***.

This question looks quite tough because there are so many words. But it's a pussycat really.

S2 Section 5 — Hypothesis Tests Warm-up Questions

1) a) All the members of the tennis club.

b) The individual tennis club members.

c) A full membership list.

It might look like I've written the same answer down three times, but there are important differences. Make sure you know exactly what's meant by the three terms tested here.

2) a) A census would be more sensible. The results will be more accurate and there are only 8 people in the population, so it wouldn't take long to find out the required information from each person.

b) A sample survey should be done. Testing all 500 toys would take too long, but more importantly, it would destroy all the toys.

c) A sample survey is the only option. The population is all the possible dice rolls — there are an infinite number of dice rolls, so you can only examine a sample of them.

3) Simple random sampling means the sample will not be affected by sampling bias.

4) a) Yes

b) No — it contains unknown parameter σ.

c) No — it contains unknown parameter μ.

d) Yes

There's no excuse for getting these ones wrong. You've just got to look for any unknown parameters — if you find one, it's not a statistic.

5) a) A two-tailed test should be used — Salma doesn't know if the coin is biased towards heads or tails.
$H_0: p = 0.5$, $H_1: p \neq 0.5$

b) A one-tailed test should be used — the typist is only interested in a decrease in the rate of errors.
$H_0: \lambda = 20$, $H_1: \lambda < 20$

6) a) The number (or proportion) of 'successes' in a random sample taken from the distribution.

b) The number of events that occur in a random interval.

7) a) (i) $H_0: p = 0.2$, $H_1: p < 0.2$, $\alpha = 0.05$ and $x = 2$:
Under H_0, $X \sim B(20, 0.2)$
$P(X \le 2) = 0.2061$
$0.2061 > 0.05$, so there is insufficient evidence at the 5% level of significance to reject H_0.

(ii) $H_0: p = 0.4$, $H_1: p > 0.4$, $\alpha = 0.01$ and $x = 15$:
Under H_0, $X \sim B(20, 0.4)$
$P(X \ge 15) = 1 - P(X \le 14) = 1 - 0.9984 = 0.0016$
$0.0016 < 0.01$, so there is evidence at the 1% level of significance to reject H_0.

b) (i) $H_0: \lambda = 7$, $H_1: \lambda < 7$, $\alpha = 0.05$ and $x = 3$:
Under H_0, $X \sim \text{Po}(7)$
$P(X \le 3) = 0.0818$
$0.0818 > 0.05$, so there is insufficient evidence at the 5% level of significance to reject H_0.

(ii) $H_0: \lambda = 2.5$, $H_1: \lambda > 2.5$, $\alpha = 0.1$ and $x = 4$:
Under H_0, $X \sim \text{Po}(2.5)$
$P(X \ge 4) = 1 - P(X \le 3) = 1 - 0.7576 = 0.2424$
$0.2424 > 0.1$, so there is insufficient evidence at the 10% level of significance to reject H_0.

These might be getting a bit tedious, but a significant amount of practice is critical when it comes to hypothesis testing.

8) a) $H_0: p = 0.3$, $H_1: p < 0.3$, $\alpha = 0.05$
Under H_0, $X \sim B(10, 0.3)$
Critical region = biggest possible set of 'low' values of X with a total probability of ≤ 0.05.
$P(X \le 0) = 0.0282$, $P(X \le 1) = 0.1493$,
so CR is $X = 0$.

Answers

b) $H_0: \lambda = 6$, $H_1: \lambda < 6$, $\alpha = 0.1$
Under H_0, $X \sim Po(6)$
Critical region = biggest possible set of 'low' values of X with a total probability of ≤ 0.1.
$P(X \leq 2) = 0.0620$, $P(X \leq 3) = 0.1512$,
so CR is $X \leq 2$.

Exam Questions

1 The possible samples are: (1, 1, 1), (1, 1, 2), (1, 2, 1), (2, 1, 1), (2, 2, 1), (2, 1, 2), (1, 2, 2) and (2, 2, 2).
[3 marks for showing that there are 8 possible samples, or 2 marks for showing 4 correct samples, or 1 mark for showing at least 1 correct sample.]
So the median could either be 1 or 2. ***[1 mark]***
$P(M = 1) = P(1, 1, 1) + P(1, 1, 2) + P(1, 2, 1) + P(2, 1, 1)$
$= 0.7^3 + (3 \times 0.7^2 \times 0.3) = 0.784$
$P(M = 2) = P(2, 2, 1) + P(2, 1, 2) + P(1, 2, 2) + P(2, 2, 2)$
$= (3 \times 0.3^2 \times 0.7) + 0.3^3 = 0.216$
[1 mark for showing that the probabilities of samples giving the same median value should be added, 1 mark for P(M = 1) = 0.784 and 1 mark for P(M = 2) = 0.216.]

Remember to check that the probabilities you've worked out for the values of the median add up to 1. If not, go back and work out where you've gone wrong.

2 a) Binomial ***[1 mark]***
'Proportion' should set the binomial bell ringing.

b) (i) Start by stating the hypotheses:
$H_0: p = 0.2$ and $H_1: p > 0.2$ ***[1 mark for both correct]***
X = number of tiramisu orders in sample
Under H_0, $X \sim B(20, 0.2)$ ***[1 mark]***
$\alpha = 0.05$

Either:
Use the binomial tables to find the probability of getting a value greater than or equal to 7, under H_0:
$P(X \geq 7) = 1 - P(X \leq 6)$ ***[1 mark]***
$= 1 - 0.9133 = 0.0867$ ***[1 mark]***
$0.0867 > 0.05$, so the result isn't significant. ***[1 mark]***
Or:
Use the binomial tables to find the critical region:
$P(X \geq 7) = 1 - P(X \leq 6) = 1 - 0.9133 = 0.0867$
$P(X \geq 8) = 1 - P(X \leq 7) = 1 - 0.9679 = 0.0321$
[1 mark for attempting to find the smallest value of x such that P(X ≥ x) ≤ 0.05.]
$0.0321 < 0.05$, so the CR is $X \geq 8$ ***[1 mark]***.
7 isn't in the CR, so the result isn't significant. ***[1 mark]***

So, there is insufficient evidence at the 5% level of significance to support the chef's theory that the proportion of dessert eaters ordering tiramisu on a Saturday is greater than on weekdays.
[1 mark for a suitable conclusion]

(ii) You're looking for the smallest value of x such that $P(X \geq x) \leq 0.05$.
You know $X = 7$ isn't significant from part (i).
Try 8: $P(X \geq 8) = 0.0321 < 0.05$,
so the answer is 8 tiramisu orders ***[1 mark]***.

Part (ii) here is really just asking for the lower boundary of the critical region. So if you answered part (i) by finding the critical region, you've already worked out the answer. Bonus.

3 a) First-serve faults must occur randomly (or independently of each other) and at a constant average rate.
[1 mark for saying first-serve faults must occur randomly or independently, and 1 mark for saying first-serve faults must occur at a constant average rate.]

b) $H_0: \lambda = 4$ and $H_1: \lambda < 4$, where λ is the rate of first-serve faults per service game.
X = number of first-serve faults in 5 service games
Under H_0, $X \sim Po(20)$
$\alpha = 0.05$
X is large so you can approximate using $X \sim N(20, 20)$
[2 marks for stating the correct normal approximation, or 1 mark for a normal approximation with only one of the mean or variance correct.]
Applying the continuity correction:
$P(X \leq 12)$ becomes $P(X < 12.5)$ ***[1 mark]***
$= P\left(Z < \frac{12.5 - 20}{\sqrt{20}}\right)$ ***[1 mark]***
$= P(Z < -1.68)$
$= 1 - P(Z < 1.68)$
$= 1 - 0.9535$
$= 0.0465$ ***[1 mark]*** < 0.05, so the result is significant.
There is evidence at the 5% level of significance to reject H_0 and to say that the rate of first-serve faults has decreased. ***[1 mark]***

4 a) $H_0: p = 0.1$ and $H_0: p \neq 0.1$
X = number of sampled residents against the plan
Under H_0, $X \sim B(50, 0.1)$ ***[1 mark]***
It's a two-tailed test, so the critical region is split into two.
For the lower end:
$P(X \leq 2) = 0.1117$, $P(X \leq 1) = 0.0338$ ***[1 mark]***,
which is the closest value.
For the upper end:
$P(X \geq 10) = 1 - 0.9755 = 0.0245$,
$P(X \geq 9) = 1 - 0.9421 = 0.0579$ ***[1 mark]***,
which is the closest value.
So CR is $X \leq 1$ ***[1 mark]*** and $X \geq 9$ ***[1 mark]***

Watch out for the wording of these questions. You want the probability in each tail to be as close as possible to 0.05 — which means it can be <u>greater</u> than 0.05.

b) The probability of incorrectly rejecting H_0 is the same as the actual significance level.
So, it's $P(X \leq 1) + P(X \geq 9)$ ***[1 mark]***
$= 0.0338 + 0.0579$
$= 0.0917$ ***[1 mark]***

Answers

c) The value 4 doesn't lie in the critical region ***[1 mark]***, so there is insufficient evidence to reject the claim that the proportion of residents against the plan is 10% ***[1 mark]***. ***(Allow follow-through for a correct conclusion drawn from an incorrectly calculated critical region in part a).)***

S2 — Practice Exam One

1 a) (i) Since the average number of houses sold per week is 2, $X \sim \text{Po}(2)$ ***[1 mark]***.

$P(X = 1) = \frac{e^{-2}2^1}{1!} = \frac{2}{e^2} = 0.271$ (to 3 d.p.) ***[1 mark]***

You can do this with tables, but here it's quicker just to use the formula.

(ii) $P(2 \le X \le 4) = P(X \le 4) - P(X < 2)$

$= P(X \le 4) - P(X \le 1)$ ***[1 mark]***

$= 0.9473 - 0.4060$ ***[1 mark]***

$= 0.5413$ ***[1 mark]***.

And you could do this one by working out P(X = 2), P(X = 3) and P(X = 4) using the formula, and then adding the results. Do it the way that seems to involve less work, that's my (obvious) advice.

b) $P(X \ge 2) = 1 - P(X < 2) = 1 - P(X \le 1)$

$= 1 - 0.4060 = 0.5940$ ***[1 mark]***.

Since the sales can be modelled by a Poisson distribution, the individual events (i.e. house sales) are independent, meaning that total sales in each week are also independent. This allows you to multiply probabilities for individual weeks.

So P(qualify for "monthly bonus") $= 0.5940^4$ ***[1 mark]***

$= 0.124$ (to 3 d.p.) ***[1 mark]***.

c) $P(X \ge 2) = 0.594$ (from part b)).

Let the random variable Y represent the number of weeks out of the next 52 weeks that the estate agent sells at least 2 houses. Then $Y \sim B(52, 0.594)$ ***[1 mark]***.

$P(Y = 30) = \binom{52}{30} \times 0.594^{30} \times (1 - 0.594)^{22}$

$= 0.108$ (to 3 d.p.) ***[1 mark]***.

A neat transition from Poisson to binomial there — don't be caught out.

d) Let Q represent the total number of houses sold over the next 26 weeks. Q will follow the Poisson distribution $\text{Po}(26 \times 2) = \text{Po}(52)$ ***[1 mark]***.

Since λ is large, this can be approximated by a normal distribution, i.e. $Q \sim N(52, 52)$ ***[1 mark]***.

$P(Q < 52) = P(Q < 51.5)$ ***[1 mark]***

$= P\left(Z < \frac{51.5 - 52}{\sqrt{52}}\right)$

$= P(Z < -0.07)$ ***[1 mark]***

$= 1 - P(Z < 0.07)$ ***[1 mark]***

$= 1 - 0.5279 = 0.4721$ ***[1 mark]***

2 a)

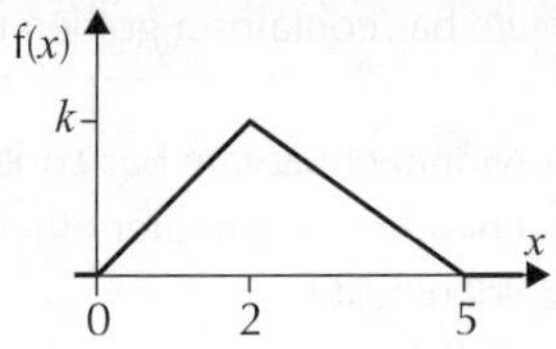

[1 mark for each sloping part of the graph correct]

b) The total area under the p.d.f. must equal 1.

So $\frac{2k}{2} + \frac{3k}{2} = \frac{5k}{2} = 1$ ***[1 mark]***.

This means $k = \frac{2}{5}$ ***[1 mark]***.

c) F(x) will be in 4 parts.

<u>First part</u>: $F(x) = 0$ for $x < 0$ ***[1 mark]***.

<u>Second part</u>: integrate $f(x) = \frac{1}{5}x$ to get $F(x) = \frac{1}{10}x^2 + c_1$, where c_1 is a constant of integration ***[1 mark]***, chosen so that $F(0) = 0$. This means $c_1 = 0$, which then gives $F(2) = \frac{2}{5}$. ***[1 mark if this part of the c.d.f. is correct]***

<u>Third part</u>: integrate $f(x) = \frac{2}{15}(5 - x) = \frac{2}{3} - \frac{2}{15}x$ to get $F(x) = \frac{2}{3}x - \frac{1}{15}x^2 + c_2$, where c_2 is a constant of integration ***[1 mark]***, chosen so that $F(2) = \frac{2}{5}$.

This means $c_2 = \frac{2}{5} - \frac{4}{3} + \frac{4}{15} = \frac{6 - 20 + 4}{15} = -\frac{10}{15} = -\frac{2}{3}$.

[1 mark if this part of the c.d.f. is correct]

This then gives $F(5) = 1$.

<u>Fourth part</u>: $F(x) = 1$ for $x > 5$ ***[1 mark]***.

So overall, the c.d.f. is:

$$F(x) = \begin{cases} 0 \text{ for } x < 0 \\ \frac{1}{10}x^2 \text{ for } 0 \le x < 2 \\ \frac{2}{3}x - \frac{1}{15}x^2 - \frac{2}{3} \text{ for } 2 \le x \le 5 \\ 1 \text{ for } x > 5 \end{cases}$$

Forgetting the constants of integration is a common problem with this kind of question. Remember... the different parts of a c.d.f. must join together smoothly — you can't have 'jumps'.

d) The median, m, of X is given by $F(m) = 0.5$.

From above, you can see that $2 < m < 5$ (since $F(2) = 0.4$).

So solve:

$\frac{2}{3}m - \frac{1}{15}m^2 - \frac{2}{3} = 0.5$, or $2m^2 - 20m + 35 = 0$

[1 mark for either quadratic].

Using the quadratic formula, this gives $m = \frac{20 \pm \sqrt{120}}{4}$,

i.e. $m = 5 \pm \frac{\sqrt{120}}{4}$ ***[1 mark]***).

But $m < 5$, so $m = 5 - \frac{\sqrt{120}}{4} = 2.261$ (to 3 d.p.) ***[1 mark]***.

Don't forget to use the right part of your c.d.f. to find the median. If you use the wrong bit, you might arrive at something that looks vaguely sensible, but it'll be completely wrong and you'll have egg all over your face. And you won't want that.

Answers

3 a) 1. The probability P(chocolate bar contains a golden ticket) must be constant.
2. Whether or not each individual chocolate bar contains a golden ticket must be independent of whether other chocolate bars contain a golden ticket.
[1 mark for each correct condition]

b) (i) $P(X > 1) = 1 - P(X \leq 1)$.
From tables, $P(X \leq 1) = 0.3991$ ***[1 mark]***.
So $P(X > 1) = 1 - 0.3991 = 0.6009$ ***[1 mark]***.

(ii) $E(X) = np = 40 \times 0.05 = 2$ ***[1 mark]***.

c) If you consider all 3 students, then there are 120 independent events with a 0.05 probability each time of 'success'. So $Y \sim B(120, 0.05)$ ***[1 mark]***.
Here, n is large and p is quite small, so you can use a Poisson approximation, $Po(120 \times 0.05) = Po(6)$ ***[1 mark]***.
So $P(Y \geq 3) = 1 - P(Y < 3) = 1 - P(Y \leq 2)$
$= 1 - 0.0620 = 0.9380$ ***[1 mark]***.

Often, the hardest bit of a question is spotting which distribution to use — and then once you've done that, you're off and running. So don't rush in when you first start a question — think it through carefully, otherwise you might start running in the wrong direction.

4 a) X is equally likely to take any value between –2 and 9, and so follows a continuous, uniform distribution: $X \sim U[-2, 9]$.
[1 mark]
You should be rubbing your hands at the prospect of a "continuous, uniform distribution" question.

b) (i) For $-2 < x < 9$, the probability density function of X takes the value $\frac{1}{(9-(-2))} = \frac{1}{11}$ ***[1 mark]***.

If it helps to draw a sketch at this point, then you should draw one:

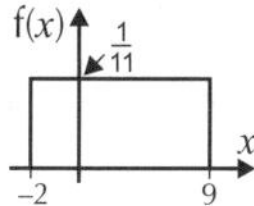

So P(train more than 6 minutes late) $= P(X > 6)$
$= (9 - 6) \times \frac{1}{11} = \frac{3}{11} = 0.273$ (to 3 d.p.) ***[1 mark]***.

(ii) P(train within 1 minute of scheduled arrival time)
$= P(-1 < X < 1) = (1 - (-1)) \times \frac{1}{11} = \frac{2}{11}$
$= 0.182$ (to 3 d.p.) ***[1 mark]***.

c) From b), the probability of the train being more than 6 minutes late is $\frac{3}{11}$. If the random variable Y represents the number of times in 5 days that the train is more than 6 minutes late, then $Y \sim B(5, \frac{3}{11})$ ***[1 mark]***.
$P(Y \geq 2) = 1 - P(Y < 2) = 1 - P(Y = 0) - P(Y = 1)$ ***[1 mark]***

$$= 1 - \left(\frac{8}{11}\right)^5 - \binom{5}{1} \times \left(\frac{8}{11}\right)^4 \times \frac{3}{11} \textbf{ [1 mark]}$$
$$= 1 - \frac{8^5}{11^5} - \frac{5 \times 8^4 \times 3}{11^5} = 1 - \frac{8^4(8+15)}{11^5}$$
$$= 1 - \frac{8^4 \times 23}{11^5} = 0.415 \text{ (to 3 d.p.) } \textbf{[1 mark]}.$$

Exam questions are often a bit like this — they'll start off talking about one type of distribution and then move on to something completely different. You need to be ready for anything.

5 Let X represent the number of defects in the 5 m roll.
Since defects occur randomly, singly and at a constant average rate, X follows a Poisson distribution, $Po(\lambda)$.
$H_0: \lambda = 5$ and $H_1: \lambda < 5$ ***[2 marks for both correct, or 1 mark for one correct.]***
So under H_0, $X \sim Po(5)$ ***[1 mark]***
$\alpha = 0.1$
Use the Poisson tables to find the probability of getting a value less than or equal to 3 under H_0:
$P(X \leq 3) = 0.2650$ ***[1 mark]***
Since $0.2650 > 0.1$, the result isn't significant. ***[1 mark]***
You could do the test by finding the critical region instead if you wanted, but that way of doing things usually takes a bit longer.
So, there is insufficient evidence at the 10% level of significance to support the manager's claim.
[1 mark for a suitable conclusion]

6 a) (i) Let the random variable X represent the number of cars in the sample of 20 that develop the rattle.
Then $X \sim B(20, 0.65)$, and you need to find $P(12 \leq X < 15) = P(12 \leq X \leq 14)$.

Since $p = 0.65 > 0.5$, you cannot use tables directly, so define a new random variable Y representing the number of cars in the sample of 20 that do not develop the rattle — then $Y \sim B(20, 0.35)$ ***[1 mark]***, and $X + Y = 20$.

$P(12 \leq X \leq 14) = P(6 \leq Y \leq 8)$
$= P(Y \leq 8) - P(Y \leq 5)$ ***[1 mark]***
$= 0.7624 - 0.2454 = 0.517$ ***[1 mark]***.

(ii) $P(X > 10) = P(Y < 10) = P(Y \leq 9) = 0.8782$ ***[1 mark]***.

b) The probability of more than half of a sample of 20 cars having the rattle is 0.8782 (using a) (ii)).
Let Q be the number of samples containing more than 10 rattling cars. Then $Q \sim B(5, 0.8782)$ ***[1 mark]***.
$$P(Q = 3) = \binom{5}{3} \times 0.8782^3 \times (1 - 0.8782)^2 \textbf{ [1 mark]}$$
$$= 0.100 \text{ (to 3 d.p.) } \textbf{[1 mark]}.$$

c) Let R be the number of cars in this larger sample that rattle. Then $R \sim B(200, 0.65)$. Here, n is large and p is not too far from 0.5, so this can be approximated with a normal distribution $N(130, 45.5)$ ***[1 mark]***.
$$P(R = 140) = P(139.5 \leq R \leq 140.5) \textbf{ [1 mark]}$$
$$= P\left(Z \leq \frac{140.5 - 130}{\sqrt{45.5}}\right) - P\left(Z \leq \frac{139.5 - 130}{\sqrt{45.5}}\right) \textbf{ [1 mark]}$$
$$= P(Z \leq 1.56) - P(Z \leq 1.41)$$
$$= 0.9406 - 0.9207 \textbf{ [1 mark]}$$
$$= 0.0199 \textbf{ [1 mark]}$$

This question is slightly autobiographical because I used to have a rattly car. I kept taking it to the garage to get it fixed, but they could never find the fault. Turned out there was a rattlesnake under the passenger seat. Was quite a common problem in that model, apparently.

Answers

7 a) All the pupils in the school ***[1 mark]***.

b) A list of the names of all the pupils in the school ***[1 mark]***.

c) One of the following: the data would be an accurate representation of the population / the data wouldn't be affected by sampling bias / the data wouldn't be affected by natural variability. ***[1 mark]***

Ah, what a nice change from all those long, complicated calculation questions. Make the most of friendly little questions like these by learning what's what in the world of sampling.

8 a) (i) A hypothesis test tests the claim made about a parameter by a null hypothesis against that made by an alternative hypothesis ***[1 mark]***. In a two-tailed test, the alternative hypothesis states that the value of the parameter is not equal to the value specified by the null hypothesis ***[1 mark]***.

(ii) The actual significance level of a test is the probability of rejecting H_0 / the probability of incorrectly rejecting H_0 ***[1 mark]***.

b) X = number of people in the sample of 20 who have done judo before. Then $X \sim B(20, p)$.
H_0: $p = 0.2$ and H_1: $p \neq 0.2$
So under H_0, $X \sim B(20, 0.2)$ ***[1 mark]***
It's a two-tailed test, so the critical region is split into two, with a probability of ≤ 0.025 in each tail.
For the lower tail:
$P(X \leq 0) = 0.0115$ and $P(X \leq 1) = 0.0692$. ***[1 mark]***
For the upper tail:
$P(X \geq 9) = 1 - 0.9900 = 0.0100$ and
$P(X \geq 8) = 1 - 0.9679 = 0.0321$. ***[1 mark]***
So CR is $X = 0$ ***[1 mark]*** and $X \geq 9$ ***[1 mark]***

c) Actual significance level = $P(X = 0) + P(X \geq 9)$
$= 0.0115 + 0.0100 = 0.0215$ or 2.15% ***[1 mark]***

S2 — Practice Exam Two

1 a) (i) The surviving bacteria are spread randomly, singly and are assumed to occur at a constant average rate, which would give rise to a Poisson distribution: $X \sim Po(6)$ ***[1 mark]***.
Using tables:
$P(X < 10) = P(X \leq 9) = 0.9161$ ***[1 mark]***

(ii) $P(5 \leq X \leq 7) = P(X \leq 7) - P(X < 5)$
$= P(X \leq 7) - P(X \leq 4)$ ***[1 mark]***
$= 0.7440 - 0.2851$ ***[1 mark]***
$= 0.4589$ ***[1 mark]***

Careful with the step: "P(5 ≤ X ≤ 7) = P(X ≤ 7) – P(X ≤ 4)" — it's easy to make a mistake there, because that '5' has somehow become a '4'. Think of it as subtracting the 'values of X you want to exclude'. So P(5 ≤ X ≤ 7) means X can be 5, 6 or 7 — that means you want all the values of X less than or equal to 7 (= P(X ≤ 7)), and then you want to subtract all the values of 4 or less (= P(X ≤ 4)).

b) $\text{mean} = \frac{\sum x}{n} = \frac{83}{15} = 5.53$ (to 2 d.p.) ***[1 mark]***

$\text{variance} = \frac{\sum x^2}{n} - \left(\frac{\sum x}{n}\right)^2$
$= \frac{543}{15} - \left(\frac{83}{15}\right)^2$ ***[1 mark]***
$= 5.58$ (to 2 d.p.) ***[1 mark]***

c) The mean and variance are approximately equal, which is a characteristic of a Poisson distribution ***[1 mark]***.

Whenever you see a mean and a variance that are roughly equal, the little bell in your head marked 'Poisson' should start ringing.

d) $P(X = 5) = \frac{e^{-\lambda}\lambda^x}{x!}$
$= \frac{e^{-5.53} \times 5.53^5}{5!}$ ***[1 mark]***
$= 0.171$ (to 3 d.p.) ***[1 mark]***.

2 a) Using the definition of F(x) for $0 \leq x \leq 1$,
$F(1) = 0.5 + 0.2 = 0.7$ ***[1 mark]***.
This means that $9.2 \times 1 - 3.5 \times 1^2 - k = 0.7$.
So $k = 9.2 - 3.5 - 0.7 = 5$ ***[1 mark]***.

Remember... the different pieces of a c.d.f. have to join together smoothly for a continuous random variable.

b) You need to find Q_3, which is given by $F(Q_3) = 0.75$.
Since $F(1) = 0.7$, you know that Q_3 must be between 1 and 1.2, so solve $9.2x - 3.5x^2 - 5 = 0.75$,
or $3.5x^2 - 9.2x + 5.75 = 0$ ***[1 mark for either quadratic]***.
Using the quadratic formula:
$$x = \frac{9.2 \pm \sqrt{9.2^2 - 4 \times 3.5 \times 5.75}}{2 \times 3.5} = \frac{9.2 \pm \sqrt{4.14}}{7}$$
You need to take the smaller of these two solutions (since the other one is greater than 1.2), which means that:
$$Q_1 = \frac{9.2 - \sqrt{4.14}}{7} = 1.024 \text{ (to 3 d.p.)}$$ ***[1 mark]***.
So the interquartile range = $Q_3 - Q_1$
$= 1.024 - 0.688 = 0.34$ (to 2 d.p.) ***[1 mark]***.

c) To find f(x), you need to differentiate F(x).
$$f(x) = \begin{cases} 0 \text{ for } x < 0 \\ 2x^3 + 0.2 \text{ for } 0 \leq x \leq 1 \\ 9.2 - 7x \text{ for } 1 < x \leq 1.2 \\ 0 \text{ for } x > 1.2 \end{cases}$$
or
$$f(x) = \begin{cases} 2x^3 + 0.2 \text{ for } 0 \leq x \leq 1 \\ 9.2 - 7x \text{ for } 1 < x \leq 1.2 \\ 0 \text{ otherwise} \end{cases}$$

[1 mark for each correct part of the p.d.f. (max. 3 marks)]

d) To find the mode, you need to find the highest point of f(x) ***[1 mark]***. As x increases from 0 to 1, $2x^3 + 0.2$ also increases. And as x increases from 1 to 1.2, $9.2 - 7x$ decreases. This means that the highest point of f(x) must be at $x = 1$. So the mode is 1 ***[1 mark]***.

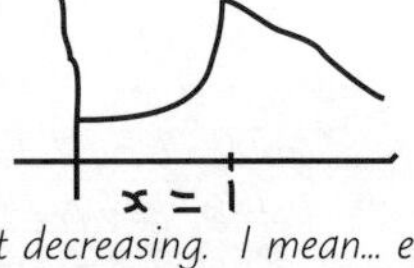

You could sketch the p.d.f. here. Just something rough would do — enough to show the first part of the p.d.f. increasing and the second part decreasing. I mean... even this feeble effort would be enough to answer the question.

Answers

3 a) C would follow a binomial distribution: $C \sim B(100, 0.07)$. ***[1 mark]***

b) (i) The mean of C is $100 \times 0.07 = 7$. So approximate C using the Poisson distribution Po(7) ***[1 mark]***.
$\lambda = 7$ is in your Poisson tables, so:
$P(5 < C \le 13) = P(C \le 13) - P(C \le 5)$ ***[1 mark]***
$= 0.9872 - 0.3007 = 0.6865$ ***[1 mark]***.

(ii) The mean of C is $100 \times 0.07 = 7$, and its variance is $100 \times 0.07 \times 0.93 = 6.51$. So approximate C using the normal distribution N(7, 6.51) ***[1 mark]***.

With a continuity correction, you need to find $P(5.5 < C < 13.5) = P(C < 13.5) - P(C < 5.5)$ ***[1 mark]***.

$$P(C < 13.5) = P\left(Z < \frac{13.5 - 7}{\sqrt{6.51}}\right) = P(Z < 2.55) = 0.9946$$

$$P(C < 5.5) = P\left(Z < \frac{5.5 - 7}{\sqrt{6.51}}\right) = P(Z < -0.59) = 1 - P(Z < 0.59) = 1 - 0.7224 = 0.2776$$

So $P(5.5 < C < 13.5) = 0.9946 - 0.2776$ ***[1 mark]***
$= 0.7170$ ***[1 mark]***.

c) A normal approximation works best when p is close to 0.5, whereas a Poisson approximation is more appropriate when p is small. The value of p here (= 0.07) is quite small, so I would expect the Poisson approximation to be more accurate ***[1 mark]***.

And in fact, the Poisson approximation is better — but only just. Both approximations give pretty good answers here, as it turns out — but that small value of p does suggest Poisson would be a slightly safer bet.

4 a) (i) X follows a continuous uniform distribution. Since the errors are randomly distributed between –0.5 and 0.5, the diameters of the cylinders must be randomly distributed between 41.5 and 42.5, i.e. $X \sim U[41.5, 42.5]$.
Between 41.5 and 42.5, the p.d.f. has value:

$$\frac{1}{b-a} = \frac{1}{42.5 - 41.5} = 1$$

So the p.d.f. of X is:

$$f(x) = \begin{cases} 1 & \text{for } 41.5 \le x \le 42.5 \\ 0 & \text{otherwise} \end{cases}$$ ***[1 mark]***

Remember... the continuous uniform distribution has a 'rectangular' p.d.f. with a total area underneath of 1. And since the width of the rectangle is 1, then the height has to be 1 as well.

(ii) Since $X \sim U[41.5, 42.5]$:

$$E(X) = \frac{a+b}{2} = \frac{41.5 + 42.5}{2} = 42$$ ***[1 mark]***

$$\text{Var}(X) = \frac{(b-a)^2}{12} = \frac{(42.5 - 41.5)^2}{12} = \frac{1}{12}$$ ***[1 mark]***

These formulas are in your formula booklet. But if you learn them off by heart so you can reel them off without having to look at the formula booklet, then so much the better.

(iii) For $x < 41.5$, $F(x) = 0$ and for $x > 42.5$, $F(x) = 1$.
For $41.5 \le x \le 42.5$, you can either state the formula if you remember it (i.e. $F(x) = \frac{x-a}{b-a}$), or you can integrate:

$$F(x_0) = \int_{-\infty}^{x_0} f(x)dx = \int_{-\infty}^{41.5} 0dx + \int_{41.5}^{x_0} 1dx = 0 + [x]_{41.5}^{x_0} = x_0 - 41.5$$

Putting that all together:

$$F(x) = \begin{cases} 0 & \text{for } x < 41.5 \\ x - 41.5 & \text{for } 41.5 \le x \le 42.5 \\ 1 & \text{for } x > 42.5 \end{cases}$$

[1 mark for 'x – 41.5' for x between 41.5 and 42.5; 1 mark for a definition of F(x) for all values of x.]

The formula for the c.d.f. of a continuous uniform distribution isn't in the formula booklet, so you really should learn this one.

(iv) The median is given by $F(m) = 0.5$.
So solve $m - 41.5 = 0.5$, giving $m = 42$ ***[1 mark]***.

You didn't really need to solve an equation in that last bit — you could have just stated the answer if you'd preferred. For a continuous uniform distribution, the mean and the median are right in the middle of the distribution.

b) (i) This is the probability that $41.7 < X < 42.3$.
You could sketch the p.d.f. to find the area under the graph between 41.7 and 42.3. Alternatively you can just find the width of this interval (= 42.3 – 41.7 = 0.6) and multiply by the height of the p.d.f. (= 1) to find that the probability of a random cylinder being acceptable is 0.6 ***[1 mark]***.

If in any doubt at all, draw a sketch — that's what I always say.

(ii) There are a fixed number of independent trials with a constant probability of 'success', so Y will follow a binomial distribution: $Y \sim B(200, 0.6)$ ***[1 mark]***.

(iii) Here, n is large and p is close to 0.5, so use a normal approximation: $Y \sim N(120, 48)$ ***[1 mark]*** (since $np = 200 \times 0.6 = 120$ and $npq = 200 \times 0.6 \times 0.4 = 48$).

65% of 200 is 130, so you need to find $P(Y > 130)$. With a continuity correction, this is $P(Y > 130.5)$ ***[1 mark]***.

$$P(Y > 130.5) = P\left(Z > \frac{130.5 - 120}{\sqrt{48}}\right) = 1 - P(Z \le 1.52) = 1 - 0.9357 = 0.0643$$ ***[1 mark]***

5 a) Let X represent the number of customers per hour.
Then, $X \sim Po(2)$
[1 mark for 'Poisson' and 1 mark for λ = 2].

b) (i) $P(X < 3) = P(X \le 2) = 0.6767$ ***[1 mark]***

(ii) $P(X = 1) = P(X \le 1) - P(X \le 0)$ ***[1 mark]***
$= 0.4060 - 0.1353 = 0.2707$ ***[1 mark]***

Answers

c) $H_0: \lambda = 2$ and $H_1: \lambda > 2$ ***[1 mark]***
Y = number of customers on a Saturday and $Y \sim Po(6\lambda)$.
Under H_0, $Y \sim Po(12)$
$\alpha = 0.01$
λ is bigger than 10, so approximate using $Y \sim N(12, 12)$
[1 mark for stating the correct normal approximation.]
Applying the continuity correction:
$P(Y \geq 25)$ becomes $P(Y > 24.5)$ ***[1 mark]***
$= P\left(Z > \frac{24.5 - 12}{\sqrt{12}}\right)$ ***[1 mark]***
$= P(Z > 3.61) < P(Z > 3.60)$
$= 1 - P(Z \leq 3.6)$
$= 1 - 0.9998$
$= 0.0002$ ***[1 mark]*** < 0.01, so the result is significant.
There is evidence at the 1% level of significance to suggest that there are more customers per hour on a Saturday.
[1 mark]

Don't let yourself be distracted by imagining Daisy, Derrick and co. plodding up and down the beach 25 times. There are 6 marks for part c) — go through your answer and check you've written down every step in the working.

6 a) Because the cards are not being replaced, the probability of choosing a picture card does not remain constant ***[1 mark]***.

b) (i) Since the cards are now being replaced after each pick, Y will follow a binomial distribution.
Since $\frac{12}{52} = \frac{3}{13}$, $Y \sim B(3, \frac{3}{13})$.
$P(Y = 2) = \binom{3}{2} \times \left(\frac{3}{13}\right)^2 \times \frac{10}{13}$ ***[1 mark]***
$= \frac{270}{13^3} = \frac{270}{2197}$
$= 0.123$ (to 3 d.p.) ***[1 mark]***.

(ii) $E(Y) = 3 \times \frac{3}{13} = \frac{9}{13} = 0.692$ (to 3 d.p.) ***[1 mark]***.

(iii) $Var(Y) = 3 \times \frac{3}{13} \times \frac{10}{13} = \frac{90}{169} = 0.533$ (to 3 d.p.)
[1 mark]

c) The probability of picking a red card is always 0.5.
So the probability of any student picking exactly 3 red cards in 4 picks is:
$P(\text{pick 3 red cards}) = \binom{4}{3} \times 0.5^3 \times (1 - 0.5)$
$= 4 \times 0.5^4 = 0.25$ ***[1 mark]***

This means that Q follows a binomial distribution:
$Q \sim B(20, 0.25)$ ***[1 mark]***.
You need to find $P(2 \leq Q \leq 8)$. $p = 0.25$ and $n = 20$ are in binomial tables, so:
$P(2 \leq Q \leq 8) = P(Q \leq 8) - P(Q < 2)$
$= P(Q \leq 8) - P(Q \leq 1)$ ***[1 mark]***
$= 0.9591 - 0.0243 = 0.9348$ ***[1 mark]***

You could do this question without tables. But it would take a while, because you'd need to find 7 individual probabilities, and add them together. That's the beauty of tables — they can tell you lots of information very quickly.

7 a) (i) No ***[1 mark]***
It's not a statistic because it contains the unknown population parameter σ.
(ii) Yes ***[1 mark]***

b) The sampling distribution of $\overline{X}$ is the probability distribution of $\overline{X}$ / the sampling distribution of $\overline{X}$ specifies the possible values $\overline{X}$ could take and the corresponding probabilities. ***[1 mark]***

8 a) X = number of people in sample of 16 who use the pool.
$X \sim B(16, p)$
$H_0: p = 0.45$ and $H_1: p < 0.45$ ***[2 marks for both correct, or 1 mark for one correct]***
So under H_0, $X \sim B(16, 0.45)$ ***[1 mark]***
$\alpha = 0.05$
The binomial tables don't give values for $n = 16$, so you need to use the binomial formula.
$P(X \leq 3) = P(X = 0) + P(X = 1) + P(X = 2) + P(X = 3)$
[1 mark]
$= 0.55^{16} + 16 \times 0.45 \times 0.55^{15} + 120 \times 0.45^2 \times 0.55^{14}$
$+ 560 \times 0.45^3 \times 0.55^{13}$
$= 0.028$ ***[1 mark]***
Since $0.028 < 0.05$, the result is significant. ***[1 mark]***
So there is evidence at the 5% level of significance to suggest that the popularity of the pool has decreased.
[1 mark]

b) For the 2nd test:
Let X be the number of people in a sample of 50 who use the pool. Then $X \sim B(50, p)$.
$H_0: p = 0.45$ and $H_1: p < 0.45$ and $\alpha = 0.05$.
So under H_0, $X \sim B(50, 0.45)$ ***[1 mark]***
The result of the test is that the manager rejects H_0, so you're looking for the biggest possible value x such that $P(X \leq x) \leq 0.05$.
Using the binomial tables, $P(X \leq 16) = 0.0427$ ***[1 mark]*** and $P(X \leq 17) = 0.0765$ ***[1 mark]***.
So the maximum possible number in the sample who use the pool is 16 ***[1 mark]***.

Answers

M2 Section 1 — Kinematics

Warm-up Questions

1)

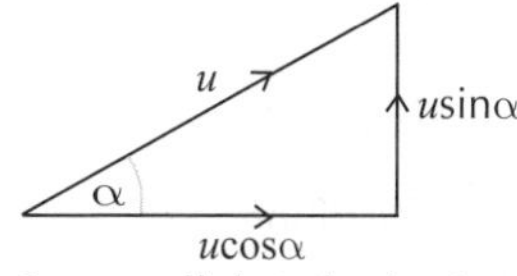

So, parallel to the horizontal, the initial velocity is $u\cos\alpha$.

2) Resolving horizontally (taking right as +ve):
$u = 120;\ s = 60;\ a = 0;\ t = ?$
$s = ut + \frac{1}{2}at^2$
$60 = 120t + \frac{1}{2} \times 0 \times t^2$
$t = 0.5$ s
Resolving vertically (taking down as +ve):
$u = 0;\ s = ?;\ a = 9.8;\ t = 0.5$
$s = ut + \frac{1}{2}at^2$
$= (0 \times 0.5) + (0.5 \times 9.8 \times 0.5^2)$
$= 1.23$ m (to 3 s.f.)

3) Resolving vertically (taking up as +ve):
$u = 22\sin\alpha;\ a = -9.8;\ t = 4;\ s = 0$
s = 0 because the ball lands at the same vertical level it started at.
$s = ut + \frac{1}{2}at^2$
$0 = 22\sin\alpha \times 4 + (0.5 \times -9.8 \times 4^2)$
Rearranging: $\sin\alpha = \frac{78.4}{88}$
$\Rightarrow \alpha = 63.0°$ (3 s.f.)
There are other ways to answer this question — you could use v = u + at and use t = 2, which is the time taken to reach the highest point, when v = 0. I like my way though.

4) a) $a = \frac{dv}{dt} = 16t - 2$
b) $s = \int v\,dt = \frac{8t^3}{3} - t^2 + c$
When $t = 0$, the particle is at the origin, i.e. $s = 0 \Rightarrow c = 0$
So, $s = \frac{8t^3}{3} - t^2$

5) $\dot{\mathbf{r}} = \frac{d\mathbf{r}}{dt}$, which represents the velocity of the particle, and
$\ddot{\mathbf{r}} = \frac{d^2\mathbf{r}}{dt^2}$, which represents the acceleration of the particle.

6) $\mathbf{r} = \int \mathbf{v}\,dt = 2t^2\mathbf{i} + \frac{t^3}{3}\mathbf{j} + \mathbf{C}$
When $t = 0$, the particle is at the origin $\Rightarrow \mathbf{C} = 0\mathbf{i} + 0\mathbf{j}$.
So, $\mathbf{r} = 2t^2\mathbf{i} + \frac{t^3}{3}\mathbf{j}$
$\mathbf{a} = \frac{d\mathbf{v}}{dt} = 4\mathbf{i} + 2t\mathbf{j}$

Exam Questions

1 a) $\tan\alpha = \frac{3}{4} \Rightarrow \sin\alpha = \frac{3}{5}$ ***[1 mark]***
Resolving vertically, taking down as +ve:
$u = u_y = 15\sin\alpha = 9$; ***[1 mark]***
$s = 11;\ a = 9.8;\ t = ?$
$s = ut + \frac{1}{2}at^2$ ***[1 mark]***
$11 = 9t + 4.9t^2$ ***[1 mark]***
Use the quadratic formula to find:
$t = 0.839$ s (3 s.f.) ***[1 mark]***

b) Resolving horizontally, taking right as +ve:
$u = u_x = 15\cos\alpha = 15 \times \frac{4}{5} = 12$; ***[1 mark]***
$s = ?;\ t = 0.8390$ s
$a = 0$, so $s = ut \Rightarrow OB = 12 \times 0.8390$ ***[1 mark]***
So, $OB = 10.07$ m
So stone misses H by $10.07 - 9 = 1.07$ m (3 s.f.) ***[1 mark]***

c) Resolving horizontally, taking right as +ve:
$s = 9;\ u_x = u\cos\alpha;\ a = 0;\ t = ?$
$s = u_x t + \frac{1}{2}at^2$ ***[1 mark]***
$9 = (u\cos\alpha)t$
$\Rightarrow t = \frac{9}{u\cos\alpha}$ — call this **eqn 1**. ***[1 mark]***
Now resolve vertically, taking down as +ve:
$s = 11;\ u_y = u\sin\alpha;\ a = 9.8;\ t = ?$
$s = u_y t + \frac{1}{2}at^2$
$11 = (u\sin\alpha)t + 4.9t^2$ — call this **eqn 2**. ***[1 mark]***
t is the same both horizontally and vertically, so substitute **eqn 1** in **eqn 2** to eliminate t:
$11 = 9\left(\frac{u\sin\alpha}{u\cos\alpha}\right) + 4.9\left(\frac{9}{u\cos\alpha}\right)^2$ ***[1 mark]***
$11 = 9\tan\alpha + \frac{4.9 \times 81}{u^2\cos^2\alpha}$
$\tan\alpha = \frac{3}{4}$ and $\cos\alpha = \frac{4}{5}$, so substituting and simplifying:
$u^2 = 145.919$
so $u = 12.1$ ms^{-1} (3 s.f.) ***[1 mark]***
Wooo. What a beauty part c) is — I'd do that again just for kicks. But then I do love a bit of substituting and eliminating. If you're confused by this question, then look back over the section — there's an example which is a bit more general, but it uses a lot of the same working.

2 a) $\mathbf{v} = \dot{\mathbf{r}} = (6t^2 - 14t)\mathbf{i} + (6t - 12t^2)\mathbf{j}$
[2 marks in total — 1 mark for attempting to differentiate the position vector, 1 mark for correctly differentiating both components]

b) $\mathbf{v} = \left(\frac{6}{4} - \frac{14}{2}\right)\mathbf{i} + \left(\frac{6}{2} - \frac{12}{4}\right)\mathbf{j}$ ***[1 mark]***
$= -5.5\mathbf{i} + 0\mathbf{j}$
Speed $= \sqrt{(-5.5)^2 + 0^2} = 5.5$ ms^{-1} ***[1 mark]***
The component of velocity in the direction of north is zero, and the component in the direction of east is negative, so the particle is moving due west ***[1 mark]***

c) $\mathbf{a} = \dot{\mathbf{v}}$ ***[1 mark]***
$= (12t - 14)\mathbf{i} + (6 - 24t)\mathbf{j}$ ***[1 mark]***
At $t = 2$, $\mathbf{a} = 10\mathbf{i} - 42\mathbf{j}$ ***[1 mark]***

d) Use $\mathbf{F} = m\mathbf{a}$ to find the force at $t = 2$:
$\mathbf{F} = 10m\mathbf{i} - 42m\mathbf{j}$ ***[1 mark]***
At $t = 2$, $|\mathbf{F}| = \sqrt{(10m)^2 + (-42m)^2} = 43.17m$ ***[1 mark]***
Magnitude of $\mathbf{F}$ at $t = 2$ is 170, so: $43.17m = 170$
$\Rightarrow m = 3.94$ kg (3 s.f.) ***[1 mark]***

e) The vectors **F** and **a** always act in the same direction, so when **F** is acting parallel to **j**, so is **a**. ***[1 mark]***
So, when **F** is acting parallel to **j**, the component of **a** in direction of **i** will be zero ***[1 mark]***, i.e.
$12t - 14 = 0 \Rightarrow t = 1.17$ s (3 s.f.) ***[1 mark]***

Answers

3 Resolving horizontally, taking right as +ve :
$u = 20\cos 30°$; $s = 30$; $a = 0$; $t = ?$

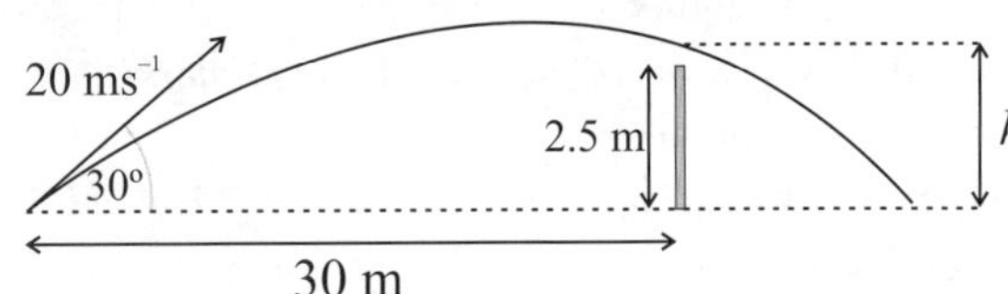

$s = ut + \frac{1}{2}at^2$ ***[1 mark]***
$30 = (20\cos 30° \times t)$
$t = 1.732$ s ***[1 mark]***
Resolving vertically, taking up as +ve:
$s = h$; $u = 20\sin 30°$; $t = 1.732$; $a = -9.8$
$s = ut + \frac{1}{2}at^2$ ***[1 mark]***
$h = (20\sin 30° \times 1.732) + (\frac{1}{2} \times -9.8 \times 1.732^2)$
$= 2.62$ m (to 3 s.f.) ***[1 mark]***
Therefore the ball goes over the crossbar. ***[1 mark]***
Assumptions: e.g. ball is a point mass/no air or wind resistance/no spin on the ball ***[1 mark]***

That was always my problem when I was taking free kicks — I didn't model the flight of the ball properly before kicking it, so no wonder I never scored.

4 a) v is at a maximum when $\frac{dv}{dt} = 0$, i.e. when $a = 0$
So, in the interval $0 \le t \le 4$,
$a = \frac{dv}{dt} = 9 - 6t$ ***[1 mark]***
Set $a = 0$:
$0 = 9 - 6t \Rightarrow t = 1.5$ s ***[1 mark]***
So, $v = (9 \times 1.5) - 3(1.5^2)$ ***[1 mark]***
$= 6.75$ ms^{-1} ***[1 mark]***

b) (i) $s = \int v\,dt$
$= \frac{9t^2}{2} - t^3 + c$ for $0 \le t \le 4$. ***[1 mark]***
When $t = 0$, the particle is at the origin, i.e. $s = 0$
$\Rightarrow c = 0$ ***[1 mark]***
So, at $t = 4$:
$s = \frac{9}{2}(16) - 64 = 8$ m ***[1 mark]***

(ii) $s = \int v\,dt$
$= \frac{-192t^{-1}}{-1} + k = \frac{192}{t} + k$ for $t > 4$ ***[1 mark]***
When $t = 4$, $s = 8$, so $8 = \frac{192}{4} + k$ ***[1 mark]***
$\Rightarrow k = -40$ ***[1 mark]***
When $t = 6$,
$s = \frac{192}{6} - 40 = -8$ m ***[1 mark]***

5 a) Resolving horizontally, taking right as +ve:
$u = 14$; $s = x$, $t = ?$, $a = 0$
$s = ut + \frac{1}{2}at^2$ gives:
$x = 14t$, so $t = \frac{x}{14}$ — call this **eqn 1.** ***[1 mark]***
Resolving vertically, taking up as +ve:
$u = 35$; $s = y$; $t = ?$; $a = -9.8$
$s = ut + \frac{1}{2}at^2 \Rightarrow y = 35t - 4.9t^2$ — call this **eqn 2**. ***[1 mark]***
Substitute **eqn 1** into **eqn 2** to eliminate t:
$y = 35\left(\frac{x}{14}\right) - 4.9\left(\frac{x}{14}\right)^2$ ***[1 mark]***
Rearrange:
$y = \frac{5x}{2} - \frac{x^2}{40}$ ***[1 mark]***
If you take down as +ve in the working, then you have to use $a = 9.8$, $s = -y$ (because y is defined as being positive), and $u = -35$. Then all the signs work out right :-)

b) Use formula from part a) with $y = -30$;
$y = -30$, because the ball lands 30 m below the point it's hit from and up was taken as positive when deriving the formula.
$-30 = \frac{5x}{2} - \frac{x^2}{40}$ ***[1 mark]***
Rearrange: $x^2 - 100x - 1200 = 0$
Solve quadratic using quadratic formula ***[1 mark]***
$x = 111$ m (3 s.f.) ***[1 mark]***

c) Distance $AH = 110.8 - 7 = 103.8$ m
Use formula from part a) with $x = 103.8$ m:
$y = \frac{5 \times 103.8}{2} - \frac{(103.8)^2}{40} = -9.861\text{m}$ ***[1 mark]***
So, when ball is vertically above H, it is 9.86 m below the level of O. Now resolve vertically, taking up as +ve:
$u = u_y = 35$; $s = -9.861$; $a = -g$; $v = v_y$
$v^2 = u^2 + 2as \Rightarrow v_y^2 = 1418$ ***[1 mark]***
In this case, you don't need to take the square root to find the value of v_y as you'd have to square it again to find the speed.
No acceleration horizontally, so $v_x = u_x = 14$ ms^{-1}
Speed, $V = \sqrt{v_x^2 + v_y^2}$ ***[1 mark]***
$= \sqrt{14^2 + 1418} = 40.2\,\text{ms}^{-1}$ (3 s.f.) ***[1 mark]***

M2 Section 2 — Centres of Mass

Warm-up Questions

1) a) Particles in a horizontal line so use $\Sigma mx = \bar{x}\Sigma m$
$m_1x_1 + m_2x_2 + m_3x_3 = \bar{x}(m_1 + m_2 + m_3)$
$\Rightarrow (1 \times 1) + (2 \times 2) + (3 \times 3) = \bar{x}(1 + 2 + 3)$
$\Rightarrow 14 = 6\bar{x} \Rightarrow \bar{x} = 14 \div 6 = 2\frac{1}{3}$.
So coordinates are $(2\frac{1}{3}, 0)$.

b) Particles in a vertical line so use $\Sigma my = \bar{y}\Sigma m$
$m_1y_1 + m_2y_2 + m_3y_3 = \bar{y}(m_1 + m_2 + m_3)$
$\Rightarrow (1 \times 3) + (2 \times 2) + (3 \times 1) = \bar{y}(1 + 2 + 3)$
$\Rightarrow 10 = 6\bar{y} \Rightarrow \bar{y} = 10 \div 6 = 1\frac{2}{3}$.
So coordinates are $(0, 1\frac{2}{3})$.

c) Particles in 2D so use $\Sigma m\mathbf{r} = \bar{\mathbf{r}}\Sigma m$
$m_1\mathbf{r}_1 + m_2\mathbf{r}_2 + m_3\mathbf{r}_3 = \bar{\mathbf{r}}(m_1 + m_2 + m_3)$
$\Rightarrow 1\binom{3}{4} + 2\binom{3}{1} + 3\binom{1}{0} = \bar{\mathbf{r}}(1 + 2 + 3)$
$\Rightarrow \binom{12}{6} = 6\bar{\mathbf{r}} \Rightarrow \bar{\mathbf{r}} = \binom{12}{6} \div 6 = \binom{2}{1}$.
So coordinates are (2, 1).

2) Use $\Sigma m\mathbf{r} = \bar{\mathbf{r}}\Sigma m$
$m\binom{0}{0} + 2m\binom{0}{4} + 3m\binom{5}{4} + 12\binom{5}{0} = (m + 2m + 3m + 12)\binom{3.5}{2}$
$\Rightarrow \binom{15m + 60}{20m} = \binom{21m + 42}{12m + 24}$
$\Rightarrow 20m = 12m + 24 \Rightarrow 8m = 24 \Rightarrow m = 24 \div 8 = 3$ kg.

3) a) Triangle (1) has area $\frac{1}{2} \times 4 \times 3 = 6$, so $m_1 = 6$.
$x_1 = 2$ (symmetry) and $y_1 = 5 - (\frac{2}{3} \times 3) = 3$ ($\frac{2}{3}$ down the median from the top vertex).

Answers

Rectangle (2) has area 1 × 2 = 2, so $m_2 = 2$.
$x_2 = 2$ and $y_2 = 1.5$ (symmetry).
Combined shape has $\bar{x} = 2$ (symmetry) and:
$m_1y_1 + m_2y_2 = \bar{y}(m_1 + m_2)$
$\Rightarrow (6 \times 3) + (2 \times 1.5) = (6 + 2)\bar{y}$
$\Rightarrow 21 = 8\bar{y} \Rightarrow \bar{y} = 21 \div 8 = 2.625$.
So coordinates are (2, 2.625).

b) Semicircle (1) has area $\frac{1}{2} \times \pi \times 3^2 = 4.5\pi$, so $m_1 = 4.5\pi$.
$x_1 = 8$ (symmetry) and $y_1 = 1 + \dfrac{2 \times 3 \times \sin\frac{\pi}{2}}{\frac{3\pi}{2}} = \dfrac{4+\pi}{\pi}$
(COM is $\frac{2r\sin\alpha}{3\alpha}$ up from the centre of the circle, where $2\alpha = \pi$).

Don't forget — the arc angle is 2α not α...

Triangle (2) has area $\frac{1}{2} \times 2 \times 1 = 1$, so $m_2 = 1$.
$x_2 = 8$ (symmetry) and $y_2 = \frac{2}{3} \times 1 = \frac{2}{3}$ ($\frac{2}{3}$ up the median from the bottom vertex).
Combined shape has $\bar{x} = 8$ (symmetry) and:
$m_1y_1 + m_2y_2 = \bar{y}(m_1 + m_2)$
$\Rightarrow (4.5\pi \times \frac{4+\pi}{\pi}) + (1 \times \frac{2}{3}) = (4.5\pi + 1)\bar{y}$
$\Rightarrow 18\frac{2}{3} + 4.5\pi = (4.5\pi + 1)\bar{y}$
$\Rightarrow \bar{y} = (18\frac{2}{3} + 4.5\pi) \div (4.5\pi + 1) = 2.167$ (to 3 d.p.).
So coordinates are (8, 2.167).

c) Circle (1) has area $\pi \times 2^2 = 4\pi$, so $m_1 = 4\pi$.
$x_1 = 14$ and $y_1 = 2$ (symmetry).
Square (2) has area 1 × 1 = 1, so $m_2 = 1$.
$x_2 = 14.5$ and $y_2 = 2.5$ (symmetry).
Using the removal method:
$m_1\mathbf{r}_1 - m_2\mathbf{r}_2 = \bar{\mathbf{r}}(m_1 - m_2)$
$\Rightarrow 4\pi\binom{14}{2} - \binom{14.5}{2.5} = (4\pi - 1)\bar{\mathbf{r}}$
$\Rightarrow \binom{56\pi - 14.5}{8\pi - 2.5} = (4\pi - 1)\bar{\mathbf{r}}$
$\Rightarrow \bar{\mathbf{r}} = \binom{56\pi - 14.5}{8\pi - 2.5} \div (4\pi - 1) = \binom{13.957}{1.957}$ (to 3 d.p.).
So coordinates are (13.957, 1.957).

4)

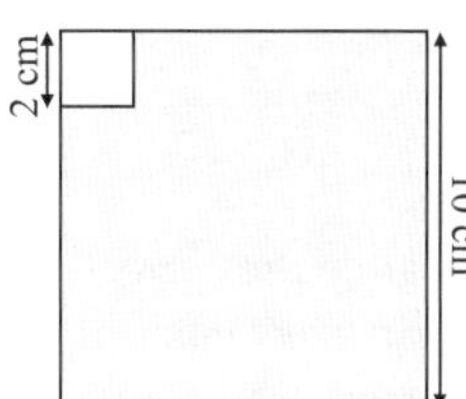

Large square (1) has area 10 × 10 = 100, so $m_1 = 100$.
$y_1 = 5$ cm from top edge (symmetry).
Small square (2) has area 2 × 2 = 4, so $m_2 = 4$.
$y_2 = 1$ cm from top edge (symmetry).
Using the removal method:
$m_1y_1 - m_2y_2 = \bar{y}(m_1 - m_2)$
$\Rightarrow (100 \times 5) - (4 \times 1) = (100 - 4)\bar{y}$
$\Rightarrow 496 = 96\bar{y} \Rightarrow \bar{y} = 496 \div 96 = 5.167$ cm from the top edge (to 3 d.p.).

You can pick any place to be the origin, but the top edge makes most sense here.

5) a)

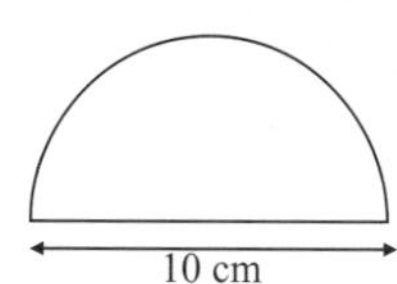

Straight rod (1) has length 10 cm so $m_1 = 10$.
$y_1 = 0$ (as it lies on the straight edge).
Arc (2) has length $\frac{10}{2} \times \pi$, so $m_2 = 5\pi$.
$y_2 = \dfrac{5 \times \sin\frac{\pi}{2}}{\frac{\pi}{2}} = \dfrac{10}{\pi}$ (COM is $\frac{r\sin\alpha}{\alpha}$ up from the centre of the circle, where $2\alpha = \pi$).
Combined frame:
$m_1y_1 + m_2y_2 = \bar{y}(m_1 + m_2)$
$\Rightarrow (10 \times 0) + (5\pi \times \frac{10}{\pi}) = (10 + 5\pi)\bar{y}$
$\Rightarrow 50 = (10 + 5\pi)\bar{y}$
$\Rightarrow \bar{y} = 50 \div (10 + 5\pi) = 1.945$ cm (to 3 d.p.).

b)

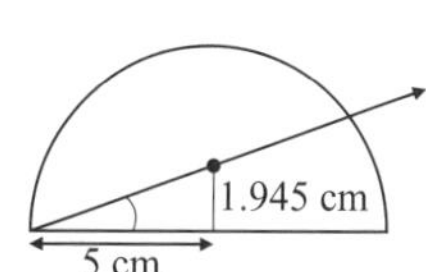

Drawing a line to represent the vertical through the COM (shown) gives a right-angled triangle. If α is the angle between the straight edge and the vertical then:
$\alpha = \tan^{-1}\left(\frac{1.945}{5}\right) = 0.371$ rads (to 3 d.p.)

Exam Questions

1 (a) Using the formula $\Sigma my = \bar{y}\Sigma m$
$m_1y_1 + m_2y_2 + m_3y_3 = \bar{y}(m_1 + m_2 + m_3)$
$\Rightarrow (4 \times 3) + (3 \times 1) + (2 \times y) = 2 \times (4 + 3 + 2)$ ***[1 mark]***
$\Rightarrow 15 + 2y = 18$ ***[1 mark]***
$\Rightarrow y = (18 - 15) \div 2 = 1.5$ ***[1 mark]***.

(b) Using the formula $\Sigma mx = \bar{x}\Sigma m$
$m_1x_1 + m_2x_2 + m_3x_3 = \bar{x}(m_1 + m_2 + m_3)$
$\Rightarrow (4 \times 1) + (3 \times 5) + (2 \times 4) = \bar{x}(4 + 3 + 2)$ ***[1 mark]***
$\Rightarrow 27 = 9\bar{x}$ ***[1 mark]***
$\Rightarrow \bar{x} = 27 \div 9 = 3$ ***[1 mark]***.

(c) Centre of mass of the lamina is at (3.5, 2.5), due to the symmetry of the shape, and $m_{\text{lamina}} = 6$ kg.
Centre of mass of the group of particles is (3, 2) (from (b)) and $m_{\text{particles}} = 4 + 3 + 2 = 9$ kg. Using $\Sigma m\mathbf{r} = \bar{\mathbf{r}}\Sigma m$:
$m_{\text{lamina}}\mathbf{r}_{\text{lamina}} + m_{\text{particles}}\mathbf{r}_{\text{particles}} = \bar{\mathbf{r}}(m_{\text{lamina}} + m_{\text{particles}})$
$\Rightarrow 6\binom{3.5}{2.5} + 9\binom{3}{2} = \bar{\mathbf{r}}(6 + 9)$
$\Rightarrow \binom{21 + 27}{15 + 18} = 15\bar{\mathbf{r}}$
$\Rightarrow \bar{\mathbf{r}} = \binom{48}{33} \div 15 = \binom{3.2}{2.2}$,
so the coordinates are (3.2, 2.2).

[6 marks available — 1 mark for the correct x_{lamina}, 1 mark for the correct y_{lamina}, 1 mark for correct entry of horizontal positions in the formula, 1 mark for correct entry of vertical positions in the formula, 1 mark for x coordinate of 3.2, 1 mark for y coordinate of 2.2.]

Answers

2 (a) (i) Setting M as the origin, the distance of the centre of mass from MP is the horizontal distance $\bar{x}$.
For each element the masses and centres are:
Particle at A: $m_A = 3m$ and $x_A = -10$ (since A is 10 cm to the left of M).
Particle at B: $m_B = 4m$ and $x_B = 10$.
Straight rod: $m_{rod} = 2m$ and $x_{rod} = 0$ (M is the midpoint of the rod, which is the centre of its mass).
Arc: $m_{arc} = \pi m$ and $x_{arc} = 0$ (due to the symmetry of the semicircular arc).

Don't forget to include the masses of all the rods and arcs — unless you're told that they're 'light'.

Combining these elements in the formula $\Sigma mx = \bar{x}\Sigma m$
$m_A x_A + m_B x_B + m_{rod} x_{rod} + m_{arc} x_{arc} = \bar{x}(m_A + m_B + m_{rod} + m_{arc})$
$\Rightarrow (3m \times -10) + (4m \times 10) + (2m \times 0) + (\pi m \times 0)$
$= \bar{x}(3m + 4m + 2m + \pi m)$
$\Rightarrow -30m + 40m = (9 + \pi)m\bar{x}$
$\Rightarrow \bar{x} = 10 \div (9 + \pi) = 0.8236$ cm to 4 d.p.

[3 marks available — 1 mark for correct total mass of system, 1 mark for correct entry into formula, 1 mark for correct final answer.]

(ii) With M as the origin still, the distance of the centre of mass from AB is the vertical distance $\bar{y}$.
So: $y_A = y_B = y_{rod} = 0$, since all three lie on the line AB.
For the arc, use the formula $y_{arc} = \frac{r\sin\alpha}{\alpha}$, where $r = 10$, and $\alpha = \frac{\pi}{2}$ (since the angle at the centre $(2\alpha) = \pi$), so

$$y_{arc} = \frac{10\sin\frac{\pi}{2}}{\frac{\pi}{2}} = \frac{20}{\pi}.$$

This is on the formula sheet if you can't remember in the exam...

Combining these in the formula $\Sigma my = \bar{y}\Sigma m$
$m_A y_A + m_B y_B + m_{rod} y_{rod} + m_{arc} y_{arc} = \bar{y}(m_A + m_B + m_{rod} + m_{arc})$
$\Rightarrow (\pi m \times \frac{20}{\pi}) = (9 + \pi)m\bar{y}$
$\Rightarrow \bar{y} = 20 \div (9 + \pi) = 1.6472$ cm to 4 d.p.

[3 marks available — 1 mark for correct value of y_{arc}, 1 mark for correct entry into formula, 1 mark for correct final answer.]

(b) On a sketch, draw a line from P to the centre of mass to represent the vertical and label relevant lengths and angles:

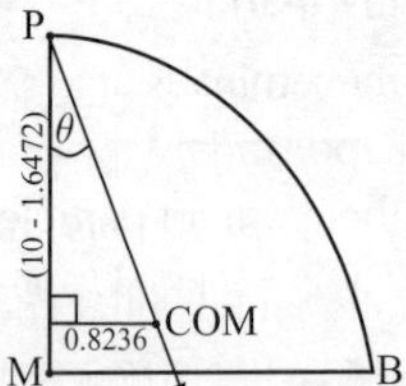

The vertical distance between P and the centre of mass = 10 – 1.6472 (from (a)(ii)) = 8.3528 cm ***[1 mark]***.

Using trig:
$\theta = \tan^{-1}\left(\frac{0.8236}{8.3528}\right)$ ***[1 mark]*** = 0.0983 rads to 3 s.f. ***[1 mark]***.

3 (a) Splitting up the shape into a triangle (1), large square (2) and small square (3), where the mass of each shape is proportional to the area, gives the following masses:
$m_1 = \frac{1}{2} \times 70 \times 30 = 1050.$
$m_2 = 50 \times 50 = 2500.$
$m_3 = 10 \times 10 = 100.$

Taking the point A as the origin, the position vectors of the centres of mass of each shape are as follows:
Triangle:
$x_1 = 25$ (due to the symmetry of the shape) and
$y_1 = 50 + (\frac{1}{3} \times 30) = 60$ (since the COM of a triangle is $\frac{2}{3}$ down the median from the vertex, and so $\frac{1}{3}$ up from the edge). So $\mathbf{r}_1 = \binom{25}{60}$.
Large Square:
$x_2 = 25$ and $y_2 = 25$ (due to the symmetry of the shape) so $\mathbf{r}_2 = \binom{25}{25}$.
Small Square:
$x_3 = 50 + 5 = 55$ and $y_3 = 5$ (due to the symmetry of the shape) so $\mathbf{r}_3 = \binom{55}{5}$.
Using the formula $\Sigma m\mathbf{r} = \bar{\mathbf{r}}\Sigma m$
$m_1\mathbf{r}_1 + m_2\mathbf{r}_2 + m_3\mathbf{r}_3 = \bar{\mathbf{r}}(m_1 + m_2 + m_3) \Rightarrow$
$1050\binom{25}{60} + 2500\binom{25}{25} + 100\binom{55}{5} = \bar{\mathbf{r}}(1050 + 2500 + 100)$
$\Rightarrow \binom{26250 + 62500 + 5500}{63000 + 62500 + 500} = 3650\bar{\mathbf{r}}$
$\Rightarrow \bar{\mathbf{r}} = \binom{94250}{126000} \div 3650 = \binom{25.8219...}{34.5205...}.$
So, to 3 s.f., the centre of mass of the sign is 25.8 cm from AB and 34.5 cm from AI.

[6 marks available — 1 mark for masses in the correct proportion, 1 mark for each individual centre of mass entered correctly into the formula, 1 mark for correct distance from AB, 1 mark for correct distance from AI.]

(b) For the sign to hang with AI horizontal, the centre of mass of the whole system (sign + particle) must be vertically below D, i.e. $\bar{x}$ must be 25 (taking A as the origin again).
Given that $m_{sign} = 1$ kg and $x_{sign} = 25.8219...$ (from (a)), and $x_{particle} = 0$ (since it's attached at the origin):
$m_{sign}x_{sign} + m_{particle}x_{particle} = \bar{x}(m_{sign} + m_{particle})$
$(1 \times 25.8219...) + 0 = 25(1 + m_{particle})$
$\Rightarrow 25.8219... \div 25 = 1 + m_{particle}$
$\Rightarrow 1.03287... - 1 = m_{particle}$
$\Rightarrow m_{particle} = 0.0329$ kg, to 3 s.f.

[3 marks available — 1 mark stating the correct required value of $\bar{x}$, 1 mark for correct entry of values into the formula, 1 mark for correct final answer.]

4 (a) The stencil is a rectangle (1) with a quarter circle (2) of radius (10 – 2) = 8 cm removed. The lamina is uniform so mass is proportional to area, so $m_1 = 12 \times 10 = 120$, and $m_2 = \frac{1}{4} \times \pi \times 8^2 = 16\pi$.
Taking O as the origin, the position of the centre of mass of the rectangle, $\mathbf{r}_1 = \binom{6}{5}$ (from the symmetry of the shape).

Answers

The sector angle $2\alpha = \frac{\pi}{2}$, so $\alpha = \frac{\pi}{4}$, and the centre of mass of the sector is $\frac{2r\sin\alpha}{3\alpha}$ from O along the axis of symmetry

$$= \frac{2 \times 8 \times \sin\frac{\pi}{4}}{\frac{3\pi}{4}} = \frac{64}{3\pi\sqrt{2}} \text{ cm.}$$

This is on the formula sheet — you just have to know how to use it. And you'll have to use trig to find the position vector... In the right-angled triangle below, cos α = x/hyp, and sin α = y/hyp, so with a bit of rearranging you can find x and y for the position vector...

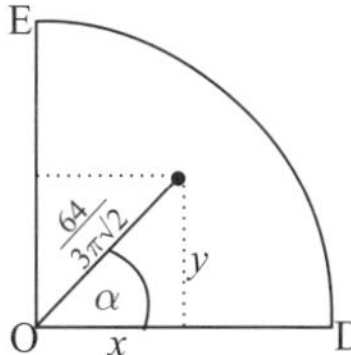

Using trig, the position vector of the centre of mass of the sector, $\mathbf{r}_2 = \begin{pmatrix} \frac{64}{3\pi\sqrt{2}} \times \cos\frac{\pi}{4} \\ \frac{64}{3\pi\sqrt{2}} \times \sin\frac{\pi}{4} \end{pmatrix} = \begin{pmatrix} \frac{32}{3\pi} \\ \frac{32}{3\pi} \end{pmatrix}$.

Using the removal method:

$m_1\mathbf{r}_1 - m_2\mathbf{r}_2 = \bar{\mathbf{r}}(m_1 - m_2)$

$$\Rightarrow 120\begin{pmatrix}6\\5\end{pmatrix} - 16\pi\begin{pmatrix}\frac{32}{3\pi}\\\frac{32}{3\pi}\end{pmatrix} = \bar{\mathbf{r}}(120 - 16\pi)$$

$$\Rightarrow \begin{pmatrix}720 - \frac{512}{3}\\600 - \frac{512}{3}\end{pmatrix} = \bar{\mathbf{r}}(120 - 16\pi)$$

$$\Rightarrow \begin{pmatrix}\frac{1648}{3}\\\frac{1288}{3}\end{pmatrix} \div (120 - 16\pi) = \bar{\mathbf{r}}$$

$$\Rightarrow \bar{\mathbf{r}} = \begin{pmatrix}7.8774...\\6.1566...\end{pmatrix}.$$

So, to 3 s.f., the coordinates of the centre of mass of the stencil are (7.88, 6.16).

[7 marks available — 1 mark for the correct total mass, 1 mark for correct r_1, 1 mark for correct r_2, 1 mark for correct entry of horizontal positions in the formula, 1 mark for correct entry of vertical positions in the formula, 1 mark for x coordinate of 7.88, 1 mark for y coordinate of 6.16.]

(b) At the point of toppling, the centre of mass will be vertically above the point D, as shown:

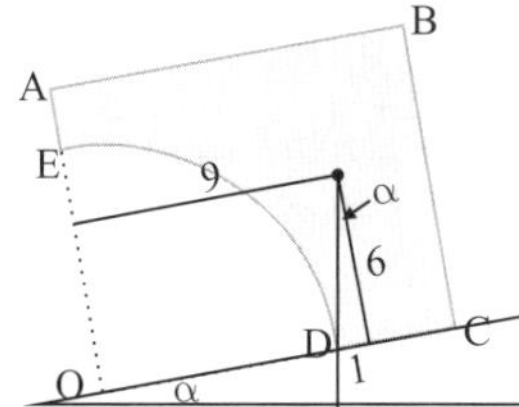

Horizontal distance from D to the centre of mass $= 9 - 8 = 1$ cm ***[1 mark]***.

Using trig, $\alpha = \tan^{-1}\left(\frac{1}{6}\right)$ ***[1 mark]*** = 0.165 rads to 3 s.f. ***[1 mark]***.

M2 Section 3 — Work and Energy

Warm-up Questions

1) Work done $= F \times s$
$= 250 \times 3 = 750$ J

2) Work done against gravity $= mgh$
$34\,000 = m \times 9.8 \times 12$
$m = 289$ kg (3 s.f.)

3) Kinetic Energy $= \frac{1}{2}mv^2$
$= \frac{1}{2} \times 450 \times 13^2$
$= 38\,025$ J $= 38.0$ kJ (3 s.f.)

4) Work done = Change in Kinetic Energy
$800 = \frac{1}{2}m(v^2 - u^2)$
$u = 0$ and $m = 65$, so:
$v^2 = \frac{1600}{65} \Rightarrow v = 4.96$ ms^{-1} (3 s.f.)

5) Increase in Potential Energy = mg × increase in height
$= 0.5 \times 9.8 \times 150$
$= 735$ J

6) "If there are no external forces doing work on an object, the total mechanical energy of the object will remain constant." You usually need to model the object as a particle, because you have to assume that the object is not acted on by any external forces such as air resistance.

7) When the hat reaches its maximum height, its velocity will be zero. Using conservation of energy:
Change in potential energy = change in kinetic energy
$mgh = \frac{1}{2}m(u^2 - v^2)$
Cancel m from both sides, and substitute $u = 5$, $v = 0$ and $g = 9.8$:
$9.8h = \frac{1}{2} \times 25 \Rightarrow h = 1.28$ m (3 s.f.)

8) "The work done on an object by external forces is equal to the change in the total mechanical energy of that object." An external force is any force other than an object's weight.

9) Power of engine = driving force × velocity
$350\,000 = F \times 22 \Rightarrow F = 15\,900$ N (3 s.f.)

Exam Questions

1 a) Increase in Kinetic Energy $= \frac{1}{2}m(v^2 - u^2)$ ***[1 mark]***
$= \frac{1}{2} \times 90 \times (6^2 - 4^2) = 900$ J ***[1 mark]***
Increase in Gravitational Potential Energy $= mgh$ ***[1 mark]***
$= 90 \times 9.8 \times 28\sin 30° = 12\,348$ J ***[1 mark]***
Increase in total Energy = Increase in K.E. + Increase in P.E.
$= 900 + 12\,348 = 13\,248$ J $= 13.2$ kJ (3 s.f.) ***[1 mark]***

b) Using the work-energy principle:
Work done on skier = Change in total energy ***[1 mark]***
$(L - 66) \times 28 = 13\,248$ ***[1 mark]***
$L = \frac{13\,248 + (66 \times 28)}{28} = 539$ N (3 s.f.) ***[1 mark]***

Answers

2 a) K.E. = $\frac{1}{2}mv^2 = \frac{1}{2} \times 0.3 \times 20^2$ ***[1 mark]***
$= 60$ J ***[1 mark]***

b) Only force acting on the stone is its weight, so use conservation of mechanical energy:
Change in K.E. = Change in P.E. ***[1 mark]***
$60 - 0 = 0.3 \times 9.8 \times h$ ***[1 mark]***
$h = 20.4$ m (3 s.f.) ***[1 mark]***

c) Stone's change in K.E. after hitting the water:
$\frac{1}{2} \times 0.3 \times 1^2 - 60 = -59.85$ J ***[1 mark]***
Call the depth the stone has sunk x m.
Change in P.E. after hitting the water:
$-mgx = -2.94x$ ***[1 mark]***
Work done on the stone by resistive force
$= Fs = -23x$ ***[1 mark]***
By the work-energy principle:
Work done on the stone = Change in total energy ***[1 mark]***
$-23x = -59.85 - 2.94x$
Rearrange to find x:
$x = 2.98$ m (3 s.f) ***[1 mark]***

3 a)

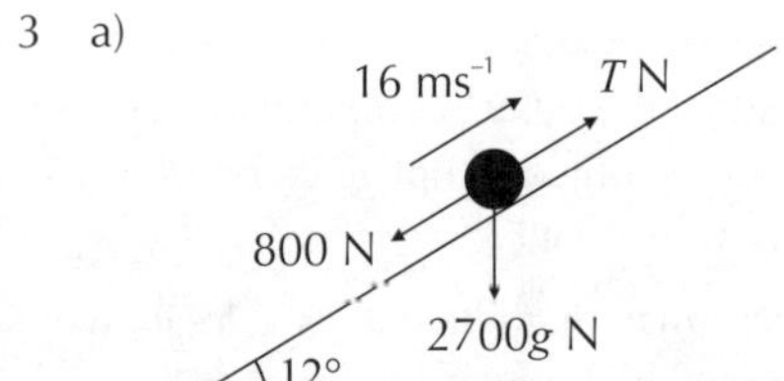

Resolving parallel to the slope using $F = ma$ with $a = 0$:
$T - 800 - 2700g\sin 12° = 0$ ***[1 mark]***
So, $T = 6301$ N ***[1 mark]***
Power of engine = Driving Force × Velocity ***[1 mark]***
$= 6301 \times 16 = 101$ kW (3 s.f.) ***[1 mark]***

b) Work done by resistive force to stop van = $-800x$ ***[1 mark]***
Change in total energy = Change in P.E. + Change in K.E.
$= (2700 \times g \times x\sin 12°) - (\frac{1}{2} \times 2700 \times 16^2)$ ***[1 mark]***
By work-energy principle,
$-800x = 2700gx\sin 12° - 345\,600$ ***[1 mark]***
Rearrange to find x:
$x = \frac{345\,600}{2700g\sin 12° + 800} = 54.8$ m (3 s.f.) ***[1 mark]***

c) Resolve parallel to the slope using $F = ma$ to find a:
$-800 - 2700g\sin 12° = 2700a$ ***[1 mark]***
$a = -2.334$ ms^{-2} ***[1 mark]***
Use $v = u + at$ to find the time taken to come to rest:
$0 = 16 - 2.334t$ ***[1 mark]***
$t = \frac{16}{2.334} = 6.86$ s (3 s.f.) ***[1 mark]***

4 a) Work done = Force × distance moved
$= 800\cos 40° \times 320 = 196$ kJ (3 s.f.)

[3 marks available in total]:
- ***1 mark for using the horizontal component of the force***
- ***1 mark for correct use of formula for work done***
- ***1 mark for correct final answer.***

b)

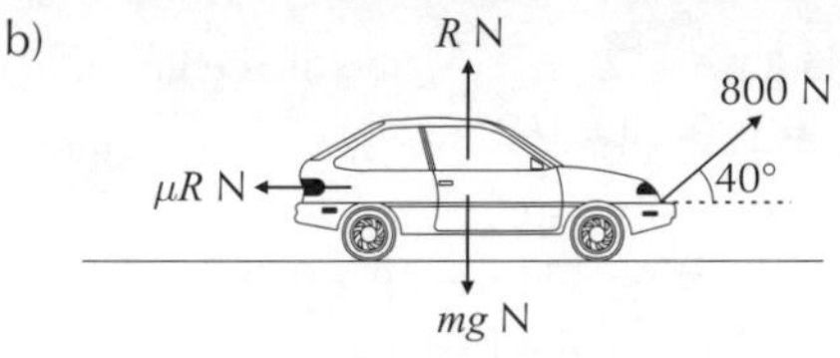

No acceleration vertically, so:
$R + 800\sin 40° = mg$
$R = 1500g - 800\sin 40° = 14\,190$ N ***[1 mark]***
Car is moving only horizontally, so:
Work done = change in kinetic energy ***[1 mark]***
$(800\cos 40° - \mu R) \times 320 = \frac{1}{2} \times 1500 \times (16^2 - 11^2)$ ***[1 mark]***
Rearrange to find μ:
$\mu = \frac{196\,107 - 101\,250}{4\,541\,000} = 0.0209$ (3 s.f.) ***[1 mark]***

5 a) Use the work rate to find the 'driving' force, F of the cyclist:
$250 = F \times 4$ ***[1 mark]***
$F = 62.5$ N
Resolve parallel to the slope: ***[1 mark]***
$62.5 - 35 - 88g\sin\alpha = 0$ ***[1 mark]***
$\alpha = \sin^{-1}\frac{27.5}{88g} = 1.83°$ (3 s.f.) ***[1 mark]***

b) Use the new work rate to find the new 'driving' force, F':
$370 = F' \times 4$ ***[1 mark]***
$F' = 92.5$ N
Resolve parallel to the slope to find a: ***[1 mark]***
$92.5 - 35 - 88g\sin\alpha = 88a$ ***[1 mark]***
$a = 0.341$ ms^{-2} (3 s.f.) ***[1 mark]***

M2 Section 4 — Collisions
Warm-up Questions

1 a) $\mathbf{I} = m\mathbf{v} - m\mathbf{u}$, so
$2\mathbf{i} + 5\mathbf{j} = 0.1\mathbf{v} - 0.1(\mathbf{i} + \mathbf{j})$
$2\mathbf{i} + 5\mathbf{j} = 0.1\mathbf{v} - 0.1\mathbf{i} - 0.1\mathbf{j}$
$0.1\mathbf{v} = 2\mathbf{i} + 5\mathbf{j} + 0.1\mathbf{i} + 0.1\mathbf{j} = 2.1\mathbf{i} + 5.1\mathbf{j}$
$\Rightarrow \mathbf{v} = 21\mathbf{i} + 51\mathbf{j}$.

b) $-3\mathbf{i} + \mathbf{j} = 0.1\mathbf{v} - 0.1\mathbf{i} - 0.1\mathbf{j}$
$0.1\mathbf{v} = -3\mathbf{i} + \mathbf{j} + 0.1\mathbf{i} + 0.1\mathbf{j} = -2.9\mathbf{i} + 1.1\mathbf{j}$
$\Rightarrow \mathbf{v} = -29\mathbf{i} + 11\mathbf{j}$.

c) $-\mathbf{i} - 6\mathbf{j} = 0.1\mathbf{v} - 0.1\mathbf{i} - 0.1\mathbf{j}$
$0.1\mathbf{v} = -\mathbf{i} - 6\mathbf{j} + 0.1\mathbf{i} + 0.1\mathbf{j} = -0.9\mathbf{i} - 5.9\mathbf{j}$
$\Rightarrow \mathbf{v} = -9\mathbf{i} - 59\mathbf{j}$.

d) $4\mathbf{i} = 0.1\mathbf{v} - 0.1\mathbf{i} - 0.1\mathbf{j}$
$0.1\mathbf{v} = 4\mathbf{i} + 0.1\mathbf{i} + 0.1\mathbf{j} = 4.1\mathbf{i} + 0.1\mathbf{j}$
$\Rightarrow \mathbf{v} = 41\mathbf{i} + \mathbf{j}$.

2 a) $\mathbf{I} = m\mathbf{v} - m\mathbf{u}$, so
$\mathbf{Q} = 2(-2\mathbf{i} + \mathbf{j}) - 2(4\mathbf{i} - \mathbf{j}) = -4\mathbf{i} + 2\mathbf{j} - 8\mathbf{i} + 2\mathbf{j}$
$\mathbf{Q} = -12\mathbf{i} + 4\mathbf{j}$.

b)

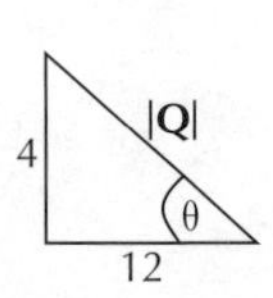

$|\mathbf{Q}| = \sqrt{(-12)^2 + 4^2} = 12.6$ Ns, to 3 s.f.

Answers

c) $\theta = \tan^{-1}\left(\frac{4}{12}\right)$
Required angle = 180 – θ = 162° (3 s.f.)

3 a) $m_A\mathbf{u}_A + m_B\mathbf{u}_B = m_A\mathbf{v}_A + m_B\mathbf{v}_B$, so:
$0.5(2\mathbf{i} + \mathbf{j}) + 0.4(-\mathbf{i} - 4\mathbf{j}) = 0.5(-\mathbf{i} - 2\mathbf{j}) + 0.4\mathbf{v}_B$
$\mathbf{i} + 0.5\mathbf{j} - 0.4\mathbf{i} - 1.6\mathbf{j} = -0.5\mathbf{i} - \mathbf{j} + 0.4\mathbf{v}_B$
$0.4\mathbf{v}_B = 1.1\mathbf{i} - 0.1\mathbf{j}$
$\Rightarrow \mathbf{v}_B = 2.75\mathbf{i} - 0.25\mathbf{j}$.
Speed = $|\mathbf{v}_B| = \sqrt{2.75^2 + 0.25^2} = 2.76$ ms^{-1}, to 3 s.f.

b) If they coalesce:
$0.5(2\mathbf{i} + \mathbf{j}) + 0.4(-\mathbf{i} - 4\mathbf{j}) = (0.5 + 0.4)\mathbf{v}$
$\mathbf{i} + 0.5\mathbf{j} - 0.4\mathbf{i} - 1.6\mathbf{j} = 0.9\mathbf{v}$
$0.9\mathbf{v} = 0.6\mathbf{i} - 1.1\mathbf{j} \Rightarrow \mathbf{v} = \frac{2}{3}\mathbf{i} - \frac{11}{9}\mathbf{j}$.
Speed = $|\mathbf{v}| = \sqrt{\left(\frac{2}{3}\right)^2 + \left(-\frac{11}{9}\right)^2} = 1.39$ ms^{-1}, to 3 s.f.

4 Call the particles A and B. If $u_A = u$ then $u_B = -u$ (as it's going in the opposite direction at the same speed). After the collision, $v_A = 0$ and $v_B = \frac{u}{2}$ (as it's going in the opposite direction to its original motion at half the speed).

$$e = \frac{\text{speed of separation of particles}}{\text{speed of approach of particles}} = \frac{v_B - v_A}{u_A - u_B}$$

$$\Rightarrow e = \frac{\frac{u}{2} - 0}{u - (-u)} = \frac{\frac{u}{2}}{2u} = \frac{u}{4u} = \frac{1}{4}.$$

5 a) For collision with a plane surface, $e = \frac{v}{u}$, so rebound speed $v = eu \Rightarrow v = 0.4 \times 10 = 4$ ms^{-1}.

b) Call the particles A and B, so

$$e = \frac{\text{speed of separation of particles}}{\text{speed of approach of particles}} = \frac{v_B - v_A}{u_A - u_B}$$

$\Rightarrow 0.4 = \frac{v_B - v_A}{10 - (-12)} \Rightarrow v_B - v_A = 0.4 \times 22$
$\Rightarrow v_B - v_A = 8.8$ ...*[1]*

Using the conservation of momentum:
$m_Au_A + m_Bu_B = m_Av_A + m_Bv_B$

$(1 \times 10) + (2 \times -12) = (1 \times v_A) + (2 \times v_B)$
$10 - 24 = v_A + 2v_B \Rightarrow v_A + 2v_B = -14$ ...*[2]*

Equation *[1]* + equation *[2]* gives:
$3v_B = -5.2 \Rightarrow v_B = -1.7333...$ ms^{-1}.

Substituting in equation *[1]* gives:
$-1.7333... - v_A = 8.8$
$\Rightarrow v_A = -1.7333... - 8.8 = -10.5333...$ ms^{-1}.
So, to 3 s.f., the original particle's rebound speed is 10.5 ms^{-1}.

6 For the first collision, between A and B:
$e = \frac{v_B - v_A}{u_A - u_B} \Rightarrow \frac{1}{4} = \frac{v_B - v_A}{3u - 2u} \Rightarrow v_B - v_A = \frac{u}{4}$ ...*[1]*
And:
$m_Au_A + m_Bu_B = m_Av_A + m_Bv_B$

$(1 \times 3u) + (4 \times 2u) = (1 \times v_A) + (4 \times v_B)$
$3u + 8u = v_A + 4v_B \Rightarrow v_A + 4v_B = 11u$ ...*[2]*

Equation *[1]* + equation *[2]* gives:
$5v_B = 11u + \frac{u}{4} \Rightarrow 5v_B = \frac{45u}{4} \Rightarrow v_B = \frac{9u}{4}$.

Substituting in equation *[2]* gives:
$v_A + 9u = 11u \Rightarrow v_A = 11u - 9u = 2u$.

For the second collision, between B and C:
$e = \frac{v_C - v_B}{u_B - u_C} \Rightarrow \frac{1}{3} = \frac{v_C - v_B}{\frac{9u}{4} - u} \Rightarrow v_C - v_B = \frac{5u}{12}$ ...*[3]*
And:
$m_Bu_B + m_Cu_C = m_Bv_B + m_Cv_C$

$(4 \times \frac{9u}{4}) + (5 \times u) = (4 \times v_B) + (5 \times v_C)$
$\Rightarrow 4v_B + 5v_C = 14u$ ...*[4]*

4 × Equation *[3]* + equation *[4]* gives:
$9v_C = \frac{5u}{3} + 14u \Rightarrow 9v_C = \frac{47u}{3} \Rightarrow v_C = \frac{47u}{27}$.
Substituting in equation *[3]* gives:
$\frac{47u}{27} - v_B = \frac{5u}{12} \Rightarrow v_B = \frac{47u}{27} - \frac{5u}{12} = \frac{143u}{108}$.
So after both collisions:
A is travelling at $2u = \frac{216u}{108}$,

and B is travelling at $\frac{143u}{108}$,

which means that A is travelling faster than B and so they should collide again.

7 Bounce 1:

Using $v^2 = u^2 + 2as$, where $v = u_1$, $u = 0$, $a = 9.8$ and $s = 1$:
$u_1^2 = 2 \times 9.8 \times 1 = 19.6 \Rightarrow u_1 = \sqrt{19.6} = 4.4271...$

Using $e = \frac{v}{u}$, $v = eu$, where $v = v_1$, $e = 0.5$ and $u = u_1$:
$v_1 = 0.5 \times 4.4271... = 2.2135...$

Then $v^2 = u^2 + 2as$, where $v = 0$, $u = v_1$ and $a = -9.8$:
$0 = 2.2135...^2 + (2 \times -9.8)s_1 \Rightarrow s_1 = \frac{2.2135...^2}{2 \times 9.8} = 0.25$ m.

Bounce 2:

From the symmetry of the vertical motion,
$u_2 = v_1 = 2.2135...$

$v = eu$, where $v = v_2$, $e = 0.5$ and $u = u_2$:
$v_2 = 0.5 \times 2.2135... = 1.1067...$

$v^2 = u^2 + 2as$, where $v = 0$, $u = v_2$ and $a = -9.8$:
$0 = 1.1067...^2 + (2 \times -9.8)s_2 \Rightarrow s_2 = \frac{1.1067...^2}{2 \times 9.8} = 0.0625$ m.

Bounce 3:

From the symmetry of the vertical motion,
$u_3 = v_2 = 1.1067...$

$v = eu$, where $v = v_3$, $e = 0.5$ and $u = u_3$:
$v_2 = 0.5 \times 1.1067... = 0.5533...$

$v^2 = u^2 + 2as$, where $v = 0$, $u = v_3$ and $a = -9.8$:
$0 = 0.5533...^2 + (2 \times -9.8)s_3$

$\Rightarrow s_3 = \frac{0.5533...^2}{2 \times 9.8} = 0.015625$ m.

8 $e = \frac{v_2 - v_1}{u_1 - u_2} \Rightarrow 0.3 = \frac{v_2 - v_1}{3 - 0} \Rightarrow v_2 - v_1 = 0.9$ ...*[1]*
And: $m_1u_1 + m_2u_2 = m_1v_1 + m_2v_2$
$\Rightarrow (2 \times 3) + (3 \times 0) = 2v_1 + 3v_2$
$\Rightarrow 6 = 2v_1 + 3v_2 \Rightarrow v_1 + 1.5v_2 = 3$ ...*[2]*
Equation *[1]* + equation *[2]* gives:
$2.5v_2 = 3.9 \Rightarrow v_2 = 1.56$ ms^{-1}.

Answers

In equation *[1]*:
$1.56 - v_1 = 0.9 \Rightarrow v_1 = 1.56 - 0.9 = 0.66$ ms^{-1}.

Loss of K.E. $= (\frac{1}{2}m_1u_1^2 + \frac{1}{2}m_2u_2^2) - (\frac{1}{2}m_1v_1^2 + \frac{1}{2}m_2v_2^2)$

$= [(\frac{1}{2} \times 2 \times 3^2) + 0] - [(\frac{1}{2} \times 2 \times 0.66^2) + (\frac{1}{2} \times 3 \times 1.56^2)]$
$= 9 - 4.086 = 4.914$ J.

Exam Questions

1 a) $\mathbf{I} = m\mathbf{v} - m\mathbf{u}$, so
$3\mathbf{i} - 8\mathbf{j} = 0.4\mathbf{v} - 0.4(-6\mathbf{i} + \mathbf{j})$ ***[1 mark]***
$3\mathbf{i} - 8\mathbf{j} = 0.4\mathbf{v} + 2.4\mathbf{i} - 0.4\mathbf{j}$
$0.4\mathbf{v} = 0.6\mathbf{i} - 7.6\mathbf{j}$ ***[1 mark]***
$\Rightarrow \mathbf{v} = 1.5\mathbf{i} - 19\mathbf{j}$ ***[1 mark]***.

Speed is the magnitude of the velocity.
Drawing this as a right-angled triangle:

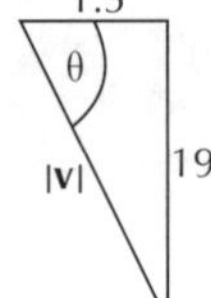

$|\mathbf{v}| = \sqrt{1.5^2 + 19^2}$ ***[1 mark]*** = 19.1 ms^{-1} to 3 s.f. ***[1 mark]***.

As always, a picture makes everything make a lot more sense.

b) Using the triangle in part a), θ is the angle with the horizontal, so:
$\theta = \tan^{-1}\left(\frac{19}{1.5}\right)$ ***[1 mark]*** = 85.5° to 3 s.f. ***[1 mark]***.

2 Using the principle of conservation of momentum for the collision:
$m_1u_1 + m_2u_2 = m_1v_1 + m_2v_2$
Since marble 2 is stationary before the impact:
$(0.02 \times 2) + (0.06 \times 0) = 0.02v_1 + 0.06v_2$ ***[1 mark]***
$\Rightarrow 0.02v_1 + 0.06v_2 = 0.04$
$\Rightarrow v_1 + 3v_2 = 2$ ...*[1]*
Since the collision is perfectly elastic, and so $e = 1$, the Law of Restitution gives a second equation:
$e = \frac{\text{speed of separation of particles}}{\text{speed of approach of particles}} = \frac{v_2 - v_1}{u_1 - u_2}$
$\Rightarrow 1 = \frac{v_2 - v_1}{2 - 0}$ ***[1 mark]*** $\Rightarrow v_2 - v_1 = 2$ ...*[2]*
Equation *[1]* + equation *[2]* gives:
$4v_2 = 4 \Rightarrow v_2 = 1$ ms^{-1} ***[1 mark]***.

Substituting in equation *[1]* gives:
$v_1 + (3 \times 1) = 2 \Rightarrow v_1 = -1$ ms^{-1} ***[1 mark]***.

So after the collision, both particles are travelling at a speed of 1 ms^{-1} (but the first particle is going in the opposite direction to its initial path).

3 a) Using the Law of Restitution for the collision between P and Q, where P is travelling at u and Q at $-u$ (i.e. in the opposite direction):

$e = \frac{v_Q - v_P}{u_P - u_Q} \Rightarrow \frac{3}{4} = \frac{v_Q - v_P}{u - (-u)}$ ***[1 mark]*** $\Rightarrow \frac{3}{4} = \frac{v_Q - v_P}{2u}$
$\Rightarrow v_Q - v_P = \frac{3u}{2}$ ...*[1]*

Using conservation of momentum:
$m_Pu_P + m_Qu_Q = m_Pv_P + m_Qv_Q$
$2mu - mu = 2mv_P + mv_Q$ ***[1 mark]***
$\Rightarrow 2v_P + v_Q = u$ ...*[2]*
Equation *[2]* – equation *[1]* gives:
$3v_P = -\frac{u}{2} \Rightarrow v_P = -\frac{u}{6}$ ***[1 mark]***.
Substituting in equation *[1]* gives:
$v_Q - (-\frac{u}{6}) = \frac{3u}{2} \Rightarrow v_Q = \frac{4u}{3}$ ***[1 mark]***.
Since P's velocity was initially positive, and is now negative, and Q's was initially negative but is now positive, the collision has reversed the directions of both particles ***[1 mark]***.
Sure about that? Yep, positive. I mean negative... erm...
$|v_Q| \div |v_P| = \frac{4u}{3} \div \frac{u}{6} = 8$,
so Q is now going 8 times faster than P ***[1 mark]***.

b) For the collision with the wall, $e_{wall} = \frac{\text{speed of rebound}}{\text{speed of approach}}$.
Q approaches the wall with a speed of $\frac{4u}{3}$ (from a)), so if v_{Qwall} is its rebound speed:

$e_{wall} = \frac{v_{Qwall}}{\frac{4u}{3}} \Rightarrow v_{Qwall} = \frac{4ue_{wall}}{3}$ ***[1 mark]***.
Since Q collides again with P, v_{Qwall} must be greater than v_P which is $\frac{u}{6}$ (from a)), so:
$\frac{4ue_{wall}}{3} > \frac{u}{6}$ ***[1 mark]*** $\Rightarrow e_{wall} > \frac{3u}{6 \times 4u} \Rightarrow e_{wall} > \frac{1}{8}$ ***[1 mark]***.

c) If $e_{wall} = \frac{3}{5}$, then (from b)):
$v_{Qwall} = \frac{4ue_{wall}}{3} = \frac{4u \times 3}{3 \times 5} = \frac{4u}{5}$ ***[1 mark]***.
Q is now travelling in the same direction as P, which is still travelling at a speed of $\frac{u}{6}$ (from a)), and the particles have a coefficient of restitution of $\frac{3}{4}$, so using the Law of Restitution for the second collision between P and Q:

$e = \frac{v_P - v_Q}{u_Q - u_P} \Rightarrow \frac{3}{4} = \frac{v_P - v_Q}{\left(\frac{4u}{5}\right) - \frac{u}{6}}$ ***[1 mark]*** $\Rightarrow \frac{3}{4} = \frac{v_P - v_Q}{\frac{19u}{30}}$
$\Rightarrow v_P - v_Q = \frac{19u}{40}$ ...*[1]*
Using conservation of momentum:
$m_Qu_Q + m_Pu_P = m_Qv_Q + m_Pv_P$
$\frac{4um}{5} + \frac{2um}{6} = mv_Q + 2mv_P$ ***[1 mark]***
$\Rightarrow v_Q + 2v_P = \frac{17u}{15}$ ...*[2]*
Equation *[1]* + equation *[2]* gives:
$3v_P = \frac{193u}{120} \Rightarrow v_P = \frac{193u}{360}$ ***[1 mark]***.
Substituting in equation *[1]* gives:
$\frac{193u}{360} - v_Q = \frac{19u}{40} \Rightarrow v_Q = \frac{193u}{360} - \frac{19u}{40} = \frac{22u}{360}$ ***[1 mark]***.
Since $v_Q = 0.22$ ms^{-1}:
$\frac{22u}{360} = 0.22$ ***[1 mark]***
$\Rightarrow u = (0.22 \times 360) \div 22 = 3.6$ ms^{-1} ***[1 mark]***.

4 a) Using the Law of Restitution for the collision between particles 1 and 2 gives:
$e = \frac{v_2 - v_1}{u_1 - u_2} \Rightarrow \frac{1}{4} = \frac{v_2 - v_1}{3u - 2u}$ ***[1 mark]***
$\Rightarrow v_2 - v_1 = \frac{u}{4}$ ...*[1]*

Answers

Using conservation of momentum:

$m_1u_1 + m_2u_2 = m_1v_1 + m_2v_2$

$(2m \times 3u) + (3m \times 2u) = 2mv_1 + 3mv_2$ ***[1 mark]***

$\Rightarrow 2v_1 + 3v_2 = 12u$ ...*[2]*

Equation *[1]* × 2 gives:

$2v_2 - 2v_1 = \frac{u}{2}$ ...*[3]*

Equation *[2]* + equation *[3]* gives:

$5v_2 = 12u + \frac{u}{2} \Rightarrow v_2 = \frac{25u}{2 \times 5} = \frac{5u}{2}$ ***[1 mark]***.

Substituting in equation *[1]* gives:

$\frac{5u}{2} - v_1 = \frac{u}{4}$

$\Rightarrow v_1 = \frac{5u}{2} - \frac{u}{4} = \frac{9u}{4}$ ***[1 mark]***.

b) Loss of kinetic energy =

$(\frac{1}{2}m_1u_1^2 + \frac{1}{2}m_2u_2^2) - (\frac{1}{2}m_1v_1^2 + \frac{1}{2}m_2v_2^2)$

$= [(\frac{1}{2} \times 2m \times (3u)^2) + (\frac{1}{2} \times 3m \times (2u)^2)] -$

$[(\frac{1}{2} \times 2m \times (\frac{9u}{4})^2) + (\frac{1}{2} \times 3m \times (\frac{5u}{2})^2)]$

$= (9mu^2 + 6mu^2) - (\frac{81mu^2}{16} + \frac{150mu^2}{16})$

$= (15 - \frac{231}{16})mu^2 = \frac{9mu^2}{16}$.

[4 marks available — 1 mark for correct values in formula for initial kinetic energy, 1 mark for correct values in formula for final kinetic energy, 1 mark for correct calculation of initial and final energy and 1 mark for correct final answer as the difference between the two.]

5 a) For the collision between A and B, the Law of Restitution gives the following equation:

$e = \frac{v_B - v_A}{u_A - u_B} \Rightarrow e = \frac{v_B - v_A}{4u - 0}$ ***[1 mark]***

$\Rightarrow v_B - v_A = 4ue$ ...*[1]*

Using conservation of momentum:

$m_Au_A + m_Bu_B = m_Av_A + m_Bv_B$

$4mu + 0 = mv_A + 2mv_B$ ***[1 mark]***

$\Rightarrow v_A + 2v_B = 4u$ ...*[2]*

Equation *[1]* + equation *[2]* gives:

$3v_B = 4u(1 + e) \Rightarrow v_B = \frac{4u}{3}(1 + e)$ ***[1 mark]***.

Substituting in equation *[1]* gives:

$\frac{4u}{3}(1 + e) - v_A = 4ue$

$\Rightarrow v_A = \frac{4u}{3}(1 + e) - 4ue = \frac{4u}{3}(1 - 2e)$ ***[1 mark]***.

Since the coefficient of restitution must be between 0 and 1, and the coefficient of restitution between B and C is $2e$, then $0 \leq 2e \leq 1 \Rightarrow 1 - 2e \geq 0$ ***[1 mark]***.

i.e. $v_A = \frac{4u}{3}(1 - 2e)$, where $u > 0$ and $1 - 2e \geq 0$. So:

v_A cannot be negative ***[1 mark]***, so the collision does not reverse the direction of A's motion ***[1 mark]***.

b) After the collision, A is travelling at $\frac{4u}{3}(1 - 2e)$ and B is travelling at $\frac{4u}{3}(1 + e)$ (from a)). In the time it takes B to travel a distance d, A has travelled $\frac{d}{4}$. So the speed of B must be 4 times the speed of A ***[1 mark]*** i.e.

$\frac{4u}{3}(1 - 2e) = \frac{u}{3}(1 + e)$ ***[1 mark]***

$\Rightarrow 4 - 8e = 1 + e$

$\Rightarrow 9e = 3 \Rightarrow e = \frac{1}{3}$ ***[1 mark]***

c) Since $e = \frac{1}{3}$ (from b)), the speed of B as it approaches C is:

$\frac{4u}{3}(1 + \frac{1}{3}) = \frac{16u}{9}$ ***[1 mark]***. The coefficient of restitution between B and C is $2e = \frac{2}{3}$ ***[1 mark]***. So, using the Law of Restitution: $e = \frac{v_C - v_B}{u_B - u_C} \Rightarrow \frac{2}{3} = \frac{v_C - v_B}{\frac{16u}{9} - 0}$ ***[1 mark]***

$\Rightarrow v_C - v_B = \frac{32u}{27}$ ...*[1]*

Using conservation of momentum:

$m_Bu_B + m_Cu_C = m_Bv_B + m_Cv_C$

$(2m \times \frac{16u}{9}) + 0 = 2mv_B + 4mv_C$ ***[1 mark]***

$\Rightarrow v_B + 2v_C = \frac{16u}{9}$ ...*[2]*

Equation *[1]* + equation *[2]* gives:

$3v_C = \frac{80u}{27} \Rightarrow v_C = \frac{80u}{81}$ ***[1 mark]***.

And that's about your lot for Section 4, a real rollercoaster ride of mathematical wonderment. Hope you had fun...

M2 Section 5 — Statics of Rigid Bodies

Warm-up Questions

1) A rod (a long, inextensible particle) where the centre of mass is not at the central point of the rod.

M2 statics is pretty rod-heavy. Think of them as a really simple stick. They don't bend, don't stretch or compress, and have no width.

2) a) $a = 0.8\sin 39.6° = 0.51$ m

b)

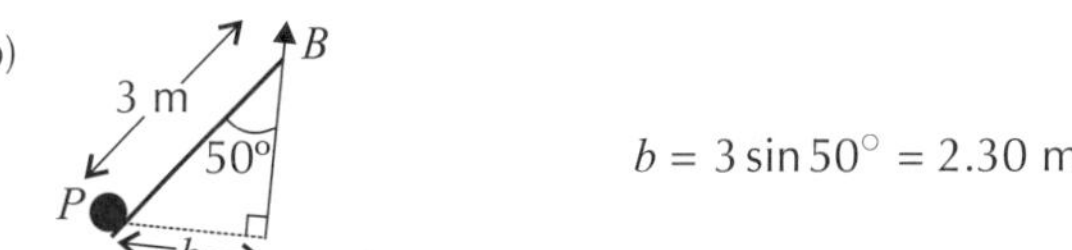

$b = 3\sin 50° = 2.30$ m

c)

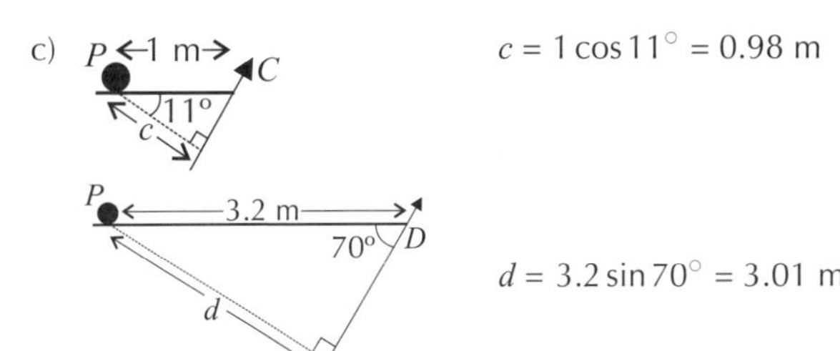

$c = 1\cos 11° = 0.98$ m

$d = 3.2\sin 70° = 3.01$ m

The perpendicular distance is always the shortest distance between a point and a force's line of action. Simple.

3) a) Resolving the forces vertically:

$42 = 28\cos 30° + T\cos 38.3°$

so $T = \frac{42 - 14\sqrt{3}}{\cos 38.3°} = 22.6$ N (3 s.f.)

Answers

b) Taking moments about the left-end:
$42xy = 28\cos30(xy + y)$
$42xy - (28\cos30)(xy) = (28\cos30)y$
$17.75xy = 24.25y \Rightarrow x = 1.37$

4) 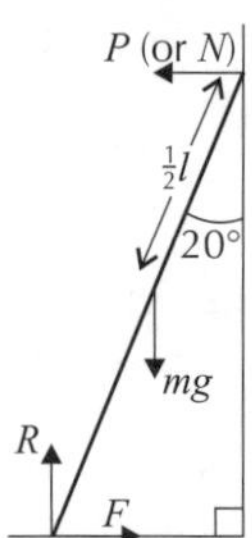

Where:
mg = weight of the ladder
F = friction between ground and ladder
R = normal reaction of the ground
P / N = normal reaction of the wall
As the rod is uniform the weight of the ladder acts at the centre of the rod (i.e. at half of l).
Assumptions: e.g. the ladder can be modelled as a rod, the ladder is rigid, friction is sufficient to keep the ladder in equilibrium, the ladder is perpendicular to the wall when viewed from above.

'Perpendicular' and 'normal' are both used in M2 (as are 'P' and 'N' to label the forces). No need to panic — they mean the same thing in all you'll do here.

Exam Questions

1 a) Taking moments about B:
$(mg\cos\theta \times 1.4) + (180\cos\theta \times 2.1)$
$= (490\sin\theta \times 4.2)$
Dividing by $\cos\theta$ gives:
$1.4mg + 378 = 2058\tan\theta = 2058 \times \frac{8}{11}$
so, $1.4mg = 1497 - 378 = 1119$
so $m = \frac{1119}{13.72} = 82$ kg (nearest kg)

AB = 4.2 m
AC = 2.8 m
BC = 1.4 m

[3 marks available in total]:
- ***1 mark for taking moments about B***
- ***1 mark for correct workings***
- ***1 mark for the correct value of m***

b) Resolving horizontally:
$F = 490$ N
Resolving vertically:
$R = 180 + 81.56g = 979.3$ N
As equilibrium is limiting, $F = \mu R$
so $979.3\mu = 490$ N and $\mu = 0.50$

[5 marks available in total]:
- ***1 mark for resolving horizontally***
- ***1 mark for resolving vertically***
- ***1 mark for using F = μR***
- ***1 mark for correct workings***
- ***1 mark for correct value of μ***

2) a) Taking moments about A:
$2g \times 0.4 = 30\cos55° \times x$
so $x = \frac{7.84}{17.2} = 0.456$ m

[3 marks available in total]:
- ***1 mark for taking moments about A***
- ***1 mark for correct workings***
- ***1 mark for correct value of x***

I've made an educated guess in the diagram above at which directions R_V and R_H act in. If I work out their values and they turn out to be negative then I just need to reverse their direction.

b) Resolving vertically:
$R_V = 2g - 30\cos55° = 2.39$ N
Resolving horizontally:
$R_H = 30\sin55° = 24.57$ N

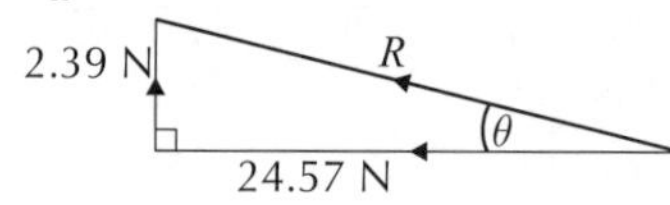

$|R| = \sqrt{2.39^2 + 24.57^2} = 24.7$ N
$\tan\theta = \frac{2.39}{24.57}$
so $\theta = 5.56°$ to the horizontal

[5 marks available in total]:
- ***1 mark for resolving vertically***
- ***1 mark for resolving horizontally***
- ***1 mark for correct workings***
- ***1 mark for correct magnitude of R***
- ***1 mark for correct direction***

3) a) Taking moments about A:
$\frac{1}{2}l \times mg\cos\theta = \frac{3}{4}l \times P$
so $P = \frac{\frac{1}{2}lmg\cos\theta}{\frac{3}{4}l} = \frac{2}{3}mg\cos\theta$

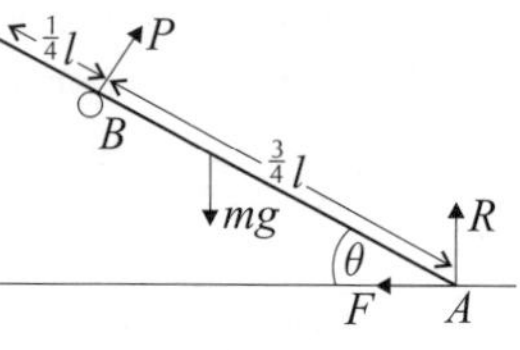

[3 marks available in total]:
- ***1 mark for taking moments about A***
- ***1 mark for correct workings***
- ***1 mark for correct answer***

Mechanics is harder with algebra than with numbers, but once you've mastered it, doing it with numbers will seem trivial. I know it's not nice, but at least it's useful.

b) $\sin\theta = \frac{3}{5}$ so $\cos\theta = \frac{4}{5}$
Using the result of part a) gives $P = \frac{8}{15}mg$
Resolving horizontally:
$F = P\sin\theta = \frac{8}{15}mg \times \frac{3}{5} = \frac{8}{25}mg$
Resolving vertically:
$R + P\cos\theta = mg$
so $R = mg - \frac{4}{5}P = mg - \frac{32}{75}mg = \frac{43}{75}mg$
Non-limiting equilibrium so $F \leq \mu R$
so $\frac{8}{25}mg \leq \mu\frac{43}{75}mg$ and $\mu \geq \frac{24}{43} = 0.56$

[6 marks available in total]:
- ***1 mark for calculating cosθ***
- ***1 mark for resolving horizontally***
- ***1 mark for resolving vertically***
- ***1 mark for using F ≤ μR***
- ***1 mark for correct workings***
- ***1 mark for correct value of μ***

That wasn't much fun, but it's good to get some use out of your calculator's fraction button. Unless you did it without a calculator, in which case, congratulations, you're officially 'hardcore'.

Answers

4) a) Resolve horizontally:

$T\cos\theta = 72.5$ N

$\tan\theta = \frac{0.8}{1.7}$

$\Rightarrow \theta = 25.2°$

so $T = \frac{72.5}{0.9048} = 80.1$ N

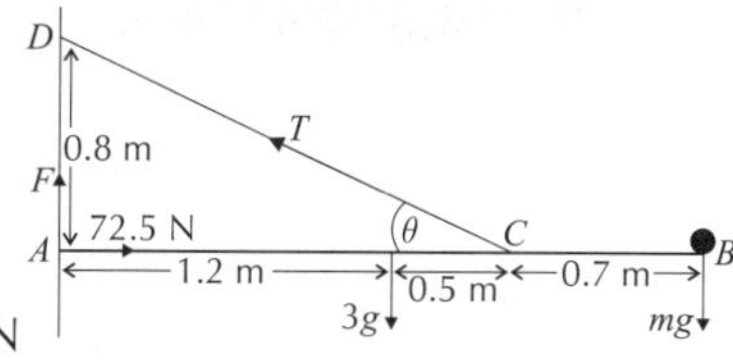

[4 marks available in total]:

- ***1 mark for resolving horizontally***
- ***1 mark for calculating θ or cosθ***
- ***1 mark for correct workings***
- ***1 mark for correct value of T***

b) Taking moments about A:

$(1.2 \times 3g) + (2.4 \times mg) = 1.7 \times 80.13\sin25.2°$

so $23.52m = 58.00 - 35.28 = 22.72$

and $m = 0.966$ kg (3 s.f)

[3 marks available in total]:

- ***1 mark for taking moments about A***
- ***1 mark for correct workings***
- ***1 mark for correct value of m***

c) Resolving vertically:

$F + 80.13\sin25.2° = 3g + 0.9660g$

so $F = 38.87 - 34.12 = 4.75$ N (3 s.f)

[3 marks available in total]:

- ***1 mark for resolving vertically***
- ***1 mark for correct workings***
- ***1 mark for correct value of F***

That, right there, is the end of the last M2 section. Only exam papers await, and now would be a good time for a cup of tea.

M2 Practice Exam One

1 a) Taking moments about C:

$1.1 \times R_V = 0.9 \times 1.8g$

so, $1.1R_V = 15.876$

and $R_V = 14.4$ N (to 3 s.f.)

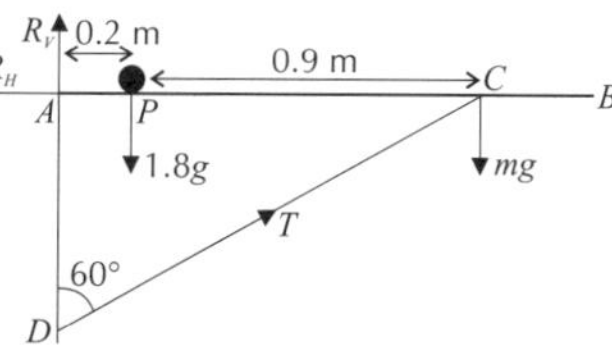

[3 marks available in total]:

- ***1 mark for taking moments about C***
- ***1 mark for correct workings***
- ***1 mark for correct value of R_V***

It's easy to get confused by which directions R_H and R_V act in. My suggestion — make an educated guess and if you're wrong they'll just turn out to be negative. No need to panic then.

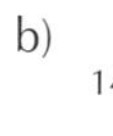

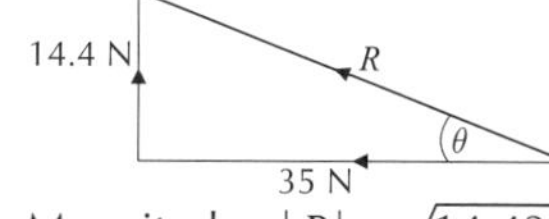

Magnitude: $|R| = \sqrt{14.43^2 + 35^2} = 37.9$ N (to 3 s.f.)

Direction: $\tan\theta = \frac{14.43}{35}$, so $\theta = 22.4°$ (to 3 s.f.) to the horizontal

[3 marks available in total]:

- ***1 mark for correct workings***
- ***1 mark for correct magnitude***
- ***1 mark for correct direction***

Pythagoras, a man of great, er, magnitude. His work is useful in pretty much any situation — try it next time you're out dancing.

c) Resolving horizontally:

$T\sin60° = R_H = 35$

so, $T = \frac{35}{\sin 60°} = 40.4$ N (to 3 s.f.)

[3 marks available in total]:

- ***1 mark for resolving horizontally***
- ***1 mark for correct workings***
- ***1 mark for correct value of T***

d) Taking moments about A:

$(0.2 \times 1.8g) + (1.1 \times mg) = 1.1 \times T\cos60°$

so, $10.78m = 22.22 - 3.53 = 18.69$

and $m = 1.73$ kg (to 3 s.f.)

[3 marks available in total]:

- ***1 mark for taking moments about A***
- ***1 mark for correct workings***
- ***1 mark for correct value of m***

2 a) Use the Law of Restitution for the collision between A and B, where A is travelling at $5u$ which changes to $-u$ ***[1 mark]*** after the collision. B has an initial velocity of 0:

$e = \frac{v_B - v_A}{u_A - u_B} \Rightarrow \frac{4}{5} = \frac{v_B - (-u)}{5u - 0}$ ***[1 mark]*** $\Rightarrow \frac{4}{5} = \frac{v_B + u}{5u}$

$\Rightarrow v_B = 4u - u = 3u$ ***[1 mark]***.

With collisions questions you're usually going to have to use either the Law of Restitution, or conservation of momentum, or both. So if you're stuck, plug the numbers you have into both formulas and see what you come up with.

b) Use conservation of momentum to find the mass of B:

$m_A u_A + m_B u_B = m_A v_A + m_B v_B$

$(1 \times 5u) + (M \times 0) = (1 \times -u) + (M \times 3u)$ ***[1 mark]***

$\Rightarrow 5u = (3M - 1)u \Rightarrow 3M - 1 = 5$ ***[1 mark]***

$\Rightarrow M = (5 + 1) \div 3 = 2$ kg ***[1 mark]***.

c) Using the Law of Restitution for the collision between B and the wall: $e = \frac{v}{u}$, so rebound speed $v = 3eu$ ***[1 mark]***, since B is travelling towards the wall at $3u$ (from a)).

For B to collide again with A, its rebound speed v must be greater than A's speed, which is u. So:

$3eu > u$ ***[1 mark]***

$3e > 1$

$e > \frac{1}{3}$ ***[1 mark]***.

3 a) Call the driving force of the car's engine T:

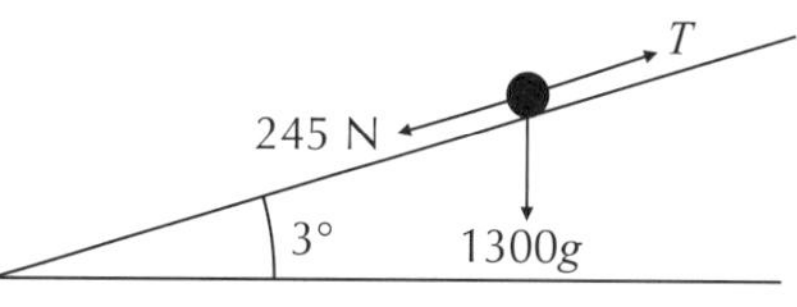

Resolve parallel to the slope to find T:

$T - (245 + 1300g\sin3°) = 0$

So, $T = (245 + 1300g\sin3°)$

Answers

Use Power = Force × Velocity to find the speed of the car:
$20\,000 = (245 + 1300g\sin3°) \times v$
$v = \frac{20\,000}{245 + 1300g\sin 3°} = 21.9\,\text{ms}^{-1}$ (3 s.f.)
[4 marks available in total]:
- ***1 mark for resolving parallel to slope***
- ***1 mark for finding correct value of T***
- ***1 mark for using Power = Fv***
- ***1 mark for finding correct speed***

b) Resolve parallel to the slope, taking up the slope as positive to find the acceleration, a: ***[1 mark]***
$-(245 + 1300g\sin3°) = 1300a$
$a = -0.7014\ \text{ms}^{-2}$ ***[1 mark]***
There's no driving force up the slope now. The only forces on the car are working to slow it down, so acceleration is negative.
Acceleration is constant, so use a constant acceleration formula to find the distance the car travels. Already know that $v = 0$ (since the car comes to rest) and $u = 21.94$ (from part a)), and need to find s, so use $v^2 = u^2 + 2as$: ***[1 mark]***
$0^2 = 21.94^2 + (2 \times -0.7014 \times s)$
$1.403s = 481.4$
$s = 343$ m (3 s.f.) ***[1 mark]***

4 a) Setting point O as the origin, the distance of the centre of mass from OA is the horizontal distance $\bar{x}$.
The frame is made from a single uniform wire, so treating each side as a separate 'rod', the masses are proportional to the lengths, i.e. $m_{OA} = 3$, $m_{OB} = 4$, and $m_{AB} = 5$.
The centre of mass of each side is at its midpoint, and so $x_{OA} = 0$ (since A is vertically above O), $x_{OB} = 2$ (i.e. 4 cm ÷ 2) and $x_{AB} = 2$ (since the triangle is right-angled, the midpoint of the hypotenuse AB is vertically above the midpoint of OB).
Combining the sides of the frame in the formula $\Sigma mx = \bar{x}\Sigma m$
$m_{OA}x_{OA} + m_{OB}x_{OB} + m_{AB}x_{AB} = \bar{x}(m_{OA} + m_{OB} + m_{AB})$
$\Rightarrow (3 \times 0) + (4 \times 2) + (5 \times 2) = \bar{x}(3 + 4 + 5)$
$\Rightarrow 18 = 12\bar{x} = \Rightarrow \bar{x} = 1.5.$
So the centre of mass of the frame is 1.5 cm from OA.
[4 marks available — 1 mark for correct individual masses of each side, 1 mark for correct centres of each side, 1 mark for correct entry into formula, 1 mark for correct final answer.]

b) With O as the origin again, the distance of the centre of mass from OB is the vertical distance $\bar{y}$. The centres of mass of each side are as follows: $y_{OA} = 1.5$ (i.e. 3 cm ÷ 2), $y_{OB} = 0$ and $y_{AB} = 1.5$ (the midpoint of the hypotenuse AB is horizontally across from the midpoint of OA).
Combining the sides of the frame in the formula $\Sigma my = \bar{y}\Sigma m$, using the masses found in a):
$m_{OA}y_{OA} + m_{OB}y_{OB} + m_{AB}y_{AB} = \bar{y}(m_{OA} + m_{OB} + m_{AB})$
$\Rightarrow (3 \times 1.5) + (4 \times 0) + (5 \times 1.5) = \bar{y}(3 + 4 + 5)$
$\Rightarrow 12 = 12\bar{y} = \Rightarrow \bar{y} = 1.$
So the centre of mass of the frame is 1 cm from OB.
[3 marks available — 1 mark for correct centres of each side, 1 mark for correct entry into formula, 1 mark for correct final answer.]

c) You'll need to find some other angles first before you get the one asked for in the question.
They say a picture paints a thousand words, so...

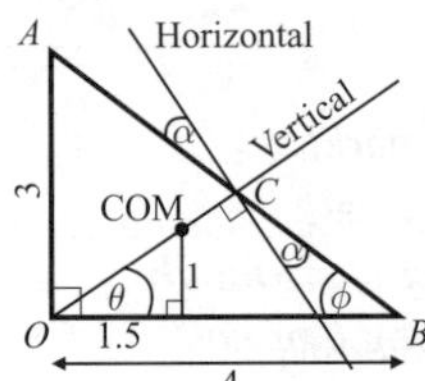

In the diagram, the angles in triangle OCB must add up to 180°, so:
$\theta + \phi + \alpha + 90 = 180 \Rightarrow \alpha = 90 - (\theta + \phi)$ ***[1 mark]***,
where α is the angle that AB makes with the horizontal, as asked for in the question.
The other angles can be found using basic trigonometry. From the right-angled triangle formed between O and the centre of mass: $\theta = \tan^{-1}(\frac{1}{1.5})$ ***[1 mark]*** $= 33.6900...°$ ***[1 mark]***
From the right-angled triangle OBA:
$\phi = \tan^{-1}(\frac{3}{4}) = 36.8698...°$ ***[1 mark]***
So the angle with the horizontal, $\alpha = 90 - (\theta + \phi)$
$= 90 - (33.6900... + 36.8698...) = 19.4401...°$
$= 19.4°$ to 3 s.f. ***[1 mark]***

5 a) Resolve vertically, taking up as positive:
$u = p;\ s = 0;\ a = -9.8;\ t = 5;$ ***[1 mark]***
Acceleration is constant, so can use a constant acceleration formula, e.g. use $s = ut + \frac{1}{2}at^2$ ***[1 mark]***
$0 = (5p) - 4.9(5^2)$
$5p = 122.5$
$p = 24.5$ ***[1 mark]***
You could also use $v = u + at$ here, with $v = 0$; $u = p$; $a = -9.8$; and $t = 2.5$ (i.e. the time taken for the ball to reach its highest point, where vertical velocity is momentarily zero). It all works out to give you the same value of p. I know, I tested it.

b) Speed $= \sqrt{29^2 + 24.5^2}$ ***[1 mark]***
$= \sqrt{1441.25} = 38.0\ \text{ms}^{-1}$ (3 s.f.) ***[1 mark]***

c)

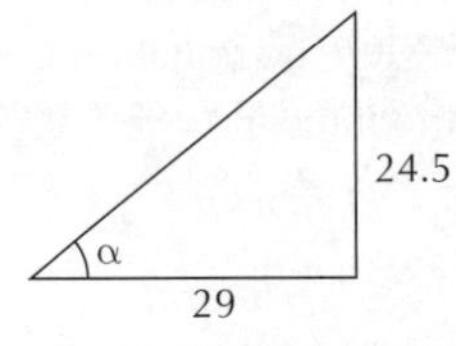

$\tan\alpha = \frac{24.5}{29}$ ***[1 mark]***
$\alpha = \tan^{-1}\frac{24.5}{29} = 40°$ (to nearest degree) ***[1 mark]***

d) No acceleration horizontally, so use $s = ut$ ***[1 mark]***
$s = 29 \times 5 = 145$ m ***[1 mark]***

Answers

e) Resolve vertically again, taking up as positive:
$u = 24.5$; $v = 0$; $a = -9.8$; $s = ?$ ***[1 mark]***
So, use $v^2 = u^2 + 2as$ ***[1 mark]***
$0 = 24.5^2 + (2 \times -9.8 \times s)$
$19.6s = 600.25$
$s = 30.6$ m (3 s.f.) ***[1 mark]***

Again, there are other ways you can do this question, and still get the same answer. You could use $t = 2.5$ in $s = ut + \frac{1}{2}at^2$ or $s = \frac{1}{2}(u + v)t$. S'up to you really.

6 a)

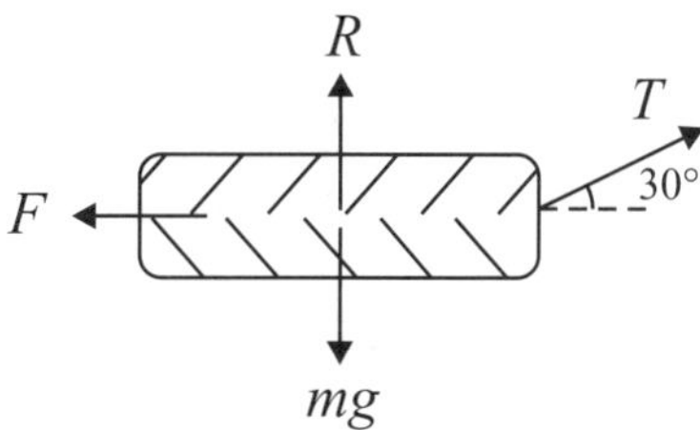

Tyre is moving only horizontally, so:
Total work done on the tyre = Change in K.E. ***[1 mark]***
i.e. Work done by T + Work done by F = Change in K.E.
Using Work done = Force × Displacement:
Work done by $F = 270 \times -75 = -20\,250$ ***[1 mark]***
Change in K.E. $= \frac{1}{2}m(v^2 - u^2) = \frac{1}{2} \times 160 \times (4 - 0.5625)$
$= 275$ J ***[1 mark]***
So, Work done by $T - 20\,250 = 275$
$\Rightarrow$ Work done by $T = 20.5$ kJ (3 s.f.) ***[1 mark]***

b) Again, using Work done = Force × Displacement:
Work done by $T = T\cos30° \times 75$ ***[1 mark]***
$T\cos30° \times 75 = 20\,525$ ***[1 mark]***
$T\cos30° = \frac{20\,525}{75}$
$T = 316$ N (3 s.f.) ***[1 mark]***

7 a) $s = \int v\,dt = \frac{11}{2}t^2 - \frac{2}{3}t^3 + c$ for $0 \le t \le 5$. ***[1 mark]***
When $t = 0$, $s = 0 \Rightarrow c = 0$. ***[1 mark]***
So, when $t = 5$:
$s = \frac{11}{2}(25) - \frac{2}{3}(125) = 54.2$ m (3 s.f.) ***[1 mark]***

b) P changes direction when $v = 0$ ***[1 mark]***
For $0 \le t \le 5$, $v = 0 \Rightarrow t = 0$ or 5.5 s ***[1 mark]***
Both of these can be ignored as one is at the origin, and the other is outside the interval for which the equation is valid.
So, P must change direction in the interval $t > 5$:
For $t > 5$, $v = 0 \Rightarrow t = \frac{25}{4} = 6.25$ s ***[1 mark]***

c) $s = \int v\,dt = 25t - 2t^2 + k$ for $t > 5$. ***[1 mark]***
When $t = 5$, $s = 54.17$ (from part a)) — use this to find k:
$54.17 = 25(5) - 2(25) + k$ ***[1 mark]***
So, $k = -20.83$
Need to find t when $s = 0$, i.e. when:
$2t^2 - 25t + 20.83 = 0$ ***[1 mark]***
Solve using quadratic formula:
$t = 0.898$ or 11.6 s. ***[1 mark]***
$t = 0.898$ can be ignored, as it is outside the interval for which the equation is valid.
So, P is back at the origin after 11.6 s (3 s.f.) ***[1 mark]***

d) Find displacement of P from origin after 8 seconds:
$-2(8)^2 + 25(8) - 20.83 = 51.17$ ***[1 mark]***
But P has already reached its point of furthest displacement from the origin (at 6.25 s as found in part b)), and is moving back towards the origin at $t = 8$.
So, find displacement of P from origin after 6.25 seconds:
$-2(6.25)^2 + 25(6.25) - 20.83 = 57.30$ ***[1 mark]***
So, total distance travelled by P in the first 8 seconds is:
$57.30 + (57.30 - 51.17)$ ***[1 mark]***
$= 63.4$ m (3 s.f.) ***[1 mark]***

M2 Practice Exam Two

1 a) Taking moments about A:
$54(3 - l) = 1.5 \times 8g\cos\theta$
$162 - 54l = 107.02$
so, $54l = 54.98$
$\Rightarrow$
$l = 1.02$ m (to 3 s.f.)

cos $\theta = 0.91$

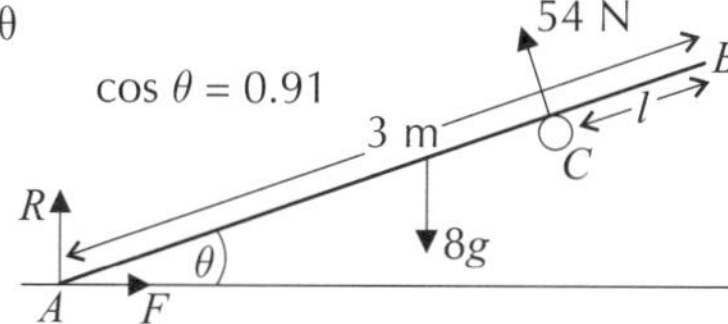

[3 marks available in total]:
- ***1 mark for taking moments about A***
- ***1 mark for correct workings***
- ***1 mark for correct value of l***

Now's a good time to remind you to take moments about points with unknown forces going through them (in this case about A, because you don't know R or F).

b) Resolving vertically:
$R + 54\cos\theta = 8g$
so, $R = 8g - (54 \times 0.91) = 29.26$ N
Resolving horizontally:
$F = 54\sin\theta$
Rod is in limiting equilibrium so $F = \mu R$:
$54\sin\theta = 29.26\mu$
As $\cos\theta = 0.91$, $\theta = 24.49°$
$29.26\mu = 54\sin(24.49) = 22.39$
So, $\mu = 0.765$ (to 3 s.f.)

[6 marks available in total]:
- ***1 mark for resolving vertically***
- ***1 mark for correct value of R***
- ***1 mark for resolving horizontally***
- ***1 mark for using F = μR***
- ***1 mark for correct workings***
- ***1 mark for correct value of μ***

Plenty of things to calculate there on the way to the final answer (μ, not 42), but nothing that's particularly difficult at least.

2 a) Find the centre of mass using the removal method, by subtracting the triangle (2) from the circle (1).
Since both the circle and the triangle that's removed from it are made from the same uniform material, their masses are in proportion to their areas:
Circle $m_1 = \pi r^2 = \pi \times 2^2 = 4\pi$.
Triangle $m_2 = \frac{1}{2} \times 1.5 \times 1.5 = 1.125$.
Taking the point P as the origin, the centre of mass of the circle, $\mathbf{r}_1 = \binom{0}{0}$, since P is the centre of the circle.
The centre of mass of the triangle is at the mean of the coordinates of $P(0,0)$, $Q(0, 1.5)$ and $R(1.5, 0)$, so:

Answers

$\mathbf{r}_2 = \begin{pmatrix}(0+0+1.5)\div 3\\(0+1.5+0)\div 3\end{pmatrix} = \begin{pmatrix}0.5\\0.5\end{pmatrix}$.

Using the removal method:

$m_1\mathbf{r}_1 - m_2\mathbf{r}_2 = \bar{\mathbf{r}}(m_1 - m_2)$

$\Rightarrow 4\pi\begin{pmatrix}0\\0\end{pmatrix} - 1.125\begin{pmatrix}0.5\\0.5\end{pmatrix} = \bar{\mathbf{r}}(4\pi - 1.125)$

$\Rightarrow \begin{pmatrix}-0.5625\\-0.5625\end{pmatrix} = 11.4413...\bar{\mathbf{r}}$

$\Rightarrow \bar{\mathbf{r}} = \begin{pmatrix}-0.5625 \div 11.4413...\\-0.5625 \div 11.4413...\end{pmatrix} = \begin{pmatrix}-0.04916...\\-0.04916...\end{pmatrix}$.

The distance of the COM from P is the magnitude of the position vector:

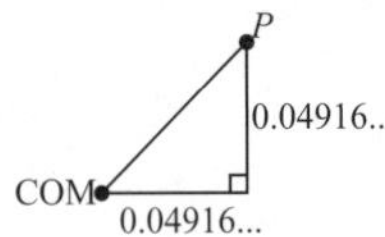

Distance $= \sqrt{0.04916...^2 + 0.04916...^2} = 0.06952...$
$= 0.070$ cm to 3 d.p.

There are other ways to find the centre of mass of this shape, because you can think of it in a different orientation, or take another point as the origin, but this way's as easy as any.

[5 marks available — 1 mark for correct masses of both shapes, 1 mark for individual centre of mass for both shapes, 1 mark for correct use of removal method formula, 1 mark for correct position vector or coordinates of centre of mass, 1 mark for correct distance from P.]

b) The shape is being hung from Q. Drawing a sketch will make it easier to see what's going on:

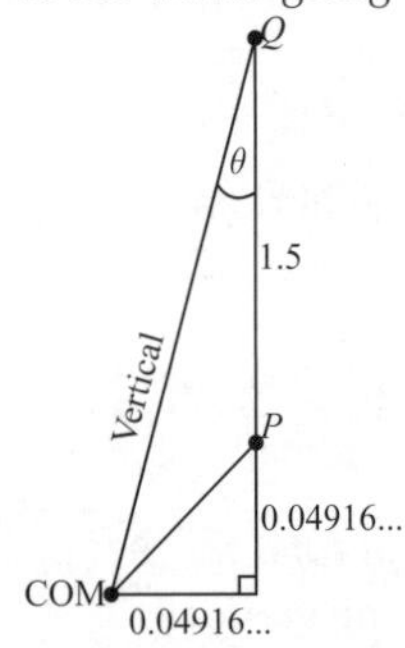

θ is the angle that PQ makes with the vertical.
Using basic trigonometry:

$\theta = \tan^{-1}\left(\frac{0.04916...}{1.5 + 0.04916...}\right) = 1.8177... = 1.8°$ to 1 d.p.

[3 marks available — 1 mark for correct sides of the right-angled triangle, 1 mark for correct working, 1 mark for correct final answer.]

3 a) Using the Law of Restitution for the collision between P and Q:

$e = \frac{v_Q - v_P}{u_P - u_Q} \Rightarrow 0.65 = \frac{v_Q - v_P}{5 - 0}$ ***[1 mark]***

$\Rightarrow v_Q - v_P = 5 \times 0.65 \Rightarrow v_Q - v_P = 3.25$ ...*[1]*.

Using conservation of momentum:

$m_Pu_P + m_Qu_Q = m_Pv_P + m_Qv_Q$

$(0.2 \times 5) + (0.6 \times 0) = (0.2 \times v_P) + (0.6 \times v_Q)$ ***[1 mark]***

$\Rightarrow 1 = 0.2v_P + 0.6v_Q \Rightarrow 5 = v_P + 3v_Q$ ...*[2]*.

Equation *[1]* + equation *[2]*:

$4v_Q = 8.25 \Rightarrow v_Q = 2.0625 = 2.06$ ms^{-1} to 3 s.f. ***[1 mark]***.

Substituting in equation *[2]*:

$5 = v_P + (3 \times 2.0625)$

$\Rightarrow v_P = 5 - (3 \times 2.0625) = -1.1875 = -1.19$ ms^{-1} to 3 s.f. ***[1 mark]***.

b) The size of the impulse on Q is the change in its momentum due to the collision, so:

$I = mv_Q - mu_Q = (0.6 \times 2.0625) - (0.6 \times 0)$ ***[1 mark]***
$= 1.2375 = 1.24$ Ns to 3 s.f. ***[1 mark]***.

Particles just can't help acting on impulse...

c) Loss of kinetic energy =

$(\frac{1}{2}m_Pu_P^2 + \frac{1}{2}m_Qu_Q^2) - (\frac{1}{2}m_Pv_P^2 + \frac{1}{2}m_Qv_Q^2)$

$= [(\frac{1}{2} \times 0.2 \times 5^2) + (\frac{1}{2} \times 0.6 \times 0^2)]$ ***[1 mark]*** $-$
$[(\frac{1}{2} \times 0.2 \times 1.1875^2) + (\frac{1}{2} \times 0.6 \times 2.0625^2)]$ ***[1 mark]***

$= (2.5 + 0) - (0.14101... + 1.27617...)$

$= 1.0828... = 1.08$ J to 3 s.f. ***[1 mark]***.

d) Using conservation of momentum for the collision between Q and R: $m_Qu_Q + m_Ru_R = m_Qv_Q + m_Rv_R$

$(0.6 \times 2.0625) + (0.7 \times 0) = (0.6 \times 0) + (0.7 \times v_R)$ ***[1 mark]***

$\Rightarrow 1.2375 = 0.7v_R \Rightarrow v_R = 1.2375 \div 0.7 = 1.7678...$
[1 mark]

Using the Law of Restitution:

$e = \frac{v_R - v_Q}{u_Q - u_R} = \frac{1.7678... - 0}{2.0625 - 0}$ ***[1 mark]*** $= 0.8571...$

$= 0.857$ to 3 s.f. ***[1 mark]***.

4 a) Bus is travelling at constant speed, so resolve horizontally with $F = ma$ to find the driving force of the engine, T:

$T - 4500 = 0 \Rightarrow T = 4500$ N ***[1 mark]***

Power of engine = Driving force × velocity ***[1 mark]***
$= 4500 \times 14 = 63$ kW ***[1 mark]***

b) Call the new driving force of the engine T':

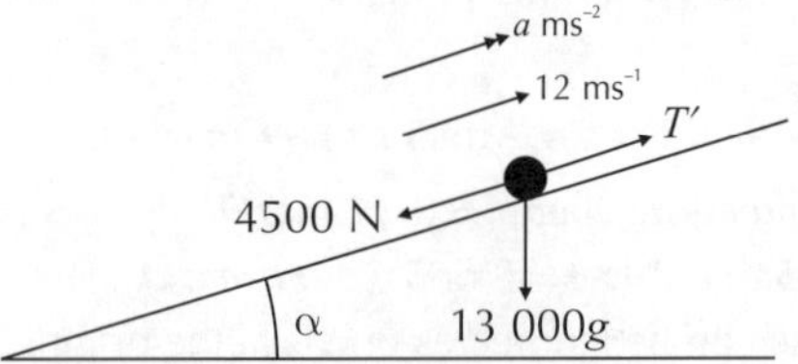

Use Power = Fv to find T':

$72\,000 = T' \times 12 \Rightarrow T' = 6000$ N

Resolve parallel to the slope with $F = ma$ to find a:

$T' - (4500 + 13\,000g\sin\alpha) = 13\,000a$

Substitute known values and rearrange:

$a = \frac{6000 - 4500 - 3640}{13\,000} = -0.165$ ms^{-2} (3 s.f.)

[4 marks available — 1 mark for using Power = Fv, 1 mark for finding the new driving force of the engine, 1 mark for resolving parallel to the slope and 1 mark for correct final answer.]

5 a) Friction is the only external force doing work on the particle, so the work-energy principle gives:

W.D. by friction = change in K.E. + change in P.E. ***[1 mark]***

Change in K.E. $= \frac{1}{2}m(v^2 - u^2)$ ***[1 mark]***

$= \frac{1}{2} \times 9 \times (0^2 - 11^2) = -544.5$ J ***[1 mark]***

Answers

Change in P.E. = mgh ***[1 mark]***

$= 9 \times 9.8 \times 8\sin30° = 352.8$ J ***[1 mark]***

So, W.D. by friction = $-544.5 + 352.8$

$= -192$ J (3 s.f.) ***[1 mark]***

Don't worry, you haven't broken maths — the work done by friction is supposed to be negative, because it's being done in the opposite direction to how the particle is moving. Phew.

b) No motion perpendicular to the plane, so resolve in this direction with $F = ma$ to find the normal reaction force, R:

$R - mg\cos30° = 0 \Rightarrow R = mg\cos30°$

$= 9 \times 9.8 \times \cos30°$ ***[1 mark]***

$= 76.38$ N

Call the frictional force F.

Particle is moving, so $F = \mu R = 76.38\mu$ ***[1 mark]***

Work done = Force × Displacement, so:

Work done by $F = F \times -8 = -611.0\mu$, ***[1 mark]***

So, from part a):

$-191.7 = -611.0\mu \Rightarrow \mu = \frac{-191.7}{-611.0} = 0.314$ (3 s.f.) ***[1 mark]***

6 a) $\mathbf{v} = \dot{\mathbf{r}} = (3t^2 - 12t + 4)\mathbf{i} + (7 - 8t)\mathbf{j}$

At $t = 5$:

$\mathbf{v} = (3(5^2) - 12(5) + 4)\mathbf{i} + (7 - 8(5))\mathbf{j} = 19\mathbf{i} - 33\mathbf{j}$ as required.

[3 marks available — 1 mark for attempting to differentiate the position vector, 1 mark for a correct expression for velocity at time t, and 1 mark for correct velocity at t = 5.]

b) When P is moving south, component of velocity in direction of $\mathbf{i}$ will be zero, i.e.

$3t^2 - 12t + 4 = 0$ ***[1 mark]***

Solving using the quadratic formula gives

$t = 0.3670$ or 3.633 ***[1 mark]***

When P is moving south, the component of velocity in the direction of $\mathbf{j}$ will be –ve, so find the velocity of P at the two values of t above, and see which is negative: ***[1 mark]***

$\mathbf{v}(0.367) = (7 - 8(0.367))\mathbf{j} = 4.06\mathbf{j}$ (so P is moving due north)

$\mathbf{v}(3.633) = (7 - 8(3.633))\mathbf{j} = -22.1\mathbf{j}$

So, P is moving due south when $t = 3.63$ s (3 s.f.) ***[1 mark]***

*Read through that bit about the components of velocity in the **j** direction a couple of times, until you're sure it makes sense to you. It can be a little bit confusing.*

c) To find force on P, will need to use $\mathbf{F} = m\mathbf{a}$, so first find $\mathbf{a}$:

$\mathbf{a} = \dot{\mathbf{v}} = (6t - 12)\mathbf{i} - 8\mathbf{j}$ ***[1 mark]***

When $t = 3$, $\mathbf{a} = (18 - 12)\mathbf{i} - 8\mathbf{j} = 6\mathbf{i} - 8\mathbf{j}$ ***[1 mark]***

So, $\mathbf{F} = m\mathbf{a} = 2.5(6\mathbf{i} - 8\mathbf{j}) = 15\mathbf{i} - 20\mathbf{j}$ ***[1 mark]***

Magnitude of $\mathbf{F} = \sqrt{15^2 + (-20)^2}$ ***[1 mark]***

$= 25$ N ***[1 mark]***

d) When $t = 5$, velocity $\mathbf{u} = 19\mathbf{i} - 33\mathbf{j}$ (from a)).

Using $\mathbf{I} = m\mathbf{v} - m\mathbf{u}$:

$\mathbf{I} = 2.5(5\mathbf{i} - \mathbf{j}) - 2.5(19\mathbf{i} - 33\mathbf{j})$ ***[1 mark]***

$\mathbf{I} = 12.5\mathbf{i} - 2.5\mathbf{j} - 47.5\mathbf{i} + 82.5\mathbf{j} = -35\mathbf{i} + 80\mathbf{j}$ ***[1 mark]***.

Magnitude: $|\mathbf{I}| = \sqrt{(-35)^2 + 80^2} = 87.3212...$

$= 87.3$ Ns to 3 s.f. ***[1 mark]***.

e) *As always, a little picture helps:*

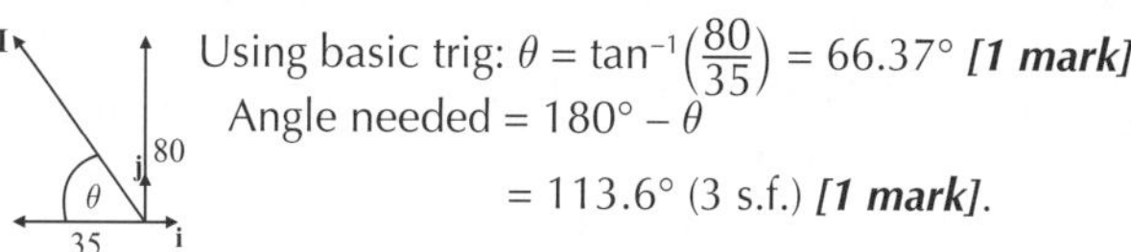

Using basic trig: $\theta = \tan^{-1}\left(\frac{80}{35}\right) = 66.37°$ ***[1 mark]***

Angle needed = $180° - \theta$

$= 113.6°$ (3 s.f.) ***[1 mark]***.

7 a) Need to find the times when the stone is 22 m above the ground (i.e. when it is at the level of projection), so resolve vertically, taking up as +ve: ***[1 mark]***

$s = 0$; $u = 14\sin46$; $a = -9.8$; $t = ?$

Acceleration is constant, so use a constant acceleration formula:

$s = ut + \frac{1}{2}at^2$

$0 = 14\sin46t - 4.9t^2$ ***[1 mark]***

$0 = (14\sin46 - 4.9t)t$

So, $t = 0$ (i.e. when the stone is thrown) or

$14\sin46 - 4.9t = 0 \Rightarrow t = 2.055$ s ***[1 mark]***

So the stone is at least 22 m above the ground for:

$2.055 - 0 = 2.06$ s (3 s.f.) ***[1 mark]***

b) Resolve vertically again, taking up as +ve to find the time taken by the stone to land: ***[1 mark]***

$s = -22$; $u = 14\sin46$; $a = -9.8$; $t = ?$

$s = ut + \frac{1}{2}at^2$

$-22 = 14\sin46t - 4.9t^2$

$\Rightarrow 4.9t^2 - 14\sin46t - 22 = 0$ ***[1 mark]***

Solve using the quadratic formula to find $t = -1.327$ or $t = 3.383$. ***[1 mark]***

Can ignore $t = -1.327$ as negative times cannot exist, so the stone lands after 3.383 seconds.

There is no acceleration horizontally, so the distance travelled is: $s = ut = 14\cos46 \times 3.383$

$= 32.9$ m (3 s.f.) ***[1 mark]***

c) No acceleration horizontally, so the horizontal component of velocity remains constant at $14\cos46$ ms^{-1}.

Resolve vertically once more, taking up as +ve to find the vertical component of the stone's final velocity:

$u = 14\sin46$; $a = -9.8$; $s = -22$; $v = ?$

$v^2 = u^2 + 2as = (14\sin46)^2 + (2 \times -9.8 \times -22)$

$= 532.6$

Don't bother finding the square root, as you'd only have to square it again in the next bit of the answer.

Speed $= \sqrt{(14\cos46)^2 + 532.6}$

$= 25.0$ ms^{-1} (3 s.f.)

[3 marks available — 1 mark for finding the horizontal and vertical components of the stone's velocity when it hits the ground, 1 mark for using Pythagoras to find the speed, and 1 mark for correct final answer.]

Index

Index

Index